Rock and Roll
Its History and Stylistic Development

Eighth Edition

Scott D. Lipscomb
San Diego State University

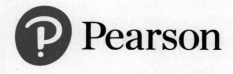 Pearson

Portfolio Manager: *Bimbabati Sen*
Portfolio Manager Assistant: *Anna Austin*
Product Marketer: *Chris Brown*
Content Developer: *Jane Miller*
Content Development Manager: *Gabrielle White*
Art/Designer: *iEnergizer/Aptara®, Ltd.*
Digital Studio Course Producer: *Rich Barnes*
Full-Service Project Manager: *iEnergizer/Aptara®, Ltd.*
Compositor: *iEnergizer/Aptara®, Ltd.*
Printer/Binder: *LSC Communications*
Cover Printer: *LSC Communications*
Cover Design: *Lumina Datamatics*
Cover Art: *Ela Kwasniewski/Shutterstock*

Acknowledgements of third party content appear on page 345, which constitutes an extension of this copyright page.

1 2019

Library of Congress Cataloging-in-Publication Data
Names: Lipscomb, Scott David, author.
Title: Rock and roll: its history and stylistic development/Scott Lipscomb.
Description: Eighth edition. Student edition. | Boston: Pearson, 2020. |
   Includes bibliographical references and index.
Identifiers: LCCN 2018017021 | ISBN 9780134202150 (pbk.)
Subjects: LCSH: Rock music--History and criticism.
Classification: LCC ML3534 .S83 2020 | DDC 781.6609–dc23 LC record available at
https://lccn.loc.gov/2018017021

Access Code Card
ISBN-10:   0-134-63874-3
ISBN-13: 978-0-134-63874-4

Loose-Leaf Edition
ISBN-10:   0-134-20215-5
ISBN-13: 978-0-134-20215-0

Revel Combo Card
ISBN-10:   0-134-62591-9
ISBN-13: 978-0-134-62591-1

Instructor's Review Copy
ISBN-10:   0-134-65418-8
ISBN-13: 978-0-134-65418-8

Rental
ISBN-10:   0-134-89908-3
ISBN-13: 978-0-134-89908-4

Dedication

Dedicated with love to my wife, Jordana, the consummate potiche;
to my children Kevin, Sterling, and Aiden;
to my siblings, Steve, Shari, Clinton, and Julia;
and to my mom, Dixie Petrey.

Brief Contents

Contents

About Revel and This Course

About This Course

The eighth edition of *Rock and Roll: Its History and Stylistic Development* introduces students to the various elements of music along with the history of rock music. Rock and roll is more than just a musical style, it is an influential social factor. While most rock history texts focus on the biographical factors of rock artists and bands, influential societal developments, and artist discographies and accomplishments, this course – while providing this same information in clear and accessible language – focuses on the *sound* of the music being discussed, working throughout each chapter to assist the reader in developing analytical listening skills and developing a comprehensive musical vocabulary, both of which can be applied to *any* style of music, including rock, jazz, classical, and world musics.

The approach taken is intended to fully engage the reader in an immersive musical experience, learning how to differentiate musical styles in an informed manner using appropriate terminology, allowing the highest level of understanding and listening enjoyment. Toward that end, this new edition of *Rock and Roll . . .* integrates numerous audio examples, created by the author, that are embedded in the text and links to official recordings and videos.

Content Highlights

The new edition has a great deal of contemporary material and exciting features to engage and inform readers:

- fully updated content to include recent events, recordings, and other changes since the publication of the 7th edition;
- Musical Close-Ups that delve deeply into particular musical elements, styles, or musicians have been integrated into the content of each chapter;
- animated audio-visual examples of most music notation images in the text have been added;
- a more complete inclusion of chart positions when referencing albums or singles;
- the glossary has been fully integrated into the text content so that hovering over a bold-faced term immediately reveals the definition of the glossary term;
- timelines are provided placing significant recordings, accomplishments, and other aspects of an artist's or group's career into a chronological, easily interpretable sequence of events; and

- journal questions, independent essay items and shared writing assignments, including recommended collaboration with peers, are integrated directly into the body of the text.

About the Author

Scott D. Lipscomb is currently Director of the School of Music and Dance at San Diego State University Dr. Lipscomb has been co-author of this text since the 3rd edition, along with his colleague Joe Stuessy. He played professionally in rock bands beginning in the late 1970s, culminating with his time with The Coupe, a Los Angeles-based rock band from 1982 to 1987, traveling and performing throughout North America. Scott played bass, keyboards, alto sax, and sang lead & background vocals. His primary areas of research interest include rock music history, understanding the role of sound and music in various forms of multimedia (especially motion pictures and video games), music perception, multimedia cognition, the impact of technology on the music learning experience, incorporation of music across the K-12 curriculum, and interactive instructional media development. He frequently presents results of his research at regional, national, and international conferences, and his work has been published in numerous peer-reviewed journals and edited volumes. Dr. Lipscomb co-edited a volume entitled *The psychology of music in multimedia* (2013, Oxford University Press) and is Editor of the *Journal of Technology in Music Learning*. Dr. Lipscomb holds a Ph.D. and an M.A. in Systematic Musicology from the University of California, Los Angeles. He received his B.M. in Jazz Performance (with an emphasis in electric and acoustic basses) from the University of Tennessee, Knoxville.

Acknowledgments

Many individuals played an important role in the preparation of this text. I am extremely fortunate to have benefited greatly over the years from the knowledge of my many students at the University of California, Los Angeles, The University of Texas at San Antonio, Northwestern University, the University of Minnesota, the College-Conservatory of Music at the University of Cincinnati, and San Diego State University. I arrive on campus every day, well-prepared for the purpose of filling the fertile minds of students with the wonders of music, and yet they manage to teach me something new every day. Some of these students have even entered into the realm of collaboration, contributing substantially to this publication, especially in the later chapters of the course. Sarah Williams, Jennifer Walshe, Michael Gaertner, and Kristin Bird were extremely helpful in providing an additional (i.e., younger) perspective regarding current groups, artists, and musical trends. In addition, I am fortunate—though some may quibble with this perspective!—to have had a teenager in my home for the past 21 years and a younger sister to fill the age gap between my children and me; to Aiden, Kevin, Sterling, and Shari, I once again express my appreciation for the many artists and musical examples you have shared with me throughout your lives. Without the input of these individuals representing two younger generations, the more recent evolutions evident in popular music would not have been covered with near the depth or level of insight that you will find here. I would also like to express my appreciation to Chelsea Valenzo-Duggan and Alissa Yatcko for their assistance with a variety of research- and library-related tasks for an earlier edition, many of which have been retained herein. Additionally, as many scholars working in the field of popular music have found, the research of Joel Whitburn and his published compilations of dates, lists, and statistics derived from the *Billboard* charts were indispensable to this work. His kind and unhesitating willingness to assist personally with requests was greatly appreciated, and his subscription-based Record Research Music Vault (http://www.musicarchivevault.com) was an oft-used resource throughout this revision process. It allowed immediate access to chart positions for recordings, both hit singles and albums. Likewise, the website for *Rolling Stone* magazine was a valuable resource. The website of the Recording Industry Association of America (http://www.riaa.com) was also useful for finding statistics related to music sales. Of course, very special thanks are due to the editors for this edition: Jane Miller, Bimbabati Sen, Gabrielle White, and Pearson Education for allowing me the opportunity to revise this eighth edition text, the sixth with which I have been involved and the first for which I am sole author.

Since the third edition of this text, I have had the privilege of revising and co-authoring along with my former colleague at The University of Texas San Antonio, Joe Stuessy, who was sole author of the first and second editions. The exemplary foundation he provided laid the groundwork for what was to become a labor of love – with all of the pleasure, excitement, and challenges that accompany any such creative relationship – since the mid-1990s. While much has changed since that time, there are sections of the text that remain almost unaltered since those early editions. Though Joe's name is no longer on the cover as an author, the spirit of the work that he contributed is strong and the content would be less informed without his valuable perspective. It is with great admiration, respect, and appreciation that I acknowledge Joe Stuessy's invaluable contributions to this work.

Most important, I want to acknowledge the essential role my family plays in every aspect of my life and the patience they have shown as I spent many late nights and weekends burning the midnight oil to complete this labor of love. I would like to express my heartfelt appreciation to my dear wife and partner for life, Jordana, and our children; Sterling, Kevin, and Aiden. Without you all, I would have had neither the stamina nor the contemporary knowledge necessary to complete this task. I should also mention that substantial amounts of comfort were provided at just the rights times along the way by our cuddly Yorkies, Xena and Madison.

Chapter 1
The Roots of Rock

 ## Learning Objectives

1.1 Describe the elements of music

1.2 Relate instrumentation with the history of rock and roll

1.3 Explain the cultural influences in the music market in the early 1950s

1.4 Summarize how the Pop music market contributed to the formation of rock and roll

1.5 Compare how each of the subculture music markets contributed to the formation of rock and roll

As we prepare to engage together in this exploration of the exciting world of rock music, I hope that you are as excited to experience this adventure as I am to write about it. Throughout this material, I will cover artists and musical developments from the 1940s up to the present day. My approach to this content focuses more directly on musical sound than any other rock history text about which I am aware. While I will also provide details concerning artist biographies, important recordings and other contributions to the art form, socio-political developments across the eras, and other essential information, the primary focus remains on the sound; for example, during the 1960s what are the musical elements that distinguish the sound of Motown from soul music?

One purpose of the following pages is to introduce you to essential musical vocabulary and the concepts they describe. I will use these words consistently throughout each chapter, and they will serve as the basis for our exploration of specific examples provided in the Listening Guides and Musical Close-Ups. Most importantly, this vocabulary and the knowledge that you will gain through its application can be used to intelligently and impressively discuss any type of music from rock to jazz to classical. So, without further delay, let's dive in …

1.1: Musical Close-Up on the Elements of Music

OBJECTIVE: Describe the elements of music

To fully understand any musical style, one must be able to analyze the various elements of music as they exist within that particular style. In this first Musical Close-Up, we shall briefly describe these elements of music and introduce a musical vocabulary that will facilitate your comprehension. In subsequent Musical Close-Ups, we shall examine one or another of these elements in greater detail as it pertains to a given style or topic.

1.1.1: Rhythm

We begin with rhythm because it is fundamental to almost all music. In its most basic form, rhythm refers to the interrelationship between music and time. Music, even in its simplest form, exists in time. Whether we are speaking of Beethoven's Ninth Symphony or just one note, there is a beginning, a duration, and an ending. Although we often compare music and visual art, they are dissimilar in at least this one respect. When you look at a painting, your eyes see it all at once. Music is more like dance, plays, books, movies, and even baseball games. All these develop

1

Rhythmic Nature of Music

In music, the composer must determine the rhythmic nature of the composition.

In the broadest sense, the composer must determine how long the piece will last. At a middle level, the composer can control the rhythmic flow of the piece. For example, the composition might have a slow-moving, rather uncomplicated opening, followed by a sudden flurry of activity; then it may build to a busy and fast climax, allowing the rhythmic tension to dissipate in the final section. At the most fine-grained level, the composer must determine the exact length of each note and how it relates to the length of the other notes sounding before, after, and simultaneously. All of this effort determines how the music exists in time—its rhythm.

Watch   MUSIC EXAMPLE A

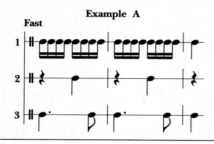

However, when we speak of rhythm, we usually mean the specific rhythmic patterns produced by the varying note durations (lengths). The two patterns shown, because the notes relate to each other differently in time, produce distinct rhythmic effects.

Watch   MUSIC EXAMPLE B

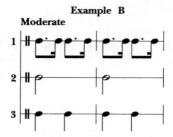

Notice the labels "Fast" and "Moderate" in the figures. These words describe the musical **tempo** (how fast all of the notes are moving through time). In the musical patterns provided here, Example A, therefore, moves faster than Example B; the former proceeds at a tempo of 120 beats per minute, while the latter is at 90 beats per minute. Tempo is part of the total rhythmic aspect of a song.

Study Examples A and B closely and listen to them each several times. You will see that, at a given moment (within each beat), there are simultaneous occurrences of long notes, short notes, and sometimes silence. If possible, perform these rhythms in class (using hand claps, nonsense syllables, or numbers); even if it is possible to simply listen to examples in an interactive course like this one, actually performing the rhythms provides a much more meaningful, visceral experience of the rhythm. Each example has a very different effect as a result of the varying rhythms.

It is not so terribly important that you understand everything about the rhythmic patterns in Examples A and B. What is important is that you realize that the rhythmic element of a piece is made up of many notes, each with different lengths compared to the others. In most musical contexts, these must be conceived and performed rather exactly for the rhythmic part of the piece to make sense.

through time. We cannot listen to Beethoven's Ninth Symphony, read *War and Peace,* or watch the seventh game of the World Series in an instant. We must allow each to unfold over its own appropriate period of time. Furthermore, each has an internal pace of activity, with moments of exciting action alternating with moments in which the level of activity subsides.

You participate personally in the rhythm of a piece when you tap your foot, clap to the beat, or dance. These reactions are natural and help explain why strongly rhythmic pieces have such appeal. Later in this course, I will review some of these comments about rhythm and show how they apply to early styles of rock and roll.

1.1.2: Melody

When a vibrating body (a guitar string, a piano string, or a saxophone reed) is set into motion fast enough, we begin to perceive a **pitch** (or **tone**). The faster the vibration, the higher the pitch we perceive. Thus, if a string vibrates 100 times per second, we hear a low pitch; if it vibrates 4,000 times per second, we hear a very high pitch. When we hear two or more pitches in succession, each with their own rhythmic duration, we begin to perceive a *melody* (or *tune*).

If you whistle or hum four to six notes (pitches) in succession, you will have created a short melody. Melodies are very important in music. Although we may physically feel the rhythm of the music, usually what we remember about a song is the melody (or tune)—and sometimes the words associated with that tune.

1.1.3: Harmony and Tonality

While *melody* is the combination of notes in succession, *harmony* is the combination of notes simultaneously. If a friend sings a certain note and you join in with a higher or lower note, you are harmonizing. When three or more notes are sounded simultaneously, we have a **chord**. If you

Terms Associated with Melody

When discussing melody, we shall encounter several new terms.

Range—The *range* of a melody describes the distance between the highest and the lowest notes of the sequence of pitches. Melodies that move from very low to very high notes have a wide range; those that move up or down very little have a narrow range.

Conjunct—The terms conjunct and disjunct tell us whether a melody is moving gradually from its lower pitches to its higher pitches smoothly (*conjunct*) or if it is jumping from high to low in a more angular fashion (*disjunct*). Examples C and D in the animations below provide examples of a conjunct and a disjunct melody.

Watch MUSIC EXAMPLE C

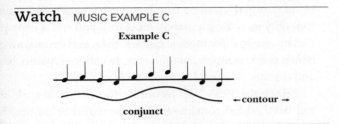

Example C

←contour→

conjunct

Disjunct—Notice that the contours of these two melodies are very different. One moves up and down smoothly (conjunct); the other is jagged and angular (disjunct). Melodic contours can be considered similar to the contours of landscapes: softly rolling hills (like the Appalachian Mountains) versus angular mountain ranges (like the Rocky Mountains or the Himalayas).

Watch MUSIC EXAMPLE D

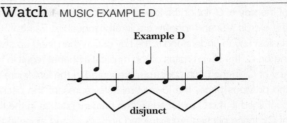

Example D

disjunct

Motive—Sometimes melodies are repetitive. In a repetitive melody, a short melodic pattern (*motive*) might be repeated over and over. This is quite distinct from the kind of melody that seems to spin itself out continually, rarely repeating itself. Finally, we should note briefly that sometimes melodies are combined with other melodies simultaneously. This is an important idea and will be discussed further when we speak of musical texture.

place your entire forearm down on a piano keyboard, the resulting sound will be a chord—not a particularly pretty chord, but a chord nevertheless.

Over the centuries, musicians have developed a way of creating chords that sound a bit better than the one you and your forearm may have just created. The most basic traditional chord consists of the minimum number of notes—three—and is called a **triad** (note the appearance of the prefix "tri-," meaning three). But as you might guess, a traditional triad is not just any three notes. There is a system for creating a pleasant-sounding traditional triad. Within the Western musical tradition, musicians commonly work with seven pitches, named according to the first seven letters of the alphabet: *A*, *B*, *C*, *D*, *E*, *F*, and *G*. There are also alterations to these notes, including sharps (slightly raised in pitch) and flats (slightly lowered in pitch), but we do not need to worry about them just yet. To create a traditional triad, one starts on any of the seven basic pitches, skips the next one, plays the third one, skips the fourth one, and plays the fifth one.

Watch MUSIC EXAMPLE E

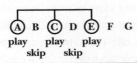

(A) B (C) D (E) F G
play play play
skip skip

Music Example E represents a triad consisting of the notes A, C, and E. We call it the A triad because A is its basic, or **root**, pitch. If one used C as the root of a triad, the three notes constituting the chord would be C, E, and G. The musical alphabet repeats up and down the pitch spectrum as follows:

Watch MUSIC EXAMPLE F

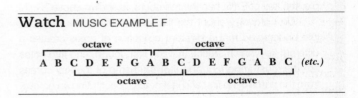

octave   octave
A B C D E F G A B C D E F G A B C (etc.)
octave   octave

The distance from a given note to the next occurrence of that same note in the musical alphabet is called an *octave*.

Chords are extremely important in music. If all we had were melody and rhythm, music would sound rather empty. Harmony is used to accompany melodies and to fill out the sound of the music. Effective harmonic practice is not a simple matter. For now, be sure you understand the concept of the traditional triad. More complicated chord structures will be explained later in this course, as necessary.

Tonality

Closely related to harmony is the concept of tonality.

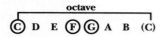

You have probably heard musicians or informed listeners speak of the **key** of B-flat or the key of E. For most traditional music, the words *key* and *tonality* are interchangeable. Perhaps the easiest key to understand is the key of C. When lined up starting on C, the seven notes of the musical alphabet result in the key of C. In the pitch spectrum presented in the last figure on the previous page, the lower brackets represent the pitches contained in the C major scale (the primary pitches in the key of C); these pitches are extracted and presented alone in the above figure.

The note C is the beginning and ending note, so we call this entire key C. Also of great importance are the fourth and fifth notes of the key, F and G.

Watch MUSIC EXAMPLE G

```
G   A   B   C   D   E   F ⌈ G
E   F   G   A   B   C   D │ E
Ⓒ   D   E   Ⓕ   Ⓖ   A   B ⌊ Ⓒ
```

Each note in the key of C can serve as the root of its own triad (represented as three vertical pitches in the figure above).

Watch MUSIC EXAMPLE H

```
B♭   C   D   E♭   F   G   A♭ ⌈ B♭
G    A♭  B♭  C    D   E♭  F  │ G
Ⓔ♭  F   G   Ⓐ♭  Ⓑ♭  C   D  ⌊ Ⓔ♭
```

Other keys have a different sequence of notes; for example, the key of E-flat has the members as shown above.

Do not worry about the flat symbols (♭) in this example; just understand that a different collection of notes creates a different key. Again, notice that the first, fourth, and fifth notes are the most important and that the name of the key comes from the name of he first and last notes, constituting an octave.

We will have more to say about keys and chords in another Musical Close-Up later in this chapter.

1.1.4: Timbre

Next, we must consider the exact quality of the sounds being produced. After all, pianos do not sound like clarinets, and clarinets do not sound like guitars. The difference in the sound quality of these instruments involves *timbre*— the tone quality of sound. Have you ever thought about how many different voices you recognize? Even if they were all speaking exactly the same words, you would probably recognize the voices of your parents, your siblings, quite a few close friends, several movie and television stars, and even some politicians. Each voice has a distinctive sound quality, or timbre (pronounced "TAM-burr").

Composers must decide whether a melody is to be played on a trumpet or saxophone and whether a chord is to be played by piano, banjo, or guitar. Should the bass be an acoustic string bass, a tuba, or an electric bass guitar? Decisions like these have a significant impact on how the final piece of music sounds. Elvis's "Hound Dog" would not be the same if it were played by a marching band, even if the melody, harmony, and rhythm were exactly the same. Certain timbres are associated with certain styles of music. Dixieland jazz sounds best when played by a small ensemble of trumpet, clarinet, trombone, tuba, banjo, and drums (possibly including a piano); most rock and roll is exemplified by one to three electric guitars, bass, and drums; swing bands need trumpets, saxophones, trombones, piano, bass, and drums.

Since the 1950s, the recording industry and rock and roll have added considerably to the world of timbre. For one thing, there is now a huge arsenal of electronic instruments to be considered. Some are basically acoustic instruments, the sounds of which are electronically amplified, like guitars. However, in many cases, the sound itself is electronically produced and modified; one of the most notable of these instruments is the synthesizer (to be discussed later in this chapter). Also, the contemporary recording studio can do much to change the timbre of the musical product. With today's technical resources for mixing, overdubbing, editing, and processing (including echo, flanging, pitch shifting ["auto tuning"], time stretching, etc.), the competent studio engineer can dramatically alter the sound of the basic raw material. This, too, is an aspect of timbre.

1.1.5: Texture

One of the factors that makes a given piece of music sound the way it does is its musical *texture*—the way the various musical lines function in relation to one another.

Types of Musical Textures

There are three basic possibilities: *monophony, homophony,* and *polyphony*.

Monophony—Monophony is the simplest musical texture. Monophonic texture exists when there is one, *and only one,* musical line. Thus, one singer, without any accompaniment, singing a solo line is an example of monophony. The essential point is not how many singers (or players) there are, but how many musical lines. Thus, 10 singers—if they are all singing exactly the same melodic line—would still create a monophonic texture.

Homophony—*Homophony* is a bit more complex. In a homophonic texture, one musical line predominates, but other lines are also present in a subservient role. One of the most common types of homophony is the melody-and-accompaniment texture. Here, one line is clearly the melody, and all other musical sounds serve as accompaniment. A folk singer accompanied by a guitar is an example of homophony. Perhaps you have heard church hymns in which the top line is the primary melodic line and the other three parts simply harmonize the melody. This is another type of homophony (chordal), but again, one line predominates and the other lines are subservient.

Polyphony—In *polyphony*, there are two or more independent lines of approximately equal importance. If you have ever sung a round like "Row, Row, Row Your Boat," you have participated in a polyphonic texture. One singer begins the song, and then a second singer begins four beats later; if a third singer is available, he or she begins four beats after the second singer. Each singer is singing the tune rather independently, but each part is just as important as the others. This type of polyphony is called imitative polyphony because one part imitates the other parts. Another form of polyphony is called nonimitative polyphony, because—though the various parts are considered equally important—they do not imitate one another musically. The nonimitative form of polyphony is more common than imitative polyphony within popular music contexts. Music that is polyphonic can be a bit difficult to listen to at first because it sounds so busy. There are, after all, multiple melodic lines to try to hear, rather than just one.

To avoid potential confusion, allow me to differentiate further the examples of monophony from imitative polyphony provided above. You may have noticed that both described the use of the same melody, but—in the imitative polyphonic example—occurrences of these melodies began at different points in time. In order for a musical texture to be considered monophonic, all voices and instruments must perform the same exact melody beginning and ending *at the same time*.

Sometimes, we speak of texture as being thick or thin. In this sense, texture may be perceived as a continuum. Two singers singing a duet would be on one end of the continuum—a very thin texture. On the opposite end, we might find a song with several vocal melodic lines, a full orchestra with the high brass playing fanfare-like material, the strings playing scale passages, the woodwinds playing frilly ornaments, the low brass playing a powerful countermelody, and the percussion pounding a frenzied rhythm. Add a background chorus

and some synthesizer chords, and we have a very thick texture.

Most popular music, including rock and roll, utilizes the melody-and-accompaniment texture, a type of homophony. On occasion, however, some musically creative minds have explored other textures; I will take special note of such cases as we encounter them throughout this course.

1.1.6: Loudness and Form

When a vibrating body (a string or drumhead) is displaced a little, it produces a relatively quiet sound; when it is displaced a lot, it produces a louder sound. If you barely touch a piano key, the hammer inside the instrument touches the string lightly and hardly moves it, producing a very soft sound. If you give the key a sharp whack, the hammer pops against the string, setting it into violent motion, and producing a louder sound. Technically, this is called the amplitude (amount of displacement) of a vibrating body. Usually, though, we call it **loudness** (or **volume**).

Most rock and roll is loud, but we will study some styles and songs that use a variety of loudness levels. As with any of the elements of music, the constant, unchanging use of a certain element leads to boredom. *Dynamics* is the term musicians use to describe the various fluctuations in loudness. The creative mind skillfully manipulates all of the available musical elements—including dynamics.

FORM *Form* is the organizational structure of a piece of music. It is the result of changes in some or all of the musical elements.

1.1.7: A Word about Words

Technically speaking, the words of a song (lyrics) are not an integral part of the music. Thus, although "Yesterday" by the Beatles certainly has words, there are many purely instrumental arrangements of this same song that are entirely recognizable, even though no lyrics are sung or spoken. Nevertheless, lyrics are intimately associated with the music of most popular songs.

The level of importance assigned to lyrics varies greatly from listener to listener. Many people say, "Oh, I don't really pay attention to the words; I just like the music (or the beat)." Yet, despite this claim, these individuals can often sing the words along with an instrumental arrangement or mouth the words as the song is being played on the radio. If the music suddenly stops, they continue singing the tune by themselves, words and all.

Too often, however, people think only of lyrics and forget about the music. For example, if asked to write a paper about the music of a 1960s folk singer or group, students often write all about the protest songs, the antiwar sentiments, the pleas for racial equality, the love songs, the symbolism, and so on. Often, little is said about the melodic lines, harmonies, forms, and other musical elements.

Lyrics constitute verbal expression, while music is a form of nonverbal expression. Frequently, we listen closely to songs with lyrics but find our minds wandering when listening to pure instrumental music. Perhaps this is because the average non-musician understands the verbal language of the lyrics but does not understand the nonverbal language of the instrumental sounds. Similarly, we can usually identify an artist or group by ear when one or more voices are singing words. But it is more difficult to identify correctly purely instrumental groups.

However, music, too, is a language. The trained musician has learned to communicate using that language. It is just as intelligible, and perhaps even more powerful, than verbal language. I hope this course will enhance your appreciation of, and ability to understand, some aspects of this nonverbal language.

One final word about words: Just as with the other aspects of rock and roll, the lyrics have undergone dramatic stylistic changes through the five decades of rock and roll history. At times, the lyrics have been the subject of derision and, at other times, the subject of heated controversy. This study will comment on the verbal aspects of rock as one part of the total picture, distinct from the music yet intimately associated with it.

An Example Illustrating Musical Form

Musical form is often considered one of the most difficult elements of music to identify. Because music flows in time and does not stop to wait for audience members to keep up, listeners must remain vigilant as they experience musical sound. This distinction is sometimes made by using the term *hearing* (passive listening, when sound simply washes over the listener) in contrast to *listening* (a proactive process of engaging with musical sound, allowing listeners to utilize listening skills at their disposal). At various times throughout this course, I will refer to the musical form of a given composition. This slide will provide you the tools necessary to begin to consider this important aspect of music listening. Through the use of a familiar analogy (the structure of a TV show), the following example will help you develop a basic understanding of musical form. As you read through later material, you will have many opportunities to apply this knowledge in a variety of musical contexts.

Think for a moment about one of your favorite television shows. Possibly, there is a short teaser, or introduction, that gives you a hint of what is to come and sets the scene. After a commercial, there is a series of scenes that set forth the primary and secondary characters and problems in that particular episode. Following another commercial, another series of scenes introduces more complications and conflicts. After another commercial, a series of scenes leads to a turning point of some kind that suggests that the end is in sight and all will be well. A final scene shows the happy participants basking in the glow of another successful escapade.

The series of scenes described, whether a television show or an episodic adventure viewed online, exists over a period of time (usually 30 to 60 minutes) and is organized into sections and subsections. The sections and subsections are delineated by changes, as characters appear and disappear, as complications arise and are resolved, and as settings change.

Musical compositions typically follow a similar organizational structure. Often, a song begins with an introduction; then, there is a section that introduces a main melody and the lyrical topic. This section may be repeated with new lyrics. Next, there may be a section with new music and new lyrics. Subsequent sections may repeat or vary earlier music with new or repeated lyrics.

Music Example I

Intro | A | A′ | B | A″ | Instr. break | A″ | Fade-out

Usually, there is an instrumental section near the middle of the piece and a fade-out section at the end. We can chart this organizational structure as shown above.

In this diagram, the repeating *A* section shows that the music is repeated; the single and double quotation marks indicate the presence of new or altered lyrics. What specifically signals that a section is ending and a new section is beginning?

The answer is simple: a change in one or more of the musical elements. From one section to the next, there may be a change in the rhythm, melody, key, texture, or lyrics. At any juncture in the musical form, there are a limited set of options: The musicians can (a) repeat previous material (*repetition*), (b) play new material (*contrast*), or (c) play something based on earlier material, but not an exact repetition (we call this last one *variation* or *development*). This may sound complicated, but you will be surprised how easy it is to perceive the changes from section to section once you begin to listen actively to musical sound as you proceed through this course.

REVIEW: THE ELEMENTS OF MUSIC

Here is an opportunity to evaluate how familiar you are with some of the important musical terms introduced so far.

Statements
1. _____ refers to the interrelationship between music and time.
2. _____ is the term musicians use to describe the various fluctuations in loudness.
3. _____ is the combination of notes, simultaneously.
4. The _____ is the most basic traditional chord.
5. _____ is the tone quality of sound.
6. When three or more notes are sounded simultaneously it is called a _____.
7. The distance from a given note to its next occurrence in the musical alphabet is called an _____.
8. _____ is the term used when a melody is jumping from high to low.
9. _____ is the way the various musical lines function in relation to one another.
10. _____ is the simplest musical texture.
11. _____ is the term used when a melody is moving gradually from its lower pitches to its higher pitches.
12. _____ is the organizational structure of a piece of music.
13. The _____ of a melody describes the distance between the highest and the lowest notes of the melody.

Feedback: 1. Rhythm 2. Dynamics 3. Harmony 4. Triad 5. Timbre 6. Chord 7. Octave 8. Disjunct 9. Texture 10. Monophony 11. Conjunct 12. Form 13. Range

1.2: Musical Close-Up on Instrumentation in Rock and Roll

OBJECTIVE: Relate instrumentation with the history of rock and roll

When we think of rock and roll, we usually think of electric guitars, drums, and singers. These have, in fact, been the essential ingredients for a rock and roll band from the early 1950s to today. However, there have been changes in the nature of these instruments, and some styles have added other instruments to the rock and roll ensemble. In this section, we shall briefly survey the instrumentation of rock from 1955 to today and then take a closer look at some specific instruments.

1.2.1: Guitar

Guitars, the basic instruments of all rock and roll, come in two basic varieties: acoustic and electric. Some early rock and rollers (e.g., Elvis Presley) started with the acoustic guitar, but most quickly learned that the unamplified acoustic guitar was no match for the electric guitars, piano, saxophone, and drums of the evolving rock ensemble. Some guitarists stayed with their acoustic instruments, merely adding electronic amplification by attaching a

History of Instrumentation of Rock

Like the sound of rock music itself, the number and types of instruments used in recording rock tunes has evolved. This simulation will take you on a brief tour of the instruments used in rock recordings from the 1950s to the 1980s.

The 1950s—The typical 1950s rock and roll band consisted of four to six players. The usual instruments included drums, bass (acoustic), two electric guitars (one rhythm and one lead), piano (acoustic), and saxophone (alto or tenor, the former playing in a higher pitch range than the latter). Some bands, of course, varied from this basic ensemble. Thus, Bill Haley's Comets included a steel guitar instead of a piano, reflecting their country and western (C&W) background. Buddy Holly's Crickets used only drums, an acoustic bass, and two guitars. Elvis Presley's early Sun recordings consist of only two guitars and a bass. Jerry Lee Lewis's early hits also incorporate a trio: piano, guitar, and drums. Little Richard's recording sessions for his big hits on Specialty Records used various instrumental lineups but usually included piano, bass, drums, guitar, and several saxophones.

The 1960s—Rock music of the 1960s included a greater diversification in instrumentation. The Beatles' lineup of two guitars (lead and rhythm), electric bass, and drums was widely imitated. If any instrument was added to this basic foursome, it was usually piano (increasingly in its electronic form and with its various electronic spin-offs). The folk movement of the 1960s went back to basics, using acoustic guitar, harmonica, banjo, acoustic bass, and sometimes bongo drums. The Motown sound featured a vocal group plus full orchestral instrumentation, similar to many early **Pop** recordings. Finally, the jazz-rock trend near the end of the decade added a horn section, consisting of trumpet(s), woodwinds (saxes or flute), and trombone.

The 1970s and the 1980s—The 1970s and 1980s witnessed the expansion of electronic instruments. Every few months, a new electronic keyboard appeared that rendered its predecessors outdated. One family of such instruments, the *synthesizer*, can emulate a myriad of instrumental sounds, from guitar to flute to drums, as well as create original sounds not produced by traditional, acoustic musical instruments. Early synthesizers were controlled by a piano-like keyboard—something most musicians know—as a way for the player to signal the note to be played. So it was natural for the pianist—now called the "keyboard player" to represent expertise beyond the piano—to be the first in rock groups to embrace the instrument.

Other than this electronic expansion, the basic instrumentation of the 1960s was simply carried forward. The ensemble of three or four guitars (including bass) and drums remained basic to hard rock and heavy metal. Some black groups continued to use brass and woodwind instruments; disco utilized full orchestral instrumentation. In recent decades, the electronic explosion has continued with increasing use of guitar synthesizers, drum machines, and computer-interfaced keyboards.

Important Developments for the Electric Guitar

If there is one instrument that represents the world of rock and roll for many people, it is the electric guitar. Almost from its beginning, the electric guitar has been an essential element of the rock sound. This simulation will provide information about some of the most important developments to this central instrument, all of which opened new doors of possibility in the sounds available to rock guitarists.

In 1954, Leo Fender introduced the Stratocaster, a solid-body guitar that became the model for electric guitars in rock and roll for many years. The Gibson company, another leading guitar manufacturer since the early part of the 20th century, introduced a solid-body electric guitar in 1952, designed by and named for Les Paul, a renowned jazz and country guitarist and himself a pioneer in the development of the electric guitar.

Among important later developments is the wireless electric guitar system, which broadcasts its electric signal to an amplifier via a transmitter connected to the guitar, so that the performer is not attached directly to the amplifier by an umbilical-like cable. This has had important ramifications for onstage performance, allowing some of the more acrobatic acts to run, jump, roll, and cavort all over a huge and elaborate stage setting (or into the audience), without fear of entangling themselves in wires. There are many other important developments to consider. Over the years, there have been various experiments with the basic guitar sound of rock and roll. Some of these include the 12-string guitars (the most common type of guitar has 6 strings) and double-necked guitars (sometimes one neck has 6 strings, while the other has 12).

In the early 1950s, near the same time as the introduction of the Stratocaster described previously, Leo Fender introduced the solid-body electric bass guitar. Some early rock and roll bands continued to prefer the acoustic bass, but, by the end of the decade, most bass players had switched to the electric instrument. By the 1960s, the old stand-up bass was gone, except in some folk- or country-influenced bands (rockabilly). The electric bass was much more portable and provided powerful bass lines that could match the loudness level of the drums, electric guitars, and electric pianos.

Through the late 1970s and early 1980s, synthesizer technology—once the province of the keyboard player—became available to the guitarist. Although the guitarist appears to be playing a typical electric guitar, she or he is really sending a series of electrical impulses to a synthesizer that has the capability to translate the notes into the timbre of a flute, trumpet, or any other sound the synthesizer can produce.

contact microphone to capture the instrument's vibrations, a fairly common practice since the mid-1930s. However, except for the folk- or country-influenced rock performers, rock guitarists quickly adopted the true electric guitar (with pickups embedded in the guitar body) as the basic instrument.

Electric guitars incorporate electromagnetic pickup devices placed below the steel strings that send a signal through an amplifier and on to a loudspeaker. Various controls operated by the hands or feet can change loudness, tone, and equalization and can add special effects, such as reverberation, distortion, wah-wah, and phase shifting. Because electric guitars do not require the wooden sound chamber of the acoustic guitar, they may be made of metal or wood, have hollow or solid bodies, and take on a variety of shapes.

1.2.2: Voice

One of the most basic and essential instruments of all is the human voice. Although there are a number of purely instrumental rock hits, the vast majority contains vocals. When asked to name rock stars, we will almost invariably name singers (some, of course, may also be instrumentalists—usually guitarists or keyboard players).

Types of Early Rock Vocalists

A primary way in which variety could be found—even in early rock and roll—was the style of the vocalist(s). A wide range of styles were represented, revealing influence from a variety of musical styles, including Pop and rhythm and blues (R&B).

The Crooners—In the early 1950s, the ideal Pop singer was the crooner, who was at his or her best singing soft, slow love songs—so-called ballads. The **crooner** (most often male) had a pleasant voice quality in the traditional sense, singing perfectly in tune with a wide pitch range and excellent control of the voice. This ideal carried over into the softer side of rock with singers like Pat Boone, Paul Anka, Frankie Avalon, the Carpenters, and Barry Manilow.

The Shouters—On the opposite end of the continuum from the crooners were the **shouters** (or screamers). There is little precedence for this style in white music prior to rock and roll. However, R&B singers had developed a shouting style several decades before rock and roll. R&B stars like Joe Turner, Big Mama Thornton, Wynonie Harris, and Elmore James half sang, half shouted their songs. There was usually a harsh, raspy quality to the voice. The general melodic contour was followed, but exact melodic pitches were only approximated. This shouting style carried over into the harder styles of rock and roll, best exemplified in the early days by Little Richard and later by Janis Joplin, James Brown, and a host of the hard rock and heavy metal bands of the 1970s, 1980s, and beyond.

The Mainstream Singers—In between the crooners and the shouters was a wide variety of vocal styles. Characterized by a harder and more powerful vocal quality than the crooners, these mainstream singers typically adhered to the correct melodic pitches but were prone to provide strong vocal accents, bend some pitches, and add various vocal embellishments to their rhythmically driving songs. This large middle ground between crooners and shouters is exemplified by such diverse singers as Jerry Lee Lewis, Fats Domino, the Beach Boys, and a good many of the Motown singers of the 1960s and later.

A Drum Set

SOURCE: Drum Kit/Dorling Kindersley Limited

Of course, some of the more versatile performers can convincingly sing two or three styles. Using Presley as an example, consider these songs: "Hard-Headed Woman" (shouter), "Can't Help Falling in Love" (crooner); and "Heartbreak Hotel" (in-between). Although the terms *crooner* and *shouter* may prove useful in describing some singers, we should not force a label on a given voice, the most personal and unique of all musical instruments.

1.2.3: Drums

If rhythm is the heart of rock and roll, drums must be the central ingredient in the rock band. Except for a few very early rock recordings (influenced by their C&W background) and some folk music of the early 1960s, drums have been an integral part of the rock music scene.

The typical rock drum set (sometimes called trap set, or just traps) is played by one person and consists of a bass drum (played with a foot pedal), a snare drum, a combination of tom-toms, a ride cymbal, a pair of hi-hat cymbals, and a cowbell. The drummer may use a variety of striking implements, including hard sticks, soft mallets, and wire brushes.

The makeup of rock drum sets remained relatively consistent from these early days until the mid- to late 1970s. Evidence of this development can be seen even earlier in the music of adventurous, musically sophisticated groups like Emerson, Lake & Palmer, and Pink Floyd. From 1975 to 1985, several important innovations occurred. The traditional acoustic drum requires a hollow-sounding chamber to shape and color its sound (thus, the big bass drum and the narrower, smaller snare drum), but innovators realized that the sound of a drumhead being struck by a stick could be produced electronically, initiating the advent of compact, solid-body drums. For example, Simmons made an early electronic drum set in which the

drumheads (or pads) have electronic pickups that sense how hard the pad is struck. Resulting pulses are then sent to a control unit that fires analog or digitally recorded sounds. Each drum was just a few inches deep, no longer needing to vary its physical dimensions to produce the desired sounds. With these systems, an entire drum set can be packed into a relatively small case and easily transported. Drummers like that.

What many drummers do not like is the development of electronic drum machines. Even in the earliest days of sound synthesis, the various drum sounds (snare, bass, cymbal, etc.) were among the easiest sounds to reproduce electronically. With the arrival of digital sampling (to be discussed in detail later in this text) and the computer-based digital audio workstation, the precision with which drum tracks can be created is truly astounding—even to the point of intentionally introducing "imperfections" (expressive deviations in time), so that the manually created drum part does not sound "mechanical." The user can program a steady bass drum beat and a variety of **subdivisions** on a snare drum, a tom-tom, and cymbals. Accents may be added using a cowbell or hand-clap sounds. Drum machines are easy to use and reproduce an impressively believable drum sound with absolute technical accuracy; most of the earliest could store about 100 patterns and 10 full-length songs in memory for instant recall. Using a more recent, computer-based system, the number of patterns that can be stored is limited only by the memory storage of your computer, resulting in a nearly limitless capacity.

1.2.4: Keyboards

In the beginning, there was the simple, upright piano with two or three pedals and 88 keys. Since rock's early days, however, a bewildering catalog of keyboards of every size, shape, and description has appeared. About the time that the performer has invested in and mastered a shiny new keyboard, a newer and shinier one with additional capabilities is marketed that makes the former one seem old-fashioned and outdated. The purpose of the present section will not be to describe every modern keyboard technology that has emerged, but to discuss a few of the principal models from which the others are derived.

One of the problems pianists faced was that they were at the mercy of the instrument they found at the performance site; if the piano was not properly maintained, pedals would fail to work, some of the keys would not play, or the instrument would be out of tune. The electric piano, which was portable enough for the keyboard player to transport it from gig to gig, solved this. In the mid- to late 1960s, it gradually replaced the acoustic piano in most rock bands. At least the performer could be sure the piano was in tune, all its notes played, and it could be placed anywhere on stage.

Even though electric pianos often had shortened keyboards (usually only 64 notes, rather than the 88 found on most upright and grand pianos) and did not sound exactly like the acoustic piano, practicality triumphed, and the electric piano became the standard keyboard for rock and roll. Soon, there were variations on the basic electric piano. For example, the clavinet allowed the pianist to switch between two different timbres; RMI made an instrument that allowed a similar switch between a piano and a harpsichord sound.

This turn to electronics launched a revolution in rock and roll keyboards. New electronic keyboard instruments appeared that attempted to imitate a wider variety of instruments. An early example was the *Mellotron*, an instrument that used tapes of prerecorded tones by various instruments. The popular Mellotron 400 contained a rack of tapes with three tracks, each of which contained a recording of acoustic instruments: brass, strings, or flute. By selecting one of these three timbres and then pressing a key, the performer produced the recorded sound of a particular instrument playing a particular note. Although a number of groups experimented with the Mellotron, its sound became especially identified with the Moody Blues. (Perhaps the most famous Mellotron solo can be heard at the beginning of "Strawberry Fields Forever" by the Beatles, another group that used the instrument.)

SYNTHESIZERS At about the same time (late 1960s and early 1970s), smaller synthesizers were being developed that were portable enough to be transported and used in live performance. Basically, analog synthesizers do two things: they generate sounds by means of oscillators and they modify sounds by means of various devices (filters, envelope shapers, and ring modulators). With the synthesizer, the keyboard player could produce an entire range of sounds by mastering a complex set of knobs, buttons, slides, and patch cords. It required some retraining, but the result was worth the trouble. Later, digital synthesizers (like the Yamaha DX7, introduced in 1983) eliminated the buttons, knobs, and patch cords, allowing sounds to be created using a small liquid crystal display (or LCD) interface and a slider. A great advantage of this next generation of synthesizers was the ability to store *patches* (different instrument sounds) in memory for later recall; it was possible to use an external library to store hundreds (or even thousands) of unique sounds that could be easily recalled in performance.

As the synthesizer revolution advanced, newer, easier-to-use models poured into the marketplace. Some specialized in string sounds, whereas others allowed for a variety of preprogrammed sounds, each available at the touch of a button. Add-ons were developed, such as the *sequencer*, which allowed the user to set up a series of pitches, rhythms, timbres, and volumes that could be set into motion at the flip of a switch. The inevitable linkage between the computer and the synthesizer was clearly established with the development of *Musical Instrument Digital Interface (MIDI)*, a protocol established in 1983 to standardize communication between computers and electronic keyboards.

Electronic organs, instruments that predate the beginnings of rock and roll, added still other sounds to the rock keyboard player's resources. Laurens Hammond introduced the electronic organ in 1939. As rock musicians discovered its sound in the 1960s (most notably the Hammond B-3 model), other companies (e.g., Farfisa and Vox) entered the market in competition with Hammond.

The keyboard player of the 1970s and 1980s was typically surrounded by four to six keyboards, each with a specialized role to play. The most elaborate electronic keyboardists (e.g., Keith Emerson and Rick Wakeman) confronted racks of instruments that resembled the cockpit of a 747. As these innovations continued into the 1990s and the new millennium, the number of keyboards necessary onstage was reduced substantially by the introduction of *soft synths*, software-based synthesizers that run as computer software, producing sounds in real time in response to MIDI messages sent from a connected keyboard controller.

1.2.5: Saxophone

There are five basic saxophones (saxes); from highest to lowest pitch range, they are soprano, alto, tenor, baritone, and bass. Because the fingering among all of the saxes is similar, the typical saxophonist can play at least alto and tenor, and many can easily switch to any of the saxes. The saxophone (sax) became a favorite instrument in jazz of the 1930s and 1940s, crossing over into R&B as well. Black bluesmen particularly favored the versatility and sensual sound of the tenor sax. Thus, it was natural that early rock and roll bands, which borrowed so much from R&B, often included a saxophone. Fats Domino's songs usually included not only a saxophone accompaniment, but frequently a sax solo at the instrumental break. Little Richard's bands included up to four saxophones. Even Bill Haley's Comets, in spite of their primarily C&W background, included a saxophone.

Since this early period, saxophones have alternately appeared and disappeared in various rock styles. The Motown sound of the 1960s utilized the saxophone, especially the baritone sax, which doubled bass lines and occasionally played solos. The jazz-rock sound of the late 1960s and early 1970s incorporated various saxophones, along with other brass and woodwind instruments. The sound of the soprano sax became particularly popular in the early 1970s, with groups such as Weather Report and Chuck Mangione's band. Throughout his career, David Bowie played saxophone on many of his recordings. Between the years 1975 to 1985, occasional specialty songs featured the sax, and many groups—such as Earth, Wind & Fire—continued to rely on its sound.

BECOME AN ACTIVE LISTENER: ROCK INSTRUMENTATION

Now it's time for you to apply some of the knowledge you have gained in this chapter. Listen to some of the listening examples described or peruse your favorite contemporary recordings. As you listen, use your developing listening skills to identify some of the instruments and other sounds discussed.

1. Find examples of these guitar sounds in songs that you like: reverb, wah-wah, and phase shifting.

2. Find examples of these vocal performance styles in songs that you like: shouter, crooner, and in-between.

3. Find examples of these drum sounds in songs that you like: bass drum, snare drum, cymbals, and drum machine.

4. Find examples of these keyboard instruments in songs that you like: piano, organ, and synthesizer.

1.3: The Early 1950s

OBJECTIVE: Explain the cultural influences in the music market in the early 1950s

Preceded and followed by turbulent decades, the 1950s seemed serene and comfortable. The late 1920s to mid-1930s were years of extreme financial pressure. The early 1940s were consumed by the most destructive war the world has ever known. From 1950 to 1952, the United States was involved in a so-called "police action" (war) in Korea. The decade following the 1950s was one of the most turbulent in our nation's history, a time of social and political unrest and another war (Vietnam).

1.3.1: The General Society

Certainly no decade is trouble-free. Even the 1950s witnessed several dramatic issues. Senator Joe McCarthy stirred up considerable controversy regarding the invasion of American society by communism. The Supreme Court issued a landmark decision in 1954 that declared the policy of "separate but equal" education for blacks and whites to be unconstitutional. A lingering fear of "the bomb" caused many people to build bomb shelters in their backyards and prompted schools to hold weekly air raid drills.

In general, despite these concerns, things were relatively good. General Dwight Eisenhower was inaugurated as president in 1953. The economy stabilized with little or no inflation. There was a feeling of well-being throughout the nation. After years of war and depression, American society was finally able to settle down and go on with the business of progress. Families looked forward to a stable and relatively predictable future. The traditional game plan was clear: Do well in school, go to college, marry, and raise a family somewhat more affluently than you were raised. This plan called for men to follow their careers and provide well for their families; women were to keep a stable and decent environment functioning at home. If one followed the game plan, personal happiness and professional success were believed to be the inevitable rewards.

Gradually, economic affluence sifted down to middle-class families that were now able to own a home, buy a new car, take a vacation, and purchase a newcomer to the entertainment scene: a television set. The fascination with television during this era was overwhelming. There were those who would watch a test pattern if nothing else was on! The programming was good, clean family entertainment: variety shows, family comedies, westerns, children's shows, news, cartoons, drama, sports, and music (e.g., *Your Hit Parade*).

The popular music of the early 1950s fit the pattern perfectly. Most of the nation was listening to a style of music we shall refer to as *Pop*. This style of music was a continuation of the popular styles of earlier decades. The lyrics typically dealt with innocent, boy-girl love; the lyrical and musical content was nonthreatening. Like society in general, Pop sought to be comfortable, pleasant, and righteous; excess was avoided. Musically, it seemed to express a society's desire to be left alone to enjoy the good life, unthreatened by the turmoil, controversy, and ugliness endured in previous decades.

1.3.2: Subcultures

Of course, we oversimplify when we speak of "society." Although we may use the term to represent the majority of average citizens, we must also recognize a number of subcultures that evidenced characteristics quite different from the norms of the idealized society in general. To begin our study of rock and roll, we must focus on two of these subcultures.

The black culture of the early 1950s was quite distinct from white, middle-class society. Racial segregation was the norm, especially in the South and the Southwest. It is hard for us to realize today that it was just over 50 years ago that blacks were required to sit in the last three or four rows of city buses. Public areas usually had separate drinking fountains and bathrooms for "colored" and "white." Blacks were routinely barred from many public accommodations, such as hotels and restaurants. Separate housing districts and schools continued to exist for blacks and whites long after the 1954 Supreme Court decision barring segregation in public schools.

With such strict segregation during the mid-twentieth century, it is not at all surprising that these segregated cultures would maintain their own distinct characteristics, including spoken dialect, dance, religion, dress, and music. Among the musical styles associated with the black culture were jazz (in a variety of substyles), gospel (a religiously oriented style), and rhythm and blues. **Rhythm and blues (R&B), one of a variety of styles evolving from the blues during the early twentieth century, is of great importance in our story of the development of rock and roll.**

Related to jazz, the spiritual and gospel styles, R&B evolved as a distinct style. Just as blacks and whites were segregated, so R&B existed separately from the Pop market. R&B had its own performers, record companies, and consumers. R&B records, often referred to as "race records" at the time, sold within their own distinct market. An R&B performer or record rarely crossed over into the national Pop market (similarly, Pop rarely infiltrated the R&B market).

A second subculture was identified with country and western (C&W) music. The poorer whites of the South developed a style of folk music often referred to as "hillbilly music." As time passed and the style spread, variations inevitably occurred (e.g., bluegrass and western swing). As with R&B, the C&W market was quite distinct from the larger Pop market. Appealing primarily to poorer rural whites in the South, Midwest, and Southwest, C&W maintained its own performers, record companies, and consumers. Pop songs rarely crossed over into the C&W market. However, a few C&W performers and songs managed to break into the national Pop scene (more about that later).

JOURNAL

The Convergence of Musical Styles

Based on the information that you have read in this chapter and on your prior knowledge of American society in the late 1940s and early 1950s, describe three ways that race, affluence, and other societal factors may have influenced the division of musical styles leading to the mid-50s into separate markets. Then, take a moment to reflect on the convergence that occurred with the popularity of Bill Haley and Elvis Presley. Do you believe that this convergence—along with rock music that followed during the next decade—had an impact on societal change that led to the civil rights movement of the 1960s? Why or why not?

 The response entered here will appear in the performance dashboard and can be viewed by your instructor.

Submit

1.4: The Pop Music Market

OBJECTIVE: Summarize how the Pop music market contributes to the formation of rock and roll

Each of the three markets described in the previous section—Pop, R&B, and C&W—contributed in varying degrees to the formation of rock and roll. R&B was by far the heaviest musical contributor; C&W also made its contribution; Pop contributed the least but must not be overlooked. In the following sections, we will delve deeper into the specific contributions made by each of these musical styles, facilitating the emergence of rock and roll.

1.4.1: Tin Pan Alley

To appreciate the tremendous impact of rock and roll, one must first understand the nature of the popular music the nation listened to in the early 1950s. Pop was derived from the long Tin Pan Alley tradition, with influences from the swing period of the 1930s and early 1940s, Hollywood movie music, and Broadway show tunes. *Tin Pan Alley* is the name given to an area of New York City that became the center of popular music publishing from the late 1800s to the late 1950s. Tin Pan Alley songs were written primarily by white, professional songwriters. Although the style changed over the decades, certain general characteristics remained constant.

Typically, the lyrics were non-offensive, noncontroversial, and, most often, dealt with simple, romantic love. Usually, Tin Pan Alley songs had a very straight, uncomplicated rhythm, with four (or sometimes three) beats to each measure. The rhythm was kept in the

Table 1.1 Ten Representative Selections of Top 50 Songs (1950–1954)

Title	Artist	Date of Peak Popularity	Comments
"Goodnight Irene"	The Weavers	August to November 1950	slow, lush, romantic ballad
"Mona Lisa"	Nat "King" Cole	July to August 1950	slow, romantic ballad
"Music, Music, Music"	Teresa Brewer	March to April 1950	upbeat, cute
"Tennessee Waltz"	Patti Page	January to February 1951	moderate tempo; cover of a C&W hit
"Too Young"	Nat "King" Cole	June to July 1951	slow, romantic ballad
"Cry"	Johnnie Ray	January to March 1952	an early example of emotive performance style; about lost love
"Wheel of Fortune"	Kay Starr	March to May 1952	moderate to slow; ballad
"Doggie in the Window"	Patti Page	March to May 1953	upbeat; cutesy, novelty song
"Wanted"	Perry Como	April to May 1954	slow; lonely-for-love song
"Hey There"	Rosemary Clooney	September to October 1954	slow love song; Broadway show tune

background of the musical fabric. Melodies were very important; they were usually rather easy to remember, so almost anyone could sing or whistle the tunes after hearing them a few times. The melodies were pretty, in a traditional sense; they usually moved freely within one octave (sometimes a little more) and moved stepwise or with small leaps. The melodic **contours** were interesting, much like a gently undulating curve. The musical material was symmetrically organized into units of four or eight measures (called *phrases*). Tempos were usually moderate to slow; faster tunes were typically bouncy and cute, often with light or humorous lyrics. Usually, the songs were recorded by professional singers with pleasing, well-trained voices and were often accompanied by a full orchestra and small chorus of background voices.

This Tin Pan Alley tradition was still very much alive in the Pop songs of the early 1950s. Songs from Broadway shows and Hollywood movies conformed to the popular style and provided a wealth of material. Table 1.1 provides 10 representative examples of Top 50 songs from 1950 to 1954, with a brief description of each.

Notice that all but two of these songs are in a slow-to-moderate tempo, most are love-oriented, and several are pure **instrumentals**. Two of the songs deserve additional comment. Nat "King" Cole's "Too Young" is a rather rare example of an early 1950s Pop song that speaks directly to youth. Specifically, it commiserates with a person who is told that she or he is too young to really be in love. Johnnie Ray's "Cry" is unusual because of the vocal style, which, due to Ray's very emotive performance, foreshadows the shouting emotionality of some early rockers. Note also that only one of the artists, Nat "King" Cole, was black, though during this period there were a few other black Pop performers, including the Mills Brothers and the Ink Spots. It is also worthy of note that commercially successful Pop

songs typically held their peak popularity for about two months. Usually, there was a period of rising popularity that lasted about four weeks and an equal period of declining popularity. Thus, a very popular hit song would exist on the charts for 16 to 20 weeks, sometimes as long as 25 weeks.

1.4.2: The Majors

Another facet of the early 1950s Pop market was its complete domination by a handful of large and powerful recording companies known as "the *majors*"—at the time, including RCA Victor, Columbia, Capitol, Mercury, and Decca. In 1954, of the 50 top-selling hit songs, 42 were produced by these five companies. Although the majors' biggest income came from Pop, they also produced classical, jazz, and some C&W recordings.

Nat "King" Cole, one of the successful artists with a major record label.

SOURCE: Eric Schwab/AFP/Getty Images

Role of the Majors in the Pop Music Market of the 1950s

The resources provided by a major record label greatly facilitated the success of signed artists. This simulation provides a detailed set of information about the many benefits these artists enjoyed.

These major companies held a large number of artists under contract. Their promotion and distribution systems were sophisticated and effective. Thus, when a new record was to be released, a nationwide promotional campaign was launched, and the product was distributed through a network of middlemen to retail outlets throughout the nation. Several of these major companies also produced phonographs (record players), were tied to radio and television networks and stations, and had subsidiary sheet music publishing operations. They truly seemed to have a stranglehold on the popular music industry.

The huge resources of these companies were used to create a very professional product. Professional composers and arrangers created the songs. The written arrangements were placed in the hands of professional, highly trained musicians. Typically, large musical forces were used, often including a full orchestra and small chorus. All of these musicians read their music; there was virtually no improvisation involved. The **lead singers** were most often also professionals; they read music and sang across a wide pitch range, with superb control and excellent voice quality.

The Pop market was national in its scope. Over a period of four to eight weeks, a song's popularity would peak in every regional market. Furthermore, it was not uncommon to have multiple versions of a hit song. Thus, if an artist on Columbia had commercial success with a particular song, the other majors would quickly produce a version of the same song, featuring one of their own artists.

Two final characteristics of considerable importance must be underscored. First, the Pop market was adult oriented. Although the 1950s were years of increasing affluence, the adults still controlled the money in the early years of the decade. The recording companies were controlled by adults, and the professional songwriters, performers, and consumers were adults. During this era, teens simply listened to and accepted their parents' music. There seemed to be no real alternative; in fact, most teens at the time saw nothing unusual about the situation.

Finally, the Pop market of the early 1950s was almost exclusively white. Again, the record company personnel, the songwriters, the performers, and the consumers were predominantly white. As with most aspects of the music industry, the basic reason had to do with the pocketbook. The adult whites were the primary consumers; thus, the recording industry aimed its product squarely at that market.

Neither the Pop consumer nor the recording industry could have anticipated that, within a few years, the music market would experience a total revolution—one that would reverse almost every one of the foregoing characteristics!

JOURNAL

Musical Elements in Pop Music

Choose three or four examples of Pop music discussed previously. Listen carefully to each song and, while the music is playing, write a description of the musical elements you can identify. Compare your responses across all of these songs. Are there some elements that are common to all? Are there other elements that are unique to a single recording? For much of the Pop music from this era, the general characteristics of the music remained relatively consistent. Why do you think that might have been the case?

▶ The response entered here will appear in the performance dashboard and can be viewed by your instructor.

Submit

1.5: The Subculture Music Market

OBJECTIVE: Compare how each of the subculture music markets contributed to the formation of rock and roll

Each of the three markets associated with different subcultures in America can be identified by distinctive musical characteristics associated with the musical elements. For example, a typical Pop recording of the late 1940s or early 1950s consists of crooning vocals and a highly memorable melody (tune), serving as a precursor to rock ballads and soft rock. The lyrical focus is frequently on romantic love and the rhythms tend to be straight and uncomplicated, remaining largely in the background so that primary attention is focused on the melody and the words. Pop incorporated a vast array of instrumental resources (sometimes a full orchestra with a choir). From a business perspective, the major labels had mastered the distribution of recordings and artist promotion, so, once the music was recorded, they were able to capitalize on these networks to achieve maximum sales.

Like Pop, the focus of C&W was largely on the melodies and lyrics, though there were significant differences between these two styles as well. For example, C&W artists introduced the yodel, which was influential as a basis for the emotional "crack" in the voices of many later rock vocalists. Artists performing this style of music also introduced the fiddle and pedal steel, which, in addition to being a direct harbinger for rockabilly, influenced the slide guitar sound that emerged in southern rock of the 1970s. The rhythmic component of C&W music was, typically, very basic and its harmonies tended to be more basic than those of Pop, a simplicity that was adopted by much rock music that followed.

In contrast to the other two styles, the primary musical element, when considering R&B, was the driving rhythm that served as the foundation for most rock music to come. R&B artists often used a shouting, highly emotional vocal style that became a common feature of mainstream rock in the late 1950s. R&B performers were primarily black and worked with independent labels; regional success was achieved without the massive distribution channels available to the majors. Many R&B songs were based on the 12-bar blues, a musical form that can still be found in rock music today. Beyond the 12-bar blues, the musical form was often loose, allowing an element of freedom and improvisation in performance; this became highly important to soul music of the 1960s and beyond.

1.5.1: Country and Western

Unlike the huge Pop market, the C&W market had a relatively small and regionally well-defined audience. Although there were C&W radio stations, performers, and recording companies all over the nation, by the early 1950s, the South, Southwest, and Midwest had become the real centers of development for this style. The most influential C&W-oriented radio show was *The Grand Ole Opry*, broadcast from Nashville's WSM radio station. During the transition from the late 1940s into the early 1950s, "the *Opry*" attracted more and more C&W songwriters and performers to Nashville.

Led by the Acuff-Rose publishing house, publishers flooded to Nashville. The recording industry was not far behind. The C&W market had been served largely by small, independent record companies scattered throughout the South, Southwest, and Midwest. Each of these small companies (called *indies*; a shortened form of "independents") was a low-budget operation with a few artists under contract. Each specialized in a certain sound that it hoped would make its products recognizable and distinct. They usually produced singles, rather than albums, because that is what they and their consumers could afford. Unlike the major companies, the indies' distribution system was simple and unsophisticated—often just a guy in a pickup truck carrying a box of records from store to store. To promote a new record, they did not need to blanket the country as the majors did. They could hit a well-defined list of radio stations in a specific set of cities in a certain geographic region. The system worked well.

This is not to say that the majors had no interest in C&W. Indeed, the majors produced a number of prominent C&W acts, often on subsidiary labels. First Decca and then Capitol, Columbia, and RCA established Nashville offices. The popularity of cowboy western movies in the 1930s and 1940s and cowboy television shows in the late 1940s and early 1950s had promoted a national market for the singing cowboy (Gene Autry, Roy Rogers and Dale Evans, and Tex Ritter). Their success opened the national Pop market to the C&W style. As a result, a number of major artists were able to escape the smaller C&W market and become national stars (Eddy Arnold and Hank Snow).

Like the Pop market, the C&W market consisted of white adults. Not generally an affluent market, what money did exist in the subculture was controlled by the adults.

CHARACTERISTICS OF C&W MUSIC   C&W music represented both similarities and dissimilarities in comparison to Pop.

Characteristics of C&W Music in the Early 1950s
C&W of the early 1950s had a very distinctive sound in comparison to Pop and R&B. This module will provide detailed information about some of these unique characteristics.

Melodies and Lyrics—As with Pop, C&W's melodies and lyrics were of prime importance. The lyrics were often love-oriented (usually tales of unrequited love or a jilted lover). The harmonies were usually simpler than those found in Pop. The form of the typical C&W song was similar to that of Tin Pan Alley songs. C&W rhythm was simple and straightforward and usually more prominent than was typical of Pop. There were, generally, three or four beats per measure, with de-emphasized subdivisions, thus creating a very simple, predictable sound. There was typically a lead singer, often with a vocal trio or quartet in the background. The musicians often performed their own original material, although there was also a repertoire of traditional songs handed down from earlier generations. Generally, the music was not notated; arrangements were worked out in rehearsal and, once set, were performed according to that plan. When instrumental solo breaks occurred, the solos stayed very close to the established melody, rather than wandering into intricate flights of fancy, as might have occurred in jazz.

Timbre—Perhaps the most recognizable characteristic of C&W music in the early 1950s was its timbre, much of which emanated from two specific sources: the vocalist and the steel guitar. C&W vocalists often sang with a rather nasal quality. Instead of carefully intoning each melodic pitch, they would often slide from note to note. A number of male C&W singers developed the ability to *yodel*—a vocal device in which the male singer cracks his voice intentionally, allowing it to move into a female range (called *falsetto*).

The steel guitar entered the C&W picture from a rather unlikely source: Hawaii. After Hawaii became a U.S. territory in 1900, the mainland was swept with a fascination for the exotic island culture. By the 1920s, the steel guitar's popularity was set. In 1931, the first electric Hawaiian steel guitar was introduced. Later developments included placing the instrument on a stand, adding a double-neck feature, and adding pedals. Being a rather conservative culture, the C&W music market was slow to include some of these innovations, especially electronic amplification.

Instruments—By the early 1950s, the typical C&W band included a vocalist, a vocal backup group, electric pedal steel guitar, piano, violin, acoustic bass (sometimes called stand-up bass or string bass), and acoustic or electric guitars. This leaves one obvious omission: drums. Although there were a few nonconformists, most traditional C&W bands avoided drums until the mid-1950s. The rhythm was set by the bass player, who slapped the strings on the accented beats, and by the guitar and piano, which reinforced all the beats.

1.5.2: Rhythm and Blues

The last of the three main tributaries leading to rock and roll, R&B, is also by far the most important. So direct is the line from R&B to early rock and roll that one may listen to certain R&B tunes recorded between 1945 and 1955 and be convinced that one is hearing 1958 vintage rock and roll.

Unlike either the Pop or the C&W market, R&B's performers and consumers were black. The R&B market was served, almost exclusively, by small, independent record companies—indies—and there were many of them, most owned and administered by whites.

Like C&W, R&B had a limited but well-defined audience. The basic center of R&B's development was the South; however, as the black population spread throughout the Southwest, the Midwest, and into major metropolitan centers across the United States, R&B went along. Thus, although most R&B singers traced their roots back to New Orleans, the Mississippi Delta, Alabama, Georgia, Tennessee, and Florida, by the 1930s and 1940s, many had relocated to other parts of the country. The small, R&B indies were located where there was talent and a market; Chicago, New York City, and Los Angeles became three leading centers for R&B recording. Many labels were formed in the late 1940s and went on to have considerable impact in the 1950s: notably, Atlantic (New York), Chess (Chicago), Specialty (Los Angeles), and Imperial (Los Angeles). The records produced by these and other indies for the R&B market served only their well-defined subpopulation of consumers. They rarely, if ever, expected sales in either the Pop or C&W markets, and, conversely, they expected no competition in their market from Pop or C&W records.

CHARACTERISTICS OF R&B MUSIC R&B paved the way for rock and roll, providing many of the signature musical characteristics that continued as part of the mainstream rock sound for decades to come.

Characteristics of R&B Music

Of the three primary markets preceding the emergence of rock and roll, R&B was by far the strongest influence on the mainstream rock style. Here you will learn about some of the characteristics that set R&B apart from Pop, C&W, and other musical styles of the period.

Musical Scheme—R&B was quite different from Pop and C&W. A large percentage of R&B songs were based on a set musical scheme known as the **12-bar blues**, introduced in the next Musical Close-Up. The music was rarely notated; as with C&W, it was usually worked out in rehearsal and then performed according to a loosely predetermined plan. Although it did not approach the melodic and harmonic complexity of jazz of the same period, R&B improvisation allowed for considerable freedom and spontaneous invention. Although some traditional songs were passed from generation to generation, most R&B songs were originals created by the performer. Many expressed personal sentiments related to love, jobs, hard knocks, and general philosophies of life.

Instruments—A typical R&B combo might consist of some or all of the following instruments: guitars (electric or acoustic or both), bass (acoustic), piano, drums, saxophone, and harmonica.

Melody—As its name implies, R&B was characterized by a hard-driving, prominent rhythm. The harmonies are those of the 12-bar blues: just three basic chords, with occasional variations. Although the words were important, the melody got minimal creative attention, generally seeming to be little more than a vehicle to carry the lyrics. In fact, there is great similarity among blues melodies, only partially because they usually conformed to the structure of the 12-bar blues and incorporated the notes of the blues scale.

Rhythm—The power of R&B resided in the strong, insistent rhythm, the personally expressive lyrics, and the vocal performance style (which was often of the shouting variety). Some outstanding R&B performers from earlier decades had a lasting impact on later versions of R&B and rock and roll in general. Listening to many of these stars, one can hear elements of 1950s rock and roll up to three decades preceding Elvis's release of "Heartbreak Hotel." For example, Memphis Slim's "All by Myself" hints at the later style of Fats Domino. In "Roll 'em Pete," by Joe Turner and Pete Johnson, one can hear the beginnings of the 1950s rock piano style and harbingers of "Bony Moronie" (Larry Williams, with a later version by John Lennon). In Elmore James's "Sunnyland," one hears hints of Chuck Berry's guitar style. And in Otis Spann's "Bloody Murder," there are fragments of bass lines that are exactly replicated in 1950s rock and roll. Although Pop and C&W played their respective roles in the creation of rock, it was R&B and its almost exclusively black performers that led most directly and forcefully into rock and roll.

Table 1.2 Some Classic 12-Bar Blues

Title	Artist	Date of Peak Popularity	Comments
"Careless Love"	Lonnie Johnson	1900s to today	A classic traditional blues that has been recorded by hundreds of artists
"St. Louis Blues"	W. C. Handy, composer; Bessie Smith, performer	Recorded 1925	One of the most popular of the urban blues that helped establish the 12-bar format
"Blue Yodel #1 (T's for Texas)"	Jimmie Rodgers	Recorded 1927	Country blues standard that features Rodgers' famous "blue yodel"
"Hootchie Cootchie Man"	Muddy Waters	Recorded 1954	Classic (electric) urban blues from the Chicago blues master
"Crossroads"	Written by Robert Johnson; performed by Cream	Recorded 1968	One of the classic country blues that has become a rock standard

MUSICAL CLOSE-UP ON THE 12-BAR BLUES The term *blues* is used many different ways in music. Various types of songs—urban blues, rural blues, country blues, jump blues, talkin' blues, rhythm and blues—share an association with the more general blues style. Originally, at least in terms of musical form, the blues had a specific meaning. Much of the music of the early blues singers and R&B artists followed a similar musical scheme. Specifically, three or four common patterns evolved using 8-, 12-, or 16-measure forms, with a consistent use of three basic chords. Over the years, one of these forms came to be favored: the 12-bar blues (see Table 1.2).

By the late 1920s, when musicians referred to the blues progression, they meant this standard form. This form became the basis for most boogie-woogie jazz of the 1930s, a large percentage of R&B of the 1930s and 1940s, and much of the **upbeat** rock and roll of the 1950s. Although used less frequently, it still appeared occasionally in the rock of the 1960s and beyond. For any one musical formula to be so durable and frequently present, it must have had considerable appeal to performers and listeners alike. It is so essential that we must study it more closely.

The Basic Musical Scheme of 12-Bar Blues

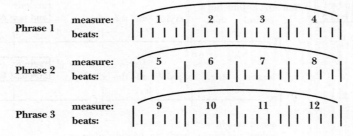

As any rock fan knows, music has beats. These are simply rhythmic pulses put into the music by the composer or performer and heard and felt by the listener. Musicians group these beats into units called *measures*, or *bars*. One blues chorus consists of 48 beats. Because the beats are usually grouped into measures of four beats each, there are 12 measures in a standard blues song; one time through this 12-bar progression is often referred to as a "chorus." A single blues chorus is comparable to a sentence in English. As with most sentences, our 12-bar "sentence" divides into smaller units called "phrases," a term common to both music and language. In the standard 12-bar blues, each phrase is four bars long. In music, we indicate phrases by large, curving lines over the measures, as shown in the example.

triads on each note

```
G  A  B  C  D  E  F  G
E  F  G  A  B  C  D  E
Notes in the key of C: → C  D  E  F  G  A  B  C
I  II III IV  V  VI VII I
```

Recall that a key is like a family of seven different notes, each of which can serve as the foundation of its own triad (three-note chord). The triads in the key of C are shown in the example.

Listen and watch the animation for this music example by clicking the play button in the Revel course.

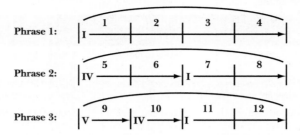

For ease of reference, we can represent these chords using Roman numerals. For the basic 12-bar blues, we can concern ourselves with only three of these chords: I, IV, and V. These three chords are distributed in the 12-bar blues form as shown in the musical phrases above.

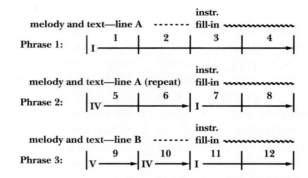

Now let us add the melody and lyrics. The words used in a 12-bar blues are usually in the form of a couplet—that is, two lines that rhyme. At this point, you may perceive a potential problem. We have two rhyming lines of text, but three phrases of music. Something must give! The blues singer's solution is to repeat the first line of the couplet, thus creating an AAB scheme. The melody of the first phrase is also repeated for the second phrase, sometimes with a slight variation to accommodate the change in harmony (notice that the chords are not identical for the two phrases). The second line of the couplet is, therefore, delayed until the third phrase of the music; the melody carrying this second line of the couplet is usually different from the melody used in the first two phrases.

In the traditional 12-bar blues, each line of text consumes about half the musical phrase (about two measures). The last two measures of each phrase are filled in by the instrumentalists.

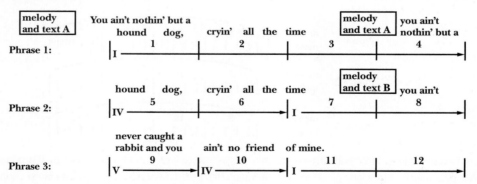

Now let us apply this scheme to an actual rock and roll record. Listen to Elvis Presley's version of "Hound Dog." Refer to the above musical example.

Elvis cheats a little by beginning each line of the text a little before the downbeat of the phrase, but, other than that, this song follows the basic 12-bar blues scheme nicely. You can actually count along by enunciating each beat ("1, 2, 3, 4"), keeping track of which measure you are in by counting the measure numbers on each downbeat: **1**-2-3-4, **2**-2-3-4, **3**-2-3-4, **4**-2-3-4, and so on. Listen several times until you really begin to feel the form; this requires repeated listening, as most listeners will not "get it" the first or second time through. During one listening, focus on the background singers. They are clearly singing the notes of the I, IV, and V chords, so this will help you hear the chord changes at the appropriate moments. As you proceed through this text, you will find that repeated listening is an absolutely essential technique you will need to utilize, since—even in the simplest, most basic styles of music—it is impossible to perceive every important aspect of a musical recording in a single pass. As the music becomes more complex, even more "listenings" may be required.

This basic 12-bar blues form has been used for thousands of songs for well over a century. Although there are many examples that follow our 12-bar blues scheme perfectly, there are many more that modify one or more aspects of this oft-used musical form. Some performers have changed some of the chords; others have eliminated the instrumental accompaniment for a few measures, while still others have varied the melodic and textual schemes. There are almost as many variations of the blues form as there are songs and performers. Yet, the basic 12-bar blues comes through. It is a very resilient feature and one that remains a fundamental aspect of R&B and early rock and roll.

The serviceability of the 12-bar blues is truly remarkable. If no singer is present, instrumentalists can still improvise over a 12-bar blues. All any musician needs to say to another is "Let's do a blues in B-flat," and, after someone counts off four beats to set the tempo, off they go! The basic scheme is adaptable to any style of rock and roll, jazz, C&W, and, of course, R&B. There are even examples of classical uses of this basic scheme.

Just in case you think the previous paragraphs describe one of the briefest songs in history—only 12 measures long—understand that the 12-bar chorus is repeated any number of times. If it is a vocal blues, the text normally changes with each chorus. Some jazz recordings repeat the chorus 40 to 50 times. With each chorus, the instrumentalist who has the lead improvises on a new musical idea, thus providing variety and interest to what might otherwise be a rather boring and repetitive musical presentation.

This musical form has enjoyed continuing use throughout the history of rock and roll, including Led Zeppelin's "Lemon Song," Frank Zappa's "Directly From My Heart to You," and Prince's "Delirious."

Listening for the 12-Bar Blues Form in Contemporary Music

Listen to several of the R&B examples provided in this chapter that are based on the 12-bar blues form so that you can familiarize yourself with the typical 12-measure form and the AAB–lyrical structure. Then, listen to a dozen of your current favorite recordings. Do any of them sound like they might also be based on the 12-bar blues or incorporate elements of that sound? Feel free to discuss this with some of your classmates to see whether, together, you can identify some contemporary examples. After completing this process, take time to write one or two paragraphs about the experience. Feel free to share both positive experiences as well as aspects that you found challenging. As you proceed through this text, you will learn to use your ears more analytically and effectively than most other listeners who simply continue to let the sound wash over them.

 The response entered here will appear in the performance dashboard and can be viewed by your instructor.

Submit

Summary: The Roots of Rock

You have now had the opportunity to learn about the three primary musical styles—along with artists representing each—that led to the emergence of rock and roll. The purpose of this next section is to review some of the most important knowledge you have gained so far.

Take Note: The Roots of Rock

- *How did key trends and subgroups in 1950s society influence the development of rock and roll?*—The economic prosperity and relative good times of the 1950s led popular music to focus on what was comfortable, pleasant, and appropriate; excess was avoided. Outside of white, middle-class America, however, there were distinct differences. Blacks were continuing their long struggle for civil rights; segregated from white society, they developed their own musical style: R&B. Another subculture was identified with C&W music, primarily the whites of the rural South.
- *What forces in popular music shaped the music that was heard before rock was popular?*—During the decades preceding the emergence of rock and roll, Tin Pan Alley had developed into the center of popular music creation. Songs were written by professional songwriters, with inoffensive and noncontroversial lyrics. Melodies were easy to remember and were designed to appeal to a mass audience. The music business was dominated by a handful of recording companies called the major labels, or "the majors." The goal was to create a very professional product that would be highly profitable.
- *What was the impact of C&W on popular music?*—C&W was a relatively small, regional style of music that appealed primarily to a southern, white audience. Like R&B, C&W was primarily recorded by indies (independent record companies) that catered to this market. C&W music reveals both similarities and dissimilarities in comparison to Pop. Like Pop, melodies and lyrics were of prime importance. However, the distinctive nasal vocal singing style and the use of the fiddle (essentially, a violin played in a different style) and steel guitar as accompaniment instruments set C&W music apart.
- *What were the primary instruments used by early rock pioneers?*—The typical 1950s rock and roll band consisted of four to six players. The usual instrumentation included drums, acoustic bass, two electric guitars (one

rhythm and one lead), acoustic piano, and saxophone (most often, either alto or tenor).

- *How was R&B different from C&W and Pop?*—Like C&W, R&B appealed to a specific audience; in this case, urban black listeners. However, unlike Pop and C&W, R&B songs generally followed a format known as the 12-bar blues and were characterized by a hard-driving, prominent rhythm designed for dancing. The power of R&B resided in the strong, insistent rhythm; the personally expressive lyrics; and the vocal performance style (often a shouting style).

- *What was the 12-bar blues, and why is this form important in the history of rock?*—The 12-bar blues form developed from traditional blues styles. As it became standardized, it consisted of a common set of three chords played across the 12 measures with lyrics for each stanza consisting of three phrases: the first phrase was repeated to form an "AAB" lyrical pattern. This musical form served as the basis for much R&B and early rock music.

SHARED WRITING

Learning to Express Your Musical Preference

Select one of the three musical styles leading to rock and roll (Pop, C&W, or R&B) that you like best and listen carefully to several of the musical examples presented to represent that style. Using the musical vocabulary you are beginning to develop, describe what it is that you like about this music. Be very specific; don't settle for vague statements, such as "I like the melody." Instead, focus on what it is specifically *about the melody* that you like, and describe it in as much detail as you are able. (This is difficult in the beginning, but, as with most things, becomes much easier and more natural with practice.)

Once you have completed this individual assignment, review three to five of the responses to this assignment submitted by fellow students. Did you provide a greater or lesser level of detail in your response? Did you utilize a sufficient amount of your musical vocabulary to communicate in a way that clearly and accurately describes the musical sound? What, if anything, would you change about your initial response after reviewing these responses by other students?

▶ A minimum number of characters is required to post and earn points. After posting, your response can be viewed by your class and instructor, and you can participate in the class discussion.

Post

0 characters | 140 minimum

Chapter 2
The Emergence of Rock and Roll

Learning Objectives

2.1 Explain the factors that led to the emergence of rock and roll

2.2 Evaluate the impact of Elvis Presley in the early development of rock and roll

2.3 Distinguish between the three basic trends of rock and roll

2.4 Identify the rhythmic elements in early rock

With the exciting emergence of rock and roll in the mid-1950s resulting from the convergence of the Pop, country and western (C&W), and rhythm and blues (R&B) markets that preceded it, it is now time to take a close look at some of the earliest and most influential developments during this period. We will review the impact of changes in the music industry (e.g., major labels vs. independent labels, and crossovers vs. covers) as well as some of the most important artists who proved to be essential leaders, propelling this new form of popular music forward and initiating a musical revolution few could have imagined.

2.1: A New Giant on the Musical Scene

OBJECTIVE: Explain the factors that led to the emergence of rock and roll

Pop, C&W, and R&B coexisted in the early 1950s as three separate and distinct markets, as if separated by tall brick walls. In a short, three-year period (roughly 1954 to 1956), those walls came tumbling down. What emerged from the ruins was a new giant on the musical scene: rock and roll.

2.1.1: Crossovers and Cover Versions

In order to develop a full understanding of this period during which rock and roll emerged, we must comprehend the related phenomena of **crossovers**.

Alternate Paths to Musical Popularity

While there are numerous examples of hit songs that were intended for a specific audience and succeeded in just the manner anticipated, there are also alternative—and relatively unexpected—paths to a similar level of success. Two possible paths are described in this section.

Crossovers—*Crossovers* were records that originated in one market but succeeded in another. Although there had been a few crossover hits before the 1950s, they became more frequent in the early 1950s and, most often, were R&B songs reaching the lower end of the Pop chart. Among the early crossover hits were "Lawdy Miss Clawdy" (Lloyd Price), "Gee" (the Crows), and "Earth Angel" (the Penguins). "Cryin' in the Chapel" (the Orioles) is a particularly good example because in July 1953, while holding the top position in the R&B market, it also climbed to number 11 on the Pop chart, thus narrowly missing the Top 10.

Covers—Observing the new interest in crossover R&B, the major companies moved quickly to produce their own popularized versions of R&B originals. These were called *cover versions*, or *covers*; that is, a subsequent version of an original song, almost always recorded by a different artist and often by another record company. Of course, multiple versions of hits were common within the Pop market long before the 1950s. Much has been written about white artists covering the songs of black musicians, but in reality, the practice worked both ways. For example, Doris Day's

Pop hit "Secret Love" was covered by the Moonglows, and "Cryin' in the Chapel" was originally a C&W ballad before being covered by the Orioles, who in turn were covered by artists creating at least five additional versions. What was new about the cover versions of 1954 was that the major companies were covering R&B originals. These Pop covers usually equaled or exceeded the sales of the original hits, and they sometimes appeared on the charts simultaneously. For example, the Penguins' "Earth Angel" reached number 8 on the R&B chart but was surpassed by the Crewcuts' version, which reached number 3 on the much more lucrative Pop chart. Sometimes, both the original version and the Pop cover version coexisted on the Pop chart; a good example is "Ain't That a Shame"—original version by Fats Domino, cover version by Pat Boone. Some of the professional composers for the Pop market also created their own originals in a style similar to the new R&B cover sound. Thus, Eddie Fisher, a Pop singer, sang "Dungaree Doll," and Kay Starr recorded "Rock and Roll Waltz," both of which contained musical elements that were similar to the R&B style but were songs created specifically for these artists by highly trained, professional composers.

2.1.2: Youth Culture

To say that 1954 and 1955 were years of turmoil and confusion in the Pop music industry would be a considerable understatement. The crossover sales, the R&B cover versions, and the Pop "sound-alikes" reflected an important new phenomenon: the emergence of a distinct youth culture.

Previously, the entertainment industry had been primarily the province of adults, who were the primary customers for entertainment; in the mid- and late 1950s, some of that money gradually flowed down into the pockets of the youth. Movies appeared that were aimed at a teenage audience; for example, *Rebel Without a Cause* (starring James Dean) and *Blackboard Jungle* (starring Sidney Poitier and Glenn Ford). If, as psychologists tell us, youth is naturally a time of rebellion, the typical 1955 young person had a problem: What to rebel against? In *Rebel Without a Cause,* Dean portrayed an angry teenager who has no real targets for his rebellious feelings. In *Blackboard Jungle,* the teenagers strike out at whatever is around: parents, the educational system (teachers), and each other.

Rebellious Teenager

Would you identify the person in this photo as a rebellious teenager?

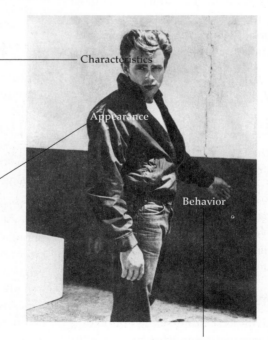

An image began to form of the rebellious teenager: sullen, brooding, and rebelling against his environment, often with little justification.

Characteristics

Appearance

The model was the so-called juvenile delinquent—black leather jacket, shirt open, collar upturned, hair slicked back into a ducktail, long sideburns, spit curl in front, and a permanent sneer.

Behavior

A "tough guy" and a "swinging chick"—cool, but ready to lash out at any moment.

Was Haley an Ideal Early Rock and Roll Icon?

As an early innovator, Bill Haley was a critically important part of the initial period of rock and roll.

Haley admired R&B music. Even when playing typical C&W jobs, he and his band would slip in the occasional R&B song in a C&W style to avoid offending his patrons. After changing his group's name to the Comets, Haley made a serious attempt to achieve national attention with his unique combination of R&B and C&W. In 1952, he released "Crazy, Man, Crazy," followed in 1954 by "Shake, Rattle, and Roll" (a cover of an original R&B hit by Joe Turner). But rock history was made that same year when Haley released his version of an R&B hit, "Rock Around the Clock" (originally recorded by Sonny Dae). Only mildly successful upon its initial release, its association with the popular movie *Blackboard Jungle* took it to the top of the Pop chart in 1955.

With the huge success of "Rock Around the Clock," the walls between Pop, C&W, and R&B began to crumble. Here was a white C&W band singing their version of an R&B song and seeing that song move up the Pop chart until it peaked at number 1 in July 1955. The song held that position for two months, and, according to *Cash Box* magazine, became the top-selling record in 1955. Even though Haley's "Shake, Rattle, and Roll" (1954) eventually sold over one million copies and was among the Top 5 for nearly five months, it was "Rock Around the Clock" that had the most dramatic impact on the nation's consciousness. Haley followed with "Dim, Dim the Lights" (1955), which crossed over to appear on the R&B chart, a particularly unusual phenomenon because so-called white records rarely appeared on the R&B chart.

Bill Haley and the Comets performing in London in 1957.
SOURCE: Pictorial Press Ltd/Alamy Stock Photo

In that crucial year of 1955, Haley and his Comets seemed to represent the raucous new style called rock and roll. His popularity continued into 1956 (and beyond) with his movie *Rock Around the Clock* (an early prototype of the teen-rock film genre that remained popular throughout the twentieth century) and several more hits, including "See You Later, Alligator," "Corrine, Corrina," and "Green Door." But Haley simply was not the right individual to personify the continuing development of the new youth-oriented rock and roll. Haley was nearly 40 years old, with a rather round, innocent baby face and a receding hairline (in spite of his 1950s-style spit curl in front). His C&W background was all too evident.

A new figure was needed to be the front man for rock and roll: someone younger, someone who could project a combination of raw power and slightly menacing rebellion. As often happens, the right person appeared in the right place at the right time.

No longer were youth content to await the passage of time until they were admitted to adult society. They coalesced into a society of their own and increasingly identified with their own movies, role models, dress code, slang, hairstyles, behavior, and, of course, music.

What music? That question was answered best by the movie *Blackboard Jungle*, which featured in its opening credits a Bill Haley song called "Rock Around the Clock." This song firmly connected the new youth culture with rock and roll, and, as a result, Bill Haley came to symbolize the emergence of this new musical sound.

2.1.3: Bill Haley and the Comets

Bill Haley was born in Detroit in 1927, and his musical career swept across the three music markets (Pop, C&W, R&B), thus encapsulating the musical integration that occurred within rock and roll as a **genre** in the mid-1950s. Haley's primary early identification was with C&W. His band originally was called the Saddlemen, and it consisted of the usual C&W instrumentation (including steel guitar), adding a drum set and saxophone from the R&B tradition.

2.2: Elvis Presley

OBJECTIVE: Evaluate the impact of Elvis Presley in the early development of rock and roll

Elvis Presley was a unique, central figure in the early development of rock and roll. He popularized the new style, disseminating it throughout society in a way few could have accomplished. It is probably not too great an overstatement to suggest that without Presley, rock might well have proven to be the musical fad its detractors claimed it to be, falling into the same category as the hula hoop and the Davy Crockett raccoon skin cap—like many sensations of American culture that consume our attention and then disappear into the realm of nostalgia.

2.2.1: Presley's Life and Career

Elvis Aron Presley was born in Tupelo, Mississippi, in 1935. During a period when the United States was a racially segregated nation (especially in the Deep South), it is hard to imagine how black and white cultures could have ever mixed. But in southern white society, those at the very bottom of the socioeconomic scale were labeled "poor white trash" and were considered to have a status equivalent to blacks. This was more than simply an abstract social stratification; it was a reality. The poorest whites lived "on the other side of the tracks" in many southern towns, often alongside blacks.

As a result, Elvis was in a position to absorb a wide variety of musical influences, including R&B, white and black gospel, C&W, bluegrass, western swing, and Pop. From the radio that brought the young Elvis both Pop music and various forms of C&W, and from his living circumstances that brought him the R&B and gospel sounds, the musical Elvis became, in effect, racially integrated.

The Presley family's economic fortunes did not improve significantly after their move to Memphis in 1948. They lived in a federally funded housing project, and Elvis attended a high school with a population drawn from predominantly lower-income neighborhoods. Naturally surrounded by white musical influences (Pop and C&W), Elvis sought out the black musical sounds with which he had become familiar in Tupelo, reportedly hanging out around the Beale Street area, a hotbed for black music.

Elvis's high school years seem to have passed rather unremarkably. He was merely an average student; he was not a member of the popular "in crowd." He just seemed different. Elvis crossed the lines of racial identity. He wore loud and outrageous clothes. He liked and sang black music. He dressed like a *hood,* wearing black leather jackets, open shirts, and upturned collars. He wore long sideburns, with his hair greased back into a ducktail. Thus, his image was not that of the typical mid-1950s, white, middle-class teenager, but a combination of black and lower-class white. His one point of popularity during high school was his singing. His peers enjoyed his musical performances, such as the one at the 1952 school variety show.

Shortly after his graduation in 1953, Presley went to a small local recording company called the Memphis Recording Service to make a record as a gift for his mother. Sam Phillips, its owner, was not present at this first recording session, but his secretary, Marion Keisker, was. She brought Presley's unique musical style to Phillips's attention when he returned.

PRESLEY'S FIRST RECORDING CONTRACT   Phillips had recorded a number of black artists in the R&B style. He also enjoyed some success in the C&W market. Phillips is said to have believed that if he could find a white artist who could perform black music with true authenticity, he could make a billion dollars (Hopkins 1971, 56). When he heard Presley's tapes, he knew he had his man. Presley signed a contract with Phillips's label Sun Records in July 1954.

Elvis released five singles on the Sun label between mid-1954 and the end of 1955. The first Sun release underscores the biracial nature of rock and roll's roots and its soon-to-be most famous practitioner. On one side of the single was "That's All Right (Mama)," an R&B song by Arthur "Big Boy" Crudup. On the flip side was "Blue Moon of Kentucky," a C&W standard by Bill Monroe. Backed by Scotty Moore (guitar) and Bill Black (bass), Presley's first record became a regional hit, and he eventually sold about 20,000 copies of this original release. Providing further evidence of the segregation in American society at the time, some white radio stations refused to play Elvis's early releases because they assumed he was of mixed race.

By the time of his fifth and final Sun release ("Mystery Train" and "I Forgot to Remember to Forget"), Presley had become an important figure in the C&W world and was named the number 1 "up and coming" C&W artist in a 1955 *Billboard* disc jockey poll. Over this same year and a half, his reputation also spread by means of personal appearances, primarily in the South and Southwest, the prime market for C&W music, and on the country-oriented *Louisiana Hayride* radio show.

However, Elvis was not the typical C&W act. His vocal and musical styles were heavily influenced by R&B and black gospel. His appearance was a mixture of black fashion and the teenage rebel look. His performance style included sexually suggestive body movements. Traditional C&W performers just did not do that. Whenever a *package show* (a show including a roster of artists) included Elvis, promoters noticed that the audience included more and more teenagers, especially females, who screamed and cried for Elvis. The other artists and their adult fans became increasingly irritated with this new phenomenon. They did not realize that they were witnessing the beginnings of a major musical, social, and economic revolution.

PRESLEY'S FIRST NATIONAL HIT   Near the end of 1955 and the beginning of 1956, two related events occurred that would set Presley up to have a national impact on the course of rock and roll. First, "Colonel" Tom Parker took over the personal management of Presley from his former manager. Parker was a shrewd industry insider who had previously built the successful careers of country singers Eddy Arnold and Hank Snow. In his first major move, he negotiated Presley's release from Sun Records, signing him with the industry giant RCA Victor. In retrospect, RCA's purchase of Elvis Presley for a total of $40,000 stands as one of the best business deals since the Louisiana Purchase, when land was purchased for about three cents an acre.

With the release of "Heartbreak Hotel" in 1956, Presley was off and running (as was rock and roll) with his first national hit (released by RCA Victor), selling more than one million copies in a matter of months. A subsequent release in July, "Hound Dog"/"Don't Be Cruel," sold over three million copies in one year. Sales orders for "Love Me Tender" exceeded one million before its release in August. In 1956, Presley's record sales surpassed the 10 million mark. Such figures were mind-boggling for the mid-1950s.

Another amazing phenomenon was that both sides of a Presley single often achieved popularity. Unlike most audio CDs, a vinyl record has two sides, so music is almost always recorded on both. Normally, the primary release (referred to as the *A-side*) is promoted for chart sales; the backup (or *B-side*) is, essentially, a bonus track to fill the second side of the vinyl record but not expected to attain significant popularity. In the case of Elvis's releases during this period, however, what was typical proved untrue. For example, "Hound Dog" and "Don't Be Cruel" (two sides of the same single) both reached number 1 on the Pop chart; "Don't" and "I Beg of You" both reached the Top 10, as did "One Night"/"I Got Stung" and "A Fool Such As I"/"I Need Your Love Tonight."

Throughout this period, Presley continued to cover C&W and R&B songs, thus continuing the biracial musicality that brought him to national prominence. Among his R&B covers were "Hound Dog" (Big Mama Thornton), "Shake, Rattle, and Roll" (Joe Turner), "Lawdy Miss Clawdy" (Lloyd Price), "Cryin' in the Chapel" (the Orioles), and a host of Little Richard's songs (including "Tutti Frutti," "Long Tall Sally," "Rip It Up," and "Ready Teddy"). There were also C&W covers (his most famous was "Blue Suede Shoes" by Carl Perkins) and even Pop covers (e.g., "Blue Moon" by Richard Rodgers, 1934). Elvis also had a number of crossover hits. "Heartbreak Hotel" reached number 1 on both Pop and C&W charts and number 3 on the R&B chart. "Don't Be Cruel," "Hound Dog," "Teddy Bear," "Jailhouse Rock," and "All Shook Up" hit number 1 on all three charts. "Love Me Tender" reached number 1 on the Pop, number 3 on the C&W, and number 4 on the R&B chart. Even as late as 1960, "Are You Lonesome Tonight?" appeared on all three charts.

PRESLEY'S INDUCTION INTO THE ARMY In 1958, Presley was inducted into the army. Two life-altering events occurred during Elvis's military service. First, his mother died during his first year of service. The effect on Elvis was profound, as he was deeply devoted to his mother. Second, in Germany, he met Priscilla Beaulieu, the teenage daughter of an army officer and the woman he would eventually marry.

On his return from Germany in 1960, Elvis's career resumed with a movie called *G.I. Blues*. It exploited his return and, of course, his identification as a soldier. This was not Elvis's first film. Beginning with *Love Me Tender* in 1956, Elvis made some 33 films over the next 16 years. Most were teen-rock exploitation films of little dramatic merit, although Elvis longed for more substantial dramatic roles.

Elvis Presley in *Love Me Tender*.

SOURCE: C20TH FOX/Ronald Grant Archive/Alamy Stock Photo

As rock and roll moved on to newer styles in the 1960s, the frequency and impact of Elvis's hits declined. He began to pull back from live performances in the early 1960s and from about 1962 to 1968 was rarely seen in person. He did produce several fine gospel albums during these years (*His Hand in Mine* [1960] and *How Great Thou Art* [1967]). He surrounded himself with a group of loyal good old boys known as the **Memphis Mafia** and retreated to his Memphis home, Graceland.

PRESLEY'S PERSONAL LIFE

Family, Health, and Career

In addition to his phenomenal artistic success, Elvis's personal circumstances and other factors also played significant roles in his life, both personal and professional.

Married Life—In 1967, Elvis married Priscilla Beaulieu; nine months later, a daughter (Lisa Marie) was born.

With a television special in December 1968 (aptly named the "Comeback Special"), Elvis returned to live performances. He retained a tremendous appeal, especially to audiences in the 30-year-old-plus age group (his original fans). Colonel Parker successfully marketed him in Las Vegas and on tour to major cities as well as at minor sites that rarely had the opportunity to host live concerts by big-name acts. A high point of Elvis's career came in 1973 with another television special, "Aloha from Hawaii," the first television show to be transmitted internationally by satellite; the audience was estimated to be one billion viewers.

Health Problems—However, Elvis's personal problems became more pressing in the 1970s. He developed a weight problem that detracted from his image as a rock sex symbol. When off the road, his weight would balloon to well over 200 pounds. Facing the beginning of a tour, he would go on a crash diet program, complete with pills, and lose 20–30 pounds in a matter of weeks. Following the tour, the weight returned. This extreme, up-and-down weight pattern and an increasing reliance on drugs wreaked havoc with his mental and physical health. His divorce from Priscilla in October 1973 and the associated loss of Lisa Marie's presence were devastating setbacks. His personal life and health continued to deteriorate throughout the 1970s. He died of heart-related problems in Memphis on August 16, 1977, at 42 years of age.

After his death, Elvis's recording of "My Way," a song written by Paul Anka and popularized by Frank Sinatra, was released and reached the Top 40. Since then, millions of Presley albums (some old, some elaborately repackaged) have been sold. Numerous books have been written about his life, and Graceland has become a major tourist attraction.

2.2.2: The Importance of Presley

Although rock's early influences are still hotly debated, many consider Elvis Presley to be the "King of Rock and Roll."

What Made Elvis Presley the King of Rock and Roll?
This status was earned as a result of the following:

He personified rock and roll.—Rock and roll developed as a biracial music, and Presley's musical style—more than anyone else's at the time—genuinely reflected those biracial influences. Perhaps the only other white artist to approach Presley's biracial style was Jerry Lee Lewis, but Lewis's short-lived career as a rock and roll artist [more about that later in this course] did not hold a candle to Presley's.

Elvis had unprecedented public appeal.—Elvis's multifaceted personality and musical versatility gave him an appeal beyond that of the typical rock and roll star. He was many things to many people: sexy, rebellious, God-fearing, patriotic, and respectful. Whether your musical tastes ran toward shouting rock and roll, softer rock, romantic ballads, hymns, gospel, country, patriotic anthems, social commentary, escapism, or tearjerkers, you could find an Elvis song to your liking. How could one person meet so many contradictory demands and still succeed? The music industry would love to know. It tried to create Elvis clones, but such attempts just did not work. He was truly unique.

Elvis was an overwhelming commercial success.—By the time of his death, at least 500 million copies of Presley records had been sold. It is estimated that over one billion Presley records have been sold worldwide (Guinness World Records), a number that will continue to grow. Over 150 albums and singles have been certified gold, platinum, or multiplatinum. "Heartbreak Hotel" returned to number 1 on the *Billboard* Hot Singles Sales chart in January 2006!

2.2.3: Elvis's Legacy

Elvis was a truly versatile performer who had a multifaceted appeal. Presley's critics argue that he began as a true rock and roller but disintegrated into a bland, somewhat pathetic Pop star, making no contributions to rock music after about 1960.

However, what is sometimes portrayed as a weakness may, in fact, be a strength. Presley assimilated the influence of many genres into his own musical style. Sometimes, his style was more of a unique mix; other times, he followed an existing style. As stated previously even his early hits included a shouting rock and roll song ("Hound Dog"), a sultry song ("Don't Be Cruel"), and a romantic Pop ballad ("Love Me Tender"). In spite of the movies and soundtracks of the 1960s, Elvis's original musical roots were still alive in him, as evidenced by his "Comeback Special" (NBC, 1968). Rejoined by members of his original group, and clad in black leather, he gave a powerful demonstration that rock and roll, raw and basic, was still alive and well within the King. His versatility and multifaceted appeal is what made him the most influential and successful proponent of rock and roll of his time. Had Presley stayed within a narrow style of so-called "real rock and roll," the new musical style might well have remained a musical subculture, like C&W, R&B, and gospel. Instead, largely because of Elvis's pivotal impact, rock and roll moved out of an identity as teen music to become the primary popular musical style of the second half of the twentieth century.

KEY EVENTS IN PRESLEY'S LIFE

In order to gain a better understanding of the trajectory of the life of an artist, it is important to know some of the most important dates associated with her or his personal and professional accomplishments, so that one can better understand the context of these events.

Time Stamp Date/Year	Time Stamp Content (Narrative)
1935	Elvis Aron Presley is born in Tupelo, Mississippi.
1948	Elvis moves with his family from Mississippi to Memphis, Tennessee.
1953	As a gift for his mother, Elvis makes his first recording at the Memphis Recording Service, a company owned by Sam Phillips.
1954	Elvis signs his first recording contract with Sun Records.
1955	Elvis is voted the number 1 "up and coming" C&W artist in a *Billboard* disc jockey poll.
Late 1955 and early 1956	Colonel Tom Parker becomes Elvis's personal manager and, after securing a release from Sun Records, signs him to a lucrative record contract with RCA Victor.
1956	Elvis stars in his first film, *Love Me Tender*.
1958	Elvis is inducted into the army.
1968	Elvis performs his "Comeback Special" after six years of relative seclusion beginning in 1962.
1973	A highlight of Elvis's later career, the "Aloha from Hawaii" television special, is transmitted internationally by satellite with an audience of one billion viewers!
August 16, 1977	Elvis died of heart-related problems, only 42 years old.

2.3: Three Basic Trends Emerge

OBJECTIVE: Distinguish between the three basic trends of rock and roll

As rock and roll developed in the 1950s, it began to break into different streams, or subgenres. Drawing on varied influences from Pop, C&W, and R&B, rock styles developed that emphasized one or more different aspects of these sources. Rock began to subdivide into three major streams: mainstream rock, rockabilly, and soft rock.

2.3.1: Mainstream Rock

As stated previously, of three primary ancestors (Pop, C&W, and R&B), R&B provided the heaviest influence on early rock and roll. In fact, some argue that rock and roll is essentially a newer, updated continuation of R&B, with other styles merely being offshoots of this main line of development.

Musical Characteristics Shared by R&B and Early Rock and Roll

Mainstream styles of 1950s rock and roll show a definite lineage back to R&B.

Reliance on the 12-Bar Blues Form—First, there was a heavy reliance on the 12-bar blues form. Many of the upbeat (fast), hard-driving 1950s rock songs were based on the 12-bar blues. Some were pure (adhering closely to all the aspects of the 12-bar blues pattern), whereas others modified one or more of the pattern's characteristics. For example, "Jailhouse Rock" expands to a 16-bar blues by extending the first 4-measure phrase of the traditional 12-bar blues to 8 measures; several songs change the traditional lyric pattern, and a few move to a middle section not related to blues. But all use the basic 12-bar blues as a point of departure.

Vocal Performance Style—Another characteristic of R&B evident in hard-driving 1950s rock and roll songs is the vocal performance style. Just as there had been R&B shouters, there were rock and roll shouters. Perhaps the best example is Little Richard. There is a distinct difference in voice production when one changes from a pure tone to a shout. Try speaking your name loudly. Then really yell it. Feel the difference? The shout has a harder sound, usually with an unavoidable raspiness. Presley approaches the shouting style in "Jailhouse Rock," "Hard Headed Woman," and "Hound Dog." Not all rock singers shouted their songs; singers such as Chuck Berry and Jerry Lee Lewis simply belted them without shouting. And not all R&B singers were shouters. Some belted out a song with a strong, hard vocal style that stopped short of shouting.

Absence of Notation—Like R&B, most of 1950s mainstream rock was not notated. The lyrics, melody, and chords for one chorus might be sketched out for the performers, but, from there, the total arrangement was worked out without notation. Also, the instrumentation of the typical rock and roll band was similar to that of the old R&B band: guitar(s), piano, drums, and saxophone.

Another important characteristic of 1950s rock that was derived from earlier R&B was the bass line. R&B bass lines were more melodic than Pop and C&W ones. The purpose of most bass lines is to provide the bottom note of the harmony (the root). In much C&W and Pop, the required bass note (usually the root or the fifth tone of the chord) was played on each beat or every other beat. In R&B, however, there was typically a more active bass line, similar to the bass lines of boogie-woogie. Thus, the bass would provide not only the root of the chord but also devise a short melodic pattern from the notes of the chord (an *arpeggio*), sometimes with a few added pitches.

Bass Line—Many patterns were devised, adding to the overall rhythmic activity of the song. Listen to the bass part of some 1940s R&B (e.g., Otis Spann's "Bloody Murder") in the following slides and you can hear the predecessors of the bass lines of much 1950s rock.

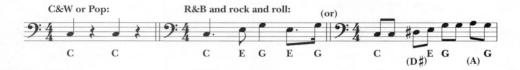

Music Example A

Bass Line #1—Click or tap the play button in the Revel course to watch a very simple bass line that was common to C&W and Pop. The repetitive nature of such a bass line serves to reinforce the root tone of each chord, providing a solid foundation upon which the sound of the other instruments can build.

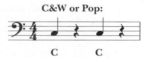

Bass Line #2—Click or tap the play button in the Revel course to watch an interesting bass line with increased interest that might be found in R&B or rock. This more active bass line provides variety and a greater sense of energy, including other chord tones in addition to the root pitch.

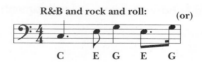

Bass Line #3—Click or tap the play button in the Revel course to watch another active bass line that appears in some examples of R&B and rock. In addition to including chord tones beyond the root pitch, this one includes a chromatic note – outside the key (D#) – and an upper neighbor tone pattern (G-A-G) near the end of the measure.

Rhythmic Aspects—Finally, the rhythmic aspect of R&B carried over to the harder styles of early rock and roll. Unlike C&W and Pop, rhythm was one of the most prominent elements of R&B. The drummer did not just provide a quiet rhythmic structure or play a simple beat; he was an integral part of the music, equal to the other members of the band. The beats were heavy and strong, and they were also emphasized in the piano and guitar parts. In 1950s mainstream rock, the beat became faster, and the emphasis on the second and fourth beats (the *backbeat*) became stronger, often reinforced by handclaps.

Hard Vocal Style Songs

Elvis Presley
"Hound Dog"
"Hard Headed
Woman"
"I Got Stung"
"Jailhouse Rock"
"(Let Me Be Your)
Teddy Bear"

Little Richard
"Lucille"
"Tutti Frutti"
"Long Tall Sally"
"Good Golly Miss Molly"
"Jenny, Jenny"

Chuck Berry
"School Days"
"Johnny B. Goode"

Bill Haley
"Rock Around the Clock"
"Shake, Rattle, and Roll"

Fats Domino
"Ain't That a Shame"

Buddy Holly
"Oh Boy"

Jerry Lee Lewis
"Whole Lot of Shakin'
Going On"

Ray Charles
"What'd I Say"

Danny and the Juniors
"At the Hop"

Bill Haley

SOURCE: David Hickes/Alamy Stock Photo

2.3.2: Rockabilly

Although most of the leading performers of early mainstream rock were black, there were a few white mainstream rockers. This was particularly true when the white performer had grown up with a heavy dose of R&B (e.g., Elvis Presley and Jerry Lee Lewis). These white performers, usually southern, most often had a C&W background. Their combination of C&W characteristics and R&B-oriented mainstream rock became known as *rockabilly*. Generally, the effect was to lighten the hard-driving, more basic mainstream style. To some, rockabilly made rock more acceptable; to others, it seemed to dilute a "purer" style.

C&W, R&B, and Pop charts in 1956. Other companies quickly jumped on the rockabilly bandwagon: with Bill Haley already on its roster, Decca added Buddy Holly and the Johnny Burnette Trio, Capitol signed Gene Vincent ("Be-Bop-a-Lula"), Chess released "Susie Q" by Dale Hawkins, and Liberty countered with "Summertime Blues" by Eddie Cochran, a Presley look-alike.

Everly Brothers (Phil and Don)—One of the most influential rockabilly acts of the period was the Everly Brothers. Their parents were C&W musicians; the boys toured with them and appeared on their radio show. This experience allowed the brothers to absorb strong C&W influences, while evolving their own rockabilly sound. With Presley as a model, they created their own personal mixture of C&W and R&B, becoming immensely popular. Between 1957 and 1960, the Everly Brothers placed 11 hits in the Top 10, including four number 1 songs. Their "All I Have to Do Is Dream" (1958) was the only song by someone other than Presley to reach the number 1 position on the Pop, R&B, and C&W charts.

Early and Eminent Contributors to Rockabilly

As a primary form of early rock and roll, rockabilly holds a unique position due to its close association with C&W, from which many of its musical elements are derived.

Bill Haley and Sam Phillips—Bill Haley laid the foundation for rockabilly along with rock and roll when he took R&B material and infused it with a C&W sound. Nonetheless, the real center for the early development of rockabilly style was Sam Phillips's Sun Studios in Memphis. Presley's success encouraged many other southern white musicians to make the trek to Memphis in the hope of finding success with the new rockabilly sound. From approximately 1955 to 1959, Sun released recordings by Carl Perkins, Jerry Lee Lewis, Johnny Cash, and a host of less significant artists. Perkins's 1955 national hit "Blue Suede Shoes" became a Top 10 hit on the

Phil (left) and Don Everly, c. 1958.

SOURCE: Pictorial Press Ltd/Alamy Stock Photo

Ricky Nelson, c. 1959.

SOURCE: Interfoto/Alamy Stock Photo

Ricky Nelson—One of the few non-southerners to be associated with rockabilly was Ricky Nelson. He and his brother appeared on the hit television show *The Adventures of Ozzie and Harriet*, in which their parents starred. Nelson developed a softer, Pop-oriented style of rockabilly and had a series of hits beginning in 1957 and continuing through 1972. The TV show provided a showcase for many of his hits and was an early use of this powerful medium to influence a teen, record-buying audience. Between 1957 and 1960, he placed 11 songs in the Top 10. Tragically, Nelson died in a plane crash in 1986.

MUSICAL CHARACTERISTICS OF ROCKABILLY The musical style of rockabilly is difficult to distinguish using precise terms. Rockabilly singers stopped short of the shouting style (sometimes emulating a crooning style in slower songs). They usually sang clearly and cleanly on pitch; the lyrics were enunciated distinctly. The instrumentation was close to that of the mainstream style, except there was less emphasis on saxophone, and acoustic guitars were used more often than electric guitars. Drums, not part of the traditional C&W sound, were added, reflecting the R&B influence. While electric bass was used by later rockabilly groups, the earliest groups used acoustic bass, upon which the bassist can slap the neck of the instrument between notes to add a percussive, often syncopated, rhythm.

Although some rockabilly songs are based, at least in part, on the 12-bar blues, most follow the 8-bar or 16-bar forms typical of C&W and Tin Pan Alley Pop songs. In some cases, the rockabilly rhythm approached the intensity of mainstream rock. More often, however, the beat was lighter, with less of the hard-driving, heavy beat of the R&B-influenced mainstream. Even so, to help identify rockabilly as a rock style, a clear and consistent backbeat on the second and fourth beats was often present. The boogie-oriented

bass lines of mainstream rock were less frequent in rockabilly, except for the harder-driving examples.

Rockabilly provided a more acceptable alternative for those who were drawn to the new rock and roll style but were not quite ready to accept the mainstream sound. It offered the excitement and appeal of rock, without the raucous, less-refined musical style evident in much of the mainstream (and without its racial associations, which some found objectionable).

2.3.3: Soft Rock

From the beginning, there has been a vital market for a softer style of rock that combines elements of rock and Pop music. Many rock purists deny that soft rock is a legitimate style of rock. They see it as the illegitimate offspring of an unholy alliance between Pop and rock, dismissing it with such derisive phrases as schlock rock or schmaltz. These purists typically dismiss this style with a condescending sniff or an incredulous "You call that rock?!" In spite of this reaction, two facts are incontrovertible: (1) Much soft rock contains clearly identifiable elements of rock, and (2) this style has retained a broad and consistent appeal (market) from the beginning of rock to the present day.

From the beginning, rock music was dance music. Whether at the high school prom or the Friday "sock hop" in the school gym, teens liked to dance to their new music. But dancing for four hours to "Tutti Frutti" and other mainstream rock tunes would be monotonous, nerve-wracking, and physically exhausting. Teens in the 1950s liked to slow dance (or close dance). With sociosexual mores being far more conservative than they later became, slow dancing was a vital part of the developing romantic relationship. In those days, holding hands and long embraces were considered socially acceptable by most, if done under the guise of dancing. Many a relationship developed during the slow tunes played as the dance evening moved into its final hours.

Soft rock of the 1950s developed two rather distinct styles: (1) white soft rock developed by Elvis, Pat Boone, and the good-looking teen idols modeled after them and (2) black soft rock developed by the numerous vocal groups referred to now (but not at that time) as **doo-wop** groups. As with so many of the developments of rock, Elvis Presley established a model for the white soft rock style. From the beginning of his RCA output, Elvis recorded soft, slow ballads, such as "I Want You, I Need You, I Love You," "Love Me Tender," "Don't," "Loving You," and "Anyway You Want Me" (all released between 1956 and 1958). The softer Pop side of Elvis continued, and even increased, during the remainder of his career. Some of these songs are pure Pop, bearing no real relationship to rock; others, however, contain clearly identifiable elements of rock.

PAT BOONE Perhaps no one better exemplifies the softer, Pop-rock style of the 1950s than Pat Boone. He was a young, handsome, and talented singer whose clean-cut appearance, performance style, and lifestyle provided an alternative to the more "menacing" styles of rock. Boone's career began with his commercially successful covers of R&B and mainstream rock originals, notably "Ain't That a Shame" (Fats Domino) and "Tutti Frutti" and "Long Tall Sally" (Little Richard). Beyond the covers, Boone also recorded the original popular versions of some upbeat songs ("Why Baby Why" and "Wonderful Time Up There"), as well as some slow- to moderate-tempo songs ("Sugar Moon," "April Love," and "Love Letters in the Sand"). Many rock historians do not categorize Boone as a rock and roll singer; after all, he did not fit the desired image of the rebellious, countercultural rock star. However, if one listens objectively to

Pat Boone, c. 1959.

SOURCE: AF archive/Alamy Stock Photo

Other Performers of Soft Rock

Soft rock is a lighter style of rock and roll with a particularly close association with Pop music and Tin Pan Alley, from which many of its musical elements are derived.

If Elvis could include soft rock and pure Pop ballads in his repertoire, others could legitimately specialize in this field. In the late 1950s and early 1960s, a large number of such performers achieved significance. Most were similar to Pat Boone and the softer side of Elvis: attractive, young, talented, and rather wholesome. This list of performers would include Paul Anka, Frankie Avalon, Bobby Rydell, Bobby Vee, Bobby Darin, Tommy Sands, and their female counterparts, Connie Francis and Brenda Lee (although the latter tended toward a soft form of rockabilly).

For the predecessors of black soft rock, we must look further back than Elvis Presley, into the 1940s and early 1950s, to groups such as the Mills Brothers and the Ink Spots. Black vocal ensembles of three to six singers were increasingly popular in the early 1950s. They usually included a particularly talented lead singer and a backup vocal ensemble that provided **close harmony**. To add rhythmic activity, the backup vocalists often sang rhythmic patterns using nonsense syllables. Although some were very simple ("doo-wah" and "doo-wop"), some became quite complex. Their acts were tightly choreographed so that the singers turned sideways, pivoted, kicked one foot, and tugged their shirt cuffs with coordinated precision. Groups such as the Ravens, the Orioles, and the Crows developed this style in the early 1950s. Landmark recordings that were representative include "Cryin' in the Chapel" (Orioles, 1953) and "Gee" (Crows, 1954).

In 1954, the Chords released "Sh-Boom," which reached number 9 on the Pop chart and number 2 on the R&B chart; a cover version by the Crew Cuts reached the number 1 position on the Pop chart and held that position for nine weeks. Further covers of "Sh-Boom" were recorded by Billy Williams, Sy Oliver, and country artist Bobby Williamson. The song also cracked the Top 20 in England. The popularity of the doo-wop sound was established. Also in 1954, the Penguins released "Earth Angel," which rose to

number 8 nationally (number 1 on the R&B chart). The cover version by the Crew Cuts also achieved a number 8 ranking. By 1955, the floodgates were opened, and the "bird groups" (e.g., Crows, Falcons, Penguins, and Flamingos), "car groups" (e.g., Imperials, Impalas, El Dorados, Fleetwoods, and Edsels), and other doo-wop groups poured into the market. Most of these groups were "one-hit wonders," achieving one or two successful hits before disappearing. Few rock styles boast such a long list of one- or two-hit artists.

Notable exceptions to the one-hit syndrome were the Platters and the Coasters. The Platters, consisting of four men and one woman, released a formidable string of hits, including the first doo-wop song to achieve number 1 status on the Pop chart, "The Great Pretender." Other Platters' hits include "Only You," "Smoke Gets in Your Eyes," "My Prayer" (a cover of an earlier hit by the Ink Spots), "Twilight Time," and "The Magic Touch." In a very different way, the Coasters also defied the one-hit syndrome. Their hits included "Yakety Yak," "Charlie Brown," "Searchin'," Poison Ivy," and "Along Came Jones." Whereas the Platters sang songs of romantic love in beautiful harmony, with the talented solo voice of Tony Williams soaring over the top, the Coasters took a humorous approach to teen life with a less-polished sound and an emphasis on the spoken bass part (e.g., "Why's everybody always pickin' on me?" from "Charlie Brown").

The Platters

SOURCE: Pictorial Press Ltd/Alamy Stock Photo

some of his performances (e.g., a national television performance of "Tutti Frutti"), one must admit that he did sing rock and roll. The vocal style is not as hard and raucous as Little Richard's, of course, but all the same, basic rock elements are present.

It is also true that many of Boone's recordings are in a pure Pop ballad style, derived from the Tin Pan Alley and Hollywood traditions, containing no pretense of rock. Boone has been criticized on the grounds that, through his cover versions, he capitalized on the original work of many black R&B artists. However, his recordings brought many of these songs to national prominence when, given the society and marketplace of the 1950s, they otherwise would likely have languished in obscurity.

JOURNAL

Describing Musical Preference

After reading about the three trends of early rock and roll (mainstream rock, rockabilly, and soft rock) and listening to representative examples, which of these trends do you like the best? Use your growing musical vocabulary to describe precisely the musical elements that factor positively into your decision.

▶ The response entered here will appear in the performance dashboard and can be viewed by your instructor.

Submit

2.4: Musical Close-Up of Rhythmic Elements in Early Rock and Roll

OBJECTIVE: Identify the rhythmic elements in early rock

Rhythm is perhaps the most basic of all of the musical elements because all sound must have a beginning, a duration, and an end—in other words, musical sound has a temporal existence. Rhythm constitutes the way in which musical sound is ordered in time.

Music psychologists believe that human beings respond naturally to the beat or rhythmic aspect of music because our own body is, in fact, a complex system of periodic vibrations and *beats* (pulses). Perhaps this is why, when we hear a strongly rhythmic piece of jazz or rock, we cannot resist tapping our feet, clapping our hands, moving our bodies, or dancing.

Although all musical styles have a rhythmic component, in some styles, the rhythm is more strongly perceived than in others. For example, in Debussy's *Prelude to the Afternoon of a Faun*, the beat is very slow and is purposely de-emphasized. The music seems to float through time. In contrast, in Elvis Presley's "Hound Dog," the beat and rhythm are much more prominent.

Basic Observations about Rhythm

There are four basic observations to make about the rhythm in almost any piece of music. The terms defined here—**tempo**, **meter**, **backbeat**, and **subdivision**—will be extremely useful in discussions of various rock songs and styles.

How fast is the beat? The musical term for the speed of the beat is *tempo*. Elvis's "Hard Headed Woman" has a fast tempo; "Return to Sender" has a moderate tempo; "Love Me Tender" has a slow tempo. The number of beats per minute (bpm) can be measured with a device called a **metronome**. The below table shows some of Elvis's songs and their tempos.

How are the beats organized? As we saw in our discussion of the 12-bar blues, Pop musicians usually organize beats into groups of four. The technical term for this organizational grouping of beats is *meter*. Thus, quadruple meter is the organization of beats into groups of four; triple meter is the organization of beats into groups of three; duple meter is groups of two; quintuple meter, five; and so on. The vast majority of rock and roll is in quadruple meter; special note of exceptions will be made as they are referenced throughout this course. Recall from earlier that each grouping of beats is called a *measure* or bar. So if we speak of eight bars of quadruple meter, we are referring to a total of 32 beats, organized into eight groups (measures) of four (beats), or 8 × 4 = 32.

Elvis's Songs and Their Tempos

Song Title	Metronome Tempo
"Hard Headed Woman"	fast 195 bpm
"Long Tally Sally"	fast 192 bpm
"I Got Stung"	fast 190 bpm
"Hound Dog"	fast 180 bpm
"Don't Be Cruel"	moderately fast 172 bpm
"Jailhouse Rock"	moderately fast 162 bpm
"Return to Sender"	moderately 132 bpm
"Are You Lonesome Tonight?"	slow 75 bpm
"Love Me Tender"	slow 72 bpm

How strong are the beats? Most people can feel the beat in a rock piece and can synchronize with that beat by tapping their feet, snapping their fingers, or clapping their hands.

All the beats in a measure are not equally strong. Traditionally, the first beat (the downbeat) has been the strongest beat; the next strongest is the third beat; the second and fourth beats are typically relatively weak. However, many rock songs emphasize beats two and four, just the opposite of the traditional approach. When this occurs, the music is said to have a strong backbeat.

To develop an ability to distinguish the backbeat, listen carefully for the strong hits of the drummer on the snare drum, which occur with a high degree of predictability in most mainstream rock songs. Music psychologists have suggested that the intense rhythmic appeal of rock may be partially due to the backbeat, creating an implicit sense of tension because the *accent* (i.e., emphasis) is placed intentionally on what are more traditionally weak beats.

Some rock emphasizes all four beats equally. For example, listen to the opening section of Chicago's "Saturday in the Park." The piano's introductory measures emphasize all four beats equally; however, when the drummer enters, he **accents**, or emphasizes, beats two and four. Or listen to the Beatles' "Why Don't We Do It in the Road?"; again, the piano part emphasizes all four beats equally, but the drum part clearly accents beats two and four.

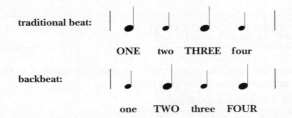

How are the beats subdivided? Rhythm would be a pretty simple matter if it consisted only of beats, but the real rhythmic interest (and resulting complexity) of most music is determined by what happens inside, or between, the beats. Each beat is usually subdivided into smaller parts. For our purposes, we shall concentrate on the **subdivision** of the beat into two, three, or four parts, though the reader should remain aware that there are even more complex possibilities:

Example of Duple Subdivision Faster rock and roll of the 1950s used a duple subdivision of the beat; the bass line of Elvis's "Jailhouse Rock" has a very clear duple subdivision of the beat.

Example of Triple Subdivision Slower, softer songs were more likely to have a triple subdivision of the beat (e.g., the Platters' "The Great Pretender" or the Flamingos' "I Only Have Eyes for You"). In these songs, notice especially the piano's repeating chords, clearly delineating the three subdivisions per beat:

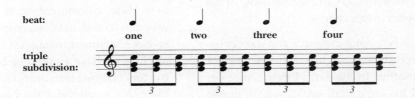

> **Practice Yourself** An interesting combination of the backbeat and a duple subdivision is found in some 1950s (and later) rock songs. Try the following exercise to make your own rock beat:
>
> right hand:
>
> left hand:
>
> Listen to "Sweet Nothings" by Brenda Lee or "Short Shorts" by the Royal Teens for examples of this combination.

Throughout the text, I will frequently refer to the rhythmic characteristics of various rock styles and certain rock pieces, referring to the tempo, the meter, the backbeat, or the subdivision pattern. The purpose of this brief introduction to rhythm in rock music is to provide a basis for understanding these later comments.

BECOME AN ACTIVE LISTENER

The ability to apply the concepts you are learning in this course to novel listening examples is a critical component of this course. These sections provide opportunities for you to practice your developing skills.

Find examples of these musical elements in the music that you enjoy:

1. fast, moderate, and slow tempos

2. a backbeat

3. subdivisions of the beat: duple, triple, and a combination of the backbeat and a duple subdivision

Review your responses below.

Summary: The Emergence of Rock and Roll

The period between 1954 and 1956 proved to be seminal to the evolution of rock and roll; in fact, this was the period of its emergence, when three previously distinct musical markets (Pop, C&W, and R&B) merged into one. The blurring of these musical boundaries was evident in the appearance of covers and crossovers. Early rock and roll eventually settled into three primary trends: mainstream rock, rockabilly, and soft rock. It is not difficult to determine connections to the three distinct musical styles that preceded rock and roll (Pop, C&W, and R&B, respectively), although record sales reflected a buying public that listened to music that crossed these lines. It is time now to turn to some of the trend-setting artists, following Bill Haley and Elvis Presley, who rose to the top during the early years of rock and roll.

Take Note

The following module reviews and summarizes some of the important content covered in this chapter.

- *What is the difference between a crossover and a cover?*— Crossovers were records that originated in one market but succeeded in another. In the early 1950s, crossover hits were achieved by some R&B artists whose music placed on the mainstream Pop chart. On the other hand, a cover is a subsequent version of a previously released song, typically recorded by another artist. Generally, during this period, white artists covered R&B hits, and their versions often performed better on the Pop chart.

- *How did Bill Haley play a key role in launching rock music?*— Bill Haley's cover of "Rock Around the Clock" was featured under the opening and closing credits of *Blackboard Jungle*, a movie that focused on teenage themes. Thanks to the film's popularity, the song was a smash hit, and Haley became a symbol of the new musical style. However, when fans saw Haley—he was nearly 40 years old at the time—they yearned for someone younger and more attractive to represent *their* music.

- *What was unique about Elvis Presley's life and career?*— Elvis Presley was a unique, central figure in the early development of rock and roll. He popularized the new style, disseminating it throughout society in a way few could have accomplished. It is probably not an overstatement to suggest that, without Presley, rock might well have proven to be the musical fad its detractors claimed it to be. Elvis's early life in Tupelo and Memphis provided a unique opportunity to absorb a variety of musical influences, including R&B, gospel, C&W, and Pop; all of those influences can be heard in his early hits.

- *What three basic trends in rock music emerged during the late 1950s in the wake of Elvis's success?*—As rock and roll developed in the 1950s, it began to break into different streams (or subgenres): mainstream rock, rockabilly, and soft rock. Mainstream rock revealed the strongest influence of R&B, emphasizing the 12-bar blues structure and a harder—sometimes shouting—vocal performance style. Rockabilly combined C&W and R&B influences and was performed by acts like the Everly Brothers and Ricky Nelson. Soft rock combined elements of rock with

Pop music and was exemplified in the performance style of Pat Boone.

- *What is distinctive about rhythm in early rock and roll?*— Although all musical styles have a rhythmic element, in some styles, the rhythm is more prominent than in others. For example, in Elvis Presley's "Hound Dog," the beat and rhythm are right up front. Rock songs vary in tempo (from very fast to very slow), in meter (how the beats are organized), in their degree of emphasis on the backbeat, and in how the main beat is subdivided. These basic rhythmic characteristics help define the rock sound and differentiate its various subgenres.

SHARED WRITING

Discuss Specific Musical Elements

Now that you are aware of the three musical styles that led to rock and roll (Pop, C&W, or R&B) and have read about the early styles of rock described in this chapter (mainstream rock, rockabilly, and soft rock), can you connect any of the pre-rock styles with these early rock subgenres? Using the musical vocabulary you are beginning to develop, what specific musical elements are consistent between similar styles, and which vary significantly between those that are quite different?

Once you have completed this individual assignment, review three to five of the responses to this assignment submitted by fellow students. Were you able to provide a greater level of detail in your response? Did you utilize a sufficient amount of your musical vocabulary to communicate in a way that clearly and accurately describes the musical sound? What, if anything, would you change about your initial response after reviewing these responses by other students?

▶ A minimum number of characters is required to post and earn points. After posting, your response can be viewed by your class and instructor, and you can participate in the class discussion.

Post

0 characters | 140 minimum

Chapter 3
1950s Style Rock and Roll

Learning Objectives

3.1 Outline the influences of the five style-setters of rock and roll in the 1950s

3.2 Summarize other influences on rock and roll in the 1950s

3.3 Explain how the emergence of rock and roll affected the music industry

3.4 Analyze the musical elements of soft rock

As rock and roll came into its own—standing on its own (proverbial) "two feet"—a number of significant artists emerged as trendsetters for the music of the era, and for much of that yet to come. Even during this early period, there was a variety of substyles already apparent, setting the stage for what would become a dizzying array of sub-genres by the 1970s. The music industry (i.e., rock music as "business") played a significant role in this process, just as signing with RCA Victor had been critical to the success of Elvis Presley. With this chapter, we step into the early world of rock and roll, a set of musical styles that provided the foundation for the vast majority of future rock artists, right up to the present day.

3.1: Five Style-Setters of the 1950s

OBJECTIVE: Outline the influences of the five style-setters of rock and roll in the 1950s

In addition to Elvis Presley, there were five other pivotal figures in 1950s rock: Little Richard, Jerry Lee Lewis, Fats Domino, Chuck Berry, and Buddy Holly. Quite different in many ways, each of these musicians broke new ground stylistically, although they were still heavily influenced by their predecessors. Together, they mark a critical era in rock's history; their musical techniques, vocal stylings, and sheer showmanship have significantly impacted the evolution of the genre.

3.1.1: Little Richard

The purest prototype of hard, mainstream rock was Little Richard. Elvis's multifaceted musical style included not only mainstream rock but also rockabilly and soft rock. Little Richard, in contrast, was, in one, self-contained package, the embodiment of the type of mainstream rock that led to the Rolling Stones, Jimi Hendrix, Alice Cooper, James Brown, David Bowie, and Prince, among others.

Little Richard

Little Richard's Life and Career

Little Richard, one of the primary mainstream rock artists of the mid- to late 1950s, effectively integrated the foundations of R&B into his rock and roll style. His flamboyance and unique appearance added significantly to his distinctive manner of performance.

Life and Influence—Although accounts of his birthdate vary, his mother reported it as December 5, 1932. Born Richard Wayne Penniman in Macon, Georgia, he was the third of 12 children. His father worked in the construction industry and "handled" moonshine (White 1984, 3). Although a simple but sincere belief in God was a part of the Penniman household, Richard was a troublemaker. This basic conflict between hell-raising and piety infused Richard's life, career, and music. In his biography of Little Richard, Charles White notes that Richard "twice discarded super-stardom for the church, typifying the conflict between sacred and secular music which is built into the black culture" (1984, xiii). Little Richard knew that his church and his family would strongly disapprove if they learned of his sexual preference. In fact, he believed this was a primary reason that his father kicked him out of the house at such an early age. After leaving home at the age of 14, he mastered a variety of musical styles, including Pop, gospel, and R&B; his experiences ran from working in a traveling medicine show to black blues bands.

Musical Career—After his father was shot and killed outside of a local tavern, Richard became the main breadwinner for the family. He continued to play and sing throughout the South and even released several gospel-oriented R&B recordings. Returning to Georgia, Richard started a new band and began listening to the music of Fats Domino, Chuck Berry, and Lloyd Price. At Price's suggestion, he sent an audition tape to Specialty Records in Los Angeles, and, after many months of effort, received a recording contract.

Specialty Records was a moderately successful gospel and R&B label. Its biggest success had been Lloyd Price's "Lawdy Miss Clawdy" in 1952. Owner Art Rupe wanted "a big band sound expressed in a churchy way," or, as Specialty's producer Robert "Bumps" Blackwell put it, "a gospel singer who could sing the blues" (White 1984, 44, 46). Blackwell had been involved in the early careers of Ray Charles and Quincy Jones and was hired to supervise Little Richard's first Specialty session in New Orleans. In 1955, after taping four rather uninspired songs by a somewhat intimidated Little Richard, the group broke for lunch. Richard went to a piano and launched into an energetic version of an off-color song called "Tutti Frutti." Blackwell knew it was what he wanted. He quickly got the local songwriter Dorothy La Bostrie to clean up the lyrics; they returned to the studio and, in 15 minutes, had recorded what was to become a rock and roll classic.

Musical Style—The chorus of "Tutti Frutti" is a 12-bar blues, as are the verses, but the latter included a modification in the third phrase with instrumental accents separated by silence over which the vocal continued to lead smoothly to the chorus. Added to Richard's pounding **boogie**-style piano are guitar, bass, tenor sax, baritone sax, and drums. Richard's shouting style and falsetto "woos" set the style for many artists to follow. The lyrics of the chorus provide a classic example of 1950s nonsense. "Tutti Frutti" is the model for most of Little Richard's hits: "Long Tall Sally," "Slippin' and Slidin'," "Rip It Up," "Ready Teddy," "The Girl Can't Help It," "Jenny, Jenny," and "Good Golly Miss Molly." Although "Tutti Frutti" sold about 500,000 copies and appealed to both black and white teens, for some, Little Richard's style was a bit too raucous and noisy. In spite of its importance in the history of rock, "Tutti Frutti" rose only to number 21 on the Pop chart, although it attained the number 2 position on the R&B chart. It was quickly covered by both Elvis Presley and Pat Boone, as was "Long Tall Sally." Richard's recording of "Rip It Up" (with "Ready Teddy" as the B-side) reached number 27 (number 1 on the R&B chart), and both were covered by Presley. Buddy Holly also recorded a cover version of "Rip It Up." Although some teens preferred the cover versions, it is not true that the Presley, Holly, or Boone recordings overshadowed Little Richard's. In fact, only two of these covers reached the Top 40 (Boone's versions of "Tutti Frutti" and "Long Tall Sally").

Little Richard's performance style was frenetic. He sang, shouted, danced, gyrated, and sweated profusely. He became the symbol for wild, unrestrained rock and roll. The parallel between his performance style and his long-held ambition to be a preacher, exhorting his congregation into frenzied expressions of praise and self-confession, reminds us of the ironic link between the southern black religious experience and the Little Richard style of rock and roll. It is reported that participants in his postconcert orgies sometimes awakened to Richard giving sincere readings of the Bible. This dichotomy ruptured in 1957 when he renounced his show business career and turned to religion.

Personal Life—In fact, Richard gave Bible college a try and even married a young Washington, D.C. secretary named Ernestine Campbell. But neither the marriage nor the religious education lasted. In 1962, he launched his comeback with a tour of England, where he met the members of two aspiring British rock groups: the Beatles and the Rolling Stones. Mick Jagger used words such as "amazing," "hypnotic," and "powerful" to describe Little Richard's performances. As a result of the performance style described above, he even compared Richard to an evangelist preaching to his flock.

By the late 1960s, Richard had slipped into self-parody. His stage act featured outrageous costumes, homosexual hype, and endless renditions of his old hits. Through the early 1970s, he attempted to make a comeback, but his growing dependence on drugs and alcohol dashed any hopes of a renewed career. As a result of several personal tragedies, he once again abandoned his wild lifestyle, and during the last half of the 1970s he again turned to religion. He even described the lyrics of some rock and punk groups as being demonic and contagious.

Perhaps Little Richard was not the king of rock and roll he claimed to be, but he was one of the most influential figures in rock history. He was dynamic, egotistical, controversial, and utterly original. Although his influence would last as long as there was rock and roll, his own personal musical style—at one time considered highly innovative—was now perceived as dated. Still, as he recalled his friends Elvis, Buddy Holly, Jimi Hendrix, Janis Joplin, Sam Cooke, and so many others, he has outlasted them all, remaining a living legend long after these artists departed.

Key Events in Little Richard's Life

In order to gain a better understanding of the trajectory of the life of an artist, it is important to know some of the most important dates associated with their personal and professional accomplishments, so that one can better understand the context of these events.

Time Stamp Date/Year	Time Stamp Content [Narrative]
December 5, 1932	Richard Wayne Penniman is born in Macon, GA
1947	Left home at the age of 14
1955	Recorded "Tutti Frutti" for Specialty Records
1957	Renounced rock and roll, turning to religion
1962	Launched a comeback tour of England

Fats Domino

SOURCE: Pictorial Press Ltd/Alamy Stock Photo

3.1.2: Fats Domino

Antoine "Fats" Domino (born on February 26, 1928, in New Orleans) represents an interesting contrast to Little Richard. Certainly, there were similarities: both were southern black artists who played piano and sang, both came from the R&B tradition, and both became very popular rock and roll stars of the 1950s. Beyond that, they were more different than alike.

Fats Domino's Life and Career

While Fats was considered one of the leading mainstream rock artists at the time, in recent decades, the acknowledgment of his high level of influence has been overshadowed by some of the other style-setters discussed in this chapter. There is no doubt that his accomplishments are as influential, if not more so, than other mainstream artists from this era who remain more familiar to contemporary audiences.

Life and Musical Career—Fats came from a musical family. He quit school at 14 to go to work as a factory worker by day and a club musician by night. Among his musical jobs, he played with a prominent New Orleans band headed by Dave Bartholomew. Bartholomew, a local representative for Imperial Records, arranged for a recording session that produced Fats's first hit, "The Fat Man," released in 1950.

By 1955, Fats had placed 12 hits in the Top 10 of the R&B chart, including a number 1 hit, "Goin' Home" (1952). Fats kept his R&B style as he was transformed into a rock and roll star of the mid- and late 1950s. This influence is obvious in "The Fat Man," where his use of the falsetto voice is particularly interesting. Unlike Little Richard's occasional falsetto "woos," Fats actually sings an entire 16-bar solo with falsetto "wah-wahs," approximating the sound of a harmonica solo. The form of "The Fat Man" is that of an **8-bar blues** (a modification of the traditional 12-bar blues). Fats preferred the 8-bar form even in his rock and roll songs. The instrumentation of "The Fat Man" is similar to the R&B-oriented rock band of the 1950s: saxes, guitar, bass, drums, and piano played in a boogie-woogie style that is less flamboyant and more refined than Little Richard's recordings.

Hits on the Pop Chart—Fats's first hit to cross over to the Pop chart was "Ain't That a Shame." Released in 1955, it became number 1 on the R&B chart and rose to number 10 on the Pop chart. A cover version by Pat Boone reached number 1 on the Pop chart in September 1955. "Ain't That a Shame" is a 12-bar blues, typical of R&B-oriented rock hits of the 1950s, but an exception to Fats's usual 8-bar blues. Subsequent Domino releases continued to do well on the R&B chart, and he placed more and more hits on the Pop chart. The Domino sound was essentially unchanged in "I'm in Love Again" (1956), "Blueberry Hill" (1956), "Blue Monday" (1956), "I'm Walkin'" (1957), "Whole Lotta Loving" (1958), and "I Want to Walk You Home" (1959).

Not all 1950s rock hits were newly composed. With hits rising and falling faster than ever before, there was a tremendous demand for material. A common practice was to resurrect old Pop favorites from previous decades and recast them in the new rock style, usually by adding a rock bass line and a familiar rock beat. Fats Domino was particularly successful at this. "Blueberry Hill," for example, had been popularized back in the 1940s by jazz big bands made up of white musicians, and "My Blue Heaven" (1956) dates back to 1927. These Tin Pan Alley songs conform to the 32-bar Pop song form, consisting of four 8-bar phrases.

Later Career—Near the end of the 1950s, performers and record companies alike assumed that rock and roll would not last. Fearing that performers would be narrowly typed as rock and roll performers only, some tried to establish themselves more as "legitimate" Pop artists, capable of continued appeal after the rock fad had run its course. Elvis Presley's success in a variety of styles seemed to confirm this strategy.

By 1960, the typical mainstream rock and roll style was indeed beginning to fade. Fats's hits were becoming less frequent.

The sound of "Walkin' to New Orleans," released in 1960, was Pop oriented. Strings were added, the old boogie-woogie rock piano disappeared, and there were no rocking saxophone solos. "Walkin' to New Orleans" proved to be Fats's last Top 10 hit. Except for a minor hit in 1968 (the Beatles' "Lady Madonna"), Fats's career after the early 1960s revolved around nostalgia tours and Las Vegas appearances.

Musical Style—Fats Domino's style was less flamboyant, hysterical, and threatening than the pounding, raucous style of Little Richard. Fats seemed more refined and controlled. He actually sat on a piano bench, playing and singing his repertoire without the histrionics of Little Richard or Jerry Lee Lewis. As we survey 1950s rock from the vantage point of history, Fats's music seems uncomplicated and enjoyable and his lifestyle rather free from controversy and trauma. He remains a lovable reminder of less troubled times.

Key Events in Fats Domino's Life

In this timeline, you will find some of the most important dates associated with Fats Domino's personal and professional accomplishments.

Time Stamp Date/Year	Time Stamp Content [Narrative]
February 26, 1928	Antoine Domino is born in New Orleans, LA
1942	Quit school and began playing in nightclubs
1950	"The Fat Man," Domino's first hit, was released
1952	"Goin' Home" hits number 1 on the R&B chart
1955	"Ain't That a Shame" is released and proves to be Fats's first crossover hit
1960	Like many rock artists, Fats began to change his sound toward a more Pop-oriented style
During the 1960s	Fats's career consisted of nostalgia tours and appearances in Las Vegas

Chuck Berry performing his infamous "duck walk."

SOURCE: Everett Collection

3.1.3: Chuck Berry

Electric guitar has become the central instrumental ingredient in rock and roll. Of the "big six" of 1950s rock, it is surely Chuck Berry who had the greatest influence on rock guitar styles, until the appearance of Jimi Hendrix a decade later.

Charles Edward Anderson Berry was born in St. Louis in 1926. He sang in the Baptist church choir and learned to play guitar while in high school. His roots were squarely in the black R&B tradition, although he was not from the South, as were Little Richard and Fats Domino. After spending three years in reform school for attempted robbery, he worked for a time in local R&B clubs and in the General Motors plant to support his wife and two children.

Key Events in Chuck Berry's Life

In the timeline below, you will find some of the most important dates associated with Chuck Berry's personal and professional accomplishments.

Time Stamp Date/Year	Time Stamp Content [Narrative]
October 18, 1926	Charles Edward Anderson Berry was born in St. Louis, MO
1955	"Maybelline" hit the charts, eventually rising to number 5 on the R&B chart
1956	"Roll Over Beethoven" is released
1959	Berry is arrested for violating the Mann Act
1972	At the age of 46, "My Ding-a-Ling" is Berry's only number 1 single on the Pop chart

Chuck Berry's Life and Career

As one of the most innovative early rock guitarists, Chuck Berry inspired generations of future musicians. In fact, there are very few rock guitarists who fail to give Berry primary credit for inspiring them and for providing a foundational rock guitar technique upon which they could build.

Musical Career—While playing at the local Cosmopolitan Club, the Chuck Berry Trio was heard by famed bluesman Muddy Waters, who suggested that the group audition for Chess Records, an independent company in Chicago. Chess and its subsidiary, Checker, had recorded some of the biggest names in R&B, including Muddy Waters and Howlin' Wolf, as well as some newer rock and roll artists (Bo Diddley, Dale Hawkins, the Moonglows, and the Flamingos). Chess was also well-connected to influential disc jockey Alan Freed, who was proactively promoting R&B music and black rock performers.

Berry's group auditioned with a song named "Ida Red," actually a C&W song made popular by Bob Wills and his Texas Playboys. Leonard Chess renamed the song, modified the lyrics, and issued Berry's recording as "Maybelline." In return for the consideration of being listed as coauthor, Alan Freed agreed to promote the record. By subsequent Chuck Berry standards, "Maybelline" is rather basic and unimpressive, both from musical and technical production perspectives. Nevertheless, with Freed's help, it hit the charts in 1955, eventually rising to number 5 (number 1 on the R&B chart).

After several intervening hits, Berry made the Pop chart again with "Roll Over Beethoven" (1956). "Too Much Monkey Business" and "Brown-Eyed Handsome Man" achieved R&B success in 1957, before "School Days," "Rock and Roll Music," "Sweet Little Sixteen," and "Johnny B. Goode" all landed in the Top 10 in 1957 and 1958. In late 1959, Berry was arrested for violation of the Mann Act, a law that made it illegal to take an underage woman across state lines for "immoral purposes." Berry's troubles began in El Paso, TX when he picked up a 14-year-old girl who had worked as a waitress and prostitute. She joined his tour, traveling through New Mexico, Arizona, Colorado, and Missouri with him. When the tour ended, Chuck put the girl to work as a hatcheck girl in his club in St. Louis. However, she proved unreliable, and Berry fired her. She subsequently filed a complaint with the police. Berry was convicted in a 1960 trial, but the conviction was overturned on appeal. A second trial resulted in a three-year sentence and a fine. He was eventually released in 1964 (White 1984, 42–44).

After his release, Berry managed several hits, including "No Particular Place to Go" (number 10 in 1964). Remarkably, he had his only number 1 Pop chart hit in 1972 ("My Ding-a-Ling") at the age of 46. Over four decades later, as he approached his 90th birthday, Chuck Berry recorded his first album in 38 years (*Chuck*, 2017). Unfortunately, the artist died of natural causes before its release.

Musical Style—Like Domino, Berry sang with a vocal style contrasting Little Richard's shouting style, and his enunciation is generally clearer than most blues-oriented R&B singers. Berry's friend Johnny Johnson adds an effective piano style to many Berry recordings; for examples, listen carefully to "Sweet Little Sixteen," "Almost Grown," "Johnny B. Goode," "Back in the U.S.A.," "Rock and Roll Music," and "Reelin' and Rockin'." Berry's lyrics speak to the newly emerging teen society and the everyday concerns of their lives: cars, girls, school, rock music, and specific problems associated with growing up. Frequently, the songs develop a story or idea ("School Days" and "Johnny B. Goode"); generally, Berry's lyrics are far superior to the "walk-talk" and "arms-charms" clichés and nonsense syllables of many 1950s rock songs. Listen to "School Days" for a particularly good example of this characteristic.

But Berry's biggest contribution to the evolution of popular music was setting the model for the rock and roll guitar style. For him, the guitar was a frontline instrument, often equal in importance to the lead vocal. Notice the alternation of voice and guitar in the chorus of "Johnny B. Goode," and also in "School Days" and "No Particular Place To Go." The *statement-and-answer* technique in which the guitar mimics the just-completed vocal line is related to the 2-bar or 4-bar **trade-offs** found in jazz. It is as if Berry and his guitar are performing a duet, a musical conversation back-and-forth.

Several of Berry's guitar introductions became famous and were widely imitated. Compare the intros to "Back in the U.S.A.," "Roll Over Beethoven," and "Johnny B. Goode." The double-note playing in his solos and the alternating chords of his rhythmic accompaniments (similar to some rock piano styles) set models that were followed for years to come.

Most of Berry's rock hits were in the standard 12-bar blues form. His stage act was not as frenetic as Little Richard's, but it was more animated than Fats Domino's. Although he was the oldest of the major rock stars of the 1950s, he developed his famous **duck walk**, a physically demanding feat. Berry would bend his knees low and lope across the stage while playing the guitar. Unlike some other 1950s rock stars, Berry never modified his style to appeal to a broader Pop audience. Throughout his career, he retained the style that made him one of the biggest stars in the history of rock and roll.

3.1.4: Jerry Lee Lewis

Jerry Lee Lewis is essentially the white counterpart to Little Richard. Jerry Lee was born on September 9, 1935, like Richard, into a rather poor family in a small southern town (Ferriday, Louisiana) with a dominant mother and a largely absent father. Both Jerry Lee and Little Richard endured an ongoing internal battle between their religious faith and their hell-raising rock and roll lifestyles. Like Little Richard, Jerry Lee's career as a rock and roll hit-maker ended prematurely.

Jerry Lee Lewis

SOURCE: Pictorial Press Ltd/Alamy Stock Photo

Million Dollar Quartet (L to R): Jerry Lee Lewis, Carl Perkins, Elvis Presley, and Johnny Cash.

SOURCE: Pictorial Press Ltd/Alamy Stock Photo

Jerry Lee Lewis's Life and Career

While reading about an artist's background and musical style can be highly informative, it is hardly a substitute for listening to the actual music. Similarly, while recordings are the ultimate goal of many rock artists or groups, the learning experience and authenticity of information provided are augmented greatly by hearing artists describe this work in their own words and, when performances are available, by watching videos of them.

Musical Style—Musically, there were also many similarities between Lewis and Richard. Both were pianists and were heavily influenced by gospel music and black R&B. Young Jerry Lee attended evangelist meetings conducted by musician-preacher Brother Janway, whose piano style included a pounding bass line and simple right-hand melodies (Lewis 1982, 15). But Jerry Lee was also captivated by R&B musicians, including B. B. King and Muddy Waters, who played at Haney's Big House in Ferriday (Lewis 1982, 15). In their mature rock and roll style, both Lewis and Richard played 12-bar blues with pounding, boogie-derived bass lines and improvised right-hand figures, including **glissandi**, repeating chords, and boogie patterns. They were best when performing hard-rocking, fast songs; their performance styles were flamboyant, including lots of physical movement while playing at the keyboard.

Personal Life—Jerry Lee's marital escapades (which would finally have a major, negative impact on his career) began in 1951, when he married a preacher's daughter. She was 17 and in the 11th grade; Jerry was 16 and in the 8th grade (he had been repeatedly held back in the 7th grade). To assuage her parents' objections, Jerry enrolled in the Southwestern Bible Institute (Waxahachie, Texas) with the goal of becoming a preacher. In a matter of months, his young wife filed for divorce, and Jerry Lee was invited to leave the institute. Meanwhile, having found a new love in a high school junior, Jerry remarried before the divorce was finalized. His second marriage was a rough one and deteriorated within several years.

Musical Career—In 1956, Jay Brown (Jerry's older cousin and bass player) persuaded Jerry to come to his home in Memphis and visit Sam Phillips's Sun Records. Jerry Lee had tried Sun Records once before but had left with a "don't call us, we'll call you" assessment. This time, things turned out better. Jerry Lee recorded "Crazy Arms" and several other country songs. Phillips was impressed and signed Jerry Lee to a contract. Late in 1956, Sun released "Crazy Arms," and it became a mild success. Also while visiting Jay, Jerry met Myra Gail, Jay's 12-year-old daughter. Something more than a family relationship developed, and by December 1957, the two were husband and wife.

Sun Records saw Jerry as another rockabilly star, but Jerry had other ideas. A pounding mainstream rock and roll song called "Whole Lot of Shakin' Going On" had been particularly successful on his most recent tour. Jerry's recording of the song, a cover version of a composition released two years earlier by the Commodores (not the later group associated with Lionel Richie), became a smash hit in 1957, reaching the top position on both the C&W and R&B charts and number 3 on the Pop chart.

In late 1957, Sun Records released "Great Balls of Fire," written by Jack Hammer and Otis Blackwell. The B-side of this release was Hank Williams's country tune "You Win Again." Aided by an appearance on Steve Allen's television variety show, Jerry Lee reached the number 2 spot on the Pop chart with "Great Balls of Fire" (number 3 on the R&B and number 1 on the C&W chart). Blackwell also wrote Jerry Lee's third major hit, "Breathless," released in February 1958, shortly after Jerry's marriage to Myra. His last major hit was "High School Confidential," the title song from an MGM movie in which the Jerry Lee Lewis Trio made a cameo appearance.

"Whole Lot of Shakin' Going On" and "Great Balls of Fire" had been Top 10 hits in England, inspiring Jerry Lee to embark on his first overseas tour there, where his arrival was enthusiastically anticipated. Against advice, he took his new 13-year-old bride (and cousin) along. No sooner had the entourage disembarked than an inquisitive reporter discovered Jerry Lee's child bride. The British were outraged. Some tour dates were canceled; others were played to half-empty halls and to jeering, taunting audiences.

Staggered by the British reaction, Jerry Lee expected more tolerance on his return to the United States, but "High School Confidential" quickly dropped from the charts, and many concerts were canceled. Jerry Lee's days as a rock and roll star were over. Repeated "comeback" attempts failed; he returned to the C&W sound from whence he had come. Between 1961 and 1975, he placed over 20 songs on the country charts, including 11 in the Top 5.

Post Rock and Roll Life—Post rock and roll life has not been kind to Jerry Lee. His marriage to Myra ended in divorce in 1970 (Jerry has had several more marriages since then). Two of his sons died tragically, as did two of his wives. There have been problems with alcohol, drugs, tax evasion, shootings, fistfights, automobile accidents, arrests, extramarital affairs, and debilitating physical illness. Not yet ready to give up, in 2010, Lewis released *Mean Old Man* (2010), featuring Keith Richards (guitar on "Sweet Virginia"), Mick Jagger (duet on "Dead Flowers"), and Eric Clapton ("You Can Have Her"). To prove he was still capable, he released *Rock & Roll Time* (2014), again including Keith Richards as a guest artist, along with Neil Young, Robbie Robertson, and Ronnie Wood.

Jerry Lee Lewis, in his brief moment of stardom, had a disproportionate impact on rock and roll. His unique blend of C&W and R&B, and his piano style, vocal style, and lifestyle, influenced many of his contemporaries and many who would follow. Although he longed to be known as the "king of rock and roll," he must settle for his lifelong nickname: "Killer."

Key Events in Jerry Lee Lewis's Life

In the timeline below, you will find some of the most important dates associated with Jerry Lee Lewis's personal and professional accomplishments.

Time Stamp Date/Year	Time Stamp Content [Narrative]
September 9, 1935	Lewis was born in Ferriday, LA
1951	At the age of 16 and in the 8th grade, he married a preacher's daughter
1956	His second attempt recording at Sun Records proved successful with the release of "Crazy Arms"
1957	Married his pre-teen cousin, Myra Gail; "Whole Lotta Shakin' Going On" becomes a smash hit, followed by "Great Balls of Fire"
1958	Lewis's marriage to his now-13-year-old wife outrages the British public and effectively ended the most commercially successful period of his career
2014	Released Rock & Roll Time, his most recent album

3.1.5: Buddy Holly

Charles Hardin (Buddy) Holley did not fit the mold of the other early rock and rollers discussed in this chapter. Born in Lubbock, Texas, in 1936, his musical foundation was almost exclusively C&W. Black R&B and gospel were not significant factors in western Texas, so Buddy grew up without the biracial musical influences that characterized Elvis's and Jerry Lee's backgrounds.

Buddy Holly

Key Events in Buddy Holly's Life

In the timeline below, you will find some of the most important dates associated with Buddy Holly's personal and professional accomplishments.

Time Stamp Date/Year	Time Stamp Content [Narrative]
September 7, 1936	Holly is born in Lubbock, TX
1956	Holly and his country-style band signed with Decca Records, making some recordings including an early version of "That'll Be the Day"
1957	Records with his new band (the Crickets), and their energized version of "That'll Be the Day" goes to number 1
1958	Holly splits from the Crickets and his manager, Norman Petty, and initiates a solo tour
February 2, 1959	Performs his last concert, in Clear Lake, IA, before dying in a plane crash early the next morning

Buddy Holly's Life and Career

Buddy Holly emerged as a unique rock artist who was influenced primarily by the C&W branch that led to the emergence of rock and roll, rather than the R&B that served as primary inspiration for the other style-setters presented earlier. His style proved particularly influential on the solidification of rockabilly as an important subgenre of rock.

Holly's Career—His country-style band signed a contract with Decca Records and, during 1956, released several straight country songs, including an early version of "That'll Be the Day." None was successful, and Decca released Buddy from his contract. (Holley's Decca contract had inadvertently dropped the e from his name; Buddy retained the misspelling as his professional name: Holly.)

In early 1957, Buddy and his new band (the Crickets) journeyed to a Clovis, New Mexico recording studio owned by Norman Petty. Among the songs recorded at that session was an energized version of "That'll Be the Day." Petty took the demo tape to New York, where, after several rejections, it was accepted by the Coral-Brunswick label. Petty became Holly's manager, and the Crickets' personnel and instrumentation solidified, including Niki Sullivan on guitar, Joe Mauldin on acoustic bass, Jerry Allison on drums, and, of course, Holly on guitar.

By August 1957, "That'll Be the Day" had risen to number 1. In the next (year-and-a-half), Holly and the Crickets released eight more singles, including "Peggy Sue," "Oh Boy!," "Maybe Baby," "Rave On," and "Heartbeat." Because separate contracts had been signed, some of these songs were released under the name of Holly on the Coral label, and some were released under the name of the Crickets on Brunswick, although all were performed by the same group of musicians.

Holly's Life—In the summer of 1958, Buddy married Maria Elena Santiago, a Puerto Rican woman from New York. Supposedly at her suggestion, questions arose regarding Norman Petty's handling of Buddy and the band, especially concerning Petty's listing as co-author of several Holly songs. Finally, in late 1958, Holly split from both Petty and the Crickets. He recruited new sidemen, planned a tour, and initiated a recording session, adopting a softer rock sound. Before this new Holly sound had a chance to be released, Buddy's new quartet (including bassist Waylon Jennings) set out on a tour with Dion and the Belmonts, Ritchie Valens, and the Big Bopper (J. P. Richardson). Following a concert at Clear Lake, Iowa, on February 2, 1959, Holly, Valens, and Richardson were killed in a plane crash in the wee hours of the next morning. Coral subsequently released a song from that last Pop-oriented recording session—a Paul Anka tune with the ironic title "It Doesn't Matter Anymore." It rose to number 13 and was, of course, Holly's last hit.

Holly's Personality—Buddy Holly was significantly different from the other 1950s rock pioneers. The R&B influence on his essentially C&W sound apparently came secondhand through his idol, Elvis Presley. Also, Buddy did not look like most 1950s rock stars. He was tall and thin; wore thick, horn-rimmed glasses; and, typically, performed in a dark suit and bow tie. He emanated none of the sexuality of Presley or the flamboyance of Little Richard or Jerry Lee Lewis.

Like Chuck Berry, vocalist-guitarist Holly wrote most of his own material, helping to initiate a trend that would characterize rock and roll of the following decades. His instrumental lineup—consisting of lead guitar, rhythm guitar, bass, and drums—would establish basic rock instrumentation for years to come. Unlike most other early rock and rollers, Holly pursued a more conservative lifestyle. He was not known as a drinker, womanizer, or druggie. In many ways, he was less like the typical rock and roll sex symbol and more like the average middle-American teenager of the 1950s. His lyrics were almost exclusively about uncomplicated boy-girl romance and reflected the rather innocent, fun-loving, teenage lifestyle of the 1950s instead of the social heaviness and angry rebellion of later rock.

Holly's Musical Style—Holly's serious approach to his music also led him into the world of production and technology, such as it was in 1957 and 1958. He experimented with **double-tracking** his voice and guitar ("Words of Love") and paid close attention to the technical side of his recordings. His turn toward a softer sound in his last recording sessions has prompted much speculation. Holly's late 1958 releases had not fared particularly well; thus, it is possible that he was attempting to broaden his reputation from that of a rock and roller to a "legitimate" Pop artist (recall Fats Domino's similar turn about one year later with "Walkin' to New Orleans").

No discussion of Buddy Holly would be complete without mentioning his unique vocal characteristics. Holly's "hiccup" style (technically, called a **glottal stop**) is derived most directly from Elvis Presley, who frequently transformed one syllable into at least two (e.g., in Presley's "Mystery Train," listen to "comin' rou-ound the li-ine"). Holly carries such divisions to new heights with his treatment of "my Pe-eggy Su-ue-ue-ue-ue-e-ue-ue" and his delivery of the words "over you-e-ou" in "It Doesn't Matter Anymore." Another Holly trademark is his habit of changing the color (or **timbre**) of his voice in mid-phrase. At times, he sings in a dark, husky, Presley-like voice; then, gradually, he changes to a thin, almost effeminate sound. This progression is very noticeable in the lines, "There's no use in me a cryin', I've done everything and now I'm sick of tryin'" in "It Doesn't Matter Anymore." The thin voice changing to his more normal voice is evident in sections of "Peggy Sue." It is almost as if Holly is running his voice through an electronic filter to alter the sound, without the need for such electronic processing.

Given the relative brevity of his recording career, Holly has had an incredible impact on the evolution of rock music. As evidence of his continuing influence, recordings of Holly tunes were released in 2010 (*Rave On Buddy Holly*), including cover versions by Paul McCartney ("It's So Easy"), Patti Smith ("Words of Love"), Graham Nash ("Raining in My Heart"), Nick Lowe ("Changing All Those Changes"), Modest Mouse ("That'll Be the Day"), Kid Rock ("Well All Right"), Florence + the Machine ("Not Fade Away"), and The Black Keys ("Dearest").

A Tragic End—Perhaps because he was the first major rock star to die suddenly and unexpectedly, an almost cult-like following emerged for Buddy Holly. Don McLean's 1971 song "American Pie," with its reference to "the day the music died," enhanced the Buddy Holly mystique. In 1959, rock and roll was a vital, dynamic new force, and its proponents were young, vigorous, and invested with the assumed immortality of youth. A pall was cast over the new rock and roll generation after his death. It was the first rock and roll death . . . but it was far from the last.

Favorite Style Setter of the 1950s

Listen to some of the cited recordings by the five style-setters described in the previous section, then listen to tracks from one of your favorite recordings released during the past decade. Can you hear influences of any of the five style-setters of the 1950s in the more recent recording? If so, write a few sentences about the specific musical elements in which you hear this influence and how the newer artist has taken this influence and made the musical style their own. What is similar between the older recording(s) and your current favorite? If you do not believe there is a significant influence, write a few sentences about the musical elements that differentiate the older and more recent recordings. Are there ways in which adopting one or more stylistic trait(s) of the earlier artist(s) might enhance the sound of the newer artist? As you continue to practice using your growing musical vocabulary, strive to be as precise and accurate as possible in your descriptions.

 The response entered here will appear in the performance dashboard and can be viewed by your instructor.

Submit

Ray Charles

SOURCE: Pictorial Press Ltd/Alamy Stock Photo

3.2: Other Rock Styles in the 1950s

OBJECTIVE: Summarize other influences on rock and roll music in the 1950s

Between July 1955 and December 1960, there were 81 number 1 hits. Of these, only 16 were recorded by the major artists discussed thus far in this chapter and the previous. In fact, 14 of those 16 were by Elvis Presley (the others were by Bill Haley and Buddy Holly). Together, Lewis, Holly, Domino, Berry, and Little Richard placed only 25 hits in the Top 10 from 1955 to 1960, meaning a host of other performers had hits during this time. The next section will provide an opportunity to survey some of the more significant of these.

3.2.1: R&B- and Gospel-Derived Rock

Several artists whose background lay in R&B or gospel found success in the late 1950s. The following section will describe a few of the most important of these, including Lloyd Price, Ray Charles, and Sam Cooke.

Successful Rock Artists of R&B and Gospel Background

You have learned about the important influence of R&B on early rock music. A primary influence on early R&B was gospel music, since many of the singers who pioneered this style gained early performance experience singing in churches. This influence of gospel will come to the fore again when we explore soul music of the 1960s and 1970s.

Lloyd Price—Lloyd Price had enjoyed several R&B hits in the early 1950s, including the crossover hit "Lawdy Miss

Clawdy." With relatively little change in style, he moved into the rock market, with songs such as "Stagger Lee" (1959) and somewhat softer hits including "Personality" and "I'm Gonna Get Married."

Ray Charles—Ray Charles started as a jazz crooner in the style of Nat "King" Cole, but through the early 1950s, his style reflected more R&B influences. In 1955, he added a strong gospel element in his performance of "I Got a Woman." An unrestrained, emotional vocal delivery over a pounding, rocking accompaniment characterized this and later R&B hits. Charles finally crossed over to the national Pop chart in 1959 with the classic "What'd I Say," his first million seller. Between 1959 and 1963, he placed nine more songs in the Top 10, including the C&W-oriented "I Can't Stop Loving You." After a long and highly influential career, Ray Charles died in 2004 at the age of 73.

Sam Cooke—The blending of gospel and blues is also evident in the style of Sam Cooke. In the early 1950s, Cooke was the lead singer for the Soul Stirrers, a popular black gospel group. His crossover to the Pop market came in 1957 with "You Send Me" (number 1). The combination of a softer sound with the gospel-flavored vocal had enormous appeal. The extended vocal *melismas* (extending one syllable over many notes) and the soulful interpolations on "I know, I know, I know" and "whoa-oh-oh-and-whoa-oh-oh-oh" seemed like a whole new world to white fans of soft rock. Cooke's voice was emotional, but not raspy or raucous. Follow-up hits included "For Sentimental Reasons," "Only Sixteen," "Wonderful World," "Chain Gang," and "Twistin' the Night Away." Tragically, Sam Cooke died in 1964, when he was shot by a hotel manager.

Rockabilly Hit Makers of the 1950s

Gene Vincent "Be-Bop-a-Lula" (1956)

Guy Mitchell "Singing the Blues" (1956)
    "Heartaches by the Number" (1959)

Marty Robbins "A White Sport Coat" (1957)
    "El Paso" (1960)

Buddy Knox "Party Doll" (1957)

Eddie Cochran "Summertime Blues" (1958)

Conway Twitty "It's Only Make Believe" (1958)

Johnny Horton "The Battle of New Orleans" (1959)
    "Sink the Bismarck" (1960)
    "North to Alaska" (1960)

3.2.2: Rockabilly

Sun Records, influential in developing the rockabilly style, had another hit with singer Johnny Cash. Cash was born in 1932 in Arkansas, and his first release, "Cry, Cry, Cry," was a moderate country hit. In 1956, "I Walk the Line" rose to number 17 on the national charts. Cash's low voice and decidedly country-style delivery set him apart from the more R&B-influenced rockabilly artists. Following several more Top 20 hits, Cash moved to Columbia Records, where he continued to score hits, including "Ring of Fire" (1963) and "A Boy Named Sue" (1969). In 1997, he was diagnosed with a degenerative nervous disorder; he died on September 12, 2003, at the age of 71. During the final four months of his life, Cash recorded 60 songs; these recordings were released posthumously as part of the *American Recording* series. A set of rarities from the artist's early years was also released posthumously (*From Memphis to Hollywood: Bootleg Vol. 2*, 2010).

In addition to those already mentioned, many other rockabilly artists enjoyed brief moments in the limelight (see list of songs and associated artists in the Rockabilly Hit Makers of the 1950s box).

3.2.3: Soft Rock

While the majority of music described during the early 1950s involves high energy, rhythmic drive, and moderate to fast tempos, listeners can become bored when music is too similar. Soft rock provided an important contrast to the musical characteristics evident in mainstream rock and rockabilly.

Soft Rock Artists

As you learned earlier in this chapter, after an initial period of creating and recording energetic, high-energy rock and roll, some of the mainstream style-setters produced music of a lighter quality. During this era, there were a number of important artists for whom the general style of their music was lighter and more relaxed. We often refer to this style of popular music as *soft rock*, and specific songs in this style are sometimes called *ballads*.

Paul Anka—One of the most talented young singer-songwriters of the 1950s was Paul Anka, a Canadian who had his first hit, "Diana," in 1957 at the age of 16. From 1958 to 1960, Anka had six more Top 10 songs, including "Lonely Boy" and "Put Your Head on My Shoulder." He continued to produce hits through the 1960s and 1970s, including a number 1 hit in 1974 called "(You're) Having My Baby." He also composed "My Way"—a hit for both Frank Sinatra and Elvis Presley.

Bobby Darin—In 1958, Bobby Darin (born Walden Robert Cassotto) produced his first hit, "Splish Splash," on Atco Records, a subsidiary of Atlantic Records. Starting with this genuine rock sound (Darin, who was white, even affected something of black enunciation), Darin gradually softened his style. "Dream Lover" (1959) and subsequent hits such as "Mack the Knife," "Beyond the Sea," "Clementine," and "Won't You Come Home Bill Bailey" are closer to a swinging Pop style. In 1973, he died of complications related to a heart condition at the age of 37.

Frankie Avalon—In the late 1950s and early 1960s, Philadelphia became a center for the handsome-male-teen-idol syndrome. With the national publicity afforded by Dick Clark's television show, *American Bandstand*, a number of young Philadelphians achieved major success. Typical of these smooth young singers was Frankie Avalon, who had a number 1 hit with "Venus." Although Avalon's songs were aimed at a young audience, they were very Pop oriented, bearing little or no relationship to mainstream rock and roll. Other teen idols followed Avalon's success.

Bobby Darin

SOURCE: Harry Hammond/V&A Images/Alamy Stock Photo

Teen Idol Hit Makers

Tommy Sands (Houston) "Teen-Age Crush" (1957)

Fabian (Philadelphia) "Turn Me Loose" (1959)
"Tiger" (1959)

Neil Sedaka (Brooklyn) "Calendar Girl"
(1960/1961)
"Breaking Up Is Hard to Do" (1962)

Bobby Rydell (Philadelphia) "Wild One" (1960)
"Swingin' School" (1960)
"Volare" (1960)

Mark Dinning (Grant County, OK) "Teen Angel"
(1960)

Bobby Vee (Fargo, ND) "Devil or Angel" (1960)
"Rubber Ball" (1960/1961)
"Take Good Care of My Baby" (1961)
"Run to Him" (1961)

Bobby Vinton (Canonsburg, PA) "Roses Are Red
(My Love)" (1962)
"Blue on Blue" (1963)
"Blue Velvet" (1963)
"There! I've Said It Again" (1963)
"Mr. Lonely" (1964)

VOCAL GROUPS Another successful form of popular music during this era was represented by white vocal groups, which ranged from the rock-oriented style of Danny and the Juniors and Dion and the Belmonts to the Pop-style sounds of the Teddy Bears ("To Know Him Is to Love Him"), the Fleetwoods ("Come Softly to Me" and "Mr. Blue"), and the Browns ("The Three Bells"). "At the Hop," a song by the Philadelphia group Danny and the Juniors, reached number 1 in early 1958 and has become a rock and roll classic. Their follow-up hit, "Rock and Roll Is Here to Stay," made the Top 20 and continues to be a rock and roll anthem. The style of Dion and the Belmonts was somewhat softer than Danny and the Juniors. The Belmonts came from the Bronx and made several modest hits before releasing "A Teenager in Love" in 1959. The follow-up "Where or When" (1960) moved to a softer Pop sound. Dion himself achieved several major hits in the early 1960s, most notably "Runaround Sue," a number 1 hit in 1961.

Popular Solo Singers of Late 50s and Early 60s

Another category of popular music artists during this period included artists who recorded with a variety of backup musicians rather than having a consistent group of supporting musicians (i.e., a band) that was considered essential to the artist's sound. In the next

section, you will learn about some of the most important of these solo singers.

Male Singers—Among the most popular black solo singers were Johnny Mathis and Tommy Edwards. Stylistically a Pop crooner, Mathis was recognized for his flawlessly expressive voice and for his remarkable vocal range. In 1957, Mathis released four ballads that reached the Top 20, including the number 1 hit "Chances Are." The unprecedented success of his greatest hits album (1958) started a trend for releasing albums that, instead of containing new material, consisted of a collection of an artist's previous hits; this early example of a greatest hits album remained on the *Billboard* album chart for some 490 weeks (almost 10 years!).

Tommy Edwards was somewhat older than the typical late 1950s Pop star. His number 1 hit "It's All in the Game" reached number 1 in 1958, when Edwards was 36. From 1958 to 1960, Edwards placed five more songs in the Top 40.

Female Singers—Female singers were rather rare in the late 1950s rock scene and mostly sang soft rock. Connie Francis (Concetta Franconero) produced some 35 Top 40 songs from 1958 to 1964. Her style ranged from cute, up-tempo songs ("Stupid Cupid," 1958, and "Lipstick on Your Collar," 1959) to soft rock ("Who's Sorry Now," 1958) to a pure Pop style ("Where the Boys Are," 1961).

Brenda Lee (Brenda Mae Tarpley) came from a C&W musical background and was only 11 years old when she signed a contract with Decca Records. In the early 1960s, she gained national attention with "Sweet Nothin's" (number 4) and "I'm Sorry" (number 1). Brenda continued to place occasional songs in the Top 10 for several years.

3.2.4: Instrumental Groups

Although singers have dominated the rock scene, the *instrumental* (a song without a vocalist singing words) has enjoyed consistent, though infrequent, popularity. Typically, a group would achieve major chart success with a particularly catchy instrumental, and then fade from view. The general public apparently finds it easier to identify and become attached to a vocalist than to recognize the stylings of an instrumentalist. For this broad audience, apparently, the verbal appeal of a song lyric may be more direct than the more subtle appeal of purely instrumental music; in fact, this may be one of the reasons that rock and roll (and other forms of popular music with vocals) consistently attains significantly greater commercial success than jazz or classical music, for which the most oft-heard works are instrumental.

One of the first successful rock instrumentals was "Honky Tonk" (1956) by Bill Doggett, a jazz and R&B player from the 1930s and 1940s (born in 1916). It had a hard blues

Table 3.1 Popular Instrumental Hits of the Late 50s and Early 60s

Song	Performer	Lead Instrument
"Rawhide"	Link Wray	guitar
"Crossfire"	Johnny and the Hurricanes	guitar
"Red River Rock"	Johnny and the Hurricanes	guitar
"Walk Don't Run"	Ventures	guitar
"Sleep Walk"	Santo and Johnny	guitar
"Topsy II"	Cozy Cole	drums
"White Silver Sands"	Bill Black Combo	piano
"The Happy Organ"	Dave "Baby" Cortez	organ
"Last Date"	Floyd Cramer	piano
"On the Rebound"	Floyd Cramer	piano
"San Antonio Rose"	Floyd Cramer	piano

and boogie-derived sound that featured a honking saxophone lead, providing an exciting "new" sound to rock and roll. A similar sound was produced in 1957 with "Raunchy" by Bill Justis, a studio musician and producer for Sun Records; this song also featured a **dirty saxophone** lead melody for which the title of the song provided a perfect description. Another instrumental featuring a dirty saxophone lead hit number 1 in 1958: "Tequila" by the Champs.

Inevitably, the rock instrumental was destined to focus on the electric guitar. Two such instrumentals achieved major success in 1958: "Rumble" by Link Wray (number 16) and "Rebel-Rouser" by Duane Eddy (number 6). Eddy's twangy guitar sound was recognizable and widely imitated. Table 3.1 shows other instrumentals that gained popularity in the late 1950s and early 1960s.

3.2.5: Novelties

Throughout the history of popular music, musical oddities known as novelty songs have appeared periodically. Usually humorous or whimsical songs with a catchy **hook**, these songs are sometimes in the prevailing popular style, but more often they have a sort of camp appeal, meaning that they are so far outside the prevailing style that they catch on. Successful novelty songs seem to happen by accident, unpredictably catching the public's attention.

Typically, the popularity of such songs is short-lived, and their creators rarely produce subsequent titles. An exception to this rule is David Seville (born Ross Bagdasarian). Seville hit the charts first in April 1958 with "Witch Doctor," a humorous song with a catchy nonsense hook. This recording used technology to produce a novel sound for the human voice by playing back the tape at a higher speed than that at which it was recorded. The success of "Witch Doctor," which used this technique, inspired Seville to create "The Chipmunk Song" later that year, a number 1 hit. The popularity of Seville's "chipmunks" continued throughout the following decades with a series of recordings (e.g., *The Chipmunks Sing the Beatles Hits*, *Chipmunk Punk*, *Urban Chipmunk*, *Chipmunk Rock*, *Chipmunks in Low Places*, and many others) into the new millennium with the release of feature-length films, including *Alvin and the Chipmunks* (2007) and *Alvin and the Chipmunks: The Squeakquel* (2010). Table 3.2 shows some of the successful novelty hits of the 1950s and early 1960s.

What Makes a Song "Novel"?

The novelty song is a unique, often humorous, form of popular music that has appeared periodically since near the beginning of the rock era. Identify any song in your own collection of more recent recordings that falls into this category (if unsuccessful in that task, reach out to a few friends until you find at least one such song). Describe thoroughly what it is about the song that makes it "novel." Are there musical elements that add to this character in addition to the vocals or lyrics? After listening to at least three of the songs in the list of early rock novelty songs above, what similarities can you identify between these early examples and the song you selected from your own collection? Are there any significant differences, musically or lyrically?

 The response entered here will appear in the performance dashboard and can be viewed by your instructor.

Submit

Table 3.2 Novelty Songs of the Late 1950s and Early 1960s

Song	Chart Position	Comments
"The Purple People Eater" (Sheb Wooley)	number 1, 1958	hook: "a one-eyed, one-horned, flying purple people eater" (using sped-up voice)
"Itsy Bitsy Teenie Weenie Yellow Polka-Dot Bikini" (Brian Hyland)	number 1, 1960	seemingly risqué lyric, but the hook line reveals that the girl in a bikini is only two years old
"Alley-Oop" (Hollywood Argyles)	number 1, 1960	nasal, off-key vocal tells of comic-strip caveman that was popular at the time; this song falls in the "so-bad-it's-good" category
"Ahab the Arab" (Ray Stevens)	number 5, 1962	another so-bad-it's good song
"The Monster Mash" (Bobby [Boris] Pickett and the Crypt-Kickers)	number 1, 1962	a parody of both TV monster shows and the dance craze

3.3: The Industry

OBJECTIVE: Explain how the emergence of rock and roll music affected the music industry

The rock revolution of the mid-1950s was more than a musical revolution. The popular music industry, which had followed rather well-entrenched, comfortable practices for decades, was literally turned upside down. The Big Five recording companies went from producing 42 of 1954's Top 50 recordings to only 17 of 1956's Top 50, a drop of 60 percent. The other 33 top discs of that later year were released by 25 different companies. A well-controlled, orderly, and predictable market had become chaotic and somewhat unpredictable.

The music publishing industry was also in turmoil. With the coming of rock and roll, **sheet music** sales dropped dramatically. In the older Pop tradition, published sheet music was an important aspect of any song's popularity and, for decades, provided a significant source of additional revenue. But the rock and rollers of the mid-1950s were teenagers, the vast majority of whom—if they played a musical instrument—played by ear rather than by reading musical notation. They simply listened to the record and imitated it. Rock and roll grew primarily from the aural tradition associated with R&B and C&W, not from the written tradition of Pop and Tin Pan Alley.

Furthermore, sheet music did not accurately reflect the sound of the new songs. The printed page could not begin to approximate the real sounds of Presley, Little Richard, or Jerry Lee Lewis and these performers' expressive deviations from the notated melodies. Finally, there was also the problem of the short-lived rock hit. By the time a song became a hit, it was too late to print, distribute, and sell a sufficient quantity of the printed music before the song faded into oblivion. In 1955 and 1956, most of the popular recordings never had a presence on the list of best-selling sheet music that was published by *Variety* magazine, the entertainment world's trade journal.

The effects of the rock revolution were also felt throughout the rest of the music industry. Established singers, instrumentalists, arrangers, orchestrators, copyists, and conductors found themselves out of the mainstream with reduced demand for their talents. Much has been said about society's protests against early rock and roll on religious, moral, musical, and racial grounds; the fact that one of the earliest and strongest reactions against rock and roll came from the established music industry itself is often overlooked. *Variety* magazine ran frequent anti-rock articles and editorials throughout 1955 and 1956. Industry representatives, from the president of MGM Records to Pop star Frank Sinatra, condemned the new style. Although their remarks were often couched in musical and moralistic terms, it is likely that underlying much of the vehemence was sheer economic distress. The music industry began to realize that the old rules no longer applied. The reaction to this revolution was convulsive, though not yet "televised" … that came later ("The Revolution Will Not Be Televised" by Gil Scott-Heron, 1970).

3.3.1: Radio

Most of the traditional music industry considered rock and roll a monstrous menace, but one segment of the business viewed the new style as its savior. Television had put a serious dent in the popularity of radio. In the early 1950s, it was reasonable to believe that radio had been superseded by television in much the same way that the automobile had replaced the horse and buggy. After all, why just listen to entertainment when you could listen and watch?

3.3.2: Payola

There was an inherent problem in the partnership between the record industry and radio. Largely because of rock and roll, record sales exploded from $213 million in 1954 to $603 million in 1959 (Gillett 1983, 39). However, the majority of this increased revenue was distributed among small, independent companies and subsidiaries, hundreds of which vied for the public attention needed to propel their unknown act to number 1 status. If a record got radio play, it stood a chance; if not, it was dead. Thus, the radio stations and the popular disc jockeys found that they had a stranglehold on the new rock and roll recording industry.

For the most part, stations blindly followed the *Billboard* charts to create their play lists. But major Top 40 stations in large markets (e.g., New York, Chicago, or L.A.) could introduce a new record locally and start it on its journey up the charts. For the promotional representatives of the record companies, vying each week with all the other "next Elvises," it was essential to obtain airplay. One could rely on the quality of the music alone or one could assist the evaluation process by offering certain advantages to disc jockeys, program directors, and station managers. Such inducements, known as **payola**, might include cash; trips to desirable locales like the Bahamas ("promotional weekends"); or partial ownership in the song, the artist, or even the record company itself.

From 1959 to 1960, the government took action. The Federal Trade Commission charged several record companies and distributors with unfair trade practices. Almost simultaneously, the district attorney of New York

Early Alliance between Rock and Radio

The quickest, easiest, and cheapest way for a small independent record company to promote its newest rock star was to obtain radio airplay. Rock and roll generally did not have access to the national television networks, which were aligned with the major record companies. *Your Hit Parade* was a popular weekly television show, but it was associated with the Pop tradition. Each week, the *Your Hit Parade* staff singers and orchestra performed live covers of the previous week's Top 10 Pop songs. But these live cover versions were, at best, pale Pop-style imitations of the rock hits that filled the charts in the late 1950s.

The show's traditional adult audience gradually lost interest because of the increasing frequency of rock and roll songs, and teenagers were not interested in, for example, singer Snooky Larson's Pop version of "Hound Dog." By 1958, *Your Hit Parade* was no longer on the air. Except for brief segments on variety shows, such as those hosted by Ed Sullivan and Steve Allen, it was not until the advent of Dick Clark's *American Bandstand* (beginning in the fall of 1957) that television offered a show specifically focused on teen rock and roll.

Not so with radio, however. Although network radio stations tended to stay with Pop music broadcasts, dramas, and serials, the smaller, independent stations primarily programmed recorded music. Many specialized in the specific styles (like C&W or R&B) that were favored in their particular locale. The announcers who played the records began to develop a personality of their own. Alan Freed, one of the first white disc jockeys to play black music for a predominantly white audience, began playing black R&B and rock and roll on his radio shows in Cleveland and later in New York City. Similar programs appeared in Los Angeles, New Orleans, Memphis, and Nashville.

Many stations were converted into chain ownership—one owner or set of owners controlling stations in a number of cities. The format, known as Top 40 radio, focused on a frequent rotation through the Top 40 hits of the week, fast-talking personalities as **deejays** (DJs; disc jockeys), and an hourly newscast. Catering to the teen audience, the stations competed for ratings. DJs such as Wolfman Jack (Bob Smith), Dick Clark, and (later) Murray the K established national reputations. By the late 1950s, radio was *the* medium for the promotion and dissemination of rock. A significant portion of the bandwidth across the AM radio dial—this was prior to the presence of FM radio—was primarily a series of competing personalities hyping the same songs in the Top 40 format. Radio was alive and well, thanks to rock and roll.

initiated grand jury hearings related to charges of commercial bribery against various disc jockeys, including Alan Freed. In February 1960, the U.S. House of Representatives Legislative Oversight Committee expanded its investigation of rigged television game shows to include payola practices in the music industry. During testimony, a number of disc jockeys admitted to taking cash, gifts, and royalty payments in return for promoting certain records. In September 1960, amendments were made to the Federal Communications Act that would prohibit payments of cash or gifts in exchange for airplay (Miller 1980, 102–03). In 1962, as a result, Freed was convicted on two counts of commercial bribery. Reports of various forms of payola, including drugs, prostitution, and promotional vacations, have intermittently surfaced throughout the history of rock and roll. Perhaps this is because one basic fact has been slow to change: Radio airplay—and, more recently, satellite radio, cable music, video channels, podcasts, and Internet resources—remains a strong factor in promoting artists and their music. As long as this is true, payola, in one form or another, is likely to persist. For example, in 2007, the Federal Communications Commission settled a lengthy investigation into pay-for-play practices by four of the country's largest radio broadcasters. Clear Channel Communications Inc., CBS Radio, Citadel Broadcasting Corporation, and Entercom Communications Corporation agreed to pay $12.5 million and reform their business practices (although they admitted no wrongdoing).

JOURNAL

Payola in the Present Day

Perform an Internet search on the word "payola." Look specifically for recent instances involving any company representing a relatively contemporary artist with whom you are familiar. Briefly summarize the charges that constitute a potentially illegal relationship between the recording industry and companies responsible for the various forms of "airplay." Compose a paragraph about the specific concerns, both legal and ethical, that come into play when considering whether or not specific behaviors exert undue influence over the sale and distribution of musical recordings.

 The response entered here will appear in the performance dashboard and can be viewed by your instructor.

Submit

3.4: Musical Close-Up on Soft Rock is Rock

OBJECTIVE: Analyze the musical elements of soft rock

Do songs like "All I Have to Do Is Dream," "Only You," "Love Letters in the Sand," and "In the Still of the Night" belong on rock and roll anthologies and in rock history publications? Although rock music does include some musical nuances and spiritual qualities that are difficult or impossible to capture in musical notation, many of its musical elements can be quite clearly defined. When these elements are found in a song, the result is a type of rock. Once categorized, we can then go on to assign it to a specific style of rock (e.g., soft rock, rockabilly, or mainstream).

Elements of Soft Rock Songs

In this Musical Close-Up, we will examine the soft rock style of the 1950s and identify the musical elements that link the style to its Pop parentage as well as its sibling rock styles.

Tempo—Most soft rock songs have a slow-to-moderate beat. One of the slowest examples is "Daddy's Home" (Shep and the Limelights), performed at a tempo of about 45 beats per minute. Quicker **tempos** can be heard in "Little Darling" by the Diamonds (145 beats per minute), "Runaround Sue" by Dion and the Belmonts (155 beats per minute), and "Wonderful Time Up There" by Pat Boone (185 beats per minute). These last three songs have fast enough tempos to move from the category of soft rock to mainstream, but tempo is not our only consideration in categorizing a song. Most soft rock songs do not have a strong *backbeat* (accents on the second and fourth beats of each measure). Boone's "Wonderful Time Up There" has a light backbeat; but, again, other factors suggest that it should be retained in the soft rock category.

Rhythm—Perhaps the most noticeable rhythmic factor in soft rock is the frequent triple subdivision of the beat. This division is often most clearly heard in the piano part, which consists of repeating right-hand chords in the middle or upper keyboard range. The list of examples of this three-notes-per-beat phenomenon would be a long one indeed. See if you can hear this triple subdivision in the following examples:

"I Only Have Eyes for You" (Flamingos)

"I Want You, I Need You, I Love You" (Elvis Presley)

"Love Letters in the Sand" (Pat Boone)

"Earth Angel" (Penguins)

"Only You" (Platters)

"Sh-Boom" (Crew Cuts)

Note: In "Sh-Boom," listen for a vocal example of the triple subdivision on "ya-da-da, da-da-da, da-da-da, da-da-da."

Melody—Like its Pop music parent, soft rock places considerable emphasis on beautiful melodies. The tunes are often **conjunct** and have a larger pitch range than those found in other rock styles. Like other rock styles, however, the singers often use **blue notes** and various **vocal interpolations** derived from R&B and gospel music. Falsetto is quite common in soft rock (e.g., "In the Still of the Night" by the Five Satins or "The Duke of Earl" by Gene Chandler). Lyrics are generally love-oriented and similar to those of the Pop music tradition. However, in soft rock of this particular era, the nonsense syllables of R&B-derived rock and roll (doo-wop) are often included, usually to create a rhythmic vocal background (e.g., "There's a Moon Out Tonight" by the Capris, "Sincerely" by the Moonglows, "In the Still of the Night" by the Five Satins). The vocal style of such black vocal groups is closer to the old R&B sound, whereas the soft rock of white performers like Boone, Presley, the Everly Brothers, and the Crew Cuts is closer to the Pop tradition

Watch MUSIC EXAMPLE 3A

I   vi   IV   V

Harmony—Along with the triple division of the beat, the most recognizable element of many soft rock songs is the harmony. Almost as common as the 12-bar blues progression is the series of chords shown above.

Tonality—For want of a better label, we shall call this the I-vi-IV-V progression. Traditionally, musicians use uppercase Roman numerals for **major triads** and lowercase Roman numerals for **minor triads**. This series of chords forms the basis for countless soft rock songs. There are variations on this series, especially where the *harmonic rhythm* (speed of the chord changes) is concerned. Thus, in some cases, each chord lasts for two beats; in other songs, each chord holds for an entire measure (four beats), and sometimes each chord sustains through two measures (eight beats). Another common variation is to substitute the ii chord for the IV. To hear this progression with each chord strummed and held, listen to the introduction to "Runaround Sue" (Dion and the Belmonts). For other examples of the I-vi-IV-V progression, listen to some of the following songs:

Two Beats per Chord
"Earth Angel" (Penguins)
"A Thousand Miles Away" (Heartbeats)
"Sh-Boom" (Crew Cuts)
"Silhouettes" (Diamonds)
"You Send Me" (Sam Cooke)
"Gee" (Crows)
"All I Have to Do Is Dream" (Everly Brothers)
"Daddy's Home" (Shep and the Limelights)
"There's a Moon Out Tonight" (Capris)

Four Beats per Chord (One Measure per Chord)
"In the Still of the Night" (Five Satins)
"Maybe" (Chantels)

Eight Beats per Chord (Two Measures per Chord)
"Little Darling" (Diamonds)
"Runaround Sue" (Dion and the Belmonts)
"The Duke of Earl" (Gene Chandler)
Note: The verse of "The Duke of Earl" reverts to four beats per chord.

Watch MUSIC EXAMPLE 3B

Doo - be - doo - be Doo - be - doo, Shoo - be - doo
I   vi   IV   V

Timbre—The timbre of soft rock is related to other rock styles. Usually, there is a lead singer with backup vocals (trio or quartet). Instrumental accompaniment includes guitar, piano, drums, and often saxophone. Vocal timbres vary from the sound of the black vocal groups performing doo-wop to the C&W-oriented sound of the Everly Brothers to the Pop-oriented sound of Pat Boone, Paul Anka, and Frankie Avalon. The bass line suggested by the I-vi-IV-V progression may be sung by a bass voice, often to nonsense syllables, for example see the example above.

Watch MUSIC EXAMPLE 3C

Bass Lines—Other songs have bass lines similar to mainstream rock. For example, listen to the bass lines in the following songs:

"Sixteen Candles" (Crests)
"Only You" (Platters)
"Sugar Moon" (Pat Boone)
"Love Letters in the Sand" (Pat Boone)

Pat Boone's "Wonderful Time Up There" makes a melodic line out of a boogie-woogie bass line, by transposing it up a couple of octaves in pitch as shown.

Form—The form of most soft rock songs is borrowed from the Pop and Tin Pan Alley traditions. A common form in this tradition is a 32-bar chorus divided into four internal sections, each of which is 8 bars long. We represent this form with the letters *AABA* because the music of the first eight measures (A) is repeated—sometimes with minimum alteration—for the second eight measures (A). Then comes some different music for eight measures (B; called the *bridge*), followed by a return to the music of the first eight measures (A). Most of the songs mentioned in this Musical Close-Up follow this formal scheme. A common variation is to add two measures to the eight-measure sections to close out (*cadence*) the harmonic progression.

The Listening Guide for "Earth Angel" by the Penguins illustrates a typical 32-bar chorus based on the I-vi-IV-V progression. As frequently happens, after the 32-bar AABA is complete, the last 16 measures are repeated, resulting in an AABABA form (musicians often describe this as "one and a half choruses").

Next to the 12-bar blues progression, the I-vi-IV-V progression cast into the 32-bar AABA form is the most commonly encountered formula in 1950s rock.

Listening Guide: Earth Angel (Penguins)

0:00–0:12	Introduction (4 measures)	I-vi-IV-V progression (2 beats per chord); 2 times
0:13–0:38	A (8 measures)	I-vi-IV-V progression; 4 times
0:39–1:04	A (8 measures)	I-vi-IV-V progression three times; 3-measure cadence (I-IV-I-I⁷); slight change in lyrics; same melody
1:05–1:30	B (8 measures)	Bridge; new words, melody, and chord progression; one chord per measure (4 beats per chord): IV-I-IV-I-IV-I-II-V
1:31–1:57	A (8 measures)	I-vi-IV-V progression three times; 2-measure cadence (I-IV-I); lyrics same as first A section (very minor change); same melody as A sections
1:58–2:23	B (8 measures)	repeat bridge
2:24–2:55	A (8 measures)	repeat last A section; ritard (slow down) in final 2 measures (cadence)

BECOME AN ACTIVE LISTENER: SOFT ROCK

In this chapter, the soft rock subgenre was described and highlighted in the Musical Close-Up. The purpose of this module is to provide an opportunity for you to identify independently music that represents some of the important components of the soft rock style.

Find a few examples of contemporary hits that would fall into the soft rock category. Give your rationale for why these songs meet the standards for this style and why you believe (or do not believe) they should still be considered a type of rock and roll.

See if you can identify examples of the I-vi-IV-V progression that have two beats per chord; four beats per chord; and eight beats per chord.

Find a current hit that follows the common AABA structure.

Early soft rock included the Pop-oriented styles of Presley, Boone, Anka, and Avalon; the black-oriented sounds of the Platters and the doo-wop groups; the C&W-oriented styles of the Everly Brothers and Ricky Nelson; and the mainstream-oriented styles of Danny and the Juniors and Dion and the Belmonts. Soft rock was very popular and set a trend that would coexist with the harder rock styles up to the present day. Is soft rock really rock and roll? Well, by elimination, it is not pure Pop, nor is it C&W, R&B, gospel, classical, or jazz. Judging by its musical elements, it is a form of rock, albeit a softer style musically and in terms of performer image. To paraphrase a familiar song title, "[soft] rock and roll is here to stay."

Summary: 1950s Rock and Roll

In this chapter, you have learned about and listened to rock music that fits into one or more of the following categories: mainstream rock, rockabilly, and soft rock. This module will briefly summarize some of the primary topics elucidated.

Take Note

• *How was Little Richard's music representative of the purest prototype of hard, mainstream rock of the late 1950s?*—Little Richard's frenetic stage presence, gospel-tinged vocals, and boogie-woogie-influenced piano playing made him the archetype for generations of hard rockers. His hit "Tutti Frutti" embodied the energy and humor of early rock.

• *Why do you think Fats Domino was among the first R&B artists to cross over to the Pop chart?*—Fats Domino's piano playing and vocals were influenced by blues and gospel music, but his singing was smoother and his piano playing less flamboyant than Little Richard's. His initial hits

(such as his first major crossover hit, 1955s "Ain't That a Shame"), were in the R&B style and were based on popular blues forms. He also recorded Pop standards like "Blueberry Hill" and "My Blue Heaven," which were mainstream hits from previous decades.

• *What role did Chuck Berry play in making the electric guitar a primary instrument in rock and roll?*—Chuck Berry was the first great electric guitarist in rock and roll, influencing generations of players to come. He was also a songwriter who was able to capture the concerns of teenagers, focusing on topics like love, school, and cars. Several of Berry's guitar introductions became famous and were widely imitated. The double-note playing in his solos and the alternating chords of his rhythmic accompaniments (similar to some rock piano styles) set models to be followed for years.

• *Why would some critics call Jerry Lee Lewis the "white counterpart" to Little Richard?*—Jerry Lee Lewis shared with Little Richard a similar piano style and a gospel-influenced shouting vocal style. His hits like "Great

Balls of Fire" shared the same power and sense of fun that were found in Little Richard's "Tutti Frutti" and "Long Tall Sally." The sexual energy of both singers made them compelling stage performers.

- *How did Buddy Holly differ from other early rock and rollers?*—Holly lacked the exposure to R&B that Elvis and Jerry Lee Lewis experienced while growing up. His background was in C&W and that influence was strongly reflected in his music. Like Chuck Berry, Holly wrote most of his own material and played lead guitar in his group, setting a standard for future generations of rock musicians.

- *Who were some of the other innovators in the 1950s, and what musical styles did they perform?*—During this period, R&B- and gospel-derived rock were among the most popular styles, performed by artists like Lloyd Price, Ray Charles, and Sam Cooke. Rockabilly continued to be popular, particularly among the artists at Sun Records (e.g., Johnny Cash). Soft rock dominated the Pop chart in the recordings of singers like Bobby Darin and others associated with Dick Clark's popular *American Bandstand*

television show. Vocal groups like Danny and the Juniors and Dion and the Belmonts celebrated young love with their smooth vocal harmonies. Instrumental performers, like pianist Bill Doggett, saxophonist Bill Justis, and guitarists Link Wray and Duane Eddy, were also popular on the charts. Novelty songs—humorous numbers with a catchy melodic hook—also fared well.

- *What was the impact of the rock revolution of the mid-1950s on the music industry as a whole?*—The musical establishment—from music publishers to singers, instrumentalists, arrangers, and others who had previously been employed working on Pop hits—suddenly found their talents in less demand as rockers stormed the charts. Radio, however, embraced rock and roll and saw its listenership swell as teenagers became devoted to deejays (DJs) who played their favorite hits. Radio's domination of the Pop chart faced a new challenge in the later 1950s when payola scandals brought attention to the record industry's payment of DJs and other radio executives in order to ensure that their records were played on the air.

SHARED WRITING

Music Distribution in the New Millennium

In this chapter, you learned about aspects of the music industry. During the era described, there was a relatively dramatic shift from control by "the Majors" to a distribution across a larger number of "indie" labels. More recently, for some artists, the Internet has proven to be a highly effectively and innovative path to commercial success. Identify one artist of the new millennium who exemplifies this use of technology and social media (e.g., YouTube, Twitter, Facebook, etc.). Enumerate at least three differences between this "new school" approach to reaching an audience and the "old school" method described in this chapter. Are there any similarities?

After you have completed this task independently, read responses of at least three other students. Have they mentioned aspects of the new approach that did not occur to you? If so, revise your initial response integrating new perspectives gained as a result.

> A minimum number of characters is required to post and earn points. After posting, your response can be viewed by your class and instructor, and you can participate in the class discussion.

Post

0 characters | 140 minimum

Chapter 4
Transitional Styles of Rock in The Early 1960s

 Learning Objectives

4.1 Explain the factors that caused the music market to fragment into new musical trends

4.2 Outline the influences that shaped the folk music trend in the 1960s

4.3 Identify the musical characteristics associated with surf music

4.4 Describe the factors that influenced the dance craze

By the early 1960s, much of the power of the first rock and roll shockwave had dissipated. Little Richard had found religion; Jerry Lee Lewis's marital scandals had essentially ended his rock music career; Chuck Berry was in jail; Buddy Holly was dead. There seemed to be declining interest in hearing yet another 12-bar blues or I-vi-IV-V progression under the harmonizing of a vocal group. The payola hearings had put a serious damper on the promotional activities of many small, independent record companies, and interest in traditional rock songs seemed to be waning. The market fragmented into a variety of directions, none of which could achieve real domination. It was a period of significant musical—and social—transition.

4.1: Fragmentation of the Market

OBJECTIVE: Explain the factors that caused the music market to fragment into new musical trends

An examination of the charts from 1960 to 1963 fails to suggest any dominant trend; it was a period of transition. A review of the seven best-selling records of 1961 gives a hint of the remarkable variation in the market (see Table 4.1). There were vestiges of the old styles as well as undeveloped seeds of new styles. As is typical of a fragmented market, each of these coexisting styles was surprisingly distinct from the others. Out of this diverse array of styles, it is possible to identify four trends: (1) vestiges of the 1950s, (2) the emerging **folk music** trend, (3) surf music, and (4) the dance craze.

Table 4.1 Best-Selling Records of 1961

Song	Artist	Comments
1. "Exodus"	Ferrante and Teicher	movie theme; instrumental (duo piano); pseudoclassical style
2. "Calcutta"	Lawrence Welk	instrumental; Pop style
3. "Will You Still Love Me Tomorrow?"	Shirelles	black female vocal group
4. "Tossin' and Turnin'"	Bobby Lewis	1950s rock style
5. "Wonderland by Night"	Bert Kaempfert	instrumental (trumpet solo); Pop style
6. "Are You Lonesome Tonight?"	Elvis Presley	Pop-style ballad
7. "Travelin' Man"	Ricky Nelson	soft rockabilly

4.1.1: Vestiges of the 1950s

As vestiges of the previous era, rockabilly and soft rock continued into the early 1960s. Instrumentals and novelty hits also appeared intermittently, but one is hard-pressed to find genuine examples of mainstream rock as established by Elvis Presley, Little Richard, Jerry Lee Lewis, Chuck Berry, Fats Domino, and Buddy Holly.

Rockabilly singers from the 1950s—including Roy Orbison, Johnny Cash, the Everly Brothers, Brenda Lee, Marty Robbins, and Ricky Nelson—continued their success into the early 1960s. Even Ray Charles, a pioneering black artist, released a successful C&W-oriented album that produced the hit single "I Can't Stop Loving You" (1962). These early 1960s rockabilly songs tended toward the soft side of the spectrum. Indeed, the early 1960s witnessed the triumph of the softer sounds, from the sound of pure Pop of the early

1950s to the soft rock sounds of the late 1950s. In the pure Pop category were songs like "Surrender," "Now or Never," and "Are You Lonesome Tonight?" by Elvis Presley and "Moody River" by Pat Boone. Traditional Pop stars returned to favor with vocal releases such as Steve Lawrence's crooning "Go Away Little Girl" (1963) and Pop-style instrumentals by Percy Faith, Acker Bilk, David Rose, Bert Kaempfert, and Lawrence Welk. During this period, the only number 1 instrumental reminiscent of the 1950s rock instrumental was "Telstar" by the Tornados, the first British group to top the U.S. charts. The soft rock of the teen idols continued with hits by Bobby Vee, Bobby Vinton, Bobby Rydell, and Neil Sedaka.

4.1.2: Musical Diversification

In the early 1960s, the black male vocal groups were joined by a host of black female vocal groups. Continuing a line that began in the 1950s with the doo-wop groups, these groups formed a link to the later **Motown** style. Table 4.2 shows some of the early 1960s black vocal groups with soft rock styles.

Table 4.2 Hits by Successful Vocal Groups in the Transition to the 1960s

Group	Description	Sample Hits	Year
Shirelles	female quartet	"Will You Still Love Me Tomorrow?"	1960
		"Dedicated to the One I Love"	1961
		"Soldier Boy"	1962
Drifters	male quintet	"There Goes My Baby"	1959
		"Save the Last Dance for Me"	1960
		"On Broadway"	1963
		"Under the Boardwalk"	1964
Marvelettes	female quartet	"Please Mr. Postman"	1961
		"Playboy"	1962
Crystals	female trio	"He's a Rebel"	1962
		"Da Doo Ron Ron"	1963

One of the most successful vocal groups in the early 1960s was the Four Seasons. Originally called the Variatones, the group and its lead singer, Frankie Valli (born Francis Castelluccio), finally caught the public's attention with "Sherry" in 1962. Their tight vocal harmonies and use of a **falsetto** lead vocal hinted at the later style of the Beach Boys and other surf groups. The Four Seasons went on to release a series of hits throughout the 1960s, including "Big Girls Don't Cry" (1962), "Walk Like a Man" (1963), and "Dawn (Go Away)" (1964). They scored a number 1 hit as late as 1976 with "December 1963 (Oh, What a Night)."

More female solo singers began to achieve success in the early 1960s. As Connie Francis and Brenda Lee continued to place hits on the charts, new female singers appeared, such as Lesley Gore ("It's My Party," 1963), Shelley Fabares ("Johnny Angel," 1962), and Little Peggy March ("I Will Follow Him," 1963).

NOVELTY SONGS There was also a steady stream of **novelty songs**: Johnny Preston's "Running Bear" (1960), Larry Verne's "Mr. Custer" (1960), and the Tokens' "The Lion Sleeps Tonight" (1961). This last song contained a South African folk song with the repeating African title, "Wimoweh," sounding, for all the world, like another variation of doo-wop. The year 1963 proved even more eclectic, with one hit by a Japanese Pop singer singing in Japanese ("Sukiyaki" by Kyu Sakamoto) and one by five Catholic nuns singing about the founder of the Dominican order ("Dominique," by Sister Luc-Gabrielle, known as the Singing Nun).

These vestiges of the late 1950s enjoyed their last big heyday before the social and musical revolutions of the mid- and late 1960s. But even as Percy Faith's "Theme from a Summer Place" was on its way to becoming the second most popular recording of the 1960s (Whitburn 1996, 809), the seeds of new and rediscovered sounds were germinating.

4.2: Beginning of the Folk Music Trend

OBJECTIVE: Outline the influences that shaped the folk music trend in the 1960s

Technically, a true *folk song* is one that has been handed down from generation to generation, the exact origins of which are unknown. It is as impossible for someone today to compose a true folk song as it would be for a carpenter to build an antique. Thus, most so-called folk music in the 1960s was not true folk music, but music composed in the style of traditional folk music. The model was the Appalachian *folk ballad*, which used various acoustic guitar or guitarlike instruments to accompany one or more vocalists singing relatively serious lyrics about contemporaneous issues of concern: money, jobs, love, death, and social issues like war and injustice.

Roots of the 1960s Folk Music Trend

The roots of the 1960s folk music trend can be traced to the 1940s.

Early in that decade, a quartet known as the Almanac Singers was formed, including Pete Seeger and Woody Guthrie. Guthrie had a long history of writing songs that reflected his experiences during the Great Depression, the dust bowl days, World War II, and the union movement. An outspoken political and social critic, he wrote columns for *The Daily Worker* and *People's World.* Among his 1,000-plus published songs is the familiar folk anthem "This Land Is Your Land."

The Almanac Singers recorded several songs before reorganizing as the Weavers (without Guthrie) in the late 1940s. They hit the Pop chart in 1950 with "Goodnight, Irene," composed by black bluesman Huddie Ledbetter (better known as Leadbelly) and their adaptation of an Israeli folksong "Tzena, Tzena." Like the Almanac Singers, they were associated with left-wing causes and organizations, and, at the height of the McCarthy era, they were blacklisted as being "subversive." The group disbanded in 1952; after

reforming for three years (1955–1958), they disbanded yet again. However, original member Pete Seeger continued his activities as a solo singer. His songs "If I Had a Hammer," "Where Have All the Flowers Gone," and "Turn, Turn, Turn" became important hits in the folk music movement of the 1960s. Seeger continued to be an important social figure and activist until his death in 2014 at the age of 94. In 2011, for example, he appeared at an Occupy Wall Street rally.

Generally, the music industry of the 1950s believed (correctly) that folk music's appeal was to a small subculture. However, in 1957, *calypso,* a style of folk music from the Caribbean, made a brief, but powerful, appearance on the charts, due primarily to singer Harry Belafonte. Born in New York City, Belafonte had spent much of his youth in Kingston, Jamaica. In the early weeks of 1957, Belafonte's "Jamaica Farewell" reached the Top 20, and later that year, "The Banana Boat Song (Day-O)" reached the Top 5. The music featured Belafonte's gentle, lyrical voice and a distinct Jamaican-English lyric. There was a hint of soft Latin bongo drum rhythms and acoustic guitars. Although considered a novelty at the time, calypso, in retrospect, helped lay the groundwork for the folk music trend of the 1960s and perhaps also paved the way for the reggae infusion that would occur during the 1970s.

4.2.1: The Kingston Trio

In 1957, college students Dave Guard, Bob Shane, and Nick Reynolds formed a vocal trio in Stanford, California, known as the Kingston Trio. Inspired by Belafonte's success, they originally performed calypso material and took their name from the capital of Jamaica.

The Kingston Trio's Origin and Musical Career

First Hit—Their first hit, "Tom Dooley" (number 1, 1958), was an adaptation of a Blue Ridge Mountain folk tune from the Civil War days. It was about a mountaineer named Tom Dula who was hanged for murder in 1868 (Bronson 1988, 45). It was a folk song according to the purest definition and may be considered the first real hit in the folk music trend.

"Tom Dooley" was a serious song compared to other hits of the time. Its spoken introduction sets the story into the historical tradition of the eternal love triangle. The song sings of murder, questionable justice, and hanging. The musical accompaniment consists exclusively of acoustic instruments—string bass, guitar, and banjo. Despite the morbid subject matter, the harmonized melody sounds quite pleasant.

Image and Personal Style—The image of the Kingston Trio was also very different from the popular rock image. They were white, clean-cut college boys with close-cropped hair, button-down shirts, and dress slacks (the so-called Ivy League look). These characteristics set a style that would influence countless other folk groups.

Musical Career—Although the Kingston Trio eventually placed 10 songs in the Top 40, no single after "Tom Dooley"

Kingston Trio

SOURCE: Everett Collection

reached higher than number 8. However, their albums sold very well—another harbinger of things to come. Their first seven *LPs* (long-playing albums), excluding reissues, were certified as gold albums (they eventually released over 30 albums). One of the other Kingston Trio hits—"M.T.A." (1959)—offered another hint of things to come. In its own lighthearted way, it was a protest song, a tongue-in-cheek song about an increase in subway fares in Boston. Like "Tom Dooley," "M.T.A." begins with a spoken introduction (accompanied only by the string bass, played with a bow like an orchestral instrument) about the citizens of Boston rallying to the defense of human rights. The song served as a gentle introduction to the protest lyric so common in earlier folk songs and a central characteristic of the folk songs of the 1960s.

Urban Folk Revival—The trend that was launched by the Kingston Trio has been called the *urban folk revival,* music produced by sophisticated, well-educated, urban collegians. For example, the Brothers Four ("Greenfields," number 2 in 1960) were fraternity brothers at the University of Washington. In 1961, the Highwaymen, a group of five Wesleyan University students, had major hits with "Michael" and "Cotton Fields." Other groups to follow the trend included the Rooftop Singers, the New Christy Minstrels, the Chad Mitchell Trio, the Limeliters, the Journeymen, and the Whiskey Hill Singers.

4.2.2: Peter, Paul, and Mary

Representing the next stage in the developing folk music trend was another vocal trio: Peter, Paul, and Mary. Unlike most of their predecessors, they produced an impressive list of hit singles, while maintaining a strong popularity on LPs and in live performance. Seven of their first eight albums were certified gold, and they placed a dozen songs in the Top 40 from 1962 to 1969.

Peter, Paul, and Mary and the Folk Revolution

Peter, Paul, and Mary

SOURCE: Pictorial Press Ltd/Alamy Stock Photo

Intellectual-Revolutionary Folknik—Peter, Paul, and Mary's image contrasted the clean-cut Ivy League look of earlier folk groups. Peter Yarrow and Paul Stookey had mustaches and beards; Mary Travers had long, straight hair. There was a gentle hint of the intellectual-revolutionary **folknik,** a type that already existed at the hard-core center of the folk movement. In 1962, however, the country was not quite ready for the harder protests of Joan Baez, Bob Dylan, and others to follow. Peter, Paul, and Mary provided a softer, more palatable version of protest that was suitable for popular consumption.

The Importance of Authenticity to the New Folk Countermovement—The tone of the new folk countermovement was set by Peter, Paul, and Mary's first album. The printed album notes included key words associated with the movement such as sincerity, authenticity, truth, good, virtue, *and* honesty. The listener was promised "no gimmicks" and told that "mediocrity has had it" and "hysteria is on the way out" (Belz 1972, 84). This music was

not for the teenybopper, but for the older, more thoughtful college student/young adult who was part of a vigorous, dynamic, and youthful new generation.

Social and Political Changes—At the age of 43, John F. Kennedy had just been elected the youngest president of the United States. It was the time of the New Frontier and the youth-oriented Peace Corps. College students and young adults believed that they could make a difference in the world, and they preferred music with a meaningful message. An entire subculture began to grow within and around college campuses, where students gathered in nearby coffeehouses to listen to campus poets and singers dispense meaningful philosophies to the accompaniment of guitar and bongo drums. This was not music to dance to; it was music to listen to and think about.

These socially aware young people did more than listen passively to the messages of the new music. They organized and were active in addressing social issues of all kinds, from racism and peace to fraternity hazing and freshman dormitory hours. They organized sit-ins, walk-ins, lay-ins, marches, and freedom bus rides.

Associations with Earlier American Folk Music—Peter, Paul, and Mary's second single (and first Top 10 hit) was "If I Had a Hammer," coauthored in the late 1940s by Pete Seeger and Lee Hays. It spoke of striking a blow for "justice," "freedom," and "love between the brothers and the sisters all over this land." In this case, they were not singing of romantic love, but of a higher order of love that ideally should exist between all people. Their follow-up hit "Puff, the Magic Dragon" (1963) spoke wistfully of the lost pleasures and innocence of childhood.

Bob Dylan's Influence—Later, in 1963, Peter, Paul, and Mary released cover versions of two songs written by Bob Dylan: "Blowin' in the Wind" (number 2) and "Don't Think Twice, It's All Right" (number 9). Peter, Paul, and Mary's polished style was more acceptable to a wider audience in 1963 than the rawer Dylan originals. As much as any other song of 1963, "Blowin' in the Wind" expressed the sentiments of the folk oriented youth culture. In this song, Dylan questions that for how long people should wait for cannon balls (violence) to cease and to be banned forever and for how many years should some people exist before they are allowed freedom.

After asking these and other similar questions, the song suggests, optimistically, that the answers are "blowin' in the wind." In other words, the youth knew the questions and had the answers. "Blowin' in the Wind" and other similar songs not only reflected the attitudes of the youth revolution, they spread these thoughts and attitudes to others. The new Kennedy administration stimulated hope that, indeed, the youth was truly capable of "changing the world."

Influences on Peter, Paul, and Mary's Image—Peter, Paul, and Mary's image was midway between the conventional Ivy League look of their predecessors and the more revolutionary look of the hard-core folkniks who would follow. They were an important link in the evolution of the folk movement of the 1960s. Their hits continued until 1969, when "Leaving on a Jet Plane" (composed in 1966 by singer-songwriter John Denver) became their only number 1 hit. The group disbanded shortly thereafter, although they staged several reunions until Travers's death in 2009.

4.2.3: Musical Characteristics of the Folk Music Trend

Folk music was quite different than the mainstream rock and rockabilly styles of the 1950s. First, there was none of the shouting style of R&B and mainstream rock. Generally, the vocalists sang perfectly on pitch, with impressive vocal control. Lyrics were important and clearly enunciated; a listener could easily understand the words, which was crucial since the message contained in the lyrics was considered of primary importance. Soloists sometimes even avoided any *vibrato* (that wiggle in the pitch that classical and Pop singers cultivated). The style employed traditional duo, trio, and quartet harmonies. The melodic lines were similar to those of the C&W and Pop styles—that is, they had interesting contours, moderate to wide ranges, and traditional, **symmetrical forms**.

Folk song harmonies were simple and *diatonic* (all notes fell within an established key) but avoided the 12-bar blues progression of R&B and mainstream rock, and the I-vi-IV-V progression of Pop and soft rock. Each song seemed to have originated as a lyric with melody, the harmonies being the result of adding chords to accompany the melody.

With slower ballads, rhythm was felt, but not emphasized. In faster tunes, the rhythm was provided by the strummed guitar (or banjo) chords. If a string bass was present, it reinforced the basic beat, but there was none of the forceful rhythm or backbeat of R&B, mainstream rock, or rockabilly.

With the folk trend of the early 1960s, we see the first of the external influences that would have an impact on the history of rock and reshape its future. As with any dynamic, growing entity, rock was susceptible to such influences as it developed.

Main Characteristics of the Early Folk Music Trend

Let us reiterate some of the main characteristics of the early folk music trend.

Lyrics—There was a new sense of seriousness in the lyrics addressing major issues of social and political importance. The writers and singers sought not only to reflect the thinking within their subculture, but to foster similar attitudes and provoke action in a wider audience. Key issues were peace, racial equality, and love.

Demographics—Folk music's appeal was principally to the older end of the youth spectrum, which split the listening audience, for the first time, into two markets: the 18- to 24-year-old age group, and the 17 and below age group.

Albums—Folk groups tended to have more hit albums than hit singles. Since the introduction of the LP in 1948 by Columbia Records, the long-play format had appealed to an older, more conservative audience. Between 1954 and 1957, almost the exact years of rock's emergence, the 45-rpm single had replaced the older 78 rpm as the most popular record format. The two-and-a-half-minute single became the primary medium of early rock. With the popularity of the folk-oriented LP, the 45-rpm single became identified more with the teenage market and the LP with the college-age and young adult market. The seriousness of the lyrics and the greater financial capacity of the 18- to 24-year-old age group made the LP the primary medium of folk music. Increasingly, albums replaced singles as the biggest share of the market.

Acoustic Instruments—The folk music purist abhorred electric guitars and elaborate studio production techniques. Remember Peter, Paul, and Mary's 1962 album notes: This was to be the "real thing" … real people playing real instruments without artificial assistance.

In late 1963 and early 1964, the initial phase of folk music's popularity absorbed several traumatic blows, addressed in the following sections. In the meantime, other changes were happening concurrently in the popular music world, contributing musical and lyrical innovations responsible for the emergence of folk rock in the mid-1960s.

JOURNAL

Contemporary Influence of the Folk Music Trend

Now that you have read about and listened to examples of the folk music trend that emerged during the transition to the 1960s, take a moment to carefully review the musical characteristics of this style enumerated in the summary above. Listen to several examples from the folk music trend section, and then find two or three present-day artists whose music provides evidence of significant influence by these earlier folk artists. Compose one paragraph about similarities between the 1960s and contemporary recordings and a second paragraph in which you identify differences between the two eras. Conclude your response by stating the era that represents the music you prefer and specifying precisely what it is about the music that causes you to prefer one over the other. (It is critically important—as you compose this response—that you consistently refer to musical elements using your developing musical vocabulary.)

▶ The response entered here will appear in the performance dashboard and can be viewed by your instructor.

Submit

4.3: Surfing Music

OBJECTIVE: Identify the musical characteristics associated with surf music

The fragmentation of the early 1960s market resulted in a variety of trends, some of which were diametrically opposed to one another. If the key words of the folk music trend were *honesty, authenticity, sincerity, freedom,* and *brotherhood,* the key words of surf music were those found in the title of the 1964 Beach Boys hit, "Fun, Fun, Fun." Seemingly, almost every characteristic cited earlier for the folk movement is exactly inverted for surf music.

Elements of Surf Music

Characteristic—The folkies avoided the artificiality of electric instruments; the surfers built their sound on electronic instruments. The folkies disliked the gimmickry of recording studio techniques; the surfers, on the other hand, exploited **echo effects**, **overdubbing,** and extensive editing. The folkies sang of heavy topics (e.g., love, peace, racial harmony); the surfers sang of cars, girls, beach parties, and big waves. The folkies advocated for social activism; the surfers appeared to be completely indifferent to such things.

Musical Style—Just as folk music was at the center of a subculture, with its norms of dress, language, and behavior, so surf music was at the heart of its own subculture. The geographic center of this subculture was southern California. As the popularity of the music spread across the country, would-be surfers (whether in Iowa, Tennessee, or Maine) acquired deep tans; bleached their hair blond; put on their sandals and cutoffs; waxed down their surfboards; and revved up their Impalas, T-birds, or Corvettes.

Beach-oriented movies highlighting the carefree southern California lifestyle began as early as 1959, when *Gidget* initiated a series of "sun-and-surf" movies.

Surf Artists—One of the first performers to become associated with the surfing subculture was Dick Dale. Dale pioneered a style of electric guitar playing that emphasized the instrument's bass notes and featured the use of heavy echo and reverb, launching a craze for guitar-led instrumentals. Enjoying regional (southern California) popularity, Dale released an album in 1962 called *Surfer's Choice,* but it failed to make any national impact. Far more successful were Jan and Dean. After several earlier hits ("Jennie Lee" in 1958, "Baby Talk" in 1959, and "Heart and Soul" in 1961), Jan Berry and Dean Torrence had a number 1 hit in 1963 with "Surf City." They eventually placed 15 songs in the Top 40. Their career effectively ended when Jan was nearly killed in an automobile wreck in 1966. After extensive therapy, Berry returned to music in 1973, and Jan and Dean enjoyed renewed popularity after the broadcast of a TV movie about them (*Dead Man's Curve*, 1978). The reunited duo opened for a Beach Boys tour during the summer of 1979 and continued to perform during the following decades until Jan Berry's death in 2004.

4.3.1: The Beach Boys

One group defined and dominated the new surf music sound: the Beach Boys. The group formed in 1961, consisting of brothers Brian, Carl, and Dennis Wilson; their cousin Mike Love; and friend Al Jardine, all living in Hawthorne, California. After an early local label hit, "Surfin'," they signed with Capitol Records, where they eventually logged over 30 Top 40 hits, including 8 in the Top 5. The musical style of the Beach Boys will be discussed in some detail in the Musical Close-Up for this chapter; in the following paragraphs, we will explore the history of this trendsetting group and briefly describe two distinct phases of their work.

The Beach Boys

SOURCE: Pictorial Press Ltd/Alamy Stock Photo

THE BEACH BOYS: SURF MUSIC PHASE Their notoriety began with "Surfin' Safari" (number 14, 1962), the song that initiated their surf music phase, and the follow-up release, "Surfin' U.S.A." (number 3, 1963). These first two songs were rockers; with "Surfer Girl," the Beach Boys showed that their sound could be adapted to the slow ballad. Subsequent hits include "Little Deuce Coupe" (number 15, 1963), "Be True to Your School" (number 6, 1963), "Fun, Fun, Fun" (number 5, 1964), "I Get Around" (number 1, 1964), "Help Me Rhonda" (number 1, 1965), "California Girls" (number 3, 1965), "Barbara Ann" (number 2, 1966), and "Sloop John B" (number 3, 1966).

The surf style of the Beach Boys was largely determined by Brian Wilson, the oldest of the Wilson brothers and the most technically proficient in the studio. Somewhat more serious and introverted than the others, Brian hardly fit the sun-and-fun, carefree Beach Boy image. Nevertheless, his musical and technical leadership of the group was beyond question.

Following a nervous breakdown in 1964, Brian stopped touring with the group and devoted himself to the creation of a new, more serious style. The result was an album released in mid-1966 called *Pet Sounds*. Using up-to-date studio techniques and extra musicians, this Beach Boys' album, which hinted at a significant stylistic change, was critically acclaimed but did not sell as well as previous albums. Its sound, however, proved highly influential to the direction of rock music and other artists, including the Beatles.

THE BEACH BOYS: POST–SURF MUSIC The Beach Boys were highly influential in expanding the possibilities for rock music. Under Brian Wilson's impeccable artistic guidance and utilizing his growing knowledge of the recording studio, they produced some highly adventurous recordings that significantly impacted the evolution of rock music after the mid-1960s.

Musical Career of the Beach Boys in the Post–Surf Music Phase

The real move into their second phase, post–surf music, came with the release of "Good Vibrations" in late 1966. Had the Beach Boys stopped prior to "Good Vibrations," they might be remembered only as a good rock and roll band of the early 1960s. Brian Wilson, Mike Love, and the rest of the band worked for over six months on "Good Vibrations." It was literally pieced together from ideas committed to tape at four different studios. After over 90 hours of studio time, 11 versions, and some $50,000 in production costs (an exorbitant amount at the time), "Good Vibrations" was released. It not only hit the number 1 position, but it became a million seller.

"Good Vibrations" was a milestone in the development of rock. Musically and technically, it was more sophisticated than any rock hit up until its time. Only the Beatles were experimenting in similar ways. Prior to this, it was assumed that a rock hit should last about two and a half minutes, and once the tempo, beat, key, and texture were established they should not change. "Good Vibrations" did not follow the formula. As Brian Wilson said, in its "three minutes and thirty-five seconds … it had a lot of riff changes. It had a lot of movements … changes, changes, changes. Building harmonies here, drop this voice out, this comes in, bring the echo chamber in, do this, put the **theremin** here, bring the cello up a little louder here. I mean it was a real production. The biggest production of our life" (Leaf 1985, 90).

The success of "Good Vibrations" encouraged Brian to pursue further experimentation. He began to plan an album, to be called *Smile*, that would expand on many of the ideas in *Pet Sounds* and "Good Vibrations." He was moving away not only from the old surf music style, but from the rest of the Beach Boys as well. His new artist friends, including Van Dyke Parks, were more associated with the new free-thinking and drug-oriented culture. Brian poured his heart and soul into *Smile,* but when the rest of the Beach Boys came off tour to record the new material, some of the group feared that Brian's new creativity was commercially risky. Hurt and confused, Brian dropped the *Smile* project.

Eight of the 20 songs were eventually released by the Beach Boys, including a Van Dyke Parks–Brian Wilson collaboration called "Heroes and Villains" (1967). Like "Good Vibrations," "Heroes and Villains" avoided rock formulas and involved frequent changes in texture, rhythm, and timbre. The album that was released in place of the aborted *Smile* was called *Smiley Smile*. Sales were poor, and *Smiley Smile* marked the beginning of the decline of the Beach Boys' popularity. Several decades later, in 2004, Brian Wilson, with the help of Van Dyke Parks, officially released *Smile* and promoted its release with a national tour, bringing his "teenage symphony to God" (Wilson's description) back from extinction. Another Parks-Wilson collaboration, *That Lucky Old Sun*, was released in 2008, and Brian Wilson took on the task of completing two unfinished compositions by American composer George Gershwin, released in 2010 as *Brian Wilson Reimagines Gershwin*.

In 2011, rumors began to circulate about a potential Beach Boys reunion tour. When Mike Love—as the sole licensee of the Beach Boys name and the only one able to use it when touring (*Rolling Stone*, February 25, 2016, pp. 42–47)—quashed the idea, Brian returned to working on new music.

In 2014, a biopic entitled *Love & Mercy* was released based on the life of Brian Wilson and starring the duo of Paul Dano as the young Brian and John Cusack as the older Brian. This film deals directly with Wilson's struggles with mental illness and, specifically, how his therapist, Dr. Eugene Landy, took advantage of these circumstances. As with all such films, of course, always be aware of the use of "poetic license" when considering the historical accuracy. *I Am Brian Wilson: A Memoir* (by the musician with the assistance of Ben Greenman) was published in 2016.

Returning to the 1960s, after the release of the Beatles' *Sgt. Pepper* album in 1967, a new world of rock exploded. Although the Beach Boys were closely paralleling the creative growth of the Beatles, they were still associated primarily with their former surf sound, hopelessly naive and innocent sounding by 1967 standards. In spite of continued efforts by Brian, Carl, and the others, their greatest successes in the 1970s and early 1980s would lie in the realm of nostalgia. In 1988, they hit the charts again with "Kokomo" (a song composed by Mike Love and friends and a recording with which Brian was not involved; Wilson 2016, p. 51), and featured on the soundtrack of *Cocktail*, a film starring Tom Cruise. One can only speculate that, had *Smile* been released at or about the same time as *Sgt. Pepper*, the musical trajectory of the Beach Boys might have been vastly different.

4.3.2: Musical Close-Up on Musical Texture in the Music of the Beach Boys

Musical *texture* refers to how the various layers of musical sounds relate to each other. If we imagine a kind of musical space, from the very lowest pitch to the very highest, how do we fill that space? We can use one note or musical line, or many. If there is more than one, how do they interact? Because the Beach Boys were one of the first rock groups to explore a variety of textures, we will take a closer look at their musical style, with a particular emphasis on texture. First, we will discuss their surf music style, and then we will examine their more mature, post–surf music style, particularly the songs "Good Vibrations" and "Heroes and Villains."

When considering musical texture, there are two primary questions a listener must ask: (1) How many musical lines (or parts) am I hearing? And (2) if more than one part, is one of these predominant or are they relatively equal in importance? If the answer to the first question is that there is one *and only one* part, the texture is *monophonic*. Otherwise (a much more common occurrence), the texture is either *homophonic* (one part is predominant) or *polyphonic* (all parts are relatively equal). The latter two textures exist in two versions each, which require a second set of considerations. Homophonic textures can either be one part that is most important, with other parts serving as subsidiary sounds (melody and accompaniment homophony), or the predominant part can be embedded in **block chords**, with all parts moving in the same rhythm, but on different pitches (chordal homophony). With polyphonic textures, the various parts can imitate one another like a "round" (imitative polyphony) or they can be independent (non-imitative polyphony). With these terms added to your growing vocabulary, you are ready to dive into a study of the music of the Beach Boys and their textural innovations.

THE SURF STYLE The surf style of the Beach Boys shows two particular influences. Brian Wilson was particularly fond of the Four Freshmen, a white Pop vocal group of the early 1950s. Their clean, sophisticated, jazz-influenced harmonies became an early model for Brian, who would spend hours singing along with their records. He especially liked the high tenor voices of the Four Freshmen and the Hi-Los, another 1950s male vocal group. Brian learned to sing in a high male voice as well as in a true falsetto. Brian's younger brother, Carl, also absorbed these influences, but he preferred the new sounds of 1950s rock and roll—especially Chuck Berry. It should not be surprising, then, that even in their early surf hits, these two influences—the quartet harmonies of the Four Freshmen and the rock and roll style of Chuck Berry—would infuse their sound.

Beach Boys Surf Hits

Surf music provided an alternative to the seriousness of the folk music trend, focusing instead on girls, waves, and cars. The Beach Boys became the ultimate representation of this musical style.

"Surfin U.S.A."—Listen first to "Surfin' U.S.A." The most obvious influence, of course, is Chuck Berry. The music is that of Berry's "Sweet Little Sixteen," with lyrics rewritten by Brian to fit the surfing theme. (It is worth noting that, following a threatened lawsuit, publishing rights for the song were given to Arc Music [Berry's publisher] and then, in 1966, the guitarist's name was added to the songwriting credits, constituting one of the first major charges of plagiarism in rock history.) After a short Berry-like guitar introduction, Mike Love's lead vocal is sung in multi-tracked unison (brief monophonic texture among the vocal parts). The vocal harmonies (chordal homophonic texture on the words "ooh" and "inside, outside, U.S.A.") are placed both above and below the midrange lead line, creating an overall melody and accompaniment homophonic texture (lead vocal as "melody" with instrumental and other vocal parts [including block chords] as

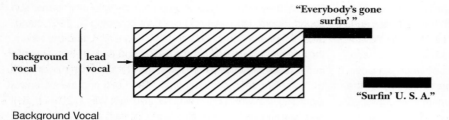

background vocal | lead vocal →

"Everybody's gone surfin' "

"Surfin' U. S. A."

Background Vocal

"accompaniment"). At the words "everybody's gone surfin'," the lead changes to high voice and the background vocal stops. The title line ("Surfin' U.S.A.") is sung in low unison (again, no background vocal). If we were to imagine a picture of this general scheme (an approximation at best), it would look like the figure above.

"Surfer Girl"—With "Surfer Girl," the texture is slightly different. In the introduction, there are background vocal harmonies under a high lead line (homophonic texture, melody and accompaniment). In the first section of the song (A section), all voices move together in block chords (chordal homophony). All are singing the same words and rhythms; there is no rhythmic independence for any one voice, though the principal melody part dominates the other, less important parts. The harmony is spread widely over the available musical space—from the high lead to the bass—and is filled nicely in the middle. This sound refers back to the Four Freshmen and the Hi-Los. At the end of this section of music, the voices split with the high voice moving independently, while the lower vocal harmony sings about my little surfer girl. (melody and accompaniment homophony). After repeating the A section, the bridge (B) features a midrange lead voice accompanied by background vocals ("aah"); at the words describing everywhere one goes the voices join again in block chords, with the highest voice predominating (melody and accompaniment homophony; note that a portion of the "accompaniment" part consists of vocals themselves in a chordal homophonic texture).

"Fun, Fun, Fun"—With "Fun, Fun, Fun," the Berry influence is particularly obvious, especially in the guitar introduction (compare with Berry's intro to "Johnny B. Goode"). The A section begins with midrange voices in unison. This monophonic texture in the vocals is sustained until the title words when a full chordal homophonic texture develops, covering a very wide pitch spectrum from high voice to bass. On the word "away," the high voice is sustained, while the other voices harmonize a rhythmic pattern on "fun ... T-bird away." another example of an overall melody and accompaniment homophonic texture within which the "accompaniment" part consists of vocals in a chordal homophonic texture. For the repeat of the A section (with different words), the mid-

range unison returns to take the lead but is accompanied by background vocals sustained from the end of the previous section. In subsequent sections of the repeated A section, the midrange voice sings the lead, accompanied by background vocals on "ooh" and the line about walking like an ace now. Skip to the end of the song (the fade section). Here, a new texture develops; the high falsetto pattern zooms off on its own, while the accompanying voices sing a repeating pattern on "fun ... T-bird away." an example of non-imitative polyphonic texture; notice how your attention tends to be drawn back and forth between the high falsetto vocal and the other chordal homophonic parts, suggesting an equal level of musical importance in contrast to the predominant importance of a single line in melody and accompaniment homophony.

Other Surf Hits—Listen to other Beach Boys surf hits and you can find examples of monophony (unison line), homophony (one part dominates as most important), and polyphony (several independent, but equally important lines). With five voices, the Beach Boys can have one solo line (often multitracked to provide a larger sound) and still have full four-voice harmony for accompaniment. Sometimes, the lead is high, accompanied by voices below; at other times the lead is midrange, with accompanying voices surrounding it, above and/or below. The frequency of change in these textures, sometimes within one phrase, adds variety and interest to the music. But compared with later Beach Boys' works, these early surf sounds seem like elementary exercises. Let us look at two of these later works.

"GOOD VIBRATIONS" "Good Vibrations" (late 1966) was the most creative and innovative single to be released in rock music up until that time. As the Listening Guide shows, there are five contrasting sections, identified by consecutive letters (A through E), arranged into a unique overall form. In several sections, there are multiple layers of voices, including an example of non-imitative polyphony (Section E). There are also some unusual timbres (for rock), including cellos, flutes, and a theremin (Section B). This innovative electronic instrument was invented in 1924 by Leon Theremin and consists of a small box with two protruding metallic rods. As the player's hand moves around one rod, a continuous tone is emitted that follows the up-and-down hand movements, producing higher and lower pitches associated with the hand position. The other hand is used to manipulate the loudness of the sound, similarly associated with proximity to the second rod.

Listening Guide: "Good Vibrations" (The Beach Boys)

0:00–0:12	Section A (8 bars)	Begins with high voice (multitracked unison and heavy echo). Accompanied by organ chords (one per beat) and a 2-bar bass pattern that repeats four times.
0:13–0:24	Section A' (8 bars)	Add percussion. Snare drum reinforces the first three notes of each bass pattern; tambourine shakes on beat 4 of odd-numbered measures; snare drum plays on beat 4 of even-numbered measures. New lyrics. Triple subdivision (snare drum) leads to next section.
0:25–0:49	Section B (16 bars)	Vocal shifts to low range. Quadruple meter with triple subdivisions in cellos; tambourine on backbeat. The gliding sound of the theremin is introduced. Background vocals added in 5th bar (2nd phrase). Third vocal layer added in 9th bar (3rd phrase).
0:50–1:15	Section A and A' (16 bars)	Repeat first 16 bars with new lyrics.
1:16–1:40	Section B	Repeat second 16 bars.
1:41–2:13	Section C (20 bars)	Contrasting section. Piano chords alternate with bass. Drums and tambourine add color. Voices enter humming. New melody and lyrics begin in measure 9. Texture changes after first 12 bars (multiple vocal layers).
2:14–2:56	Section D (24 bars)	Sustained organ chords and percussion color. Midrange vocal line ("gotta keep ... with her.") enters in 5th bar (2nd phrase). Voices shift to high range and bass added in 9th bar (3rd phrase). Fourth phrase adds high organ line and voices fade out. Multilayered texture continues until broken by jazzy, vocal chord in 23rd bar, followed by 1 bar of silence (24th bar).
2:57–3:12	Section B (10 bars)	Repeat last 8 measures of section B (plus 2 bars of cello/percussion accompaniment).
3:13–3:25	Section E (8 bars)	Polyphonic section. Accompaniment limited to bass and tambourine. First voice (falsetto) enters on rising line; 2nd voice (3rd bar) enters on descending line; other voices enter (5th bar) to create full polyphonic texture.
3:26–3:34	Coda (about 5 bars)	Accompaniment (cello, percussion, theremin) for section B returns and fades out.

"Good Vibrations" goes well beyond the Beach Boys' earlier surf style, yet, in spite of its complexity, preserves the basic Beach Boys sound. It remains one of the musical milestones in the history of rock.

BECOME AN ACTIVE LISTENER: MUSICAL TEXTURES

One of the most challenging musical elements to understand is musical texture, but it is one that truly distinguishes a trained listener (an active, analytical listener) from one who is untrained (a passive listener).

Find examples of these vocal styles in the music that you enjoy:
1. Monophony (unison line)
2. Homophony (all voices moving together or melody and accompaniment)
3. Polyphony (several independent, equally important lines)

"HEROES AND VILLAINS" Listen to "Heroes and Villains" and see whether you can discern the many sectional changes and multiple layers of instrumental and vocal sounds within each section. A few of these are enumerated below.

As the first section closes, the rhythm stops, and there is a pause while the voices slide into a chord that is *dissonant* (does not harmonize traditionally, creating a sense of unease) with the instrumental chord. Both the break in the rhythm and the dissonance were generally no-no's in rock music prior to this. The following section has at least two vocal layers. One sings the line "heroes and villains," while another sings a "bomp-bomp-bomp" accompaniment over

sustained organ bass notes. The voices fade, and only the organ remains.

After the "la-la" section, another complex, multilayered vocal ("doo, doo, doo") is introduced, pulling together just at the end of the section. This section (like several subsequent sections) is *a cappella*; that is, without instrumental accompaniment. In the "my children were raised...." section, note the method of producing the vocal accompaniment tones: a hard glottal attack, followed by a decay. The subsequent section removes all accompaniment and echo, resulting in an old **barbershop quartet** sound.

Do not be discouraged if you are unable to separate all of the various sound layers in "Heroes and Villains." Get what you can and try to appreciate the complexity involved in conceptualizing and producing this song. Although the Beatles had a greater impact on rock history overall, Brian Wilson and the post–surf music style of the Beach Boys were doing work just as creative, if not more so, at about the same time (1966–1967). To a large extent, Brian did it himself; he had no George Martin (the integral producer who is often called "the fifth Beatle").

4.4: The Dance Craze

OBJECTIVE: Describe the factors that influenced the dance craze

From its beginnings, rock and roll has been associated with dancing. Teen dances in the 1950s usually fell into two categories: slow, in which couples held each other close and moved romantically but leisurely around the dance floor, and fast, usually the jitterbug, a holdover from the big band swing era of the 1930s and 1940s.

4.4.1: The Twist

In 1959, Hank Ballard and the Midnighters recorded a song called "Teardrops on Your Letter." The flip side of the single was a song called "The Twist." When it began to catch on, a cover version was released on Cameo-Parkway Records (Philadelphia) by Ernest Evans, who went by the name Chubby Checker (note the obvious derivation of this name when compared to Fats Domino). The song reached number 1 on two separate occasions (September 1960 and January 1962)—an unequaled feat in rock history at the time—and it stayed on the Hot 100 chart for a total of over 38 weeks, also an unparalleled achievement. "The Twist" initiated an explosion of dance-oriented records that came to be known as "the dance craze."

Chubby Checker, c. 1960

SOURCE: Michael Levin Photography/Alamy Stock Photo

Checker and "The Twist" were popularized on *American Bandstand*. The song and the dance became a national fad, spinning off countless twist records for Checker and others. For examples, listen to the following songs:

"Let's Twist Again," Chubby Checker
"Slow Twistin'," Chubby Checker
"Twist It Up," Chubby Checker
"Twist and Shout," Isley Brothers; Beatles
"The Peppermint Twist," Joey Dee and the Starlighters
"Twistin' the Night Away," Sam Cooke
"Twistin' U.S.A.," Danny and the Juniors
"Twist, Twist Senora," Gary "U.S." Bonds
"Twistin' Mathilda," Jimmy Soul

4.4.2: New Dances

The dance craze spread to an older, adult crowd. New dances followed: Chubby Checker had hits with "Pony Time" (1961), "The Fly" (1961), "Limbo Rock" (1962), "Popeye the Hitchhiker" (1962), "Let's Limbo Some More" (1963), and "Let's Do the Freddie" (1965). Others, led by

black artists from Philadelphia, often on the Cameo-Parkway label, invented a seemingly endless string of new dances (see Table 4.3).

Table 4.3 Examples of Dance Craze Recordings

Song	Artist	Year	Label
"Continental Walk"	Hank Ballard and the Midnighters	1961	King
"The Fish"	Bobby Rydell	1961	Cameo
"Bristol Stomp"	Dovells	1961	Parkway
"Wah Watusi"	Orlons	1962	Cameo
"Mashed Potato Time"	Dee Dee Sharp	1962	Cameo
"Loco Motion"	Little Eva	1962	Dimension
"Hully Gully Baby"	Dovells	1962	Parkway
"Do the Bird"	Dee Dee Sharp	1963	Cameo
"The Hitch Hike"	Marvin Gaye	1963	Tamla
"Monkey Time"	Major Lance	1963	Okeh
"Do the Freddie"	Freddie and the Dreamers	1965	Mercury
"The Jerk"	Larks	1965	Money
"The Shake"	Sam Cooke	1965	RCA
"The Cool Jerk"	Capitols	1966	Karen

Most often relying on the 12-bar blues structure, these songs usually contained lyrics that provided instructions about how to do the given dance. Sometimes, teens invented their own dance variations without the aid of any such instruction. Dancers faced each other without actually touching, sometimes drifting several feet apart, perhaps a harbinger of the era's new emphasis on individualism. Certainly, these dance records kept black music on the charts in the face of the folk trend, the surf trend, and the coming British invasion, all three of which involved mostly white artists. The dance craze of the early 1960s also served as a precursor to disco (1970s) and break dancing (1980s).

JOURNAL

Contemporary Dance Craze

Dancing has almost always been associated with musical performance—from the minuet in classical music through swing bands in the 1930s and 1940s and right into the rock era. In fact, as you have learned, it became a central focus of the dance craze. There have been more recent dances like the electric slide. Take a moment to reflect on your own experience of listening and dancing to music. Describe one dance, either performed as a couple or in a larger group. Search the Internet to find two or three examples of more contemporary dance moves, whether or not you are able to think of such a dance on your own. Write a short paragraph detailing how you would instruct someone to perform this dance. If possible, gather together several of your classmates and teach them the steps for one of these as you learn the dances they discovered in their own research.

 The response entered here will appear in the performance dashboard and can be viewed by your instructor.

Submit

Summary: Transitional Styles of Rock in The Early 1960s

The 1960s rock scene splintered in many directions. There were Pop-oriented teen idols, female groups in the doo-wop tradition, novelty songs, folk singers, surfers, and twisters. No one style predominated. Rock seemed to be losing its direction in a hopeless fragmentation of the market. Was it possible to pull this diverse musical universe together and send rock in a new direction? The answer was yes. A far-reaching musical revolution was about to begin.

Take Note

- *Why did the rock music market become fragmented in the early 1960s?*—The initial excitement that had been created by rock and roll had ebbed somewhat by the early 1960s. Major performers were no longer on the charts because of scandal (Jerry Lee Lewis), imprisonment (Chuck Berry), or death (Buddy Holly). While no one musical style dominated, the early 1960s saw four major trends on the charts: (1) vestiges of the 1950s, (2) the emerging folk music trend, (3) surf music, and (4) the dance craze.
- *How did folk music arise as one of the key musical trends of this era?*—Folk music first came to the forefront in the 1940s and early 1950s, thanks to the success of singer/songwriters like Woody Guthrie and Peter Seeger, as well as groups like the Weavers. In the later 1950s, a new folk music craze arose illustrated by the success of popular trios like the Kingston Trio and the more politically oriented Peter, Paul, and Mary. Folk music promoted authenticity, serious lyrics, and acoustic instruments. Albums sold better than singles and the music appealed primarily to the older portion of the teen Pop market and college-age listeners.
- *What was surf music and what was its significance to the history of rock?*—Surf music was inspired by California's youth culture, which celebrated "fun in the sun" as opposed to the more serious audience that preferred folk music. Surf groups featured electric instrumentation and used plenty of special effects on their recordings. Dick Dale was a key proponent of the surf guitar sound, emphasizing the instrument's bass notes and featuring the use of heavy echo and reverb. But surf vocal groups were the ones who truly popularized the style, notably the duo of Jan and Dean and, the most successful of all surf groups, the Beach Boys.
- *What was the association between rock and roll and dance crazes?*—From the very start, rock and roll was associated with dancing. While teenagers of the 1950s mixed slow dancing and the jitterbug, the early 1960s saw the rise of highly energetic specialized dances that were perfectly suited to express rock and roll's drive. "The Twist," a 1959 song by Hank Ballard and the Midnighters, was covered by Chubby Checker a year later, which launched dozens of imitators, initiating a major dance craze.

SHARED WRITING

Factors Associated with the Emergence of Musical Styles in a Period of Transition

After learning about the markets leading to the emergence of rock and roll (Pop, C&W, and R&B) and then identifying early rock styles as soft rock, rockabilly, and mainstream rock, you have been made aware that the pre-rock and early rock styles share a clear relationship. However, during the transition to the 1960s, some genuinely new approaches to popular music emerged. Choose one of the four styles discussed in this chapter and write two paragraphs in which you provide your own assessment of how that particular style came to be. You should carefully consider the audience for the music, the geographic region from which it emerged, the artists themselves, and other significant factors. After you have composed your independent response, seek out the responses of two or three other students and consider them carefully. After reading the responses of your fellow students, are there insights you have gained that might allow you to further develop your own assessment of the music you chose?

A minimum number of characters is required to post and earn points. After posting, your response can be viewed by your class and instructor, and you can participate in the class discussion.

Post

0 characters | 140 minimum

Chapter 5
The Beatles

 ## Learning Objectives

5.1 Summarize the factors that transformed rock music in the 1960s

5.2 Outline the early social and musical transformations leading to Beatlemania in the UK

5.3 Analyze the events leading to Beatlemania in the United States

5.4 Explain the maturation of the Beatles' musical style in the middle period of their musical career as a band

5.5 Outline the important developments in the music of the Beatles during the late period

5.6 Describe the Beatles musical innovations

Early rock and roll of the 1950s had a transformative impact on popular music and the recording industry in America. During the late 1950s, that impact proved to be international. After a brief gestational period, an impressive array of musicians born in England began to share their own versions of rock music with the world. The present chapter provides, via its examination of the phenomenal events and innovative music of the Beatles, a prelude to what would soon become a full-blown British Invasion.

5.1: Revolution within a Revolution

OBJECTIVE: Summarize the factors that transformed rock music in the 1960s

The coming of rock and roll turned both music and the music industry upside down. The Pop sounds of Perry Como, Eddie Fisher, and Doris Day yielded to the rocking sounds of Elvis Presley, Little Richard, and Jerry Lee Lewis. An industry dominated by five major record companies was now populated with hundreds of successful, small, independent companies. A well-ordered succession of predictable hit records, each sustaining its popularity for months at a time, was replaced by a dizzying sequence of hits and artists, many of whom zoomed to popularity only to fade to obscurity within a few weeks. Even general society felt the changes. A white, adult-oriented society was transformed into a youth-oriented society with a growing

acceptance of, and admiration for, black culture—and all of this took place in the space of about three years. Rock and roll was a revolution.

5.1.1: Rock Enters Its Second Decade

By the beginning of 1964, rock was entering its second decade. Much of the power of its original thrust had dissipated. Music was in a state of confusion. Fans listened, interchangeably, to Elvis, soft rock teen idols, silly novelty tunes, doo-wop groups, increasingly serious folk groups, equally unserious surfers, and a plethora of twists and other dance records. What was rock and roll in the early 1960s? Half a dozen answers would be equally valid.

5.1.2: Rapid Social Change

Society, too, was in a state of disarray. The 1960s had begun as "the Kennedy years," as America entered a New Frontier (John F. Kennedy's label for his overall political program). The folk musicians sang of peace, racial justice, and "love between the brothers and the sisters all over this land." There was a new kind of optimism "blowin' in the wind." But, as the shots echoed through Dealey Plaza in Dallas on November 22, 1963, the dream shattered. America's youngest president, both the symbol of this new hope for a utopian future and the youth culture's philosophical leader, was killed by an assassin's bullet. The hope, optimism, and faith of the youth movement were simultaneously staggered by that same gunshot.

The nation's emotional reaction is difficult for us to understand today. Since 1963, many prominent political and social figures have been the targets of violence; our society has become accustomed (and comparatively desensitized) to it. But in November 1963, the shock of Kennedy's assassination sent the nation into a prolonged period of depression and self-doubt. The United States was a civilized nation; things like that just did not happen here! But no matter how hard we tried to deny it, we could not. Were we a sick society? How could American culture allow such an assassin to emerge? And then, to our horror, the assassin was assassinated! Even today, many people who were alive at the time can tell you exactly where they were and what they were doing when they first heard the shocking news that President Kennedy had been shot.

5.1.3: America's Cultural Inferiority Complex

The United States has always been a nation with a cultural inferiority complex; "real culture" came from Europe. Americans considered their native cultural products to be unsophisticated at best and downright embarrassing at worst. Not until the early years of the twentieth century did classical composers begin to create a uniquely American style; previously, they had merely based their work on European models. For example, when classical performers aspired to the concert stage, it was obligatory that they journeyed to Paris, Rome, Vienna, or London for study. Similarly, many music scholars enthusiastically studied and wrote about the folk music of Europe or the Far East but rarely, until more recently, considered American folk music worthy of serious academic pursuit. Jazz was perhaps the most embarrassing of all (until rock and roll, of course). Although Americans viewed jazz as merely "fun music" (or worse), many important European composers included elements of jazz in their "serious" compositions. It was only after the European music community took jazz seriously that Americans decided that it must be okay.

Rock and roll was an even bigger embarrassment than concert music, jazz, or folk music. No one could take *that* seriously! It was just noisy, American teenage music (with a heavy influence of black R&B). To be legitimized, it would need to receive the European seal of approval.

With the Kennedy assassination generating national self-doubt, our cultural inferiority complex reached an all-time low; we were vulnerable to a cultural invasion. The Beatles would lead that invasion, bringing a new level of sophistication to rock music, while at the same time reintroducing America to what was most important about the music of Chuck Berry, Buddy Holly, Elvis Presley, and the other 1950s innovators … much of which had been lost during the early 1960s. With that invasion, rock and roll—itself an American revolution—would experience its own revolution. The rules were about to be rewritten. Rock would never be the same again.

5.2: The Early Beatles

OBJECTIVE: Outline the early social and musical transformations leading to Beatlemania in the UK

John Winston Lennon was born in Liverpool, England, on October 9, 1940. His mother, Julia, was a fun-loving and carefree soul who, within a year of John's birth, left her husband to live with another man. John's father was a ship's steward who was rarely home. John was left in the care of his Aunt Mimi (Julia's sister) and Uncle George, who became his substitute parents. From his earliest days in primary school, it was obvious that John was bright. He loved to read and frequently created poems, short stories, and drawings. Equally obvious was a streak of impishness that gradually progressed through mischievousness into a mild form of delinquency. After Uncle George's sudden death in 1955, John became a burden to Aunt Mimi; his grades dropped, and his rebellion became more troublesome.

In 1956, John first heard Elvis Presley's recordings; he was mesmerized. Julia shared her minimal knowledge of banjo with John, who had obtained an inexpensive guitar. Although the BBC declined to play rock and roll, the independent station Radio Luxembourg did, and John listened constantly. He adopted the rebellious teddy-boy image: greasy hair with a ducktail in back and pointed slide of hair in front, and tight "drainpipe" pants. Then, John heard Lonnie Donegan's smash hit "Rock Island Line," representing the *skiffle* style—a simple, three-chord style featuring an instrumental lineup of guitar and/or banjo and homemade instruments, such as a washboard (played with thimble-capped fingers) and bass made from a broom handle, wooden chest, and a tightly strung wire. John organized his own skiffle group, the Quarry Men (named after Quarry Bank High School, which John attended). Working wherever they could find jobs, the Quarry Men played both skiffle and rock and roll. In July 1957, they were playing at a garden party when band member Ivan Vaughan introduced John to his friend from Liverpool Institute, Paul McCartney; several days later, John invited Paul to join the group.

James Paul McCartney was born on June 18, 1942. Like John, Paul was naturally bright, excelling in English composition and art, but unlike John, Paul enjoyed his success at school. When Paul was 14, his family was staggered by the death of Mary McCartney, Paul's mother. Paul's father, Jim, had run a successful society band in the 1920s, and his musical background was an influence in the McCartney home. When the skiffle rage hit Britain, Jim bought a guitar for Paul, who imitated the vocal and guitar styles of Presley, Little Richard, Carl Perkins, and the Everly Brothers. At the Woolton garden party—where he first heard the Quarry Men—Paul amazed John Lennon and the others with his skillful and authentic performance of Little Richard songs.

5.2.1: The Quarry Men

In the Quarry Men, Paul and John became close friends. They shared a passion for guitars and for rock and roll; both were quick-witted and fascinated with language and art. But in many ways, they were vastly different. John was rebellious and iconoclastic; he fought any form of authority or inhibition. He could be rude and callous, reveling in "cruelty jokes" and deprecatory remarks; nevertheless, he was generous to a fault. Paul, on the other hand, was practical to the point of being downright stingy. He strove for the approval of authority figures and consciously fostered an image of the "good boy." In their commonalities lay the foundation of one of the most successful songwriting teams and entertainment acts in music history. In their differences lay the seeds of the eventual disintegration of the act and also, in some ways, the dual directions British rock would take from the mid-1960s to the present day.

By 1957, John had flunked out of Quarry Bank High School. Yielding to pressure from Aunt Mimi, he enrolled in an art college in Liverpool. The skiffle style had run its course, and now the Liverpool groups, including the Quarry Men, concentrated solely on rock and roll. In late 1957, a young (14-year-old) friend of Paul's started hanging around the Quarry Men; his name was George Harrison.

George (born February 25, 1943) met Paul at the Liverpool Institute in 1954. Like John, George resented formal education and did not do well in school. Also like Lennon, he adopted the rebellious teddy-boy look and was easily hooked by Lonnie Donegan's skiffle sound. George's mother bought him a guitar, and he began to teach himself to play, copying the chords and bass lines from American rock and roll records, especially Buddy Holly's hits. When Paul finally introduced him to the Quarry Men, he demonstrated a few of the patterns he had learned and sat in with the group whenever possible. John looked condescendingly on this quiet 14-year-old, who was, even then, rather somber and introverted; nevertheless, he was tolerated as a friend of Paul's.

In July 1958, John's mother, Julia, was killed by a car near Aunt Mimi's house. Despite this loss, John continued his studies at art college where he met Cynthia Powell, his future wife. Meanwhile, the Quarry Men continued playing odd jobs around Liverpool.

5.2.2: The Silver Beetles

One of the most talented students at the art college was Stu Sutcliffe. Gifted but antisocial, he looked, dressed, and acted the part of the countercultural brooding artist. It was only natural that he and John would become friends. Although he had no idea how to play, Stu bought a bass guitar, determined to join John's group. Through local club owner Alan Williams, the group was booked on shows and even a Scottish tour. Tour promoter Larry Parnes suggested a name change. Stu suggested the name "Beetles" in homage to Buddy Holly's Crickets. The group extended it to Silver Beetles and, for a while, Long John and the Silver Beetles. John, who had a never-ending fascination with word play, suggested the misspelling that was to become a legend—Beatles, a pun on the word "beat."

Silver Beetles: George Harrison, Pete Best, Paul McCartney, and John Lennon

SOURCE: Keystone Pictures USA/Alamy Stock Photo

Early Performances of the Silver Beetles

The Scottish Tour—The Scottish tour was a low-budget, second-rate affair that found them backing up some of Parnes's less impressive acts. But the Silver Beetles were hardly a sophisticated musical act themselves: Paul was clearly the most competent, John was playing well enough, and George was barely more than a beginner. Stu could hardly play at all, and he knew it; he frequently played with his back to the audience. The group had no coordinated stage costumes, no image, and no set act. Simply put, in May 1960, the Silver Beetles were not very good.

The Germany Trip—Back in Liverpool, Alan Williams contacted a club owner from Hamburg, Germany, named Bruno Koschmider, who had successfully featured British groups in the past. Koschmider wanted to book another Liverpool group, and Williams recommended the ill-prepared, drummerless Beetles. Paul Mc-

Cartney approached local drummer Pete Best about joining the group for the two-month booking, and Pete promptly agreed.

In 1960, Hamburg was an attractive city, having been largely rebuilt after its destruction in World War II. Its entertainment district, known as the Reeperbahn (somewhat comparable to "the strip" in Las Vegas) was well known throughout northern Europe for its free, hedonistic lifestyle, offering alcohol, drugs, and sex to its fun-seeking patrons. However, the Indra, the club where the Beetles were booked, was at the wrong end of the strip; it was a dive. Faced with the necessity of performing four and a half hours per night, night after night, week after week, the group began to forge a set repertoire and the beginnings of a stage act. Through fellow musicians, they were introduced to the Reeperbahn's after-hours nightlife—including large quantities of beer, free and easy sex, and "prellys" (Preludin, a German diet pill that, in effect, was an upper). Good news came when Koschmider decided to move the Beetles to the Kaiserkeller, his more prominent club.

Although his drumming was certainly adequate for the Beatles, Pete Best was otherwise rather distinct from the other four. The girls stared past John, George, and even Paul, and made eyes at Pete, whose athletic good looks upstaged the others. Furthermore, he did not join in the increasingly outrageous stage antics of John and Paul, nor in the off-hours revelries. Meanwhile, Stu Sutcliffe began dating Astrid Kirchherr, a beautiful young woman, who was a talented artist and photographer. She convinced Stu to let her cut his hair in a "French cut"—short, with hair down on his forehead. One by one, George, Paul, and John converted to the new hairstyle; only Pete retained his greased pompadour.

The Beatles' first German trip ended after they abandoned Koschmider's club for a competitor. Possibly through Koschmider, the German police discovered that George was too young to work in clubs, and he was deported back to Liverpool. Shortly thereafter, Paul inadvertently set some curtains on fire and found himself in trouble with the German police. Soon, all of the Beatles decided to follow George home.

5.2.3: The Cavern Club

The Cavern Club, literally a cellar below a warehouse near the Liverpool docks, had been a jazz club since opening in 1957. Realizing the growing popularity of the new "beat" sound, owner Ray McFall gradually presented some local rock groups. He hired the Beatles for his noontime shows, and they were soon attracting a large clientele of (mostly female) office and shop workers. The club consisted of a small, crowded room with a small bandstand against one wall. The acoustics were poor and the atmosphere was stifling, but the Beatles began to create a loyal Liverpool following.

In mid-1961, they returned to Hamburg to play at the Top Ten Club, alternating sets with singer Tony Sheridan. Trouble emerged as Paul became increasingly critical of Stu's lack of musical ability. Meanwhile, Stu was becoming increasingly serious about his painting and about Astrid, gradually losing his interest in rock and roll. He was also suffering from severe headaches, and his moods fluctuated wildly. Except for occasional performances, he dropped out of the Beatles, allowing an eager Paul to move to bass guitar.

On this second trip to Hamburg, the Beatles made their first commercial recording, backing Tony Sheridan on the standards "My Bonnie Lies over the Ocean" and "When the Saints Go Marching In." Under the name the "Beat Brothers," the group recorded "Ain't She Sweet" and an instrumental called "Cry for a Shadow." The Sheridan recording was released in Germany and was a fair success; the Beat Brothers' record remained in the vaults. John, Paul, George, and Pete headed back, once again, to Liverpool and the Cavern Club.

5.2.4: Brian Epstein

Disc jockey Bob Wooler was an early fan of the Beatles and encouraged his listeners to ask their favorite record shop for the group's recording of "My Bonnie." In October 1961, several teens went to one of the largest and most successful Liverpool record stores and asked the manager, Brian Epstein, for the new Beatles record. Epstein knew nothing of the Beatles, the Cavern Club, or rock and roll. The son of an upper-middle-class family, Brian was a sophisticated businessman whose passions were clothing design, theater, and classical music. A meticulous and organized man, he had taken over the record department of his family's large store. Brian took pride in being able to fulfill any customer's request, no matter how obscure. Nevertheless, he searched unsuccessfully for "My Bonnie" by Tony Sheridan and the Beat Brothers (the Beatles). Since the teenage customers had said that the group was playing at the Cavern Club just a few hundred yards from his store, Brian decided the easiest way to locate the record was to visit with the group itself.

The Cavern Club was hardly Brian's cup of tea; however, he was fascinated with the four rough boys who nonchalantly tossed off song after song with a defiant disregard for their audience or the accepted standards of good taste. For the next month or so, Brian continued to visit the club and even had several formal meetings with the Beatles. He had been quietly learning from his friends in the industry what it was like to manage a rock band. Against all advice, he finally proposed to the Beatles that he become their manager. To his surprise and delight, they accepted.

Although 1962 was to be a big year for the Beatles, it did not begin well. Brian's first priority was to obtain a recording contract. He started at the top with Decca, EMI, Philips, and Pye Records. In early January, the Beatles recorded some 15 songs (including three originals) in Decca's London studios. Their nerves got the best of them, and their performance was not impressive. Decca passed, and Epstein stomped out of their offices, warning them that one day his group would be bigger than Elvis Presley!

Many promoters and managers have made similar statements, but never has one been as right as Epstein was proven. More bad news came in April. As the Beatles landed in Germany for a booking at Hamburg's Star-Club, they learned that Stu Sutcliffe had died that very day (the cause was subsequently diagnosed as a brain tumor).

5.2.5: George Martin and Parlophone

In early June 1962, the Beatles returned to London to audition for Parlophone Records. Among the large British label EMI's various subsidiaries, Parlophone was at the bottom of the totem pole. Its normal fare included spoken comedy and some light-music groups. The head of Parlophone was a knowledgeable, sophisticated musician named George Martin. He had ambitions to bring Parlophone to a more competitive and respectable status. The new beat sound seemed to be one way to boost the label's sales, so he listened with interest to the demo tape Brian Epstein sent him. In June, he listened to John, Paul, George, and Pete in person as they played through their repertoire. Martin liked the Beatles both personally and musically, sensing the hidden potential for a new and fresh sound. In July, he offered Brian the minimum EMI contract for one year and four songs, at a royalty of one penny per double-sided record.

The Path to Success of the Beatles

Several crucial changes occurred during 1962–1963 that set the foundation for what would become British—and then American—Beatlemania.

Final Pieces Fall into Place—Things started moving fast. In August, the band agreed that Pete Best was not fitting in personally or musically with the rest of the group. The boys gave Brian the job of informing Pete that he was being dropped. It was a crushing blow for Pete, a two-year Beatles veteran, coming just as they had finally secured a recording contract. His replacement would be one of Liverpool's best-known drummers, Richard Starkey, a.k.a. Ringo Starr.

Richard Starkey was born on July 7, 1940, in Liverpool. In spite of a broken home and poor economic resources, Ritchie (as he was called) was a cheerful child. A series of illnesses took their toll on his education and his physical health. After a brief experience in a skiffle band, Ritchie joined Rory Storm and the Hurricanes. Because he wore so many rings, he earned the nickname "Ringo," and Starkey was shortened to "Starr." The band established a strong reputation around Liverpool and Hamburg. They were certainly well ahead of the rough-edged Beatles. In Hamburg, Ringo hung around the Beatles during their off-hours binges. In August 1962, shortly after Pete Best's departure, the Beatles invited Ringo to join them. He acquired a Beatle hair-

cut, shaved his beard, and said good-bye to Rory Storm. Paul McCartney recalled the moment when Ringo played with the band at the Cavern Club in 1962 as the moment when they truly became a band (*Rolling Stone*, April 9, 2014, p. 39). The last of the six major pieces of what would become the Beatle legend—John, Paul, George, Ringo, Brian Epstein, and George Martin—was finally in place.

Public Appearance—In September 1962, the Beatles recorded "Love Me Do" and "P.S. I Love You." Ringo was replaced by a session drummer on this first recording. The record was released on October 4 but was given minimal publicity by EMI. "Love Me Do" eventually climbed to number 17 in the UK by December 1962. In late November, George Martin set up another recording session. On hearing the final version of "Please, Please Me," he assured the Beatles that it was destined to be number 1. Television appearances on *Thank Your Lucky Stars* and a radio appearance on the BBC's *Saturday Club* helped George's prediction come true. On March 2, 1963, the *Melody Maker* chart showed the Beatles' second release as number 1. They were the heroes of Liverpool.

George Martin wisely followed immediately with a full album of newly recorded songs from the Beatles' live repertoire. It was a mix of Lennon-McCartney songs (e.g., "I Saw Her Standing There" and "Do You Want to Know a Secret?") and cover versions (most notably the Isley Brothers' "Twist and Shout"). Brian busily arranged radio, television, and tour appearances, not only to publicize the group and its record releases, but also to ensure adequate revenue should the record successes prove to be short-lived.

Climbing the Charts—The Beatles' third release, "From Me to You," hit number 1 in late April 1963. By then, Gerry and the Pacemakers, old friends from Liverpool, had joined the Beatles on the charts. People began to speak of the Liverpool or the **Mersey sound** (the Mersey River runs through Liverpool). Brian added several more groups to his agency, and promoters and record companies flocked to Liverpool to sign any group that combed their hair forward, wore high-buttoned coats, and could hold a guitar. By midsummer, Brian was managing the number 1, 2, and 3 acts on the British charts: the Beatles, Gerry and the Pacemakers, and Billy J. Kramer and the Dakotas.

The Beatles' fourth big hit, "She Loves You," fared even better than its predecessors, zooming to number 1 on the basis of advance orders, and holding that position for two months. In September, the *Melody Maker* poll showed the Beatles as the top British Pop group. Their most notable television appearance of the year came in October on *Sunday Night at the London Palladium* before a viewing audience estimated at 15 million. In late October came a successful tour of Sweden, followed in November by an appearance as part of the 1963 Royal Command Performance for an exclusive audience that included the Queen Mother and Princess Margaret. At this show, John made his famous quip: "Will the people in the cheaper seats clap your hands? All the rest of you, if you'll just rattle your jewelry."

Beatlemania Begins—Late 1963 saw the British version of *Beatlemania* in full swing. Newspapers overflowed with Beatle interviews and articles portraying them as lovable, innocent, charming, witty lads; Beatles products were rampant. Their second LP, *With the Beatles,* was successful, as was their fifth single, "I Want to Hold Your Hand." Parlophone, EMI's poor relation just a year earlier, had held the number 1 position for 37 out of the past 52 weeks. And the Beatles, who just 18 months earlier had been thrilled to see the inside of a real recording studio, now held seven out of the Top 20 positions on the British chart. But if British Beatlemania surpassed their wildest dreams, they were about to find the reaction in America even more breathtaking.

The memorable melodies and happy, uptempo sound of the Beatles were instantly accessible to a broad range of listeners. Some of the most important recordings of this early period in the Beatles' career included the following hit singles.

Key Hits from the Beatles' Early Years

Please, Please Me
Love Me Do
I Saw Her Standing There
She Loves You
I Want to Hold Your Hand
Twist and Shout

JOURNAL

Musical Characteristics of Early Beatles Songs

Listen to recordings of the six songs listed above from this early period of the Beatles. What three aspects of the Beatles' musical sound do you find most infectious? Using your knowledge of musical elements, compare these songs to the music of one of your favorite artists or groups of the last decade. What aspects of this contemporary artists' sound clearly differentiate it from other recording artists of the same period?

▶ | The response entered here will appear in the performance dashboard and can be viewed by your instructor.

Submit

5.3: Beatlemania— American Style

OBJECTIVE: **Analyze the events leading to Beatlemania in the United States**

In 1963, everyone knew that real rock and roll was exclusively American music. Any other country's "rock" was merely a pale imitation. So when George Martin approached EMI-owned Capitol Records in the United States about releasing a Beatles record, he was virtually ignored. The fact that "Please, Please Me" was number 1 in Britain did not impress Capitol's American executives. After all, other British acts, such as Cliff Richard, had bombed miserably in the United States. Instead, Martin turned to two small American independent labels (Vee Jay and Swan) to release the Beatles' first three singles in the United States, but none made the Top 100.

In November 1963, Brian Epstein flew to New York to try to break down the barriers. After much hesitation, Capitol agreed to release "I Want to Hold Your Hand" in January 1964. Brian convinced promoter Sid Bernstein to present the Beatles in concert at Carnegie Hall. Finally, he contacted Ed Sullivan, host of a CBS television variety show that had aired for some 20 years. Sullivan, on a recent trip to England, had seen Beatlemania firsthand; he booked the group for two shows in February—as a novelty act. (It was estimated that the Beatles' first *Ed Sullivan Show* appearance was seen by some 70 million people— approximately 60 percent of the viewing audience.) The Beatles hoped to do what no previous British group had done: crack the American pop rock scene. There was no way anyone could have foreseen that they would not only crack it, but blow it wide open.

Beatles making their first appearance on the *Ed Sullivan Show*, 1964.

SOURCE: Trinity Mirror/Mirrorpix/Alamy Stock Photo

Rise of the Beatles in American Music

With the assistance of Brian Epstein as their manager, the Beatles used radio and TV extremely effectively to announce their arrival in America.

The Beginning—When several U.S. disc jockeys began playing "I Want to Hold Your Hand," Capitol moved its release date up to December 26, 1963. By the time the Beatles stepped off the airplane in New York, their song had been number 1 for one week. Beatlemania—American style—had begun. A crowd estimated at 5,000 awaited the Beatles at the airport. There were 50,000 applications for seats at the *Ed Sullivan Show*; the auditorium seated 700. The nation's disc jockeys played Beatle records nonstop, pausing only to announce "Beatle time" and "Beatle temperature."

First Press Conference—Many Americans watched the Beatles' first U.S. press conference to see what these strange, mop-haired people were like. Their quick-witted charm came through loud and clear:

> *Reporter:* Was your family in show business?
>
> *John:* Well, me Dad used to say me Mother was a great performer.
>
> *Reporter:* What do you think of the campaign in Detroit to stamp out the Beatles?
>
> *Paul:* We've got a campaign of our own to stamp out Detroit. (Norman 1982, 279)

The lines were delivered with good humor, posing no threat to anyone; the Beatles were intelligent, yet fun: They were talented rock and rollers, yet nonthreatening. America went wild.

American Pop Chart Domination—The Beatles returned to Britain having accomplished more than they ever expected with their American "invasion." By April 1964, they dominated the American Pop chart. With Capitol, Vee Jay, Swan, and three other labels issuing Beatles songs, the market was glutted. "I Want to Hold Your Hand" hit number 1 on February 1 and stayed there for seven weeks. On March 21, it yielded the number 1 position to "She Loves You." Two weeks later, "She Loves You" gave way to "Can't Buy Me Love." In December 1956, Elvis Presley had placed nine singles in the Top 100 in one week. That incredible feat was surpassed on March 28, 1964, when the Beatles placed 10 singles in the Top 100. By mid-April, there were 14 Beatles singles in the Top 100 (Bronson 1988, 145). For the week of April 4, 1964, the top five songs on the chart were all Beatles' songs. Amazingly, 60 percent of the singles sold in the first quarter of 1964 were Beatles recordings (Belz 1972, 145).

5.3.1: A Hard Day's Night

The Beatles' first movie, *A Hard Day's Night* (released in the summer of 1964), was a huge commercial success. The Beatles toured Scandinavia, Holland, Australia, and the Far East. In August, they returned to the United States, where they found Beatlemania to be even greater than before. They performed in 23 cities, and the mobs at airports, hotels, and concerts engulfed them. Girls hid in hotel air-conditioning shafts; fans were injured in the mad rush of the crowds; kids fell from overhead beams, balcony rails, and elevated walkways; they climbed onto the wings of the Beatles' airplane; often, the Beatles escaped concerts in armored trucks.

MULTIMILLION-DOLLAR ROCK LIFESTYLE By early 1965, the multimillion-dollar rock lifestyle was in full swing for the Beatles. There were elaborate new cars, new homes for themselves and their families, and steady girlfriends, along with a dizzying array of one-nighters. Marijuana became a regular habit in 1964; by 1965, their pill popping had widened to become a regular rainbow: French blues, purple hearts, black bombers, and yellow submarines. Finally, George and John were introduced to LSD—one of the most mind-altering of drugs. Meanwhile, the new government of Britain, headed by Prime Minister Harold Wilson, had named each of the Beatles a Member of the Most Excellent Order of the British Empire—an honor previously reserved for war heroes (which they were not), members of titled families (which they were not), and the very wealthy (which they had recently become).

5.3.2: Help!

Their second movie, 1965's *Help!*, was as successful as *A Hard Day's Night*. A third tour to the United States began in August 1965 with a concert at Shea Stadium. Some 55,000 screaming fans nearly drowned out the sound of the music. By now, the Beatles had placed 23 songs in the American Top 100 in 18 months. Most of the songs were Lennon–McCartney creations and were relatively consistent in musical style. They tended to be pleasant, upbeat rock and roll tunes, easy to listen and dance to. These were good, solid rock and roll songs, but not revolutionary—and certainly not profound. In September 1965, it was reasonable to believe that the Beatles were nothing more than a delightful and incredibly successful rock and roll band with a distinctive but not shockingly creative sound.

JOURNAL

The Influence of Skiffle Music

Use your preferred Internet browser to access YouTube or another large video archive to search for examples of skiffle music (you can find a lot of Lonnie Donegan). After listening to four or five of these, exercise your growing musical vocabulary to accurately describe the sound of this music, focusing on specific musical elements (e.g., melody, rhythm, harmony, loudness, instrumentation, etc.). Now, listen to several examples of the Beatles' early singles released in 1963 and 1964. Identify at least three influences of the skiffle style that you can hear in these popular rock and roll hits that initiated the British Invasion.

 The response entered here will appear in the performance dashboard and can be viewed by your instructor.

Submit

5.4: Experimentation During the Beatles Middle Period

OBJECTIVE: Explain the maturation of the Beatles musical style in the middle period of their musical career as a band

By late 1965, the Beatles were in a position enjoyed by few stars in any field: They could do no wrong. Usually, once popular music artists establish a successful style, they cling to it desperately, because to experiment with new sounds is to risk the loss of a familiar aural identity and, as a result, fans. But the Beatles were in the unique position of being able to do whatever struck their fancy. Such freedom can be bewildering, but the creative mind strikes out into the new and uncharted territory, always with the burning question, "What if I try this?" The Beatles had that spark of creativity.

At this time, the basic differences between Paul McCartney and John Lennon began to emerge in serious ways, as their muses led them in different directions. Paul was rather conservative, sentimental, anxious to please, willing to conform, and extremely talented in a musically traditional way. John was rebellious, aggressive, bitterly cynical, linguistically adept, and more experimental musically. Both, within the constraints of their very different personalities, possessed hyper-creative minds.

5.4.1: "Yesterday"

In the spring of 1965, Paul approached George Martin with a song called "Yesterday." He intended to sing it himself, accompanied by his acoustic guitar. It had a beautifully flowing melody, an unusually sophisticated chord pattern (for pop rock music), and sensitive lyrics. Martin suggested that this refined song be set to strings—possibly a string quartet. At first, Paul reacted negatively. After all, what would people think of the world's most successful rock band singing to the accompaniment of a string quartet—the medium used by Mozart, Haydn, and Beethoven for some of their most eloquent musical statements in the classical idiom? Nevertheless, Paul and George worked out an arrangement and recorded it. "Yesterday" was released on the *Help!* album in Britain and as a single in the United States. It not only climbed to number 1 in the United States but eventually became the Beatles' most recorded song with thousands of cover versions. Predictably, John hated the song. A soft love ballad with sentimental lyrics was just not his style.

"Yesterday" is not a rock song; it is pure Pop and, thus, did not initiate a new style of rock. However, it did serve notice that the Beatles were no longer a predictable rock band, content to grind out hits according to a proven formula. If "Yesterday" had not been followed by more surprises, it would simply be another example of a rock group occasionally straying into the legitimate Pop field; Elvis Presley, Fats Domino, and Buddy Holly had done so during the previous decade. But in light of what followed over the next five or six years, "Yesterday" takes its place as the first hint of what was to come. The musical revolution begins.

5.4.2: Rubber Soul

In late 1965, the first of two important Beatles albums appeared: *Rubber Soul*, followed in August 1966 by *Revolver*. These albums would show a gradual increase in experimentation, providing a transition from the Beatles' early period to their mature style. *Rubber Soul* even *looked* different.

Features of the Rubber Soul Album

Unique Cover—The front cover showed the slightly distorted faces of the four Beatles, and the magical words *The Beatles* were purposely left off. It was an artsy cover, somewhat surreal, and gave a hint of what would later be labeled "**psychedelic**."

Innovative Music—Gone, too, were the "yeah, yeah, yeah" songs. John had discovered the lyrics of Bob Dylan, and George Harrison had discovered the sitar. All four had heard the new American folk rock. Four-track recording replaced the older two-track technology. As a result, rhythm, voices, and instruments could be recorded, erased, rerecorded, and mixed separately. Putting together a song became a constructive process, not unlike creating a fine painting, layer by layer. New ideas for sounds were contributed by Paul, John, and George, and then refined by George Martin. Sometimes, Martin would propose new ideas or changes himself. It was a dynamic and collaborative creative process.

During a tour to India, George Harrison was introduced to the **sitar**. Anxious to integrate the unique sound of this instrument into rock, Harrison found the perfect opportunity in John's new song "Norwegian Wood." Thus, the experimentation with timbres new to rock (string quartet, and now sitar) continued.

Lyrics—In "The Word," John's lyrics take a turn from the usual boy-girl Beatle songs toward his emerging philosophy of love as the answer to world problems. Again, this is a hint of things to come ("All You Need Is Love"). Paul's song "Michelle" is more traditional in its lyrics, but its harmonies are more interesting. As with "Yesterday," Paul creates a fascinating melody and a sophisticated sequence of chords. The bilingual lyrics (English and French) were not without precedent in popular music, but were unusual for a rock group.

Instrumental Breaks—"In My Life" is a good song, but what is particularly interesting is the instrumental break. According to the common formula for a rock song, somewhere in the middle, there should be a brief break that features an instrumental lead—usually a guitar. But the Beatles rarely followed the usual. Instead, there is what sounds like a harpsichord solo in a polyphonic texture more closely associated with Bach than the Beatles. To create this peculiar sound, George Martin played the solo on piano, recorded at half speed and an octave lower than desired; when mixed back in at double speed, the tempo and pitch are corrected, but the timbre is altered to approximate that of a harpsichord. This extra touch of creativity is what increasingly set the Beatles apart from other rock bands of the era.

Because of the growing complexity of their recordings, it was taking the Beatles longer to create new albums than in their first years. Anxious for product, the group's American label assembled an album to fill the gap between *Rubber Soul* and *Revolver*. *Yesterday and Today* was assembled from singles and extra U.K. album tracks to cash in on the Beatles' popularity. The album nonetheless contains some important songs in the Beatles' catalog ("Nowhere Man," "Yesterday," and "Day Tripper").

The "Nowhere Man" lyrics are a social commentary, showing an awareness of the more serious, relevant lyrics of the folk and folk rock movement. The song describes the sort of person who refuses to get involved, who wanders down the middle of life's road, voicing no opinions, supporting no vital causes, and never speaking his mind. Heavier, socially oriented lyrics were to become more common in subsequent Beatle songs.

5.4.3: Revolver

The release of *Revolver* in August 1966 was coordinated with yet another tour of the United States. The Beatles arrived to find themselves in the midst of the biggest controversy yet. Back in February, John had given an interview to an English reporter, in which he said, in part,

> Christianity will go. It will vanish and shrink. I needn't argue with that; I'm right and I will be proved right. We're more popular than Jesus now: I don't know which will go first—rock 'n' roll or Christianity.
>
> — (Coleman 1984, 312)

The British public, accustomed to John's iconoclastic remarks, took the comments in stride. However, when *Datebook,* an American teen magazine, quoted the interview, there was a burst of outrage. Over 30 radio stations banned Beatles' records; there were protest marches and record-burning sessions. Brian Epstein offered the press "clarifications" and "explanations" aimed at taking the sting out of John's remarks. Epstein asserted that John was bemoaning the apparent decline of Christianity's influence, as illustrated by the regrettable fact that the Beatles were more popular than Jesus. But the pressure still mounted for an apology from John himself. Yielding to the pressure, the usually articulate John stumbled through a so-called apology at a press conference in Chicago. Gradually, the furor died away. Seemingly preferring to avoid a similar controversy, the media and the public ignored several potentially inflammatory remarks about the Vietnam War made by John during the American tour.

The 1966 tour was a success, but the Beatles were tiring of the drudgery of live performance. Although no one knew it at the time, the Beatles' appearance on August 29, 1966, at San Francisco's Candlestick Park would be the group's last live concert ever. (Although this was their final ticketed concert, the Beatles did play an impromptu concert on the rooftop of the Apple Corps headquarters to an audience of surprised passersby on January 30, 1969.) One of the problems was that the increasingly experimental nature of their recorded music made its replication in live concert virtually impossible. Another problem was that the music could barely be heard over the screaming voices of the audience.

The new album, *Revolver*, continued the trend of experimentation. The cover took the *Rubber Soul* design one step further. Again, the group's name appeared nowhere on the front. The black-and-white cover showed sketches of the four famous faces; flowing up to the top of the cover was a montage of photos of the individual Beatles. The album itself contained more Indian-influenced sounds ("Love You Too"). There was a mainstream rocker ("Got to Get You into My Life") with added trumpets and saxes and "Tomorrow Never Knows," with its tape sounds mixed in backward and at varying speeds, along with John's continuing love theme.

MATURING MUSICAL STYLE Now past the middle of the 1960s, the recordings of the Beatles began to evolve from memorably infectious, hit singles into a period of musical experimentation, pushing the boundaries of what had previously been considered appropriate territory for popular music. Moving into the late 1960s, a new path was opening before them, leading to an undeniable musical revolution.

Songs Indicating Beatles' Mature Style

Two songs stand out as further indicators of what would become the Beatles' mature style.

Eleanor Rigby—Paul's "Eleanor Rigby" carries the string quartet of "Yesterday" a step further by using a string *octet* (an ensemble of eight string players). The song's lyrics focus on two lonely persons—Eleanor Rigby and Father McKenzie—who find themselves out of life's mainstream. In many ways, this song seems to be a precursor to the subsequent *Sgt. Pepper* album. The nihilism of "Nowhere Man" is carried forward in "Eleanor Rigby" ("writing the words of a sermon that no one will hear" and similar phrases). Lines like "Eleanor Rigby puts on a face that she keeps in a jar by the door" show that Paul is not far behind John in his ability to turn the English language to his needs. "I'm Only Sleeping" includes a unique feature: Its guitar sounds are mixed in backward (a musical device to be used many times in later recordings). Yet another hint of things to come is the song "And Your Bird Can Sing," with its obtuse, surrealistic lyrics. Beatles fans quickly came to recognize these kinds of songs as the work of John Lennon.

Yellow Submarine—The other interesting song is "Yellow Submarine." Drug-oriented lyrics were creating controversies throughout the music industry. These songs were usually written with liberal use of *double entendre*: lines that had two possible interpretations, one drug oriented and the

other more innocent. When challenged, the performers could provide the straight interpretation, but to the initiated, the drug-oriented message was understood. The Beatles, although by this time into marijuana, pills, and LSD, had previously avoided this particular controversy. "Yellow subs" were a type of pill, and the lyrics described a dreamlike fantasyland. The recording included extramusical sounds, including gushing water, tinkling ice, bubbling sounds, and a military band. Heard at one level, it was what would later be called psychedelic. However, on another level, it could be heard as an amusing, childlike cartoon, much like the Beatles themselves: innocent, lovable, and cute. Double entendres and eventually overt drug references would also become a factor in the later Beatles style.

Key Songs from the Beatles' Middle Period

Yesterday
Norwegian Wood
In My Life
Nowhere Man
Got to Get You Into My Life
Eleanor Rigby
Yellow Submarine
Penny Lane
Strawberry Fields Forever

5.4.4: "Penny Lane" and "Strawberry Fields Forever"

In late 1966, the Beatles drifted in different directions. When they regrouped in December, they began work on what would be a double-sided single: "Penny Lane" and "Strawberry Fields Forever." "Penny Lane" is a nostalgic look back to Liverpool, specifically the area where the Quarry Men had begun. Paul had heard a piccolo trumpet (a small, higher-pitched trumpet, often used in Baroque music) and asked George Martin to use it in his song. Together, they worked out the familiar piccolo trumpet countermelody heard near the end of the song.

John's "Strawberry Fields Forever" was also a nostalgic look back to Liverpool—and much more. Strawberry Field was a Salvation Army home not far away from Aunt Mimi's house. But the lyrics convey more of an impression of nostalgia than anything specific. The words continue the surrealistic trend evident earlier in "And Your Bird Can Sing." Two versions of "Strawberry Fields Forever" were recorded in different tempos and in different keys: one with a heavy guitar sound and the second with the softer sound of cellos and brass. When John heard them, he liked the beginning of one and the ending of the other. A simple splice would not work because of the different tempos and keys. With considerable technical skill and almost unbelievable good luck, George Martin managed to modify the tape speeds enough to bring the two versions together. The result is a very eerie sound that, with John's stream-of-consciousness lyrics, creates a purely psychedelic impression. Further coloration was added by mixing in (backward and at varying speeds) pieces of tape with the sounds of piano runs and arpeggios. John, who was sinking more and more into an LSD-oriented lifestyle, had created (with George Martin's help) a psychedelic, musical trip.

Released in February 1967, "Penny Lane" and "Strawberry Fields Forever" both reached the Top 10 ("Penny Lane" hit number 1). The year 1967 would be pivotal not only for the Beatles but for the history of rock music. They were to experience several life-altering changes, and they would produce an album that would "put it all together," launching them into their most impressive period of musical productivity, while simultaneously revolutionizing popular music.

JOURNAL

The Beatles Make a Movie

Watch the opening scene of *A Hard Day's Night*, which consists of a re-enactment of Beatlemania as the Beatles are being chased by fans in London, though the location was filmed to look like Liverpool. Let the movie play for about 10 minutes past the opening chase scene, so that you get a sense of the personalities portrayed by each member of the Beatles. (I hope you will be inspired to watch the entire film.) Take a moment to appreciate the energy inherent in that opening scene. Can you imagine being a member of a group that generates such hysteria? How would it make you feel? Identify at least three positive aspects associated with garnering such a high level of attention. Identify at least three negative consequences of receiving that much attention. If you had a chance to be a star at this level, would you choose to take the opportunity? Why or why not?

▶ The response entered here will appear in the performance dashboard and can be viewed by your instructor.

Submit

5.5: Revolution in the Late Music of the Beatles

OBJECTIVE: Outline the important developments in the music of the Beatles during the late period

Beginning with "Yesterday" and *Rubber Soul* and culminating with "Penny Lane" and "Strawberry Fields Forever," the Beatles (with the essential creative participation of George Martin) had pushed, pulled, poked, and tugged at the outer walls of rock and roll. In 1967, they would gather all their creative forces, synthesize all the experimental bits and pieces from their middle period, and produce a classic rock album: *Sgt. Pepper's Lonely Hearts Club Band*.

5.5.1: Sgt. Pepper's Lonely Hearts Club Band

If the decade of the 1960s was the century's most interesting period (as many would argue), 1967 was that decade's most interesting year. For the Beatles, the winds of change had begun shortly before the new year. On November 9, John had attended a preview of an art exhibit opening at the Indica Gallery. Both puzzled and fascinated by the avant-garde exhibition, he was approached by a small woman dressed in black. She silently handed him a card that contained one word: *Breathe*. It was Yoko Ono whose work was being displayed.

The period also contained tragedy. Early in 1967, Brian Epstein attempted suicide. When the Beatles decided to stop touring, Brian felt that he was no longer needed. His personal life was in turmoil; two factors playing into his psychological state were the lack of societal acceptance regarding his sexual orientation and a formidable drug habit. On August 27, 1967, he finally succumbed to an apparently accidental drug overdose. Ironically, Brian Epstein was Beatlemania's creator and, at the age of 32, its first victim. But Brian had underestimated his importance to the Beatles. Without his sometimes unwanted and certainly unappreciated guidance, the Beatles' personal and corporate lives began to come unglued.

On August 4, 1967, the Beatles attended a lecture on spiritual regeneration given by an Indian guru, the Maharishi Mahesh Yogi. Fascinated by his words, they accompanied him to Bangor, North Wales, for further study. They were there when the telephone call about Brian's death reached them. In numerous documentaries about this period in the career of the Beatles, one can observe the stunned disbelief apparent on each member's face shortly after hearing the news, revealing both the high regard in which they held Epstein and the tragic loss they realized.

The Beatles and friends with Maharishi Mahesh Yogi, September 1967.
SOURCE: Daily Mail/Rex/Alamy Stock Photo

Meanwhile, the *Sgt. Pepper* album had been released on June 1, 1967, and had begun its 168-week stay on the chart. It had begun as a whimsical song (by Paul) called "Sgt. Pepper's Lonely Hearts Club Band." The idea grew to become a unifying theme for the album. As the recording begins, the Beatles actually "became" Sgt. Pepper's band, presenting a series of "acts" in a psychedelic concert atmosphere. As work progressed, George Martin and the Beatles were energized by the gradual awareness that they were creating something truly innovative and unique—a revolutionary masterpiece.

Components of the Sgt. Pepper Album

Side 1 Introducing Sgt. Pepper's Lonely Hearts Club Band—The album begins with crowd noises; the music enters, and Sgt. Pepper's band is introduced. The mix of sounds includes brass band music and crowd reactions. Next, we are introduced to Billy Shears (Ringo), who moves directly into "A Little Help from My Friends." A simple and catchy song, it contains drug-oriented double entendres and the dialogue between Billy and a Greek-like chorus.

"Lucy in the Sky with Diamonds"—"Lucy in the Sky with Diamonds" is one of the album's most interesting songs. The initials, *L, S,* and *D,* send a fairly clear signal that the song is drug related, but, as usual, an alternative explanation was offered: John said that the song was inspired by a drawing by his four-year-old son, Julian. Certainly, the lyrics evoke an LSD trip through fantasy-like images. Musically, there is a shift of meter from the triple meter of each verse to the quadruple meter of the choruses. This is a first for mainstream rock and roll; such meter changes almost destroy the song's dance-ability. Experimentation with timbre also contributes to the overall effect (e.g., the modified organ sounds near the beginning; the echoless voice at the beginning, which is then doubled only to return to solo voice, but with heavy echo).

"She's Leaving Home"—Paul's song "She's Leaving Home" draws on several earlier experiments. As with "Yesterday" and "Eleanor Rigby," the accompaniment is provided by a string ensemble, but this time adding a harp. The triple meter suppresses any potential for a frenetic rock feeling. Paul begins the story as a narrator: in the first chorus, falsetto voices comment as outsiders while voices in the normal male range play the role of parents. This pattern continues throughout the song. Internal ironies abound in several lines. Overall, the story allows a sympathetic insight into both the girl's problems and the parents' perspective. It was a common story in 1967, when thousands of teenagers ran away from home to live in communes; it was, after all, the Summer of Love.

"Being for the Benefit of Mr. Kite!"—The lyrics of John's "Being for the Benefit of Mr. Kite!" came almost directly from an old theater bill he had purchased in an antique shop. The primary musical interest in this track lies in the instrumental sections at the words "Henry ... waltz." and "Mr. Kite ... bill." both are accompanied by a dazzling blend of calliope sound effects that were cut into irregular lengths and then mixed in at different speeds—sometimes backward, sometimes distorted—all over a steady, simple waltz beat.

Side 2 "Within You Without You"—Side two of the album opens with a sitar and other Indian instruments, announcing George Harrison's song "Within You Without You." The resulting trance-like effect accompanies a philosophical discourse in the lyrics drawn from George's readings in Eastern theology. One hardly perceives a regular meter in this song, partially because of changes from quadruple to quintuple to triple meter, but also because of the irregular phrase lengths that tend to obscure the development of any strong metrical effect.

"When I'm Sixty-Four"—Seemingly incongruous crowd noises yank us out of this otherworldly experience into the totally different sound world of "When I'm Sixty-Four." For this composition, Paul has traveled back in time to evoke a musical style of the 1930s. In tribute to his dad, who had recently turned 64, Paul may have been imagining what his dad's jazz band sounded like. The square beat and symmetrical form are throwbacks to the older Pop style; the bridge sections break the symmetry and otherwise antique sound of this song. Of course, there is a bit of irony inherent in his more recent live performances of this piece, as he continues to give concerts well into his 70s.

"Good Morning, Good Morning"—A crowing cock signals the beginning of "Good Morning, Good Morning." The lyrics comment on the emptiness of the average person's life. Unlike the old-fashioned clarinet sounds of Paul's "When I'm Sixty-Four," the heavier sound of saxes provides John's accompaniment. The bridge section includes saxes playing a bass line drawn from earlier R&B-inspired rock and roll. The song ends with more barnyard noises.

The Final Track—Finally, the musical potpourri represented on this album ends with a reprise of the *Sgt. Pepper* theme, thanking us for our attention and closing out the album's story line. But we are not quite finished. With no break, we are pulled into the final track: "A Day in the Life." John begins with a tale gleaned from his habitual newspaper reading. As the meaning of the lyrics becomes disjointed, John delivers the line about him loving to turn you on. This line (referring to drugs, music, sex, or spirituality?) is followed by a building wall of sound made by some 40 musicians hired for this session. Their starting and ending points were established, and, in between, they improvised. As instruments are added and the notes climb in range, a seething, yet stationary, musical wall is erected. Suddenly near its peak, it is cut off, and Paul enters with a new section ("Woke ... bed." etc.). As he describes going to the upper deck (smoking section) of a double-decker bus, he goes into a (marijuana-induced?) dream. As his voice floats rather aimlessly on the syllable "aah," heavy echo is added, and the voice fades behind a steadily louder unison line performed by the orchestral musicians that finally takes over and moves with a transitional cadence into the next section. John returns to the same music with which the song began. Again, he ends with the line about loving to turn you on, followed by the building wall of sound. This time, however, the wall is not curtailed until it reaches its peak. A dramatic silence follows, and then a huge chord is struck; the chord is allowed to decay (diminish in loudness) until it disappears into silence after some 45 seconds.

What is the purpose of this chord? Although we are unable to say for sure, it is fun to speculate. There is no doubt that the Beatles knew they had produced a monument in rock and roll. It would have been discouraging for them to have invested over four months (and some 700 hours) of creativity into an album only to have their listeners pay casual attention to the record and, the second it ends, give it no further thought, moving right on to another record or to other activities. The ending chord of *Sgt. Pepper* does hold us up for what seems to be an interminable 45 seconds. It almost forces us to reflect. Perhaps that is the point.

Watch "A Day in the Life" by the Beatles.*
https://www.youtube.com/watch?v=usNsCeOV4GM

*By clicking this link in the Revel course, you will be redirected to a third-party site.

Sgt. Pepper was a success, both commercially and critically. Virtually every phase of the popular music industry recognized it immediately as revolutionary. Almost as important as the music itself was the album cover. Folding like a book, it was more elaborate than any previous Pop or rock album. On the front cover, in addition to the Beatles in their Sgt. Pepper costumes, there are some 60 other familiar faces (including Stu Sutcliffe's). On the back cover are the complete lyrics (another new idea for rock albums) and the four Beatles, with Paul's back to the camera (more about that later). Inserted in the album cover along with the record, listeners discovered a paper cutout sheet that included a *Sgt. Pepper* armband (a paper version of the one worn by the Beatles in the photo in the second column), a paper moustache, and other miscellaneous items. After *Sgt. Pepper,* elaborate album packaging became the norm.

The idea of unifying the entire album with one thematic concept also became widely imitated. The term **concept album** became a chic catchword in the industry. It suddenly seemed that every group was producing them (sometimes the concept was more imagined than real). Frequently, a specific theme song opened and closed these albums, as was suggested by the "Sgt. Pepper" theme and its reprise.

5.5.2: Magical Mystery Tour

The year 1967 was not yet over for the Beatles. In June, they appeared as British representatives on an international television special beamed to millions of viewers via satellite, singing "All You Need Is Love." These huge successes were followed by their first flop. Paul's idea for a film called *Magical Mystery Tour* featured the Beatles and a weird entourage of "friends" touring the British countryside in a psychedelically painted bus. Unlike their earlier experiences, it seemed that everything that could possibly go wrong went wrong. Their fans and the media surrounded them at every stop. Without a script, the film failed to develop, and the enthusiasm of the Beatles waned—but Paul persisted. After its television premiere on December 26, the film was massacred by critics, and, for once, the public agreed. The days of "the Beatles can do no wrong" were over. Insiders agreed that if Brian had still been around to shepherd his headstrong foursome, this disaster might have been averted.

Fortunately, the *Magical Mystery Tour* album was a successful follow-up to *Sgt. Pepper.* The American release contained the six songs from the movie plus other collected singles. Of particular note are "The Fool on the Hill," a simple yet beautiful ballad by Paul, and "I Am the Walrus," an eccentric song by John. In the latter, John infuses more of his masterful wordplay and surrealistic lyrical combinations, with the content based loosely on Lewis Carroll's *Through the Looking Glass.* There are orchestral instruments playing traditional sections and then sliding from one pitch to another, adding the psychedelic touch. There is a chanting chorus mixed in, various verbal interpolations, and even a reading of Shakespeare's *King Lear.*

THE BEATLES' VISIT TO INDIA   In February 1968, the Beatles announced that they were giving up drugs now that they had discovered a better way to obtain their spiritual goals. They followed the Maharishi to Rishikesh, India, for a full-fledged immersion into the guru's theology. There was fasting, chanting, mass prayer, and meditation. Slowly, the individual members grew disillusioned with the guru's teachings and left; Ringo left first, while John and George remained the longest.

The Beatles, c. 1968.

SOURCE: Pictorial Press Ltd/Alamy Stock Photo

YOKO ONO During his two months in India, John had been corresponding with Yoko Ono, the avant-garde artist whose exhibit he had seen the previous year. He was intrigued by her iconoclasm and the apparent profundity of her artworks and writings. At times, he made fun of her artsy eccentricity, but he also felt that she could lead him into intellectual and philosophical realms he had only imagined. John had previously confessed to Cynthia his innumerable infidelities. Now, he began to flaunt openly his developing relationship with Yoko Ono. The other Beatles became increasingly aware of Yoko during mid-1968. She sat beside John in the recording studio during sessions, she attended their business lunches and meetings, and she seemed to the other members omnipresent and intrusive. Their resentment grew as they realized that Yoko was not simply John's latest fling but a permanent addition to the Beatles' family.

The public became aware of Yoko Ono's relationship with John in June 1968 and was even less amused than the other Beatles. Almost wherever they went, John and Yoko were greeted with catcalls and racial slurs; hate mail arrived regularly. For years, Cynthia had endured John's sharp tongue, endless touring, LSD trips, inability to handle liquor, and persistent infidelity. To the utter amazement of all, John sued Cynthia for divorce on the grounds of adultery. Flabbergasted and hurt, Cynthia countersued on the same grounds. John and his lawyers righteously denied the charges, until it became obvious that Yoko was pregnant, weakening their argument considerably. Cynthia was granted a divorce in November 1968 and retained custody of their son, Julian.

5.5.3: The Beatles (the White Album)

The most important Beatles album to come out in 1968 was simply titled *The Beatles*. It has become known as the "White Album" because its cover is completely white and devoid of any print or graphics, except on the spine, and a number on the front cover representing the order of production. Having launched an explosion of garish, elaborate album art with *Sgt. Pepper*, the Beatles went to the opposite extreme with the ultimate in plain simplicity.

Characteristics of the White Album

As the Beatles continued to innovate during their late period, eclecticism in a wide variety of styles was evident in their recordings. Many of these will be detailed in the Musical Close-Up later in the chapter.

The Extreme Eclecticism of the Music—The White Album was a double album (previously rare in Pop, except for special collections) and contained 30 songs. Beatles' fans consider it either the group's best or worst album. The controversy arises from the extreme eclecticism of the music; although the reason was not apparent at the time, it has since become obvious that the White Album was not so much the work of one group but of four individuals, each of whom was heading in a different musical direction. In retrospect, the album seems to telegraph the message that the breakup of the Beatles was imminent. The sessions that produced *The Beatles* were characterized by tension, bickering, resentment, and egocentricity. John's songs were harsh, eccentric, avant-garde, and purposely noncommercial. Paul's contributions seemed (at least to John) sentimental, bland, and overly commercial. George added four songs to the White Album, but tried to stay out of the escalating Lennon-McCartney tug-of-war. Ringo, musically the most conservative of the group, seemed beaten down by the battles; he even resigned, leaving the sessions for several weeks before being talked into returning. These problems would have been enough to doom the average rock group's album. But the White Album somehow managed to emerge as a success musically and commercially. It reached number 1 on the album chart and held that position for nine weeks (144 weeks in the Top 200).

Tribute to the Musical Predecessors—There may be a secondary, more subtle reason for the extreme variety of style on the White Album. Jan Wenner, in *Rolling Stone* magazine, said, "*The Beatles* is the history and synthesis of Western music" (Schaffner 1977, 113). Although that might be an overstatement, it nonetheless contains an element of truth. Throughout the White Album, there are musical and verbal references to a wide variety of pre-existing musicians and styles, each of which had contributed to the musical fabric from which the Beatles had grown. Whether it was consciously done or not, the White Album seems to pay tribute to the Beatles' musical predecessors … to the many influences that had to have come first before there could be a "Beatles." Their tributes are genuine and authentic. However, it is hard to imagine that the White Album's songs were performed by the same group, much less included on the same album. This is the exact opposite of the concept album trend they themselves had begun just one year earlier with *Sgt. Pepper*.

VARYING STYLES OF THE WHITE ALBUM "Back in the U.S.S.R." is a straight-ahead rock song. The overall concept derives from Chuck Berry's "Back in the U.S.A." At the bridge, the Beatles pay a musical and verbal tribute to the Beach Boys. The historic connection of Berry and the Beach Boys is particularly appropriate (recall "Surfin' U.S.A." and "Sweet Little Sixteen," the song upon which the former was based).

Different Musical Styles Used in the White Album

The White Album is a perfect example of the eclecticism evident in the Beatles' late recordings. In fact, on first hearing, it is difficult, if not impossible, to predict the style of the next track at any given moment.

12-Bar Blues—While some British bands were basing their entire approach on the 12-bar blues form, the Beatles rarely featured it. Nonetheless, the White Album contains three 12-bar blues: "Yer Blues," "Birthday," and "Why Don't We Do It in the Road?" This last song is just about as basic as a 12-bar blues can be. The harmonies are pounded out on the piano, and the lyrics are shouted in true R&B tradition. Whereas we might have expected the Beatles to produce a sophisticated, modified interpretation of the blues, instead we get Paul's raw, authentic performance.

The Old Pop Style—Picking up where he left off with "When I'm Sixty-Four," Paul creates a replica of the old Pop style of the 1920s in "Honey Pie." Imitating the sound of a scratchy 78-rpm record, Paul begins with a verse section without a regular beat. The verse sets the scene for the chorus, which is accompanied by a regular quadruple beat. The instrumental backing is a perfect representation of pre-swing era bands, with their emphasis on the clarinet ensemble. Again, the form, melody, harmony, and timbre combine to recreate the earlier style with impressive authenticity.

The Folk Ballad Style—"Rocky Raccoon" is a humorous narrative that seems to poke gentle fun at the folk ballad style. Paul is accompanied by acoustic guitar and harmonica, bringing to mind the sound of pre-1965 Bob Dylan. Paul even allows his voice to slump off pitch, especially at the end of phrases, a trait of Dylan's vocal style (listen, for example, to the line about booking a room in the local saloon. "Rocky" pays good-natured tribute to Dylan, albeit tongue-in-cheek.

The Lennon-Style—John's "Happiness Is a Warm Gun" begins with typical Lennon-style surrealistic lyrics, but midway through the song, the music turns to a late 1950s doo-wop style, complete with I-vi-IV-V progression, doo-wop background nonsense syllables, and vocal falsetto. In "Julia," John writes a beautiful, sentimental song in loving memory of his mother. He refers to the Maharishi in "Sexy Sadie," with lyrics directly critical of the guru, although John thought better of specifically naming him and substituted the new title; note how "Marharishi" and "Sexy Sadie" contain the same number of syllables. Paul's "Blackbird" provides hints about his views of the shaky status of the group and suggests his own ambitions ("fly away").

The Miscellaneous Styles—If the varying styles of other White Album cuts seem surprising, John's "Revolution 9" provides a true shock to the system. It offers over eight minutes of miscellaneous sounds welded into a musical montage. There are bits and pieces of various conversations, musical segments played backward and forward, and sound effects at various speeds. Intermittently, a voice clearly enunciates "number 9, number 9, number 9." There is hysterical laughter, radio distortion, and some moaning and heavy breathing, sped up to sound like the gurgling sounds of a baby. The other Beatles and George Martin pleaded with John not to include the song on the album, but his determination was unwavering. Although the piece may have mystified Beatles fans, it was nothing new to the classical avant-garde. Composer John Cage had worked for years with musical montages of this type. His *Variations IV* is actually quite similar to "Revolution 9," except that Lennon added the rather attractive unifying "theme" of the recurring "number 9." John and Yoko both knew and admired Cage's work, so, in that sense, "Revolution 9" fits in nicely with the other works on the album that authentically reflect the work of other musical predecessors and contemporaries. John's obsession with the number 9 derived from his belief that the number had been an uncanny part of almost every significant aspect of his life.

The Early Beatles Style—After the cacophony of "Revolution 9," we are transported into the Pop world of the early 1950s with John's "Good Night" (sung by Ringo). It is a perfectly authentic representation of this earlier style, including the lush orchestral accompaniment, the background choir, the lyrical melody, the beautiful harmonies, and the subdued rhythms. This performance does not seem to have been intended as a parody, but as an authentic rendering of another musical predecessor of the Beatles.

5.5.4: Apple Corps Ltd.

The White Album was released on the Apple Records label, part of the Beatles' new company, Apple Corps Ltd., designed to allow them to dabble in music, film, and other artistic ventures. Not the least of the new organization's components was the Apple Foundation for the Arts, an agency that would provide money and other resources for struggling, unknown artists in all fields. But the Apple Foundation was soon submerged in a sea of tapes, musical manuscripts, novels, paintings, plays, and so on. Though a nice concept, it was highly impractical.

That music can have a remarkable effect on human behavior is a fact that has been known for centuries. A regrettable example arose in mid-1969, when Charles Manson led his communal "family" on a bloody spree that resulted in the gruesome murder of actress Sharon Tate and others. Manson viewed the Beatles as prophets, and his interpretation of "Helter Skelter," "Blackbird," "Revolution 9," and "Piggies" convinced him that his heroes were instructing him to commit bloody atrocities on wealthy white society. The scenes of his crimes were adorned with titles of Beatles' songs written in the blood of his victims. As Brian Epstein had learned earlier, and John Lennon's death would exemplify later, Beatlemania had its darker side.

Apple Records' first single release proved to be the Beatles' biggest seller of all time: "Hey Jude" backed with "Revolution" (not the same as "Revolution 9"). "Hey Jude" (number 1 for nine weeks) was slightly over seven minutes long—nearly three times the length of a typical Top 40 song. Beginning only with Paul's piano and vocal, the song builds steadily by adding vocal and instrumental accompaniment. Once the peak level is reached, it generates even greater impact by constant repetition; the fade-out lasts some four minutes. With "Revolution," John attempted to clarify his role within the youth revolution: He agreed that the world needed change, but he felt that a line should be drawn short of destructive revolution. The song naturally created controversy. To the more radical youth, it sounded like a sellout—a namby-pamby revolutionist who espoused the cause only to the extent that it remained comfortable. However, to most, it seemed a responsible statement of the ideal of constructive change. John and Yoko's philosophy of nonviolence would become a primary theme for them in the years to come.

OTHER BEATLES PRODUCTIONS Several other Beatles productions occurred in 1968, including a cartoon feature film (*Yellow Submarine*) and albums by George (*Wonderwall Music*) and John and Yoko (*Two Virgins*). There were few bright spots for the Beatles in 1969. One single, "Get Back," proved successful, rising to number 1 in the spring, but tensions had developed over their management problem. After Brian's death, the Beatles had tried to manage their empire on their own, but the situation devolved quickly into a chaotic disaster. John wanted New Yorker Allen Klein to become the Beatles' new manager. Klein had managed numerous rock acts, including the Rolling Stones. Paul advocated hiring Lee Eastman, father of his new bride, Linda Eastman McCartney. George and Ringo lined up with John, possibly fearing the consequences of a McCartney-Eastman arrangement. Klein became the new manager and began to put Apple's house in order, but the inherent problems were overwhelming, and the inevitable end was not far off.

After Paul and Linda's high-society wedding and John and Yoko's marriage, both occurring in March, fans were beginning to wonder whether there would ever be another Beatles album. John and Yoko seemed to be drifting further into eccentricity. They spent their honeymoon in the Amsterdam Hilton with some 50 reporters in attendance. They stayed in bed for a week, growing their hair for peace. In April, the couple held another "happening." This time, they concealed themselves under a bag on top of a table. This posture, said John, promoted honest communication and would encourage world peace.

5.5.5: Abbey Road

In the beginning of 1969, recognizing the fragmenting priorities of the group's members, Paul began urging them to return to their roots by performing live. Various ideas were bandied about, including making a live appearance in India. Paul also was anxious to have the Beatles create a new film. They finally decided to attempt to film the process of making an album, and sessions were begun in a large studio in London. However, the early morning hours and the cold space—plus the growing animosity between the Beatles themselves—led to hours of tape with little finished music. Discouraged, the group decided to shelve this project, temporarily at least. (Later, this material would form the basis for the film and record *Let It Be*.)

The best thing to come from the Beatles in 1969 was the *Abbey Road* album. This album continued the level of excellence achieved by *Sgt. Pepper* and *The Beatles*. The album title refers to EMI's Abbey Road studios, where the Beatles had been recording throughout most of their career. Even as the group was disintegrating, they managed to "Come Together" (the album's opening song) one more time, literally and musically. Even though each Beatle contributed individual songs, the entire group played and sang on almost every track.

Interesting Feature of Abbey Road

There are a number of aspects of this 1969 album that are noteworthy. The members of the Beatles and their collective creative processes continued to evolve innovatively.

George's Emergence as a First-Rate Songwriter—Perhaps the most interesting feature is George's emergence as a first-rate songwriter. His contributions to the White Album had shown considerable promise, but with "Something" and "Here Comes the Sun," Harrison achieved qualitative, if not quantitative, equality with Lennon and McCartney. "Something," with its clever harmonic progressions (especially its instantly recognizable cadence) and double-time metrical shifts, has become a standard. Similarly, "Here Comes the Sun" contains effective shifting accents in the chorus and changing meters in the instrumental break. These two are among *Abbey Road*'s most attractive songs.

John's Two Opposite Musical Directions at the Same Time—John was going in two opposite musical directions at the same time. There were the avant-garde experiments with Yoko Ono, but there were also genuine rock songs in which he seemed to be going back to basics. "Come Together," for example, is a throwback to basic rock and roll (although the lyrics are typical Lennon). "I Want You (She's So Heavy)" is a more modern example of the harder mainstream rock of the late 1960s. Almost eight minutes long, "I Want You" builds up to a powerful ending, with a unison instrumental riff in the midst of electronic distortion.

Paul's Slow Rock Song—Paul's "Oh! Darling" is a slow rock song, in which the lyrics are screamed by the usually more lyrical Paul. It is also a throwback to earlier rock, complete with 1950s bass lines and chord progressions. "Because" is an effective song, using jazz-like vocal harmonies in which the Beatles' voices unite in a sophisticated blend. Harpsichord adds color to the accompaniment to create a beautifully delicate texture.

> **Conclusion with a Series of Songs Unified into a Set**—The album concludes with a series of songs unified into a set. Lyrics and instrumental fragments unite the songs, which otherwise display considerable variety. Beginning with Paul's "You Never Give Me Your Money," the set moves to "Sun King" by John. Almost a variation of George's "Here Comes the Sun," this song recalls the sophisticated harmonies and textures of "Because." "Golden Slumbers" alternates with "Carry That Weight," a rock riff that leads to a strong example of the Beatles' guitar work. The beautiful and majestic "The End" closes the album on the recurring Beatles' theme of love.

Abbey Road was the Beatles biggest-selling album, holding the number 1 position for 11 weeks. Subsequent albums consist of reissues, unreleased songs, or specially recorded single tracks. Never again would the Beatles gather for the purpose of recording an entire album.

Songs from the Beatles' Late Period

Lucy in the Sky with Diamonds
Being for the Benefit of Mr. Kite
Good Morning, Good Morning
A Day in the Life
Revolution (single version)
Back in the U.S.S.R.
Yer Blues
Revolution 9
Come Together
Hey Jude

5.5.6: The "Death" of Paul and the Breakup of the Beatles

As the 1970s approached, the Beatles as a group were on their last leg. While the music they produced continued to be creative, the personality clashes and differing musical trajectories reached a breaking point. The dissolution of one of the greatest rock bands in history was imminent.

5.5.7: After the Beatles

The four Beatles continued to produce music individually after the group disbanded formally in 1970.

Over a quarter of a century after the Beatles disbanded, their recordings continued to sell. *Live at the BBC*, featuring 56 performances from the early 1960s, reached number 3 on the album chart in 1994. *Anthology 1*, *Anthology 2*, and *Anthology 3* were released from 1995 to 1996, and all reached the number 1 position. "Free as a Bird" and "Real Love" were new songs based on two John Lennon demos from the late 1970s. "Real Love" reached number 11 and became the

---

End of the Beatles

After an incomparably successful musical career that was initiated by Beatlemania and followed by recordings that significantly expanded the boundaries of rock and roll, The Beatles, as a band, were coming to an end.

The "Paul is Dead" Hoax—Near the end of 1969, the famous "Paul is dead" hoax became an international rage. Charles Manson was not the only person who carefully studied Beatles' lyrics, music, and album covers for hidden meanings. Especially with Lennon's enigmatic lyrics, dedicated fans began to analyze every line for the "real" message. Fans found hidden messages in "Strawberry Fields Forever" ("I buried Paul") and backward messages in "Revolution 9," and between "I'm So Tired" and "Blackbird" ("Paul is dead, man … miss him; miss him"; Schaffner 1977, 127). The inclusion of backward messages (*backmasking*) on records was not a hoax, and indeed, if one listens to these spots, the suspected messages do seem to be present, though not necessarily intentional.

The Paul is dead hoax spread like wildfire. Assiduous Beatles' fans discovered numerous clues to confirm their suspicions. The theory developed that Paul had been killed in an automobile accident in 1966 (when the Beatles stopped touring) and that the first hints had appeared in *Sgt. Pepper* (e.g., Paul's armband on the inside cover reads "O.P.D." (Officially Pronounced Dead, the British version of DOA: Dead On Arrival). Reinforcing clues were found on *Magical Mystery Tour*, the White Album, and *Abbey Road*. The personal appearances of Paul McCartney did little to lessen the convictions of the believers. They were convinced that an impostor had taken his place. As of this writing, it appears to be a safe conclusion that the rumors of Paul's death were greatly exaggerated. (In 1993, he released an album titled *Paul Is Live* and has continued a prolific post-Beatles career, touring well into his 70s.)

Independent Work by Each Member—The death of the Beatles as a group was no hoax, however. In the summer of 1969, John and Yoko released a single called "Give Peace a Chance." The record was credited to the Plastic Ono Band, which was simply a group gathered hastily for this recording. In September, John and Yoko traveled to Toronto for a rock revival concert. John's real musical and spiritual life was now outside the Beatles. By 1970, it was clear that the Beatles were each going separate ways. In January, John and Yoko released an album from their Toronto concert. In May, Ringo released a solo album (*Sentimental Journey*), as did Paul (*McCartney*). George quietly joined Eric Clapton's band on tour and prepared his own solo album, *All Things Must Pass*, to be released in December.

Announcement of Paul's Withdrawal—Paul's album included a "press interview" that, in effect, indicated that Paul was withdrawing from the Beatles. John, having agreed months earlier to keep his own plans to resign private, was furious with Paul for making such a public declaration.

Let It Be—In April 1970, the Beatles' film *Let It Be* was released, along with an accompanying album. It consisted of tracks recorded a year earlier. The four Beatles were no longer interested in the *Let It Be* album project, so producer Phil Spector was hired to sift through the various tracks and edit and remix them. Spector added strings, chorus, and layers of sound to the basic Beatles songs. His production work seems overdone when compared to the more refined and understated albums previously released by the Beatles. The album does contain an earlier Beatles' single "Get Back," which is a good basic mainstream rock tune, and, of course, there is the title song, which, in many ways, sums up the Fab Four's attitude … not only toward the album, but also toward the group's demise. Perhaps it was also the best advice to offer to their many distraught fans: Let it be.

Life of the Members After the Breakup of the Beatles

Though none of the Beatles attained the level of success in solo careers that they experienced together, they each made a significant mark on their own during the post-Beatles years.

George Harrison—George Harrison's *All Things Must Pass* was a boxed triple album and contained the single hit "My Sweet Lord," a song with such similarities to "He's So Fine" by the Chiffons (1963) that it resulted in a lawsuit. In 1971, he sponsored a benefit concert to raise money for victims of the Pakistani civil war; appearing with him were Ringo, Eric Clapton, Bob Dylan, and others. George continued to produce albums reflecting his Indian theology and musical style. In the late 1980s, he also performed as part of super-group playfully called the Traveling Wilburys, consisting of Jeff Lynne (Electric Light Orchestra), Tom Petty, Roy Orbison, and Bob Dylan. Tragically, Harrison died of cancer in 2001.

Ringo—Ringo followed *Sentimental Journey* with a country-oriented album called *Beaucoup of Blues*. He stayed with a gentle, uncomplicated style of rock in subsequent albums, and, in the early 1970s, had several hit singles ("Photograph" and "You're Sixteen"). Unlike John, Ringo strove for commercial success and uncontroversial popularity; unlike George, he was not selling any heavy theological messages or trying to save the world; unlike Paul, he preferred simple, uncomplicated music to sophisticated experimentation. Ringo's touring continues at the time of this publication.

Paul McCartney—Paul McCartney emerged as the most commercially successful ex-Beatle. With Linda McCartney, he formed Wings and produced several albums that were huge musical and commercial successes (e.g., *Ram* in 1971 and *Band on the Run* in 1973). Beginning with *Red Rose Speedway* (1973), he produced five consecutive number 1 albums. *Tug of War* (1982) included a hit single "Ebony and Ivory," sung with Stevie Wonder, and his next album, *Pipes of Peace* (1983), included "Say, Say, Say," sung with Michael Jackson. His movie *Give My Regards to Broad Street* was a reasonable success. By the 1990s, Sir Paul McCartney had become an elder statesman of music. Among other things, he turned his energies to large-scale, pop-rock-classical efforts such as *Standing Stone* (1991). He continued to release recordings into the new millennium.

John Lennon—For John Lennon, the 1970s were difficult times. He and Yoko moved to the United States in 1971. For a while they involved themselves in politics and a variety of social causes. When their visas expired, they began a four-year battle to avoid deportation. Although prior drug arrests were cited as the cause for deportation, there is reason to suspect that the couple's outspoken support of controversial socio-political causes angered the authorities. From 1973 to 1975, they were separated, with John moving to Los Angeles. Life began to improve after his return to New York. In late 1975, John and Yoko's first child, Sean, was born—on John's birthday. Sean himself went on to become a musician, releasing recordings and touring with his own bands.

In spite of all the personal difficulties, John had some success in his solo career. His *Imagine* album (1971) was a huge success, as was the hit single of the same name. Subsequent albums in the early 1970s also reached the Top 10, but, in 1976, he retired from the music business to become a full-time husband and father. It was not until the autumn of 1980 that he and Yoko returned to the studio to cut an album of songs that would reflect the new John Lennon. There were no drugs and no alcohol at the sessions. The songs spoke of family relationships, clean living, and a very simple kind of love. The resulting album, *Double Fantasy*, pointed toward a new direction in rock music. But events were to leave that new direction undeveloped. In December 1980, John was shot by Mark David Chapman, a Beatles' fan since the early days. Incomprehensibly, he murdered John not long after obtaining his autograph.

Beatles' 23rd gold single (the most of any group to that point). In 2000, the Beatles had sold over 113 million albums, more than any previous recording artists. An anthology of the band's number 1 hits (appropriately entitled *1*) became their 19th number 1 album; by 2011, this album had sold over 11 million copies, with *The Beatles*, their top-selling album, rising to 19 million units sold. Their 2011 arrangement to allow their catalog to be sold as digital downloads through iTunes made their recordings even more readily available to a new generation of listeners. One can only wonder when, or *if*, Beatlemania will ever end.

5.6: Musical Close-Up on the Technical Side of the Beatles Music

OBJECTIVE: Describe the Beatles' musical innovations

Before 1966, everyone knew what rock and roll was: simple, enjoyable music that was loud and usually fast with a strong 4/4 beat (and backbeat); it had silly words, simple melodies, and three-chord harmonies; the songs lasted for about two and a half minutes, and the song forms contained lots of repetition. Many songs still fit the old model, but, by the last half of 1967, the boundaries had been pushed back. By the end of the 1960s, there were basically no limits to what a rock band could do, assuming they were creative and talented enough. Although others contributed to this revolution, primary impetus emerged from the music of the Beatles. Certainly, their early songs revealed moments of creativity, but it was 1965's "Yesterday" that began a revolution within rock and roll that would leave no parameter of rock music untouched.

5.6.1: Rhythm and Meter

If there were one fundamental element of early rock and roll (other than the 12-bar blues form), it was the beat. Rock's rhythmic underpinnings were its insistent quadruple meter, the moderate-to-fast tempos, the heavy backbeat, and the duple division of each beat. Slower tempos and triple subdivision of the beat were typically reserved for soft rock styles. The Beatles challenged these conventions and freed rock and roll from the tyranny of quadruple (4/4) meter.

Finally, the Beatles even challenged the concepts that "real" rock and roll should have a moderate-to-fast tempo and that soft rock should have a slower tempo. "Come Together" moves at about 80 beats per minute (bpm); that is, just slightly faster than Presley's "Are You Lonesome Tonight" (75 bpm), yet it can hardly be considered a soft rock ballad. Paul begins "Golden Slumbers" in a soft rock

The Beatles' Experiments with Rhythm and Meter

Some of the specific rhythmic and metrical innovations evident in recordings by the Beatles are discussed here. Though their level of creativity continued to evolve impressively throughout their time as a band, they were already including unexpected musical manipulations in some of their early work.

> "Say want re   well   know   world"
> | ↓ ↓ ↓ | ↓ | ↓ | ↓ | | ↓ |
> | 1 - 2 - 3 - 4 | 1 - 2 - 3 - 4 | 1 - 2 | 1 - 2 - 3 - 4 | 1 - 2 - 3 - 4 | 1 |

Musical Notation #1: "Revolution"

One of the least disruptive metrical changes in a 4/4 song results from adding a single measure of 2/4. A quadruple (4/4) measure is basically a combination of two duple measures (2/4); adding an extra pair of beats does not disrupt the alternating flow of strong and weak beats. Listen to "Revolution" from the White Album. The song is basically in 4/4 meter, but there is a 2/4 measure inserted in the first two phrases. Beginning on the second word of the song ("say"), you can follow along by counting two measures of 4/4 (eight beats), then two extra beats, and then resume counting two measures of 4/4 (eight more beats). You should land on beat one on the word "world."

Another example of a 2/4 measure inserted into a 4/4 song is "Golden Slumbers" (*Abbey Road*). After counting seven measures of 4/4 (beginning on the words "Once, there was a way"), insert one 2/4 measure before returning to 4/4, and everything works out fine.

Click or tap the play button in the Revel course to watch musical notation #1: "Revolution."

$$| \frac{3}{4} | \frac{4}{4} \vdash\!\!-\!\!-\!\!-\!\!\dashv | \frac{6}{4} \vdash\!\!-\!\!\dashv | \frac{4}{4} | \frac{6}{4} |$$

Musical Notation #2: "Blackbird"

Triple meter (3/4 time) is more typically associated with the waltz than with rock and roll. But in "Lucy in the Sky with Diamonds," each verse is in 3/4. One measure before the entrance of each chorus, there are four strong beats on the tom-toms played by Ringo, signaling the change to 4/4 meter. As the song alternates verse and chorus, the meter alternates from triple to quadruple and vice versa. "She's Leaving Home" is in triple meter throughout. In some songs, the Beatles toss in one or more measures of triple meter. In "Back in the U.S.S.R.," on the second time through the opening section, the meter shifts to 3/4 for two measures at the words "back ... U.S." (Alternatively, one could hear these measures as continuing in quadruple meter, with an extra duple measure added on the words "U.S.S.R.") "Blackbird" begins with a guitar introduction of seven beats (a measure of triple and a measure of quadruple). The verse follows the metrical structure as shown in the musical notation #2 on the previous page.

The chorus also moves between measures of three, four, and six beats.

Click or tap the play button in the Revel course to watch musical notation #2: "Blackbird."

Musical Notation #3: "All You Need is Love"

In the "love, love, love" opening of "All You Need Is Love," quadruple and triple meters are alternated. The verse follows the metric scheme shown in the image above.

Click or tap the play button in the Revel course to watch musical notation #3: "All You Need is Love."

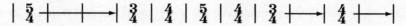

Musical Notation #4: "Good Morning, Good Morning"

The Beatles occasionally experimented with five beats per measure. The introduction to "Good Morning, Good Morning" is in 4/4, but as the verse begins ("nothing to do to save his life"), the meter switches to quintuple (5/4). After three quintuple measures, there is a measure of 3/4 followed by a measure of 4/4. The verse continues to shift between triple, quadruple, and quintuple meters before the chorus settles into a more normal 4/4.

Click or tap the play button in the Revel course to watch musical notation #4: "Good Morning, Good Morning."

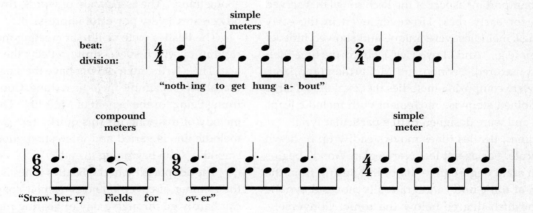

Musical Notation #5: "Strawberry Fields"

"Strawberry Fields Forever" introduces still another metrical shift. In simple meters (e.g., 4/4 and 2/4), there are two eighth notes per beat (duple subdivision). But there is another metrical structure called *compound meter*, in which there are three eighth notes per beat (triple subdivision). If the eighth notes are of equal duration in both cases, the beat in compound meter is slower because each beat must accommodate three eighth notes instead of two. As an example, study the above diagram of the rhythmic structure of five measures from "Strawberry Fields Forever."

Notice that if the eighth-note divisions move at a steady pace the beat gets further apart (slower). In the section where John sings "living ... closed." the melody includes three notes put into the space of two beats (where four eighth notes normally go), confusing the metrical feeling even more.

Musical Notation #6: "A Day in the Life"

Accenting notes irregularly also confuses the perception of meter. In the middle section of "A Day in the Life," listen to the piano after Paul sings about dragging a comb across his head. Each beat is divided neatly into four equal parts (called 16th notes, or quadruple subdivision). But the accents fall almost anywhere but on the beat as shown in musical notation #6 on the previous page.

When songs have three or five beats per measure, accents are irregular, and the speed of the beat is shifting; in such musical compositions, the standard rock and roll backbeat is nullified. Although most Beatles tunes retain the rock backbeat, some do not. In John's "Give Peace a Chance," not only is the backbeat not present, but the first and third beats are heavily accented—just the opposite of the rock backbeat.

Click or tap the play button in the Revel course to watch musical notation #6: "A Day in the Life."

style with the tempo about 80 bpm. Gradually, Paul's voice hardens, and we move imperceptibly into "Carry That Weight"—certainly not a soft rock song, but still at the same tempo. For the best example, consider the coda of "I Want You (She's So Heavy)." Using compound meter, the beat slows to about 45 bpm, much slower than Elvis's "Love Me Tender" (72 bpm), but no one has ever called "I Want You" soft rock. In fact, one author even suggested that it could be considered an early example of heavy metal (Schaffner 1977, 125).

5.6.2: Melody

Prior to the Beatles, mainstream rock melodies were generally repetitive and rather unimaginative. Melody had not been an important aspect of the R&B songs that served as models for early rock. However, even in the early Beatles songs, melodies were unique and showed hints of melodic flair (e.g., "And I Love Her"), but by the time their talents had matured, Lennon and McCartney (and later, Harrison) were composing melodies that exploited a large range, combined stepwise movement with melodic leaps effectively, and were designed to fit a particular lyric.

Sometimes, Beatles tunes move steadily up or down an entire scale. For example, "Norwegian Wood" begins on the fifth **scale degree** (five diatonic notes up from the **key center**, or **tonic note**) and gradually moves down the scale to the fifth degree below the tonic. Conversely, "Yesterday" begins on the first and second scale degrees and then moves up the scale to the tonic note an octave higher, before beginning a gradual descent back down the scale:

Other tunes are less scalar; they move by small leaps to outline chords. For example, "Got to Get You into My Life" begins by outlining the notes of the **tonic chord** (scale degrees 1, 3, and 5). The melody moves through scale degrees 5–3–3–3–1–5– 5–5–3–3–3–(4)–3–(2)–1, before ending with a large leap from 2 to 8.

The appeal of many Beatles tunes cannot be fully explained through technical analysis. Some writers simply have an instinctive feel for creating catchy melodies that stay in our minds. The melodies for "Hey Jude" and "Yellow Submarine" are not particularly sophisticated; they are simple enough to be remembered and sung by the average listener, but different enough to be distinguishable from other songs. The same can be said for the beautifully lyrical melodies of "Yesterday," "Michelle," and "Something." The association of words, rhythms, and melody creates a very powerful impression.

The Beatles were skillful at creating melodic lines, the rhythm of which successfully reflects the prosody of the text. Their lyrics often did not have the singsong regularity that allows for simple melodic writing. Consider the words from "Being for the Benefit of Mr. Kite!" The rhythm in the melody of this song fits this quirky text perfectly, and the melodic line is varied and interesting enough to carry us smoothly from beginning to end.

The adaptability of the Beatles tunes is exemplified by the number of cover versions of their songs. Indeed, one can hardly go through a day of hearing piped-in music in grocery stores, doctor's offices, shopping malls, and elevators without hearing "Eleanor Rigby," "Let It Be," "Hey Jude," and others being played by a million and one strings.

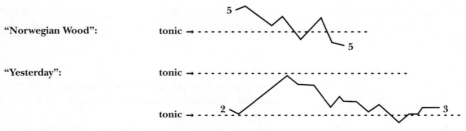

Musical Notation #7: "Norwegian Wood" & "Yesterday"

BECOME AN ACTIVE LISTENER: CHANGING TEMPOS AND METERS

One of the most fundamental aspects of rock music is the beat, and most songs establish a beat and keep it consistent for the duration of the songs. As you have seen from the examples above, the Beatles found ways to alter the meters and tempos within a song that was very uncommon in popular music of the era. This Active Listener module challenges you to identify some of these same changes in music with which you are familiar. Just a word of warning … this may take some time and effort, because these changes are quite infrequent … this sense of variety and innovation is one of the many reasons that the Beatles' music remains so prominent and fresh-sounding even today.

Find examples in the music you enjoy that feature:
1. 4/4 meter with the addition of a single measure of 2/4, as in "Revolution"

2. Changes in meter, like "Strawberry Fields Forever"

3. Changes in tempo, like "Golden Slumbers"

4. A slow tempo but hard rock style

5.6.3: Harmony and Tonality

With the possible exception of the Beach Boys, hit songs displayed little significant creativity in harmonic or tonal aspects of rock music prior to the Beatles. There had been hundreds of 12-bar blues and an almost equal number of I-vi-IV-V progressions. Melodies and chords were drawn almost exclusively from the major or blues scales. Once a song was determined to be in a certain key, the chords stayed close to just that limited collection of notes. The technical term for this practice is *diatonic*—that is, adhering to the notes of a given scale. The opposite of diatonic is *chromatic*—using notes outside of the prevailing scale. For rock's first 10 years, diatonic harmonies prevailed, but the Beatles did not want to sound like everyone else. With very few exceptions, they avoided the 12-bar blues and the I-vi-IV-V formulas. Their refusal to fall into the easy acceptance of rock clichés led them into some interesting harmonic territory.

Even early Beatles' songs feature chord progressions that are surprising. "I Saw Her Standing There" begins normally enough, but after the words "so how could I dance with another," there are falsetto voices on "oh." The chord at this moment is a **major triad**, the root of which is the lowered sixth scale degree. This chord is found in neither the major nor blues scales. It is a flat sixth chord (notated as ♭VI) and is a chromatic harmony, meaning a chord consisting of one or more note(s) outside of the scale.

"Penny Lane" uses this same chord situated in a sophisticated harmonic progression. The song begins as if it will be a I-vi-IV-V progression. In "Penny Lane," there is a barber showing photographs: I-vi-IV-V. Then, the harmonic motion goes in a different direction. The second phrase begins with I and vi and then moves to a minor chord on tonic (the song is in a major key, so the I chord *should* be major). The bass line then moves to the sixth scale degree, but instead of the diatonic vi chord, we get a chromatic chord on vi (technically, trained musicians call it a half-diminished seventh chord). Next, the bass line descends one-half step to ♭VI. Finally, the bass line moves down to the fifth scale degree, harmonized diatonically as V, and the verse is repeated.

The middle section of "Penny Lane" moves to a new tonal center on ♭VII. This is rather adventurous harmonically for a Pop-oriented rock song.

The use of chromatic chords is one reason the Beatles' music sounded different. In "Back in the U.S.S.R.," the verse moves from the tonic chord (I) to the IV chord, but, then, to harmonize a *blue third* (lowered third scale degree), the Beatles build a major triad, using the blue note as the root of the chord. This same chord (♭III) is used in the middle section of "Birthday." There, the chord alternates with ♭VII so persistently that the song seems to change keys.

Over the centuries, a tradition of common chord progressions has evolved. Many Beatles songs depart from these traditions.

Sometimes, it is difficult to determine the key in a Beatles song (see "Being for the Benefit of Mr. Kite!"). Even in an early song like "Can't Buy Me Love," the introduction and choruses are in a major key, but the verses, which comprise an inserted 12-bar blues, lie in a minor key. Similarly, "Come Together," which is basically in minor throughout, turns to major on the words "come together." Another song that contains some tonal ambiguity is "She Loves You." Although this song is basically in G major, there is considerable emphasis on E minor, a closely related key because it shares the same **key signature**. The song begins on an E minor chord, and there is an important cadence on E minor at the words "and you know that can't be bad." The final cadence of each verse is also interesting because it moves from a minor iv chord (a chromatic chord built on the fourth note of the scale, but a minor triad rather than major) to the diatonic V chord.

Beatles Songs Representing Chromatic Chords and Nontraditional Progressions

The following examples represent three Beatles songs that include chromatic chords (indicated by an asterisk) and nontraditional progressions (indicated by a bracket). Also, when you see a Roman numeral with a flat or a sharp (♭ or #) in front of it, the chord is a chromatic chord:

$$| \text{ ii } | \text{ ii } | \overset{*}{♭\textbf{VII}} | \overset{*}{♭\textbf{VII}} | \text{v}^7 | \text{v}^7 | \text{ I } | \text{ I } \|$$

$$| \text{ I } | \text{ I } | \text{ iii } | \text{ iii } | \text{ vi } | \text{ vi } | \text{IV } \overset{*}{♭\textbf{VII}} | \text{ I } \|$$

Musical Notation #8: "Help!"

"Help!" — "Help!" — Published key: A major

Click or tap the play button in the Revel course to watch musical notation #8: "Help!"

$$| \text{ I } | \text{ vi } \overset{*}{\text{I}^7} | \text{ IV } \overset{*}{\text{iv}} | \text{ I } | \text{(repeat 4 measures)} |$$

$$| \text{vi}^7 | \text{ IV } | \overset{*}{♭\textbf{VII}} | \text{ I } | \text{vi}^7 | \overset{*}{\textbf{II}^7} \overset{*}{\text{iv}} | \text{ I } |$$

Musical Notation #9: "In My Life"

"In My Life" — "In My Life" — Published Key: A major

Note: With chords such as I^7, iv, and II^7, the root of the chord is diatonic, but at least one of the other notes of the chord is chromatic.

Click or tap the play button in the Revel course to watch musical notation #9: "In My Life."

$$| \overset{*}{\text{I}} | \text{iv}^7 \text{ VI } | \overset{*}{♭\textbf{VII}} \overset{*}{\#\textbf{VI}} | \overset{*}{\text{VI}^7} | \text{ v } \text{ VI } | \text{ v } |$$

Musical Notation #10: "Michelle"

"Michelle" — "Michelle" — Published key: F minor (however, the verse represented in the music notation is in F *major*)

Click or tap the play button in the Revel course to watch musical notation #10: "Michelle."

$$| \overset{*}{♭\text{vii}} \overset{*}{\text{iv}^+} \text{(augmented)} | \text{ VI } \text{ i } | \overset{*}{\text{IV}^7} | \overset{*}{\text{IV}^7} |$$

$$| \overset{*}{♭\text{vii}} \overset{*}{\text{iv}^+} | \text{ VI } \text{ i } | \text{ v}^7 | \text{ i } \overset{*}{\text{i}^7} |$$

$$| \text{ VI } \text{v}^7 | \text{ i } \text{ VI } \text{ i } | \text{ VI } \text{ v } | \text{ i } |$$

Musical Notation #11: "Being for the Benefit of Mr. Kite"

"Being for the Benefit of Mr. Kite!" — "Being for the Benefit of Mr. Kite!" — Published key: D minor

Note: This song begins with so many chromatic chords that the actual key is ambiguous. Even though it settles into D minor, the opening measures emphasize the key of C minor.

Click or tap the play button in the Revel course to watch musical notation #11: "Being for the Benefit of Mr. Kite."

$$| \text{ I } | \text{ I } | \overset{*}{\text{v}}^{\text{min7}} | \overset{*}{\text{v}}^{\text{min7}} | \overset{*}{\text{VI}^7} | \overset{*}{\text{VI}^7} | \text{IV } \text{v } \overset{*}{\text{VI}} | \overset{*}{\text{VI}} | \overset{*}{\text{IV}}^{\text{maj7}} \text{ v } | \text{ I } |$$

Musical Notation #12: "Strawberry Fields Forever"

"Strawberry Fields Forever" — "Strawberry Fields Forever" — Published key: A major

Click or tap the play button in the Revel course to watch musical notation #12: "Strawberry Fields Forever."

The Beatles rarely resorted to the old 12-bar blues form, but with "Yer Blues," the Beatles modify the form to suit their needs. For every 4/4 measure of the standard 12 measures of the blues form, the Beatles substitute 2 measures of 3/4:

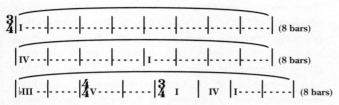

Musical Notation #13: "Yer Blues"

Of course, one could also hear this as 12 measures of 6/4, instead of 24 measures of 3/4. Notice the chromatic chord that begins the third phase and the meter change to 4/4 for 2 measures in that same phrase. This is the blues, Beatles style.

Much has been said about the modality of the Beatles' melodies and harmonies. This is because many of their melodies and chord progressions seem to be based on **modes**—a system of scales that predates our major and minor scales by centuries. Many of these modal references contain the lowered seventh or the lowered third degrees, or both. However, it is more likely that the Beatles' use of these scale degrees was guided by the blues tradition than by the pre-seventeenth-century Greek modes.

"Eleanor Rigby" has often been cited as using the Dorian mode—a scale that is like our minor scale but uses a raised sixth scale degree. Indeed, in this song, although the minor scale predominates, the sixth scale degree is sometimes raised (as it would be in the Dorian mode) and sometimes not. But these modal references are probably the result of harmonic considerations: using the raised sixth in association with the diatonic i chord and the lowered sixth as the root of the diatonic VI chord.

Much more could be said about the Beatles' use of harmony and tonality. Later songs, such as "Because" and "Sun King" (with its surprising 11th chord initiating a new key), show creative musical minds at work. To keep these harmonic practices in perspective, however, what seemed fresh and innovative in rock was well known in classical music, jazz, and even in more sophisticated types of popular music (e.g., Broadway show tunes). Nevertheless, if rock was ever to move beyond the mundane simplicity of three or four chords, simple rhythms, and repetitive melodies, someone had to lead the way, and the Beatles did just that.

5.6.4: Timbre

Although the Beatles' experiments with rhythm, melody, and harmony were important, perhaps the innovations that were most obvious to the untrained ear involved timbre—the new sound colors they brought to the world of rock and roll. In their early music, the instrumentation of the Beatles consisted of voices accompanied by two guitars, bass, and drums. But, as any Beatles fan can tell you, that was only the beginning. Where sound color was concerned, George Martin truly became "the fifth Beatle." Sometimes, the ideas were his; at other times, he refined ideas proposed by the group.

The Beatles' Experiments with Timbre

The Beatles introduced many new sounds into their recordings by including instruments that are not commonly used in rock recordings, and by using studio technology to manipulate recorded sound directly (e.g., speeding up the tape or playing it backwards). Some of these timbral innovations are described in the following section.

The voice is the most fundamental instrument at any group's disposal. As with Presley and Holly, Paul McCartney was especially capable of a variety of vocal timbres. At times he could project a soft, lyrical voice, as in "Yesterday" or "The Long and Winding Road." At other times, he could use the shouting style of the old R&B tradition, as in "Why Don't We Do It in the Road?" and "Oh! Darling." In "Golden Slumbers," Paul begins as a crooning ballad singer, but, as the song progresses, his voice becomes more harsh and distorted. Finally, he reverts to the softer sound, before moving into "Carry That Weight." These changes in vocal timbre are accomplished naturally by the singer. However, there are also instances where the Beatles use electronics to modify the voice; for example, listen to the electronically modified spoken voice in "Honey Pie" ("Now, she's hit the big time").

The guitar was also subjected to timbral modification in some Beatles recordings. The opening of "I Feel Fine" (1964) uses intentional electronic **feedback.** In "I'm Only Sleeping," the guitars are **overdubbed** (one ordinary and one with fuzz); some parts are also mixed in backwards.

Beyond these timbral experiments, within their own instrumentation, the Beatles added a variety of other instruments and ensembles to their recordings. We have already mentioned several innovations (the string ensembles in "Yesterday," "Eleanor Rigby," and "She's Leaving Home"). In various songs, we hear flutes ("You've Got to Hide Your Love Away"), harpsichord ("Because"), piccolo trumpet ("Penny Lane"), brass and saxes ("Got to Get You into My Life"), sitar ("Norwegian Wood"), brass band ("Yellow Submarine"), organ and bass harmonica ("Being for the Benefit of Mr. Kite!"), clarinets ("Honey Pie"), full orchestra ("A Day in the Life"), and a little bit of almost everything in "Strawberry Fields Forever." In "Within You Without You," we hear tabla (drums) and dilruba (a long-necked Indian lute). The addition of extramusical sounds, although not new to popular music (e.g., "409" by the Beach Boys), is a technique commonly found in Beatles recordings. Examples include the airplane sounds in "Back in the U.S.S.R.," the various sound effects in "Yellow Submarine," animal sounds in "Good Morning, Good Morning," and the alarm clock in "A Day in the Life."

Still another category of timbral experimentation involves tape effects. This would include the sped-up piano solo in "In My Life" described previously, the remarkable mixing of two versions of "Strawberry Fields Forever," the spliced-together and overdubbed fragments that conclude "Being for the Benefit of Mr. Kite!," and the tape-generated and manipulated sounds of "Tomorrow Never Knows." The end of the middle section of "A Day in the Life" (the dream section), with its heavily echoed and fading vocal line against the increasingly predominant unison string and brass line,

is a particularly effective manipulation of sound. There are examples of backwards instrumental segments ("Tomorrow Never Knows") and backward verbal messages, whether intentional on the part of the Beatles or not. Finally, of course, there is the sonic montage of "Revolution 9" that makes use of all of these techniques.

These examples provide only a small sample of the timbral experiments evident on various Beatles records. Choose almost any song from the *Revolver* album or later Beatles recordings, and you will hear (1) an uncommon use of a common instrument, (2) the addition of an uncommon instrument, (3) the addition of extramusical sound effects, and/or (4) the electronic manipulation or modification of sounds. Imagine the listener's excitement as each new Beatles album was placed on the turntable, revealing what new rainbow of sounds had been cooked up *this* time.

5.6.5: Form

In rock music, the Beatles led the way toward expanded and irregular forms. Most Pop and rock songs from the 1950s and early 1960s conformed to one of several traditional patterns:

Typical twelve-bar blues pattern:

| | 12-bar | 12-bar | | Instrumental | 12-bar | | Fade- |
| Intro | chorus | chorus | (etc.) | break | chorus | (etc.) | out |

Typical AABA pattern:

| Intro | A | A | B (bridge) | A | Instrumental break | B | A | Fade-out |

Musical Notation #14: typical 12-bar blues & AABA patterns

Internal phrases were typically four or eight measures long; the total song length was around 2 minutes and 30 seconds. Although exceptions may be found, these were the generally accepted norms for successful hits.

Although many of their songs conform to the Top 40 "two-and-a-half-minute rule," a significant number of Beatles songs extend well beyond that time frame: "Yer Blues" (four minutes), "Helter Skelter" (four and a half

minutes), "While My Guitar Gently Weeps" (four minutes), "A Day in the Life" (five minutes), "Hey Jude" (seven minutes), "I Want You (She's So Heavy)" (over seven and a half minutes), and "Revolution 9" (eight minutes). Of course, anyone can make a long song simply by repeating a short song ad nauseam. In fact, "Hey Jude" and "I Want You (She's So Heavy)" use considerable repetition to create length. But some songs achieve their length by incorporating a variety of sections that gradually build to the total length. "A Day in the Life" is one such example.

The form of "A Day in the Life" is unique. There probably is not another song in the world with exactly the same structure. The closest precedent is called *ternary form* (three parts: ABA). The uniqueness of this musical form is compounded by the use of some overlapping sections, where one section begins before the preceding one has ended (the third chorus of section A and the following transition). Except for the introduction and some internal phrases, none of the sections are the usual four- or eight-bar lengths. Irregular phrase lengths abound in Beatles songs. Examples include early songs such as "Love Me Do" (13-measure sections) and "Do You Want to Know a Secret"

Listening Guide: "A Day in the Life" (The Beatles)

0:00–0:12	Introduction (4 bars)	Sets the basic accompaniment.
0:13–0:43	Section A; first chorus (10 measures)	"The line about reading the news today." Two 4-bar phrases with a 2-bar extension.
0:44–1:10	Section A; second chorus (9 measures)	"Line about blowing his mind out." A 4-bar phrase followed by a 5-bar phrase.
1:11–1:44	Section A; third chorus (11 measures?)	"Line about seeing a film today." A 4-bar phrase followed by a 5-bar phrase, then a 2-bar (overlapping) third phrase that dovetails with the next section (*transition*).
1:45–2:15	Transition (10 measures?)	Orchestral buildup provides transition to section B.
2:16–2:48	Section B; part 1 (13 measures)	Two-bar introduction. First phrase is 6 bars (includes two duple measures); second phrase is 5 bars (includes one duple measure).
2:49–3:17	Section B, part 2 (10 measures)	Dream sequence. Heavy echo; voice fades, leaving prominent string and brass line.
3:18–3:49	Section A; fourth chorus (11 measures)	"Line about hearing the news today." Similar to third chorus. A 4-bar phrase followed by a 5-bar phrase, then a 2-bar phrase that overlaps with the coda.
3:50–5:03	Coda (11 measures)	Repeat of transition, with the addition of one final bar. Last bar has a brief break, then a major triad that is allowed to decay for almost 45 seconds.

(14-measure section created by two 6-measure phrases plus a 2-measure extension); middle period songs such as "Michelle" (6-measure phrases and a bridge of 10 measures), and "Yesterday" (7-measure phrases); and later songs such as "I Am the Walrus" (3-measure phrases) and "Hello Goodbye" (a 15-and-a-half-measure section, divided into phrases of 4, 4½, 3, and 4 measures).

Beyond matters of phrase lengths and internal sections are larger considerations of groups of songs and entire albums. The innovativeness of the concept album (*Sgt. Pepper*) has already been mentioned. Even the eclectic White Album has some interesting balances between songs. There is "Revolution 1" and "Revolution 9"; there is "Honey Pie" and "Wild Honey Pie"; there is a song about a weeping guitar followed by a song referring to the happiness of a warm gun; there is a sequence of "Blackbird," "Piggies," and "Rocky Raccoon" (and, later, a song referring to a monkey); and after the harsh avant-gardism of "Revolution 9," the album ends with the soft nostalgia of "Good Night." The *Abbey Road* album ends with a series of songs and fragments, woven together into a kind of multi-movement suite. The Beatles were obviously thinking of larger structures.

5.6.6: Texture

The Beatles' contributions in the area of texture were less impressive. The overwhelming majority of Beatles songs are homophonic, with emphasis on the melody-and-accompaniment format. Where vocal polyphony exists, it is rather simple. For example, in the chorus of "She's Leaving Home," the lead vocal sings a slow-moving upper line ("she ... home."), while a lower line moves in faster note values ("we gave ... lives.").

Sometimes a **countermelody** is devised to operate against the lead vocal. For example, in "Help!," there is a slow-moving countermelody below the melody; this counter-line follows the harmonic progression and is more a part of the accompaniment than a true polyphonic line that assumes equal importance to the other melody. A brief example of vocal polyphony is found in the *a cappella* (without accompaniment) sections of "Paperback Writer." A vocal falsetto above the lead line adds to the texture, but, again, this line seems more an extension of the harmonic accompaniment than true polyphony. A cappella sections are rather rare in Beatles songs (as they are in most rock and Pop styles), though they do occur infrequently ("Nowhere Man" and "Paperback Writer").

Of course, with the added instrumental components in so many songs (e.g., strings and brass), a thicker and more interesting texture is a natural result. In the quasi-classical moments (e.g., the instrumental break of "In My Life" and the string accompaniments of "Yesterday," "Eleanor Rigby," and "She's Leaving Home"), there are varying amounts of polyphony (often the creative contribution of George Martin). The piccolo trumpet line in "Penny Lane" adds a refreshing touch of polyphony to the texture of that song.

5.6.7: Lyrics

While early recordings by the Beatles were not particularly innovative, they did develop a clear style of their own that was based on the foundation provided by earlier, influential rockers like Little Richard and Chuck Berry, incorporating nonsense syllables and vocal interpolations ("yeah yeah yeahs") and falsetto "oo's." As the group, and their music, matured, the lyrical content too took on a more meaningful role, beyond simple entertainment and romantic topics venturing into socio-political commentary and symbolism.

Characteristics of the Beatles' Lyrics

The Beatles' lyrics have been analyzed, reanalyzed, and probably overanalyzed.

Innovative and Meaningful—Hidden messages, backward messages, social profundities, and global prophecies, whether or not intended or accurately interpreted, have been "found" in their words. Although we should not downplay the Beatles' skill in lyric writing, we cannot claim for them the role of innovators of the meaningful rock lyric. That award lies in the area of the folk music trend and with Bob Dylan, in particular, as discussed elsewhere in this text.

Concepts/Themes—Early Beatles lyrics were fairly typical in comparison to most Pop and rock songs of the period. Most were love songs, complete with hand-holding, letter writing, and lots of "yeah, yeah, yeahs." However, in 1964, the Beatles met Bob Dylan and became acquainted with his songs. Within the next year, subtle differences became apparent in the Beatles' lyrics. For example, Dylan's 1964 song "My Back Pages" speaks of the black-and-white, false self-assuredness of youth in contrast to a greater willingness to consider the gray aspects of issues that comes with maturity. A similar theme is addressed by John Lennon in his 1965 song "Help!"

From mid-1965, Beatles lyrics became increasingly thoughtful and thought provoking. The sensitive lyrics of "Yesterday," the social commentary of "Nowhere Man," and the poetic images and turns of phrase in "Eleanor Rigby" revealed that the Beatles were capable of growing beyond the simple lyrics of romance to concerns about major social issues, socially disaffected individuals, more sensitive aspects of mature relationships, and, of course, drugs. In the 1967 to 1970 albums and singles, one can find considerable variety in the lyrics, but the Beatles music of this era represents more emphasis on nostalgia ("Penny Lane" and "Get Back"), personal criticism ("Sexy Sadie"), surrealism and nonsensical stream-of-consciousness texts ("I Am the Walrus"), and love and peace ("All You Need Is Love" and "Give Peace a Chance").

Symbolism—Dylan used imagery, metaphor, and symbolism artistically in his lyrics. From 1965 onward, so did the Beatles. Much of this symbolism is obvious, while some is obscure and subject to interpretation. It is a short step from obscure symbolism to meaningless surrealism. But, accustomed to finding the meaning of such obscure symbols, some fans were driven to determine a specific meaning in the surreal. This led to the fascination with detecting the "hidden meanings" in meaningless lyrics and the questionable individual interpretations of Charles Manson and the Paul is dead hoax. As already noted, fans also enjoyed deciphering the Beatles' deliberate drug references and sometimes carried this practice forward into songs with innocent or meaningless use of words that, if the context were sufficiently contorted, could be construed as drug-related.

Certainly, the Beatles' lyrics were extensive in their subject matter, and they were skillfully written. Because of their position as trendsetters and spokesmen for a generation, their

influence on subsequent rock lyrics was significant. However, in this aspect of their music, they themselves had been significantly inspired by an earlier revolutionary: Bob Dylan.

JOURNAL

The Influence of *Pet Sounds*

As discussed in the preceding Musical Close-Up, one of the primary innovations in the music of the Beatles was their expansion of the harmonic and tonal language of rock and roll. Listen to several songs from the Beach Boys' album *Pet Sounds*, which was released the year before *Sgt. Pepper*. The Beatles themselves have given Brian Wilson significant credit for opening the door to their own tonal experimentation. Choosing one song from *Pet Sounds*, identify at least three lyrical phrases where the harmonic progression surprises you. Using an informed musical vocabulary, do your best to describe your emotional, and perhaps visceral, reaction to these musical moments. While performing this task, notice the musical influence of the sounds on *Pet Sounds* upon the Beatles' *Sgt. Pepper's Lonely Hearts Club Band*.

 The response entered here will appear in the performance dashboard and can be viewed by your instructor.

Submit

Summary: The Beatles

Many of the Beatles' experiments in rhythm, melody, harmony, timbre, and form led to copious imitations and the establishment of new norms. In a broad sense, they created an environment of creativity, experimentation, and innovation in the world of rock music. No longer was it limited to proven formulas and strict norms. Even though an artist or group might not directly imitate a specific Beatles innovation, they could discover their own unique sound. No longer bound to traditional instrumentation, established forms, or trite lyrics, truly creative artists could give their musical minds free reign. This establishment of a climate of freedom in musical creativity is of greater importance than any single Beatles innovation or experiment.

The typical Beatles fan was not attracted to the music as a result of a conscious appreciation for these technical innovations. It is highly doubtful that, on hearing a new Beatles song, one teenager telephoned another to report with excitement the group's use of the Dorian mode in a five-measure phrase accompanied by a ♭III chord. However, it is likely that many fans sensed that there was something different about the Beatles' music. It simply did not sound like other rock and roll. The specific technical devices, many described in the previous section, are the reasons why the music sounded different, but one should not conclude that the fans' conscious awareness of these devices was the reason for their fascination with the music. In fact, it is quite impressive—and significant credit is due to the Beatles for the fact—that such highly innovative music was accepted into the mainstream and that this highly creative music was

accepted as simply the next step in the evolution of rock and roll.

Finally, the Beatles' innovations were not really firsts in the truest sense of the word. Precedence for almost every one of these musical devices can be found in classical music, jazz, and even Broadway tunes. However, they do seem innovative within the world of rock music. Even there, though, it is possible to cite some prior examples. However, to have a truly innovative influence, one must be in a position to have an impact on a general society. Although arguments over the Beatles' innovativeness have raged for years (and will undoubtedly continue), it seems fair to conclude that, because of their very visible position as trendsetters, they brought to the world of rock many new ideas (whether they were literally their own original ideas or not) and had a major influence on the direction of rock and roll.

It is common to divide the history of rock into two periods: pre- and post-Beatles. Simply put, they were musical pioneers. Their influence on rock music is undeniable. But there were other influences beyond the music … on clothing, hairstyles, lifestyles, and philosophies. As with Presley, they covered the entire spectrum of Pop and rock. Within their work, there are examples of hard-driving mainstream rock, avant-garde rock, psychedelic rock, symphonic rock, and lighthearted rock ditties. They had gathered together the first 10 years of rock's development, molded it to their style, added their own creative innovations, and then slung it into the future. In the coming years, rock would fragment into a bewildering variety of styles and trends, as others would pick up and develop one or another of the stylistic fragments. No longer was rock simply fun music; it had become serious. Scholars would analyze the music and lyrics: There would be university courses in rock music (unthinkable in 1962). The Beatles' legacy, some of it good and some of it dubious, would influence rock for decades to come.

Take Note: The Beatles

- *How did the social change that occurred in the early 1960s influence rock and roll?*—American society was rapidly changing in the early 1960s, symbolized by the election of the youthful John F. Kennedy as president. Almost as quickly as the new era dawned, however, tragedy overshadowed this rebirth when Kennedy was assassinated in 1963 while visiting Dallas, Texas. The tension between hopeful rebirth and American anxiety about cultural status resulted in an openness to the arrival of new musical sounds from abroad.

- *How did the Beatles evolve from a skiffle group into a major Pop sensation in their early years?*—John Lennon began playing music in high school with a skiffle group he formed called the Quarry Men. While playing at a local party, he met Paul McCartney, and the two quickly became friends and began writing songs together. After graduating from high school—and adding guitarist George Harrison, bass player Stu Sutcliffe, and drummer Pete Best (later replaced by Ringo Starr)—the group eventually became the Beatles, playing small clubs in their native Liverpool and also abroad in Hamburg, Germany. A local record store manager named Brian Epstein heard the Beatles play at Liverpool's Cavern Club and became their manager. They were signed to Parlophone Records and began working with producer George Martin. Their third single, "Please Please Me," reached number 1 on the British chart in March, 1963. About nine months later, the Beatles took America by storm, with the release of "I Want to Hold Your Hand" and their initial appearances on the *Ed Sullivan Show*. Beatlemania erupted, and American popular music was never the same.

- *How did the Beatles expand their sound during their middle years through studio experimentation?*—The Beatles could have continued to produce upbeat, teenage Pop songs, enjoying continuing success. However, primary songwriters Paul McCartney and John Lennon were not content to rest on their laurels. The Beatles stopped touring in the mid-1960s and focused instead on working in the recording studio. Their most notable experiments came on two albums, *Rubber Soul* and *Revolver*, culminating in the two-sided single release of "Penny Lane" and "Strawberry Fields Forever" in 1967. They experimented with different instrumentation, from string quartet accompaniment ("Yesterday") to sitar ("Norwegian Wood"), as well as studio effects such as playing tapes backwards to give their music a "psychedelic" sound.

- *What were the most notable of the Beatles' later achievements?*—The Beatles' final years were marked by further experimentation as well as growing tensions between members of the group, particularly between Lennon and McCartney. In late 1967, they released what many consider the first concept album, *Sgt. Pepper's Lonely Hearts Club Band*, an attempt to create a series of rock songs around a unifying theme. It was followed by the two-LP set known as the White Album, an eclectic mix of songs, revealing the strains in the group (many tracks were recorded by one or two of the Beatles working alone, rather than as a group). A final effort to return to their roots as a band performing live resulted in the *Let It Be* album and an associated film, followed by their swansong, *Abbey Road*. After the group broke up, the individual members continued to record, although their level of accomplishment and musical innovation—while quite impressive—never rivaled that of the Beatles.

The Lyrics for "Lucy in the Sky with Diamonds"

Search online for the lyrics for "Lucy in the Sky with Diamonds." Read through all stanzas several times. Identify three to five phrases that represent potential references to drug use. Provide your own interpretation of the meaning of these phrases. Now, search for an example of a modern poem that makes similar use of the English language, presenting a surrealistic, perhaps even nonsensical, meaning. Notice how words can be used to create a rhythmic flow or paint mental pictures that vary widely in their interpretation from individual to individual. Share your response to this exercise with three other students. How do your interpretations differ? In what ways are they similar? If you are so inclined, take some time to compose a stanza of a poem of your own in this style.

 A minimum number of characters is required to post and earn points. After posting, your response can be viewed by your class and instructor, and you can participate in the class discussion.

Post

0 characters | 140 minimum

Chapter 6
The British Invasion

 Learning Objectives

6.1 Explain the influences on the transformation of the Rolling Stones' image during the early years of the band

6.2 Analyze the musical style of the Rolling Stones

6.3 Summarize the success of other British groups during the 1960s

The Beatles were responsible for many innovations and trends in rock and roll, but perhaps none was more significant than their initiation of the British Invasion. Prior to 1964, rock and roll was an American product, exported to other parts of the globe in varying degrees. The British were particularly passionate about American stars, including Buddy Holly, Little Richard, Gene Vincent, Eddie Cochran, and Jerry Lee Lewis. Imitating these performers, many British rock musicians attained popularity in their own countries, but they found it impossible to export their success to the United States. Only the Tornadoes, Lonnie Donegan, and Cliff Richard had made fleeting appearances on the U.S. charts.

In 1964, beginning with the Beatles, British rock groups became the rage in rock and roll's homeland. Of the 23 number 1 hits in 1964, 9 were by British artists (6 by the Beatles). By 1965, 13 out of 26 number 1 songs were of British origin (5 by the Beatles). Although the trend abated slightly after 1967, a new premise had been established: rock and roll was no longer an exclusively American product. From 1964 onward, British and American rock artists competed more or less equally in the market. As we shall see, several important trends were initiated or cofounded by British rock artists. However, it is not true that the British, exclusively, dominated the charts, as is sometimes thought. In fact, of the 124 number 1 hits from 1964 to 1969, only 35 were by British artists—a dramatic change from the pre-1964 Pop chart (2 British number 1 hits in the 10 years from 1954 to 1963), but not a complete takeover.

With the British Invasion came a split in rock's mainstream—a duality that would weigh heavily on subsequent decades. The Beatles' Paul McCartney and John Lennon embodied this duality. Although history may view them as a songwriting team, they were, in fact, two divergent individuals who cooperated (sort of) in a highly successful corporate venture. Paul was more refined, more traditionally talented musically, and more compliant to societal norms. John was iconoclastic, rebellious, and inclined to nonconformity. Paul tended toward the elegant, the nostalgic, and the sentimental, while John leaned toward the raw, the raucous, and the shocking. This tension is reflected in the White Album and in the double-sided hit singles "Penny Lane" and "Strawberry Fields Forever."

This dichotomy is the prototype for an even larger division within the British Invasion as a whole. The British groups that constitute that "invasion" seem to split into two camps: the softer, more refined, less rebellious bands on one hand and the raw, basic, R&B-oriented mainstream rock bands on the other. In spite of their own internal duality, the Beatles became the representatives of the former trend (probably because of their early image as being cute and lovable and their later reputation as being eclectic experimenters). The Rolling Stones personified the latter camp. Most rock fans of the later 1960s could identify themselves as either Beatles' fans or Rolling Stones' fans. Rarely was anyone an equal fan of both. The difference was musical, but it also involved image, lifestyle, and personality type. One could quickly assess a new acquaintance with one basic question: "Are you a Beatle or a Stone?"

At the risk of oversimplification, this basic split in British rock is a useful model for post-1964 rock. Many of the trends we observe in rock after 1964 seem to fall in line behind the

Beatles or the Stones. The softer British groups discussed later in this chapter, jazz rock groups of the late 1960s and early 1970s, virtuosic art rock bands, and several of the other trends of the 1970s and 1980s owed much, directly or indirectly, to the Beatles. The harder British groups; many San Francisco groups; and, later, the hard rock, punk, and heavy metal groups owed much (again, directly or indirectly) to the Rolling Stones. There are still other influences to be considered, of course, as well as individual innovations and stylistic variations and the basic trends evident in rock of the 1950s and early 1960s: mainstream, rockabilly, soft rock, and folk.

As the Beatles are discussed elsewhere in this course, let us cross to the other side of the street and meet the Rolling Stones.

6.1: The Rolling Stones

OBJECTIVE: Explain the influences on the transformation of the Rolling Stones' image during the early years of the band

The Beatles' formative years were influenced by American rock and roll stars of the 1950s: Presley, Holly, and Little Richard. But the Rolling Stones' earliest influences went back to the roots of rock and roll: black R&B. Young Michael Jagger (born July 26, 1943) and several friends formed what can loosely be called a band (they had no equipment and never performed in public), just for the fun of playing and singing their favorite R&B songs as well as some 1950s rock tunes, especially those by Chuck Berry. To make their R&B roots clear, they called themselves Little Boy Blue and the Blue Boys. Jagger lived in Dartford, Kent, in a middle-class home and attended the respectable London School of Economics (LSE). Living several blocks away was Keith Richards (born on December 18, 1943), a guitarist who sometimes sat in on rehearsals with the Blue Boys.

The Rolling Stones
SOURCE: Lebrecht Music and Arts Photo Library/Alamy Stock Photo

There was an active subculture of R&B aficionados in London. One of the most ardent was Alexis Korner, who led his own R&B-oriented band called Blues Incorporated; he eventually opened his own club, the Ealing Club. On occasion, Korner used a drummer named Charlie Watts (born June 2, 1941) who was a fairly accomplished jazz drummer but also enjoyed playing R&B. Also hanging around Korner and his club was a young blues enthusiast named Brian Jones (born February 28, 1942) who dropped out of school at the age of 14 and began playing sax in jazz and R&B bands. At Korner's Ealing Club, Brian tried to establish himself as a guitarist, calling himself "Elmo Lewis."

The Blue Boys often attended the sessions at the Ealing Club, hoping for a chance to perform. Jagger was given an occasional opportunity to sing with Korner's band, but he did not make a positive impression. Nevertheless, the Blue Boys and Elmo Lewis became acquainted and decided to join forces. Their debut performance on July 12, 1962, was as an intermission band at the Marquee Club (another R&B and jazz club). The group consisted of Jagger, Richards, Jones, pianist Ian Stewart, bassist Dick Taylor, and drummer Mike Avory. Taking their name from a song by blues singer Muddy Waters, they called themselves the Rolling Stones.

6.1.1: The Years before "Satisfaction"

The jazz-oriented audience at the Marquee Club thought the Stones were too close to rock and roll. Brian Jones was sufficiently irritated by the criticism to write a letter to *Jazz News* that revealed a rather thoughtful assessment of the situation. He opined that the jazz scene was contaminated by pseudo-intellectual snobbery. He stated further that rock and roll was actually closer to R&B than R&B was to jazz. According to Brian, rock is a direct descendant of R&B whereas jazz was "Negro music" that was emotionally less intense but on a higher intellectual level (Norman 1984, 70).

For the balance of 1962, the Rolling Stones played wherever work could be found. When Taylor quit the group, he was replaced by Bill Wyman (born William Perks, October 24, 1936), an "older" man at 26 years of age. By 1963, Charlie Watts had become the band's regular drummer, although he continued to prefer his first musical love: jazz. In 1963, a public relations agent named Andrew Loog Oldham approached the Rolling Stones about becoming their manager. Brian Jones signed a management contract with Oldham and a more established agent named Eric Easton. Jones also negotiated a larger salary for himself as leader of the Rolling Stones.

The Initial Milestones of the Rolling Stones

The early career of the Rolling Stones was marked by a number of important developments, including forming their own distinctive image and making a name for themselves amidst the initial wave of the British Invasion. This module describes some of the important accomplishments of the band during this period.

Forming a Counterimage to the Beatles—Decca Records' Dick Rowe had become known as the man who turned down the Beatles in favor of Brian Poole and the Tremeloes. Needless to say, when George Harrison recommended to Rowe that he sign a new group called the Rolling Stones, he jumped at the chance. In May 1963, the Rolling Stones made their first recording. "Come On," a Chuck Berry song, was the A-side; the B-side was an R&B song called "I Want to Be Loved." To promote their new record, the group appeared on the television show *Thank Your Lucky Stars*, uncharacteristically dressed in coordinated suits, Beatles' style. "Come On" reached number 26 on the British chart. The Stones began the arduous grind of performing and touring in hopes of building a following. Everywhere they went, they were confronted with British Beatlemania; irked and resentful, they dropped the Beatle-like coordinated suits, electing to appear in street clothes. Their second release, "I Want to Be Your Man" (ironically, a Lennon-McCartney song), rose to number 3 in late 1963.

Through 1964, the Stones gradually formed their counterimage to the Beatles. Their stage act became more sexually suggestive; they allowed their hair to grow longer and attained a scruffy, unkempt look. Oldham purposely built the image of "surliness, squalor, rebellion, and menace" (Norman 1984, 113). Brian continued to think of himself as the group's leader, taking his extra salary and claiming the better hotel rooms. Meanwhile, Oldham was insisting that Jagger and Richard (Keith had dropped the *s* from his name) become a songwriting team like Lennon and McCartney. Their early attempts were unsuccessful, except for one song called "Tell Me (You're Coming Back)"—a Beatles-like tune complete with some "whoa, yeahs," included on their first LP, released in April 1964. The album's other cuts are either R&B-oriented mainstream rock (covers of songs by Bo Diddley and Chuck Berry) or actual R&B songs originally performed by older black artists like Jimmy Reed and Willie Dixon. The sexually oriented "I'm a King Bee" suggests the Jagger image that would be so successfully exploited as the band's popularity grew.

Joining the British Invasion—The time had come for the Stones to join the British Invasion of America. Their first U.S. and Canadian tour was launched in June 1964, four months after the Beatles. "Not Fade Away," backed with "I Wanna Be Your Man," had barely made the U.S. charts. Their arrival at Kennedy Airport drew hundreds instead of the thousands the Beatles had drawn. Unlike the Beatles' Ed Sullivan television appearance, the Stones were hosted by Les Crane on an obscure late-night talk show and on Dean Martin's *Hollywood Palace*, where their host paid them little attention, except to make fun of them. In Omaha, 600 fans "jammed" an auditorium seating 15,000; in San Antonio, they performed in a 20,000-seat arena to a few hundred listeners. The Stones' first attack on American Beatlemania was largely unsuccessful, except for their final concerts at a sold-out Carnegie Hall in New York City. While in the United States, the Stones stopped by the Chess studios in Chicago, where so much early R&B had been recorded. There they met Muddy Waters, Chuck Berry, and Willie Dixon and recorded "It's All Over Now."

The balance of 1964 was spent on a European tour and a second, more successful American tour (this time, they appeared on the *Ed Sullivan Show*). It was on this second U.S. tour that Jagger saw James Brown perform. Fascinated and impressed, Jagger set out to imitate Brown's dancing and incorporate these moves into the Rolling Stones' act.

6.1.2: The Impact of "Satisfaction"

In January 1965, the Stones' second album, *12 X 5*, was released. Again, it leaned heavily on the R&B sound that was the foundation of the group's sound. "Time Is on My Side" reached number 6 in the United States, and "The Last Time" reached number 1 in England and number 9 in the United States. By spring 1965, the Rolling Stones had the top single, the top *EP* (*extended play:* a 45-rpm album, usually containing four songs on a 7-inch disc) and the top LP in Britain. Though they did not know it at the time, they were only months away from topping the American Pop chart.

Rolling Stones' Journey to Success

The Rolling Stones have proven to be one of the longest-running bands in rock history, recording and touring for over half a century. This section describes some of the early events that laid the foundation for their success.

During their third U.S. tour (Spring 1965), the Stones made a return appearance on the *Ed Sullivan Show* and appeared on the youth music-oriented *Shindig*. While resting in a motel room, Keith began playing a guitar pattern that he thought sounded catchy. Mick improvised some words, and the result was "(I Can't Get No) Satisfaction." It zoomed to number 1 in the United States that summer. Controversy surrounded the song: Some argued that it referred to masturbation; others thought it was about sex in general. Jagger, following the old double entendre explanation often used by rock artists, said that it referred to the general lack of any kind of satisfaction (sexual, artistic, spiritual, etc.) obtainable when a rock group was touring in a foreign country.

Allen Klein, who became the Beatles' manager in 1969, was known for his ability to find the soft spots in his clients' recording contracts, thus getting them more money. His client list was impressive, including Steve Lawrence, Eydie Gormé, Bobby Darin, Sam Cooke, Buddy Knox, the Dave Clark Five, the Animals, Donovan, and Herman's Hermits. However, Klein was also known for his cut-throat business sense. In describing Klein, Philip Norman (the Rolling Stones' biographer) noted that a piranha might be somewhat more polite than Klein (Norman 1984, 155). Klein offered to become Andrew Oldham's "business manager," thus leaving Oldham free to pursue the purely creative aspects of the Stones' career. Oldham accepted. His partner, Eric Easton, who objected, was edged out (amid lawsuits, of course).

The Stones rushed out a new album called *December's Children (and Everybody's)* just in time for Christmas 1965. It contained another number 1 hit, "Get Off My Cloud." On tour, in Los Angeles, Brian Jones met and began dating Anita Pallenberg; he and Keith also tried a new drug: **LSD**. In fact, Brian's alcohol and drug intake was becoming quite a problem. He had missed the "Satisfaction" recording session because he was wasted on booze and pills. He had hash and marijuana lying all over his house. His drug-induced paranoia led him to think that the other Stones were "out to get him." When LSD was added to this picture, matters got worse. Once, he refused to enter a recording studio because he was convinced that the studio was crawling with black beetles.

For the Stones, the year 1966 began with yet another successful single: "19th Nervous Breakdown." The song was an unsympathetic portrait of upper-class party girls. The B-side contained "As Tears Go By," accompanied by a string ensemble and acoustic guitars. It sounded like a rather blatant imitation of McCartney's "Yesterday." The Stones' fourth album, *Aftermath* (April 1966), was their first to feature only Jagger and Richard songs. The song "Paint It Black" hit number 1 in the United States. During this period, the Stones' touring schedule was fierce: Australia, New Zealand, and Europe in the first half of 1966 and Great Britain in the fall. Their live performances were met with increasingly wild behavior and outright violence among fans.

Unfortunately, 1967 was a year of scandal and increased controversy about the Rolling Stones. The album *Between the Buttons* contained two hit singles: "Ruby Tuesday" (number 1 in the U.S.) and "Let's Spend the Night Together," which didn't make the Top 40. The latter, especially, seemed to be another blatant step into overtly sexual lyrics. The press began digging out all sorts of drug and sex stories about the Stones. Although Mick Jagger initially denied LSD use, by the end of the year, he, too, was using the drug. During the year, Jagger, Richard, and Jones were arrested on drug charges.

To the Stones, the release of the Beatles' *Sgt. Pepper* was a shock. Ever competitive with the only other British group to attain comparable popularity, the Stones promptly went into the studio to record what they hoped would be an appropriate response. Brian Jones slept through recording sessions; when he played, he played so badly that the others quietly disconnected his guitar from the amplifier. When it was finally released in December, *Their Satanic Majesties Request* was a gross disappointment. Even the Stones themselves realized that they had failed to "out-Beatle" the Beatles. They had tried earlier in 1967 with "We Love You," an attempt to answer the Beatles' "All You Need Is Love." The Stones' song was even accompanied by a promotional film, similar to the pioneering film produced for the Beatles' monster hit.

In spite of the competition between the two groups, they were actually rather good friends. In fact, when the Beatles traveled to Bangor, North Wales, in August 1967 to absorb the Maharishi's wisdom, they were accompanied by Mick Jagger and Marianne Faithfull, who had begun living together in late 1966.

As though they had learned their lesson, the Stones' next single, "Jumpin' Jack Flash," was a basic R&B-oriented mainstream rock song, unclouded by efforts at Beatle-like sophistication or chic psychedelia. It was the kind of basic raw rock and roll the Stones did best. It was followed by the more lyrically sophisticated "Sympathy for the Devil." Jagger and Richard were inspired to write this song when Marianne Faithfull told them about Mikhail Bulgakov's *The Master and Margarita,* a book about a smooth-talking Satan who visits Russia to assess the effects of the revolution. It was included on their late 1968 album *Beggar's Banquet*. The album also contained the single "Street Fighting Man" that was suppressed in the United States because the nation was already a powder keg of street violence, from race riots to the havoc at the Democratic National Convention that same year.

Meanwhile, Brian Jones had been arrested again on drug charges. The time had come for the Stones to be rid of him. They were preparing for another U.S. tour, and there was no chance of Brian's obtaining a U.S. work permit with two drug convictions. Furthermore, his mental and physical condition had deteriorated badly. He was no longer an asset and would have to be fired. Mick, Keith, and Charlie Watts let him go, softening the blow by hinting that the separation was temporary. Brian, in turn, pretended to be elated at the prospect of solo work or work with other British groups.

As a replacement, they hired Mick Taylor, who had played in John Mayall's Bluesbreakers. His public debut was planned for July 5 at a free concert to be given by the Stones at Hyde Park in London. On July 2, Brian Jones, drunk and high, drowned in a swimming pool. The Hyde Park concert went on as planned. Some 250,000 fans attended. Films of the occasion reveal that the Stones played very badly, possibly as a result of Brian's death, their lack of recent public performances, and/or the presence of a new guitarist.

6.1.3: Altamont

In mid-1969, the Rolling Stones were at the peak of their career, yet they were almost flat broke. With a new manager, Ronnie Schneider, they promptly released two albums, a greatest hits album called *Through the Past Darkly,* and *Let It Bleed.* Designed to highlight the group's R&B roots, the American tour to accompany the album was to feature artists such as B. B. King and Ike and Tina Turner as warm-up acts. However, as the tour progressed, it attracted more and more negative publicity. Ticket prices were unusually high, and the Stones' habit of showing up hours late compounded the problems. The tour was being filmed in hopes of creating a full-length documentary.

Jagger decided that what was needed to turn things around was a big finish. Woodstock, a free outdoor concert in upstate New York earlier that year, was being described as the biggest and most positive event in rock's tumultuous decade of the 1960s. Jagger decided that the big finish for their American tour would be a free outdoor concert on the West Coast—"Woodstock West." After several other sites were considered and dropped, an offer to use the Altamont Raceway near Livermore, California (about 40 miles southeast of San Francisco), was accepted only one day before the concert's scheduled date of December 4. For a security force, Jagger invited various California chapters of Hell's Angels, motorcycle gangs known for their violence and disruption of similar events, perhaps with the intention of avoiding such violence.

The Rolling Stones on stage at Altamont, December 1969.
SOURCE: INTERFOTO/Personalities/Alamy Stock Photo

ROCK'S "DARKEST DAY" By Saturday morning, the crowd had already reached 100,000. The Angels appeared, armed with their lead-weighted pool cues and other more conventional weapons. By early afternoon, fights were breaking out all over the grounds. There were beatings, and many members of the crowd were already high on cheap drugs. As Santana began to play, violence erupted around the stage and continued into Jefferson Airplane's set. The Angels punched, kicked, and bludgeoned many of those present, from cameramen to stoned and nude audience members. As Crosby, Stills, Nash, and Young performed, the violence approached riot status.

Finally, the Rolling Stones took the stage. Mayhem abounded. As Jagger began "Sympathy for the Devil," all hell broke loose. Twice, the Stones stopped the music and pleaded for people to "cool out." Keith Richard

threatened to enter the melee personally. Jagger pathetically pleaded for sanity. They finished "Sympathy for the Devil," but there was little applause. After angry exchanges between the band and Angels, Taylor and Richard attempted to initiate some cool-down music (blues) with Wyman and Watts joining in. After a couple of choruses, Jagger added lyrics from Jimmy Reed's "The Sun is Shining" (Selvin 2016, 190), then launched into the calmer "Under My Thumb." Suddenly, a fight erupted between the Angels and an 18-year-old black youth named Meredith Hunter. The Angels grabbed him and plunged a knife into his neck and back and then stomped him in the face. Unaware that a murder was taking place right before his eyes, Jagger called for a doctor, saying, "Someone's been hurt." The concert continued, largely because the Stones were afraid of what might happen if they cut their set short. Finally, Jagger thanked everyone for a wonderful time and, astoundingly, expressed appreciation to the Angels for helping out. The Stones made a rapid getaway in their helicopter.

Hunter was not the only casualty at Altamont. Two other youths were killed when a car ran over them while they lay sleeping on the ground; another youth drowned in an irrigation ditch; yet another jumped from a traffic overpass and sustained multiple injuries. The documentary film of the tour was more than anyone could have expected. *Gimme Shelter,* with its climactic footage of a silver blade descending on Hunter's back, is a sobering film. The rock community was disheartened by the violence at Altamont. Even *Rolling Stone* magazine, in a major article published some six weeks later, suggested that the real blame for Altamont lay with the Stones.

Following this tragedy, the Stones did not perform "Sympathy for the Devil" for some six years. As Mick Jagger said onstage at Altamont, "We always have something funny happen when we start that number."

6.1.4: After Altamont

Altamont created considerable resentment toward the group for their apparently callous attitudes toward the tragedies that had occurred there. But it also seemed to spur on even more violence in subsequent concerts. Meanwhile, Mick, Keith, and Bill Wyman were in deep tax trouble. To escape payment, they moved to France. In April 1971, *Sticky Fingers* was released. It contained "Brown Sugar," a song with lyrics that were widely condemned as being both sexist and racist; it became the Stones' sixth number 1 hit in the United States.

The year 1972 found the Stones returning to America for another tour. Their album *Exile on Main Street* was number 1 in the United States. Mick hoped for smaller concert sites and tightly controlled circumstances to avoid another

Altamont. But the Stones were victims of their own creation. They had largely invented the economics of the large rock concert event, often characterized by fans who were snorting cocaine and throwing bottles at the performers (Norman 1984, 360).

For an opening act, the Stones hired Stevie Wonder, again presumably to emphasize their black musical roots. Jagger's act became even more sexually provocative. Violence and arrests abounded.

Recorded in Jamaica, *Goat's Head Soup* was released in 1973. It contained another number 1 single, "Angie." Around this time, Anita and Keith were arrested several times for possession of marijuana, heroin, and unlicensed weapons. Meanwhile, Mick and his new wife, Bianca, lived the high life, bouncing between the United States, France, and England—largely to avoid paying taxes.

In 1974, Mick Taylor, now a heroin addict, quit the Rolling Stones and was replaced by Ronnie Wood. The following albums were disappointing, and the Stones had no Top 10 hits in 1974 and no Top 40 hits in 1975. In August 1976, the Stones were to be part of a rock festival in England. Some 200,000 fans showed up, and so did the Stones—four hours late. They were not well received; as odd as it may sound now (with the benefit of hindsight), the end of the band seemed near.

Keith and Anita finally separated, and Keith began to pull out of his heroin habit. *Some Girls* was released in 1978 and contained the Stones' first number 1 hit in five years ("Miss You"). The album seemed to announce the return of the Rolling Stones. The albums *Tattoo You* (1981) and *Undercover* (1983) continued in the vein of *Some Girls*. In 1983, the Stones separated from Atlantic and signed with CBS. The first album on their new label

was released in 1985, and, ironically, it was a solo album by Mick Jagger. Keith bitterly resented Mick's solo venture. Nevertheless, they subsequently released a group album (*Dirty Work*) that contained a hit called "Harlem Shuffle."

The Stones toured the United States in 1981 and 1982. Throughout the next two decades, as Mick Jagger did solo work and Keith Richards (he added the *s* back to his name) played with other bands, rumors spread that the Rolling Stones were finally breaking up. To be sure, their real heyday had been the 1960s and 1970s. After all, by 2000, Jagger, Richards, and Watts were nearly 60 years old (Bill Wyman left the band in 1993). Nevertheless, the Rolling Stones were still performing to huge sellout audiences, and their albums continued to sell very well. *Voodoo Lounge* (1994) reached number 2 and won a Grammy. *Bridges to Babylon* (1997) reached number 3 and was the band's 19th platinum album. A live album, *Live Licks*, was released in 2004 and added a few guest artists. The band's "A Bigger Bang" tour in 2005 (supporting the CD of the same name) was a huge success, as was the release of their DVD box sets, *Four Flicks* (four full-length Stones concerts) in 2003 and *The Biggest Bang* (a seven-hour documentary) in the summer of 2007, followed in 2008 by a Martin Scorsese documentary entitled *Shine a Light* (the soundtrack reached number 11). Although the Stones have not had a Top 40 hit on the Billboard Hot 100 since 1989 ("Rock and a Hard Place"), they continue to perform to sold-out audiences and release recordings; however, the most successful of these in recent years have been rereleases of earlier albums (e.g., *Exile on Main Street [Deluxe Edition]*). It appears that the Stones are likely to keep on rolling until they drop.

Key Events in the History of the Rolling Stones after Altamont

The Rolling Stones are undeniably one of the most successful bands in the history of rock and roll. The following timeline provides a selected list of important events, both positive and negative, that had an impact on their career.

Date/Year	Content [Narrative]
December 1970	*Gimme Shelter*, a documentary about the Stones tour in 1969, is released containing shocking footage of Meredith Hunter's murder
April 1971	The Stones move to France to avoid tax-related problems in the UK
June 1972	*Exile on Main Street* reaches number 1 on the U.S. charts
September 1973	Release of *Goat's Head Soup* containing a number 1 hit, "Angie"; on the negative side, Keith was arrested several times for possession of drugs and unlicensed weapons
April 1975	Mick Taylor, who joined the band after Brian Jones' death, is replaced by Ronnie Wood
June 1978	Released *Some Girls*, containing the Stones' first number 1 hit in five years
March 1985	First album under CBS record contract was Jagger's solo album (*She's the Boss*, number 13), causing resentment among members of the band
October 1997	*Bridges to Babylon* (number 3) becomes the group's 19th platinum album
Summer 2007	*The Biggest Bang*, a seven-hour documentary about the Stones is released
2008	Martin Scorsese releases *Shine a Light*, another documentary about the Stones

6.1.5: The Bad Boys of Rock

An analysis of the Rolling Stones' music will be reserved for the Musical Close-Up in a later section. Of equal, or perhaps even greater, importance to the history of rock and roll is the band's image. There can be no doubt that Presley, Berry, Lewis, Little Richard, and even the lovable Beatles were less than cherubic choirboys, but many of the less socially acceptable escapades of these and other rock stars were kept deliberately quiet. Certainly, none of them had consciously provoked public displeasure and condemnation (except possibly John Lennon, who sometimes enjoyed controversy for controversy's sake).

The Rolling Stones, however, were the first significant rock group to foster an overtly negative image. Although Oldham consciously hyped their bad-boy image, they seemed to project the image quite effectively by simply being themselves. This image was fostered in two ways: (1) through their personal lives (specifically, Brian Jones, Mick Jagger, and Keith Richards) and (2) through the outrageous antics of their fans.

6.1.6: Rock Listeners Identify as "a Stone" or "a Beatle"

There can be little doubt that the Beatles and the Stones were the leaders of the British Invasion. Both groups

Development of the Rolling Stones' Bad Boys Image

To distinguish themselves from other groups of the era, the Stones intentionally adopted an image that contrasted mightily with that of the Beatles, focusing on already-established stereotypes: sex, drugs, and rock and roll!

Personal Lives—Brian Jones had encountered trouble as early as 1958, when, at the age of 14, he was named as the responsible party by a female classmate who was pregnant. By the age of 20, he had fathered two sons by different girlfriends; he provided no support for either son—both of whom he had named Julian. By 1965, Brian had taken up with Anita Pallenberg. Their relationship was characterized by drugs and alcohol. Anita soon moved on to Keith Richards.

In May 1967, Brian was arrested on a drug charge. He eventually received a sentence of three years' probation and a small fine, plus psychiatric treatment. Brian celebrated his victory with an orgy of drinks and pills that put him into a hospital two days later.

In May 1968, Brian was arrested for drugs again. Among his escapades around this time were a suicide attempt and a fight with Mick that ended when Brian threatened Jagger with a knife. Brian's death in 1969 was hardly a shock to those who knew him.

Keith Richards had started using drugs while a student at Sidcup Art College. A raid on his home in 1967 uncovered drugs and paraphernalia. At a trial in June, Keith was found guilty and sentenced to one year in prison and a £500 fine, later overturned. By 1971, Keith and Anita were buying heroin in consignments that cost £4,000 and using it up in about a month. Keith endured three more drug arrests in 1976 and 1977. Mick Jagger was also arrested in the 1967 raid and was ultimately sentenced to a one-year conditional discharge. The judge lectured Mick, noting that as a celebrity, he was the idol of many young people. The judge continued by saying that due to this serious

responsibility, Mick's punishment should include higher penalties (Norman 1984, 236).

Aggressive Behavior by Fans—The other factor in the bad-boy image was the fans' behavior at Rolling Stones concerts. Granted, fans had rushed the stage at Elvis's performances, and Beatles' fans were capable of all sorts of silliness, but Stones concerts brought fan misbehavior to a whole new level. In 1966, Paris police used clubs and tear gas to subdue 3,000 rioters. In Marseilles, a chair was thrown at Jagger, opening a two-inch cut above his eye. A concert in Lynn, Massachusetts, was stopped by police after only a few minutes. In Vancouver, there were 36 injuries, ranging from minor wounds to broken bones and concussions. In London, a concert was stopped after three minutes when Jagger was attacked by three girls, thus starting a tidal wave toward the stage.

By the late 1960s, the love-and-peace generation had been transformed into the drug-and-violence generation. The decade's political events—the assassination of the president, then Robert Kennedy, then Dr. Martin Luther King, Jr., as well as violence at the National Democratic Convention and rioting in cities—were changing the tenor of the times.

More than any other rock group, the Rolling Stones, with their bad-boy image, became the musical rallying point for anti-social violence. Stones' biographer Philip Norman referred to the *Let It Bleed* album of 1969 as background music for a new, more violent society (Norman 1984, 321–22).

Publicity to Personification—Between the well-publicized personal lifestyle of the individual Stones and the outrageous behavior of their fans, the group became the personification of the most rebellious, most antisocial, most hedonistic side of rock. Many of these activities are captured in great detail in Keith Richards' entertaining—if one-sided—autobiography entitled *Life* (2010). More than any other group, they initiated a path within rock that would lead through the hard rock of the 1970s, the punk rock of the late 1970s and early 1980s, the heavy metal of the 1980s, and the gangsta rap of the 1990s.

Importance of Rolling Stones in Rock History

When Andrew Oldham approached Eric Easton about co-managing the Stones, Easton's only reservation was that they needed to replace Mick Jagger with someone who could sing! So why is this group important? Consider the following:

Since the end of the 1950s, rock had gradually moved away from its R&B roots. Indeed, mainstream rock had seemed on the verge of extinction in the early 1960s. There was soft rock, folk music, surf music, and dance songs, but very little real, raw, basic rock and roll. The British Invasion brought with it the return of mainstream rock. As the Beatles generally veered toward a more sophisticated style, the Stones stimulated a rebirth of more basic, R&B-derived mainstream rock.

This fundamental split within the ranks of the British Invasion is central to the history of rock since the mid-1960s. The Rolling Stones and the Beatles eventually veered off from each other—in close proximity at first, but with widening separation as their styles developed. This fork in rock's mainstream not only determined much about subsequent British rock but also much about rock and roll in general.

Since its beginnings, rock had always had a seamier underside. The Rolling Stones were the first to blatantly shove the darker side of rock into the open, capitalizing on—and reveling in—their reputations as bad boys. Drugs, sex, violence, and the occult—the whole range of the Stones' antisocial behavior—were flaunted as part of their image, and their fans responded in kind, bringing new levels of violence and misbehavior to the rock scene. This trend persists today, as some rock groups fall all over themselves trying to out-shock and out-repulse their predecessors.

Finally, the Stones deserve an important place in rock history simply because of their longevity. Since 1962, they have persevered through changing styles and all manner of personal adversity. Few other rock groups in history have held a comparable position of importance for such a long time.

sprang from the same musical soil: a fascination with 1950s rock and roll and its R&B roots. But the Stones were more interested in basic R&B for its own sake. They were the most prominent among the bands referred to as the British blues bands. With only a few side excursions along the way, they continued to develop their R&B-influenced mainstream rock style. The Beatles, on the other hand, struck out into new musical territory, developing precedents for new variants of rock and roll and significantly expanding the boundaries of the style.

Yet the two groups were not on exactly equal footing. The Beatles were considered *the* group and the Stones their challengers. It is not surprising that, although the Stones were, at times, resentful of the Beatles' success, they sometimes expressed the sincerest form of flattery: imitation.

However, the eventual success of the Rolling Stones did not lie within their Beatles simulations. Their reputation and successes were based on their contrasts with the Beatles. Perhaps it finally took the disappointment of *Their Satanic Majesties Request* to show them that they would need to let the Beatles be the Beatles and allow themselves to be the Rolling Stones.

6.1.7: Relevance of the Rolling Stones

The Rolling Stones hold an important position in the history of rock and roll. To be sure, they were not musical creators and innovators at the level of the Beach Boys and the Beatles.

JOURNAL

Contrasting Images

While the musical styles of the Beatles and the Rolling Stones varied significantly, the difference in the image each band portrayed in the 1960s was equally distinctive. After reading the material presented so far in this chapter, search a video archive, like YouTube, for performances by the Beatles and the Rolling Stones during the mid to late 1960s, acknowledging that performances by the Beatles are limited during the late 1960s. In your own words, compare the two groups on their manner of performance, dress, musical styles, interactions with the audience, and other distinguishing characteristics. Had you been a listener during this period, would you have considered yourself "a Beatle" or "a Stone"? Provide at least three reasons for your choice.

 The response entered here will appear in the performance dashboard and can be viewed by your instructor.

Submit

6.2: Musical Close-Up on the Musical Style of the Rolling Stones

OBJECTIVE: Analyze the musical style of the Rolling Stones

The key words in considering the musical style of the Rolling Stones are *simplicity* and *repetition*. In this Musical Close-Up, we will briefly examine a dozen or so Stones' songs and then take a more detailed look at two of their

Examples of the Musical Style of the Rolling Stones

In an earlier section of this course, we examined the complexity of the innovative musical style of the Beatles. In contrast, the music of the Stones remained rooted in the blues and R&B, excluding a brief foray with *Their Satanic Majesty's Request* in 1967 a few months after the release of the Beatles' *Sgt. Pepper.* This module provides an opportunity to closely examine the music of the Stones.

Musical Example #1: "Heart of Stone"

"Heart of Stone" —"Heart of Stone" is also based on a 12-bar form, but the chords do not follow the traditional blues progression.

    Click or tap the play button in the Revel course to watch this musical example of "Heart of Stone."

    Introduction (two measures)

    A (12-bar blues plus 4-bar extension and 1-bar connection)

    A (12-bar blues plus 4-bar extension)

    B (8-bar bridge)

    A (12-bar blues plus 4-bar extension)

    Instrumental Break (3 bars)

    B (8-bar bridge)

    A (12-bar blues)

    Fade-out on repeated I-chord **riff**

This chorus is repeated three times, followed by a fade-out that repeats the last two measures. Remember the key words: *simplicity* and *repetition*. (Throughout these examples, an asterisk indicates a *chromatic chord*; i.e., one that is outside the prevailing key.)

Musical Example #2: "Paint It Black"

"Paint It Black" —"Paint It Black" uses only two progressions, each four bars long, that alternate until near the end of the song, as shown above. For the fade-out, the first four bars (i and V) are repeated over and over.

    Click or tap the play button in the Revel course to watch a musical example of "Paint It Black."

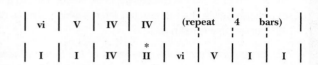

Musical Example #3: "Under My Thumb"

"Under My Thumb" —"Under My Thumb" is based on a 16-bar chorus, as shown above. This 16-bar chorus is repeated until the fade-out, which consists of an extended repetition of the I chord.

    Click or tap the play button in the Revel course to watch a musical example of "Under My Thumb."

| I | IV | V | IV | (repeated 7 more times; total phrase = 16 bars) |

| I | iii | IV | V | (repeat 2 more times) | ♭VII | V | (= 8 bars) |

Musical Example #4: "Get Off My Cloud"

"Get Off My Cloud" —"Get Off My Cloud" uses only two simple harmonic patterns that appear throughout the song.

    Click or tap the play button in the Revel course to watch a musical example of "Get Off My Cloud."

---

most famous songs: "Satisfaction" and "Sympathy for the Devil."

    In their many hits of the mid- and late 1960s, the Stones preserved the general feeling of the blues, the shouting vocal style, and the blues scale. But they rarely adhered to the traditional 12-bar blues form and its prescribed chord pattern. An exception to this rule is "19th Nervous Breakdown," which begins with what sounds like a traditional 12-bar blues. However, it is extended by two extra measures of the IV chord and two extra measures of I (plus one connecting measure of I). This extended 16-bar blues chorus plus an eight-measure bridge forms the basis of the song.

6.2.1: Analyses of the Style of the Stones

As these analyses suggest, the Stones tended to favor *diatonic* chords (i.e., chords within the prevailing scale) set into traditional, symmetrical phrases of 4, 8, 12, or 16 measures.

    The Rolling Stones have remained masters of the blues- and R&B-based mainstream rock sound, creating high energy music with songs built on a foundation of Keith Richard's guitar riffs and chord progressions that remain mostly diatonic. While to the elite music listener, their recordings may not match the level of musical innovation inherent in the music of the Beatles or the Beach Boys, the sound of the Stones has certainly remained popular and the group has outlasted either of the more musically innovative groups.

Musical Elements of the Rolling Stones' Songs

Chord—The chord progressions are simple and repetitive. Chromatic chords are not used frequently (confirmed by the minimal presence of asterisks in the figures above), the major chord on the second scale degree (II) being the most common. Also encountered are the ♭VII and ♭III, both of which are common in blues-related styles, since they are simply major triads built on the "blue" seventh and "blue" third scale degrees. The 4-bar, 8-bar, and 16-bar units are simply repeated to create the total song length.

Rhythm—Similarly, there is little rhythmic variance from the norms established by earlier rock styles. The Stones adhere primarily to quadruple meter with a strong backbeat on the second and fourth beats usually present. Most Stones songs divide each beat into duple divisions, while a few slower songs (e.g., "Time Is on My Side" and "Heart of Stone") use a triple division of the beat.

Timbre—The common timbre of the Stones' music is modified occasionally by the use of additional instruments: marimba on "Under My Thumb," some fine saxophone work on "Brown Sugar," and a variety of instruments on "Ruby Tuesday" (recorder, cello, and piano) and "You Can't Always Get What You Want" (French horn, organ, piano, and choir).

Mick Jagger's vocal timbre is heavily influenced by the shouting blues style (listen to "Get Off My Cloud" for a good illustration). Jagger lacks a rich vocal quality and is often slightly off pitch. He frequently adds spoken improvisations and interpolations like "oh, my, my, my," "easy, baby," and "yes, it is." Listen to "Time Is on My Side" for a good example of Jagger's spoken interpolations. There is also occasional use of vocal falsetto.

Melody—The Stones' melodies are not as sophisticated as those by Lennon and McCartney (or Harrison). Melody was not a particularly important parameter in R&B nor is it with the Stones. Like their harmonic style, their melodic style usually adheres to the prevailing scale and is rather repetitive. Use of the blues scale is common ("Gimme Shelter"). It is not accidental that relatively few of the Stones' tunes have been covered in Pop versions (as happened frequently to Beatles tunes). Taken out of their blues-based rock context, they do not seem to lend themselves to other stylistic interpretations.

BECOME AN ACTIVE LISTENER: A MUSICAL "TREASURE HUNT"

Mainstream rock based on the blues and R&B continues to provide inspiration for contemporary rock music. Now that you have studied more carefully some examples from the Rolling Stones' catalogue, it is time to use your ears to find some of the common elements of mainstream rock in the music you listen to today.

Find examples of these elements in the music that you enjoy
1. Repeated, simple harmony pattern
2. Shouted, blues-style vocals
3. The blues scale
4. A memorable riff (like the guitar in the opening bars of "Satisfaction")

6.2.2: "Satisfaction"

Before leaving the Stones, let us take a close look at two of their most popular works: "Satisfaction" and "Sympathy for the Devil."

Analysis of the Musical Style of "Satisfaction"

phrase A:	I	I	IV	IV
phrase A (repeated):	I	I	IV	IV
phrase B:	I	V	I	IV
phrase C (riff):	I	♭VII*	I	♭VII*

"(I Can't Get No) Satisfaction"

"Satisfaction" has as its nucleus a 16-bar chorus consisting of four 4-bar phrases as shown above.
   Click or tap the play button in the Revel to watch a musical example of "(I Can't Get No) Satisfaction."

scale degrees: 5 5   5 6 ♭7   ♭7 ♭7 6 6 5

E: I   ♭VII

"(I Can't Get No) Satisfaction" Guitar Riff

Phrase 2 is a repetition of phrase 1; phrase 3 is contrasting; phrase 4 is the signature guitar riff from which the other sections of the song are derived as shown above.

Click or tap the play button in the Revel to watch a musical example of the guitar riff in "(I Can't Get No) Satisfaction."

Note: Phrase C = guitar riff (R)

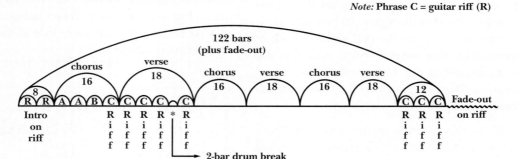

Phrase C- Guitar Riff

The entire song consists of the 16-bar chorus described and represented above alternating with the verses that are sung over this guitar riff. The figure above shows the formal scheme of the entire song.

The verses consist of four repetitions of the 4-bar guitar riff interrupted between the third and fourth repetitions by a 2-bar drum break, resulting in an asymmetrical 18-bar section.

6.2.3: "Sympathy for the Devil"

"Sympathy for the Devil" never reached the Top 40, but most Stones' fans consider it one of the group's most representative songs from the 1960s. It consists of two four-measure progressions that are repeated throughout the song's six-minute length:

E: I   ♭VII   IV   I   V   V   I   (IV)   I

"Sympathy for the Devil"

Thus, the basic harmonic vocabulary is limited to four chords: I, IV, V, and ♭VII. Each chorus consists of six phrases: four repetitions of pattern A and two repetitions of pattern B. On the fourth occurrence of pattern A, the last measure is repeated, creating a 5-bar phrase. The entire formal structure is represented in the following Listening Guide.

Listening Guide: "Sympathy for the Devil" (the Rolling Stones)

0:00–0:20	Introduction (10 bars)	Establishes a samba-like accompaniment; maracas added in measure four.
0:21–0:56	Chorus I: first section (17 measures)	Lead vocal ("Please . . .") and full accompaniment enter. Four repetitions of chord pattern A; three 4-bar phrases and a 5-bar phrase (last measure is extended).
0:57–1:13	Chorus I: second section (8 measures)	"Pleased . . ." Two repetitions of chord pattern B resulting in two 4-bar phrases.
1:14–1:57	Chorus II (25 measures)	Same as Chorus I (with new lyrics in first section).
1:58–2:50	Chorus III (25 measures)	Same as Chorus I (with new lyrics in first section). Add background vocals ("ooh-ooh").

2:51–3:42	Chorus IV (25 measures)	Same as Chorus III. Guitar lead replaces vocal in first section; vocal returns for second section.
3:43–4:35	Chorus V (25 measures)	Same as Chorus III (new lyrics in first section).
4:36–6:24	Closing Section	Chord pattern A (4-bar phrases) repeated to fade-out (about 1 minute, 48 seconds). Lead vocal and guitar improvise interjections.

Based on a comparative analysis of the musical parameters (harmony, rhythm, melody, form, texture, and timbre), "Sympathy for the Devil" is really rather simple, basic, and repetitive. Its appeal, via its insistent rhythm and repetitive melodic and formal units, is visceral, rather than challenging to the musical mind. For example, compare the analysis above to the analysis of Blood, Sweat, and Tears' version of the same song that is featured in a discussion of jazz rock later in the course. The greater sophistication of that arrangement is reflected in the more complex analysis required. However, it is the Stones' simplicity and repetitiveness that are at the heart of their appeal to many listeners—fans who do not wish to be bothered by innovation and complexity. Certainly the Stones represent a marked contrast to the Beatles, with all the latter's creativity and musical experimentation. Starting from similar positions, these two British groups diverged onto different paths, each leading the way to very different but highly successful styles of rock and roll.

JOURNAL

Identifying Musical Form

As an opportunity to exercise listening skills you are beginning to develop, select one of your favorite songs in which you can identify a significant amount of musical repetition. (It is important to differentiate between lyrical repetition [i.e., the words spoken or sung] and repetition of the musical melodies or chord progressions.) Listen to the song several times, carefully identifying repeating sections and sections that provide musical contrast. Using either the arch form diagram format

used for "Satisfaction" or the textual format used in the Listening Guide, provide a representation of the form of your chosen song.

> The response entered here will appear in the performance dashboard and can be viewed by your instructor.

Submit

6.3:   All the Others

OBJECTIVE: Summarize the success of other British groups during the 1960s

In the wake of the Beatles and the Rolling Stones came a tidal wave of English rock groups. These artists achieved considerable success from 1964 to 1966, before the first wave of the British Invasion dissipated, leaving only the Beatles and Stones as continuing hit makers. In the late 1960s, there was a second wave that would have its primary effect in the early 1970s and beyond.

6.3.1: The First Wave

The first-wave British groups were often identified by their geographic origin. For our purposes, however, it is more useful to think of them as they line up stylistically behind the Beatles or the Stones. The most numerous and commercially successful were the Beatle-like groups.

The table below summarizes some of the more successful of these groups.

Table 6.1 Successful First-Wave Groups in the British Invasion

Group	Geographic Origin	Representative Hits	Comments
The Dave Clark Five	London	"Glad All Over" (number 6, 1964); "Bits and Pieces" (number 4, 1964); "Over and Over" (number 1, 1965)	Clark was drummer and manager; group used guitars, bass, drums, and tenor sax; "Bits and Pieces" was slightly harder than most of their songs
The Searchers	Liverpool	"Needles and Pins" (number 13, 1964); "Love Potion No. Nine" (number 3, 1964)	Sang many covers of American hits; a softer style; sophisticated and pleasant
Peter and Gordon	London	"A World Without Love" (number 1, 1964)	Peter Asher and Gordon Waller had hits with several McCartney songs; Asher became a producer for Apple Records and, later, an important U.S. producer (for James Taylor and Linda Ronstadt, among others)
Billy J. Kramer and the Dakotas	Manchester	"Little Children" (number 7, 1965); "Bad to Me" (number 9, 1964)	Followed Beatles' pattern (managed by Epstein, Hamburg appearances, Parlophone recordings produced by Martin); recorded many Beatles songs; more popular in England than in the United States
Gerry and the Pacemakers	Liverpool	"Don't Let the Sun Catch You Crying" (number 4, 1964); "Ferry Across the Mersey" (number 6, 1965)	Popular in England, along with the Beatles in 1963; followed the Epstein-Martin pattern; soft, sophisticated style

Group	Geographic Origin	Representative Hits	Comments
Freddie and the Dreamers	Manchester	"I'm Telling You Now" (number 1, 1965); "Do the Freddie" (number 18, 1965)	Successful in England prior to American hits; the "Freddie" capitalized on the U.S. dance craze; lovable and humorous
Wayne Fontana and the Mind-Benders	Manchester	"Game of Love" (number 1, 1965); "A Groovy Kind of Love" (number 2, 1966)	Slightly harder sound
Herman's Hermits	Manchester	"I'm into Something Good" (number 13, 1964); "Can't You Hear My Heartbeat" (number 2, 1965); "Mrs. Brown You've Got a Lovely Daughter" (number 1, 1965); "I'm Henry VIII, I Am" (number 1, 1965); "There's a Kind of Hush" (number 4, 1967)	The most popular of these groups; lead singer was Peter Noone; if the Beatles were lovable, Herman's Hermits were downright squeezable
The Hollies	Lancashire (debut in Manchester)	"Bus Stop" (number 5, 1966); "Stop Stop Stop" (number 7, 1966)	Group's name derived from Buddy Holly; numerous personnel changes; they continued through the 1970s and into the 1980s

6.3.2: Blues-Based British Groups

When discussing the Rolling Stones, we noted that they were a blues-based band. Their general sound, basic harmonic vocabulary, shouting vocal style, and frequent use of the blues scale suggest their derivation from the older R&B style. A significant number of first-wave British Invasion groups followed the lead of the Stones as they moved away from the Beatles' image and musical style. Actually, the real initiator of the British blues trend was John Mayall, whose group, the Bluesbreakers, never enjoyed a Top 40 hit in the United States; their highest charting single was "Don't Waste My Time" (number 81 in 1969), which remains relatively unknown. Mayall's Bluesbreakers, formed in 1962, and they were an authentic blues band (as opposed to a blues-based rock and roll band). Mayall used a number of young musicians who would go on to play in other significant British rock bands (e.g., Mick Taylor of the Rolling Stones, John McVie and Mick Fleetwood of Fleetwood Mac, and Eric Clapton of the Yardbirds and Cream). The Bluesbreakers played an authentic style of basic R&B, incorporating the 12-bar blues progression, the blues scale, and the shouting vocal style. Mayall has continued performing extensively into the new millennium, placing several albums in the Top 10 on *Billboard*'s top-selling blues albums chart: *Blues for the Lost Days* (1997), *Along for the Ride* (2001), *John Mayall & the Bluesbreakers* (2004), *Road Dogs* (2005), *In the Place of the King* (2007), and *Tough* (2009).

The blues purity of Alexis Korner's Blues Incorporated and Mayall's Bluesbreakers was converted into a blues-based rock style by the Rolling Stones and their followers in the first wave of British Invasion groups.

The table below describes some of these bands.

Table 6.2 Blues-Based Rock Groups in the First Wave

Group	Geographic Origin	Representative Hits	Comments
The Animals	Newcastle upon Tyne	"House of the Rising Sun" (number 1, 1964); "We Gotta Get Out of This Place" (number 13, 1965); "Don't Let Me Be Misunderstood" (number 15, 1965)	Lead singer: Eric Burdon; occasionally used a shouting vocal style
Manfred Mann	Johannesburg, South Africa	"Do Wah Diddy Diddy" (number 1, 1964); "Sha La La" (number 12, 1965); "Pretty Flamingo" (number 29, 1966); "Mighty Quinn (Quinn the Eskimo)" (number 10, 1968)	Mann (Michael Lubowitz) attended the Juilliard School of Music; originally a blues-based band (e.g., "Why Should We Not," "Got My Mojo Working," and "Hoochie Coochie"); drifted toward folk-oriented style ("With God on Our Side") and soft rock ("Sha La La")
The Kinks	London	"You Really Got Me" (number 7, 1964); "All Day and All of the Night" (number 7, 1965); "Tired of Waiting for You" (number 6, 1965)	Organized by Ray and David Davies; built an image similar to the Rolling Stones, both on- and offstage
The Zombies	St. Albans	"She's Not There" (number 2, 1964); "Tell Her No" (number 6, 1965); "Time of the Season" (number 3, 1969)	Like Manfred Mann, their style varies; "She's Not There" and "I Want You Back" have the harder blues-based sound; "Tell Her No" moves closer to the Beatles' sound
Troggs	Wiltshire	"Wild Thing" (number 1, 1966); "Love Is All Around" (number 7, 1968)	Began by trying to out-Stone the Stones, but their third U.S. hit ("Love Is All Around") was a softer ballad

6.3.3: From Blues-Based Rock to Hard Rock

If one is looking for a direct line from these blues-based bands to the hard rock and heavy metal bands of the 1970s and 1980s, one need only look at the Yardbirds. The Yardbirds realized their initial success with a song called "For Your Love" (number 6 in the U.S., 1965). A quintet, the Yardbirds boasted a series of lead guitarists, each of whom would have a significant impact on later rock: Eric Clapton (earlier a member of the Bluesbreakers and later a founder of Cream), Jimmy Page (Led Zeppelin), and Jeff Beck.

Prior to their first hit, the Yardbirds played straight R&B but moved to the newer blues-based rock sound popularized by the Stones and the Animals. Their third hit, "I'm a Man," recorded earlier by Muddy Waters and Bo Diddley, is closer to the traditional blues style. The next hit, "Shapes of Things," contains a guitar instrumental break that sounds way ahead of its time—closer to the sounds of the hard rock groups of the 1970s. Clapton, when he was with the Yardbirds in the band's early days, had initiated such improvisatory breaks, calling them **rave-ups**. These instrumental sections could go on for as long as 30 minutes and were the forerunners of the lengthy instrumental solos that typified the San Francisco bands in the later 1960s. The Yardbirds' last U.S. Top 40 hit, "Happenings Ten Years' Time Ago," presages the hard rock and heavy metal sounds of the 1970s and 1980s. In 1968, the Yardbirds disbanded; Jimmy Page tried at first to organize a group known as the New Yardbirds but finally changed the name to Led Zeppelin, a band that would become seminal in the transition to the 1970s.

Summary: The British Invasion

In his article on the British Invasion in *The Rolling Stone Illustrated History of Rock and Roll*, Lester Bangs poses a reasonable question: "It might legitimately be asked whether more than a handful of British Invasion bands would have made the States, and rock history, if they hadn't ridden in on the Beatles' coattails" (Miller 1980, 176). While true, the fact remains that all the bands discussed here (and more) did cross the Atlantic in the wake of the Beatles and the Stones. In doing so, they reinforced the musical directions established by the Beatles and the Stones and, thus, laid the groundwork for many more British rock groups throughout the 1970s.

Take Note: The British Invasion

- *What was the impact of the British Invasion on American popular music?*—From the Beatles' arrival in America in early 1964, it seemed as though the Hot 100 was dominated by British Invasion acts. In fact, the British bands only produced about a quarter of all the number 1 hits from 1964 to 1969. However, the impact of these groups was undeniable in terms of sound and style. The British Invasion groups fell into two basic categories: soft rockers and more rebellious R&B-derived groups. This split set a precedent for post-1964 rock.

- *How did the Rolling Stones transform rock music during the 1960s and early 1970s?*—The Rolling Stones represented the more rebellious, iconoclastic, blues- and R&B-derived side of rock, compared with the "safer" sound and look of the Beatles. They cultivated an image as the "bad boys" of rock and roll, capitalizing on their reputation for dabbling in drugs, sex, violence, and the occult. While this image helped sell records, it also inspired unfortunate incidents of violence at their concerts, such as the murderous actions of the Hells Angels at the Altamont concert in 1969, an event that lives on in infamy.

- *What other British Invasion bands played a role in shaping rock during this period?*—Most British Invasion bands fell neatly into two major categories, softer rockers in the Beatles' mold and more rebellious blues-based rockers like the Stones. Beatles-like groups included the Dave Clark Five, Gerry and the Pacemakers, Herman's Hermits, and the Hollies; while blues-influenced groups included the Animals, Manfred Mann, the Kinks, and the Troggs.

SHARED WRITING

Primary Influences on Your Favorite Music

In this chapter, you read about and listened to music by the Beatles and the Rolling Stones, and learned that most bands in the first wave of the British Invasion tended to identify more strongly with one approach or the other ("a Beatle" or "a Stone" method). Listen to several of your current favorite songs. Do you hear direct influences of either or both of these approaches? Using your developing musical vocabulary, identify which approach—the Beatles or the Stones—appears most influential on the recording(s) you selected. Identify at least five specific examples of this influence and, using your own words, describe them as thoroughly as you can. After you have completed this assignment, share your answer with two or three of your peers and carefully consider their work. Do you hear the same influences as your friends? Are there any points of disagreement that might lead to intense discussion about these musical styles of the mid- to late 1960s?

 A minimum number of characters is required to post and earn points. After posting, your response can be viewed by your class and instructor, and you can participate in the class discussion. \

Post   0 characters | 140 minimum

Chapter 7
Folk Music and Folk Rock

 Learning Objectives

7.1 Relate socio-political events of the 1960s to the folk music trend

7.2 Explain how Bob Dylan's music impacted the folk music trend

7.3 Describe the musical forms used most commonly by Bob Dylan

7.4 Describe the role of the Byrds in establishing the foundation of folk rock

7.5 Compare the significant contributions of other folk musicians of the 1960s

During the transitional period from 1950s rock and roll (mainstream rock, rockabilly, and soft rock) to the styles that emerged in the early 1960s, we have discussed the important role played by the folk music trend represented by the Kingston Trio; Peter, Paul, and Mary; and other artists, in which the musical accompaniment was typically provided by acoustic instruments and the lyrics took on a role of much greater significance, addressing important social and political issues. That musical trend laid the foundation for the folk music and **folk rock** described in this chapter, including the central role of the protest song during a period of unrest.

7.1: The Youth Generation of the 1960s

OBJECTIVE: Relate socio-political events of the 1960s to the folk music trend

The early phases of the folk music movement were characterized by a new sense of optimism under the Kennedy administration, but Kennedy's assassination on November 22, 1963, burst that optimism; by the end of the decade, disillusionment, violence, drug abuse, and generally antisocial behavior (as at Altamont) seemed to prevail. So what were the youth of the 1960s really like?

7.1.1: Generational Perspectives

The 1950s were dominated by a Republican administration and tended to be years of political and social conservatism. The 1960s, in contrast, were liberal years dominated by Democratic administrations, and they witnessed significant social change. One of the first issues to be taken up by the youth was racial integration—the civil rights movement. Young people participated in a variety of demonstrations intended to focus attention on racial segregation and discrimination. The movement achieved an important milestone in 1965 with the passage of major civil rights legislation. Impressed with their ability to have a measurable impact and to effect change, the youth turned their attention to another major problem: the Vietnam War. This one proved to be an even bigger challenge. As American involvement grew and more youth were involuntarily drafted to participate in a war of which they disapproved, the protests grew more adamant. The youth were less successful in this effort than they had been in the civil rights campaign. The war escalated throughout the 1960s and did not end until the early 1970s; the frustration caused by the war may be a partial explanation for the city riots and other violence that erupted in the late 1960s.

There was also growing concern about the environment: air and water were being polluted, oil and gas resources were dwindling, and forests were being used up at an alarming rate. These concerns led to a new consciousness of the value of natural products. Natural foods became an important trend. Along with this awareness came a deep suspicion of technology, from the automobile to the newly evolving (at the time) computer industry.

7.1.2: Self-Exploration and Sexual Revolution

Interestingly, the concern for the rights and well-being of others was counterbalanced by a growing concern for the self. Spiritual paths, such as Zen Buddhism, transcendental meditation, and various gurus, along with recreational drugs, such as marijuana and LSD, were touted as ways to achieve greater self-knowledge and hyped as "mind expanding" experiences. The coexistence of the interest in drug use and a new emphasis on natural health foods was one of the odd contradictions of this period.

Ironically, the peace-conscious youth ultimately resorted to violence. Peaceful demonstrations often got out of hand when protesters were confronted by police who were dispatched to exercise crowd control. Political violence flared at universities across the nation, culminating in 1968 with riots at the Democratic National Convention and the tragic killing of four students by members of the Ohio National Guard at Kent State University (1970), hauntingly referenced in Crosby, Stills, Nash, & Young's "Ohio," recorded just weeks after the shooting. Undoubtedly, youth violence was exacerbated by the frustration resulting from the assassinations of the U.S. president and such youth heroes as Robert Kennedy and Martin Luther King, Jr.

In response, many youth just "dropped out." They grew their hair longer and longer, dressed in ever more outlandish styles, and ran away to communes in San Francisco and other points west. Increasingly, cultural heroes were not good-looking, righteous knights on white horses, but antiheroes. Movie heroes were often bums, prostitutes, and general ne'er-do-wells, and popular rock and roll groups made up of drug abusing, womanizing bad boys (the Rolling Stones) were admiringly accepted. Cultural icons like Timothy Leary—an ex-Harvard professor who became a proponent of LSD use—urged young people to "turn on, tune in, and drop out." The original idealistic goals of transforming mainstream society were abandoned for a life of self-exploration (some would say self-indulgence).

A poignant "Port Huron Statement" was written in 1962 by Students for a Democratic Society, a brief excerpt of which is provided below:

> Doubt has replaced hopefulness—and men act out of a defeatism that is labeled realistic. The decline of utopia and hope is in fact one of the defining features of social life today.... To be idealistic is to be considered apocalyptic, deluded. (Otto 2016, 145)

Bertrand Russell, a highly respected British mathematician, provided little help to alleviate the fear and disillusion felt by the youth generation when he stated in a 1963 interview for *Playboy* magazine that

> The human race may well become extinct before the end of the present century. Speaking as a mathematician, I should say that the odds are about three to one against survival. [Thankfully, his prediction was wrong.] The risk of war by accident—an unintended war triggered by an explosive situation such as that in Cuba—remains and indeed grows greater all the time. (Otto 2016, p. 147)

This was the same era during which The Who proclaimed loudly on their first album, "I hope I die before I get old" and Jack Weinberg, free-speech activist at Berkeley warned, "Don't trust anybody over thirty" (Otto 2016, p. 151). Otto goes on to encapsulate these feelings and acknowledge one proactive step taken: "Feeling powerless, these baby boomers needed an outlet for their anger and distrust of science, government, and the older generation. They adopted the protest song of folk music" (p. 152).

Finally, there was the sexual revolution. Women began to be seen as equals, and youth began to abandon the sexual stereotypes of the past. Skirts were shortened to well above the knee. Cohabitation and communal living became more common. The slogan "Freedom Now" referred not only to the end of racial discrimination, but also to the loosening of sexual mores.

The 1960s were turbulent, troublesome, exciting, tragic, and revolutionary, and the results of that decade continue to affect society well into the twenty-first century. To be sure, music was an essential part of the 1960s. The music reflected much of society's concerns and feelings, but it also reinforced attitudes and beliefs and helped modify value systems, spreading the changes to an ever-widening segment of the population. Many were motivated by music to act, and music became the soundtrack for national tragedies, upheaval, and unrest. The Beatles, Bob Dylan, the Rolling Stones, soul music, and acid rock—for those who lived through those times, it is impossible to separate the music from the experience itself.

JOURNAL

Finding a Path out of Disillusionment

While the level of disillusionment was undeniably high during the mid- to late 1960s, every youth generation is faced with its own unique challenges. Identify one specific social, political, or personal issue about which you feel extremely passionate—the greater the passion, the better. Describe the factors that led to the present situation and enumerate three to five actions that you and your peers could take to resolve this matter. Can you identify any rock artists who address these issues directly in their music? Do you feel that the role of popular music artists today is as central to resolving significant societal issues as it proved to be during the 1960s? Explain the basis for your conclusion.

 The response entered here will appear in the performance dashboard and can be viewed by your instructor.

Submit

7.2: Bob Dylan

OBJECTIVE: Explain how Bob Dylan's music impacted the folk music trend

The youth movement of the early 1960s was closely identified with the folk music trend exemplified by the Kingston Trio and Peter, Paul, and Mary. These serious, socially conscious youth shunned rock and roll as commercial junk. The result seemed to be an irreparable split between the "folkies" and the "rockers." But from within the folk movement came a singer who would bring together the two factions and have a revolutionary impact on the nature of rock and roll. His name was Bob Dylan.

Robert Zimmerman was born in Duluth, Minnesota, on May 24, 1941. Six years later, he and his family moved 75 miles northwest to the small town of Hibbing. He attended the University of Minnesota for several months but dropped out late in 1960. He hung around the coffeehouses and small clubs in Dinkytown (adjacent to campus), singing and playing guitar whenever he could. In this atmosphere, he absorbed a good dose of folk music, especially songs by his hero Woody Guthrie. Hearing that Guthrie was dying of Huntington's disease in a New York City hospital, Bob Dylan (Zimmerman's newly adopted professional name) decided to leave Minnesota, to seek fame and fortune in the big city, and to meet Guthrie.

After moving to New York City in 1961, Dylan visited with Guthrie on numerous occasions and, through this seminal folk musician, was welcomed into the city's folk scene, centered to a large degree in Greenwich Village. Accompanied only by his own acoustic guitar and harmonica, Dylan auditioned for Columbia Records' John Hammond. Among the songs Dylan sang at that audition was "You're No Good," an old folk song by Jesse Fuller. Listen to that song (on his first album) and honestly decide whether you would have recommended Mr. Dylan for a major label recording contract. Hammond's instincts and intuitions as a talent scout should be truly appreciated. For whatever reasons, John Hammond foresaw a future for this scruffy, raw, and untrained singer.

7.2.1: Dylan's Early Music

Dylan's first album (*Bob Dylan*) was released in March 1962. It contained traditional folk songs and blues tunes plus two original songs by Dylan: "Song to Woody," a tribute to his hero, and "Talkin' New York," sung in the **talking blues** style developed by blues singer Huddie Ledbetter (Leadbelly) and popularized by Woody Guthrie. In this type of song, a story is half-spoken, half-sung (or intoned) over a simple chordal accompaniment. Dylan's "Talkin' New York" is autobiographical as it tells of his leaving the "Wild West" to settle in New York City. Even in

this early song, there are hints of Dylan's primary talent: the ability to write lyrics with artistic skill. The song also reveals the dry wit and sarcasm that would be heard in many future Dylan songs.

Bob Dylan recording his first Columbia album, 1963.
SOURCE: Everett Collection Historical/Alamy Stock Photo

The follow-up album, *The Freewheelin' Bob Dylan* (1963), contained all original material and caught the attention of the folk community. It contained one of Dylan's most important songs: "Blowin' in the Wind." This song was covered by Peter, Paul, and Mary, resulting in a number 2 hit that became an anthem for the youth movement. This song provided a strong indication of the skill and promise evident in this young artist, expressing the optimism and confidence inherent in the youth movement prior to those tragic gunshots in Dallas. But the album also contained one of Dylan's most bitter songs, "Masters of War," as well as the, typically, wry love song, "Don't Think Twice, It's All Right" (also covered successfully by Peter, Paul, and Mary). Finally, there is the sheer poetic beauty of "A Hard Rain's a-Gonna Fall," which refers to a whole spectrum of humanity's self-destructive tendencies.

In the summer of 1963, Dylan appeared at the Newport Folk Festival, a major annual gathering for fans of folk music. Introduced by Joan Baez, he brought the concert to an emotional climax with "Blowin' in the Wind." Joining Baez; Peter, Paul, and Mary; Pete Seeger; Theodore Bikel; and other folk stars, he sang the civil rights anthem, "We Shall Overcome."

With *The Times They Are a-Changin'* (1964), Dylan emerged as a major star of the folk movement. Still accompanied only by his acoustic guitar and harmonica, he sang songs about war (the sarcastic "With God on

Our Side") and racial prejudice ("The Lonesome Death of Hattie Carroll"). The title song on this album, "The Times They Are a-Changin'," is another youth anthem in the vein of "Blowin' in the Wind." Compared to the earlier anthem, however, this song has a rougher edge. Dylan warns the establishment that there is a new force in the nation and that they had better adapt to it or they'll "sink like a stone" in the floods of change. By this time, Dylan was widely recognized as the messiah of the youth folk movement.

7.2.2: Folk Rock is Born

As the mid-1960s approached, Dylan's music began to evolve in both lyrical content and sound. In the next section, we will look closely at some of those specific changes.

7.2.3: Dylan's Later Music

In January 1968, Dylan released his first album since the accident. *John Wesley Harding* reflected yet another change in direction. His voice was more mellow and pleasing; there was little of the old anger and protest against world problems or the heavy folk rock of *Highway 61 Revisited* or *Blonde on Blonde*. True to Dylan's enigmatic style, though, the jacket notes are surrealistic and almost impossible to decipher logically. Dylan's lyrics followed this same pattern. For example, "All Along the Watchtower" seems to be an interesting story, but we are never exactly sure what it is about.

Dylan's last album of the 1960s was *Nashville Skyline* (1969), containing a number 7 hit, "Lay Lady Lay." Once again, he surprised fans with an unexpected turn, this time toward a country sound. Among the musicians on the album were Charlie Daniels, Johnny Cash, and Chet Atkins. The presence of steel guitars made the country influence obvious.

Bob Dylan's Contributions to the Origin of Folk Rock

Prior to 1965, Bob Dylan was identified as a recognized leader of the folk music trend, into which he fit perfectly with his socially conscious lyrics accompanied by acoustic instruments. As his musical style evolved, the sound of his music, in particular, began to change. Some of the most important of those changes are enumerated in this section.

Dylan's next album, *Another Side of Bob Dylan,* was a bit of a surprise. He seemed to pull back from the leading edge of protest and appeared to be more mellow and contemplative. Throughout his career, Dylan seemed to dislike being stereotyped; as soon as he felt his image was becoming too stabilized, he moved in a new direction. If *Another Side* was a mild surprise to Dylan's following, the single that hit the Hot 100 chart in May 1965 was even more unsettling. "Subterranean Homesick Blues" only rose to number 39 but started a ripple that would become a tsunami. The "problem" was the music. It used a drum set and electric guitars; in fact, it sounded suspiciously like rock.

Dylan's next album, *Bringing It All Back Home,* used electric instruments on half of its songs. The folkies' worst fears were confirmed in July 1965 at the Newport Folk Festival, when Dylan's much-anticipated appearance created a near-riot as he strolled onto the stage with an electric guitar and proceeded to perform to the accompaniment of the Paul Butterfield Blues Band. Amid the booing and hissing, few realized that a new musical style had been born: folk rock. To Dylan's horrified followers, it seemed that he had "sold out" and "gone commercial." For others, he had presciently provided a path to an alternate future.

Actually, in March 1965 (prior to Dylan's performance in Newport), the Byrds had adapted his "Mr. Tambourine Man" to their rock style and released it as a single, but it did not reach number 1 until

June 26. So, who invented folk rock—the Byrds or Dylan? Dylan's "Subterranean Homesick Blues" hit the Hot 100 first, but the Byrds' single hit number 1, whereas Dylan's barely cracked the Top 40 (and then only for one week). Let us just say that the Byrds and Dylan hit on the folk rock style at about the same time and can share the credit—or blame, depending on your perspective.

As if to further confound his fans, Dylan released another electrified single called "Like a Rolling Stone" (August 1965). This six-minute song (included on the *Highway 61 Revisited* album) became his first major hit, rising to number 2 and breaking the radio industry's two-and-a-half-minute norms. "Like a Rolling Stone" was rock music with folk-like (or at least Dylan-like) lyrics. Therein lay the basis of the new folk rock style. Dylan's next album, *Blonde on Blonde* (1966), continued the new combination style. It was rock's first double album (two 12-inch vinyl discs), preceding *The Beatles* by about two and a half years.

Of particular note is "Rainy Day Women #12 and 35," another number 2 hit (Dylan himself has never had a number 1 hit). The song seems to be an answer to his critics—those hard-core folkies who saw him as a traitor to the cause. "He nonchalantly notes that people will criticize you no matter what you do. He tosses off the criticism with a double entendre, stating that everyone should get stoned. This hook line can mean that everybody must endure criticism (getting stoned in the biblical sense) or that one is best advised to shrug off criticism and simply get stoned (with drugs or alcohol). Either way, Dylan seems generally unaffected by his critics' disapproval.

Bob Dylan, at the height of his career, virtually disappeared for a year and a half, following a serious motorcycle accident in late July 1966. During much of 1967, Dylan recuperated in Woodstock, New York, a small town that had attracted artists for many decades. There, he and a Canadian group known as The Band rehearsed and recorded a series of new songs (eventually released as *The Basement Tapes* in 1975).

Dylan's Later Career

Although our main concern here is the Dylan of the 1960s, since he was truly one of the pioneers associated with both the solidification of folk music as a force for social change and the emergence of folk rock, we would be remiss if we did not at least survey Dylan's later career.

1970s—He became a model for the singer-songwriter trend of the 1970s. His most interesting album of the 1970s was *Blood on the Tracks*, a number 1 album in 1975. The album includes "Tangled Up in Blue," an insightful song about the dissolution of a relationship; at the time of the album, Dylan was recovering from the end of his marriage. There are other exemplary songs on this album, such as "Simple Twist of Fate" and the long, western ballad "Lily, Rosemary, and the Jack of Hearts."

In a series of San Francisco concerts in 1979, Dylan again shocked his fans by turning to a Christian message. A subsequent album, *Slow Train Coming*, contained a collection of born-again songs.

1980s—Two more Christian-themed albums, *Saved* and *Shot of Love*, were released in the early 1980s. His 1983 album, *Infidels*, seemed to withdraw back into Dylanesque vagueness; some felt it was a move away from his born-again message, but others argued that it was simply a more subtle statement of that same philosophy. It seems that Dylan and his obtuse lyrics simply cannot avoid being the center of controversy.

1990s and later—After a period of less significant output, Dylan returned in the late 1990s with a series of albums, beginning with 1997's *Time Out of Mind*, announcing a renewed vigor in his songwriting and performing. Turning to his original inspirations in folk, blues, and other roots music, Dylan's work found new recognition among a new generation of fans. This success continued unabated into the new millennium with *Love and Theft* (number 5 in 2001), *Modern Times* (number 1 in 2006), and *Together Through Life* (number 1 in 2009). In 2017, Dylan released his 38th studio album, *Triplicate*, his third collection of American standards, including "That Old Black Magic" and "Polka Dots and Moonbeams," recordings that might have been seen as more appropriate for Frank Sinatra than Bob Dylan. Also, in 2016, as a "recording dump" with few peers, he released a 36-disc box set entitled *1966 Live Recordings*, containing a recording of every show during his tour that year. Expanding into other artistic realms, a collection of 40 Dylan paintings—a mix of cityscapes, landscapes, and scenes of everyday life in the country—was exhibited at the National Gallery of Denmark in 2010.

Also during 2016, which was a banner year in an already-impressive career, Dylan was awarded the Nobel Peace Prize in Literature. At the age of 75, he was the first musician ever to win the award, further establishing the importance of his lyrical contributions to the art form. Naturally, once again, this initiated a conflict between those who felt the choice was justified (including Stephen King and Salman Rushdie) and those traditionalists who were opposed, citing the decision as misguided. Perhaps the times truly are "a-changin'." Since the late 1980s, Dylan has been touring "almost constantly, inspiring an unofficial name for the itinerary, the Never Ending Tour" (Sisario, Alter, & Chan 2016).

Before leaving Dylan, we must restate his most significant contribution to the history of rock, now evidenced on a global scale in his becoming a recipient of the Nobel Prize in Literature. His lyrics—with their symbolism, internal ironies, sarcasm, thought-provoking messages, dry wit, surrealism, and graceful flow—were the most influential and sophisticated since the beginning of rock and roll. Through his influence on the Beatles, especially on John Lennon, the Dylanesque lyric found its way into the very heart of 1960s rock. It is undeniable that rock lyrics have not been the same since.

JOURNAL

Bob Dylan's Lyrics

Find a copy of the lyrics for "Blowin' in the Wind." Read through them very carefully three or four times. What do you believe is the message that Dylan was trying to communicate through these stanzas? Don't be overly influenced by the interpretation presented earlier in this chapter; your assessment is every bit as valid. After all, one of the beauties of poetry (and Dylan's lyrics certainly fall now within that category) is that there can be multiple interpretations. What contemporary rock musicians can you identify who focus as intently on their lyrical content, specifically in regards to addressing socio-political topics of significant import?

 The response entered here will appear in the performance dashboard and can be viewed by your instructor.

Submit

7.3: Musical Close-Up on The Musical Form of Bob Dylan's Songs

OBJECTIVE: Describe the musical forms used most commonly by Bob Dylan

Thus far, we have mentioned three basic types of musical forms: the 12-bar blues, the AABA form, and a unique approach to song form in which a new and different form is created for each song. This last is sometimes called the *through-composed form*; that is, for each new section of text, new music may be composed. This form has had

The Strophic Principle

One of the most common musical forms used by folk musicians is known as strophic form. The basic elements of this musical form will be described in this module.

If you have ever heard the music performed in a religious service, you are familiar with strophic song form. Recall that the music is printed just one time, but below the music are the words to verses 1, 2, 3, 4, and so on. So it is with most early folk songs.

Bob Dylan grew up admiring this folk song tradition, and his basic approach to song form reflects this influence. Many old folk ballads consist of four lines of text, each one of which is set to a 4-measure musical phrase, thus creating a 16-measure strophe (four lines times 4-measure phrases equals 16 measures). This 16-measure strophe is simply repeated for each new stanza (verse) of text, providing us an opportunity to distinguish between two aspects of musical form: microform and macroform.

At the **macroform** level, strophic form would simply be represented as a series of repetitions: $A_1A_2A_3A_4 \ldots A_x$. At the **microform** level, however, the differentiation between phrases within each strophe becomes apparent; music theorists often use lowercase letters to distinguish between microform and macroform levels of analysis, a technique we shall follow in the discussion below.

As we have seen, a large percentage of early rock followed either the 12-bar blues form (in its own way a very specific kind of strophic form) or the AABA pattern. With the Beatles, a new freedom emerged regarding form, and, often, each song would have its own unique form (e.g., "A Day in the Life"), somewhat like the concept of the through-composed song. With Dylan and the other folk-oriented singers, the strophic form typically prevailed. Sometimes Dylan adhered rather closely to the old folk pattern; other times, he used the strophic form as a general organizing structure but took considerable liberties regarding the microform within each strophe.

considerable appeal for classical composers, because it means that the music can respond to variations in mood, images, and situations in the lyrics as one proceeds through the total length of the text. This is a very different approach from one that sets each and every verse to the same music, regardless of its semantic content. This latter approach is called the *strophic form* and is commonly used in folk music, which brings us to Bob Dylan.

In the following Musical Close-Up, we shall examine a few representative examples of Dylan's songs to see how they illustrate the strophic principle. We can begin by finding a sort of norm and then going from there. We will also address (a bit later) another common form: verse and chorus.

7.3.1: Dylan's Songs in Strophic Form

You are beginning to amass a knowledge of musical forms that are often found in rock and roll. Elsewhere in this course, you have been introduced to the 12-bar blues, the AABA form, and the I-vi-IV-V progression. In this chapter, we added strophic form; the following module will provide specific examples of songs that were composed by Bob Dylan using this form.

Please access the following link and search for the appropriate songs to access the lyrics to all the songs referred to in the following section:

https://www.bobdylan.com/songs/

Examples of Songs in Strophic Form

The previous section provided a detailed explanation of strophic form as it has been used in popular and folk music contexts. The following section provides specific examples of this form as implemented by Bob Dylan.

"Blowin' in the Wind"—Let us start with "Blowin' in the Wind" (Dylan 1973, 33). Each of the three stanzas of this song contains four lines. The first stanza (beginning with the words "How many roads ...") can serve as a model.

Each of the lines is given a four-measure melody, resulting in a 16-measure strophe. The first three melodic phrases are very similar, and the fourth is contrasting. Thus, the musical form inside each strophe can be represented as: aaab. The same music is then used for the second, third, and all following strophes. "Blowin' in the Wind" provides a good example of the strophic song form.

"Don't Think Twice, It's All Right"—"Don't Think Twice, It's All Right" is quite similar, except that the first two musical phrases are parallel, with the third and fourth phrases having new melodies. Thus, the internal pattern would be represented as: aabc. As you are listening to this song, note that each 4-measure phrase breaks into two half-phrases, or subphrases. This is fairly common even in the 4-measure phrases of classical music. "Don't Think Twice" has four strophes, each 16 measures long.

"My Back Pages"—"My Back Pages" follows a similar pattern. Its six stanzas are all set to the same music; each strophe is 16 measures long, consisting of four 4-measure phrases. The internal melodic scheme is like that of "Blowin' in the Wind" (aaab), though the chord progressions and other musical aspects represented by the "a" and "b" phrases are different.

"Positively 4th Street"—Using these three songs as our basis, we can find some interesting variations. For example, "Positively 4th Street" consists of 12 short stanzas, each of which is set to the same two 4-measure phrases (ab). This microform (with 8-measure phrases) is unusually short for Dylan, who generally prefers the 16-measure length. Even more interesting, each 8-measure strophe ends up "in the air," rather than on a solid tonic chord. This is what theorists call a *half cadence* (ending on the V chord); it propels us forward from one stanza into the next, rather than solidly closing off each one.

"The Times They Are a-Changin'"—"The Times They Are a-Changin'" is another strophic song, this time with five stanzas, but these do not follow the traditional four-measure phrase structure (4 + 4 + 4 + 4). Instead, there are basically six lines per stanza. ("Come senators . . . a'changin'.")

The first and third lines are set to a 5-measure melody; the other lines are set to 4-measure melodies. Thus, we have a 26-measure strophe. Granted, it is irregular, but Dylan makes it work.

"Rainy Day Women #12 and 35" and "Subterranean Homesick Blues"—Rather unusually, Dylan sets each of the five stanzas of "Rainy Day Women #12 and 35" to the traditional 12-bar blues form. Moreover, "Subterranean Homesick Blues" is based

loosely on the 16-bar blues (like 12-bar blues, except there are 8 measures of I instead of 4 at the beginning of each verse; see table below).

	16-Bar Blues	Subterranean Homesick Blues
Phrase 1	4 bars of I	4 bars of I
Phrase 2	4 bars of I	4 bars of I
Phrase 3	2 bars of IV; 2 bars of I	2 bars of IV; 4 bars of I
Phrase 4	2 bars of V; 2 bars of I	2 bars of V; 2 bars of I

As you can see, there is a 2-measure extension of the third phrase (two extra bars of the I chord). Thus, we have an 18-bar form. Furthermore, strophes 3 and 4 are varied slightly. Such variations within the strophic form are quite common in Dylan's compositions.

7.3.2: Dylan's Songs in Verse-and-Chorus Form

Finally, we will examine two songs that use the **verse-and-chorus form**. In this approach, there is a chorus, the words and music of which are always the same; this chorus alternates with a series of verses, each of which has the same music but different words.

Please access the following link and search for the appropriate songs to access the lyrics to all the songs referred to in the following section:

https://www.bobdylan.com/songs/

(Note: Clicking on the link will direct you out of the Revel course.)

While the outline of the musical form of "Mr. Tambourine Man" was provided below, the next section

Examples of Verse-and-Chorus Form Songs

The following section provides two examples of Dylan songs that were written in the verse-and-chorus song form. This is a frequently used musical form in the realm of popular music.

"Like a Rolling Stone"—The verse for "Like a Rolling Stone" contains five musical phrases, each 4 measures long, thus creating a 20-bar form. The chorus ("how does it feel," etc.) is normally 12 measures long (three 4-bar phrases), though you can see that there is an exception even to this standard in the first chorus. The chorus alternates with the four verses as follows. (Note: "How does it feel" initiates the chorus everytime.)

Verse 1: 20 measures

Chorus: 10 measures

Verse 2: 20 measures

Chorus: 12 measures

Verse 3: 20 measures

Chorus: 12 measures

Verse 4: 20 measures

Chorus: 12 measures

Note that the first chorus is shortened by 2 measures (one subphrase of music is skipped). This verse-and-chorus form is related to the strophic concept, inasmuch as the same musical sequence is repeated four times, with new words for each verse.

"Mr. Tambourine Man"—"Mr. Tambourine Man" also follows the verse-and-chorus approach. The song opens and closes

Music Example

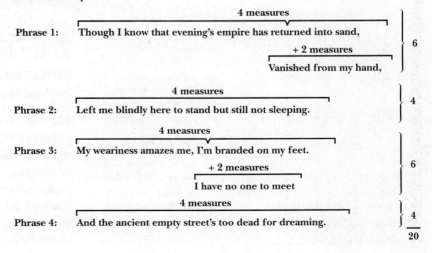

	4 measures	
Phrase 1:	Though I know that evening's empire has returned into sand,	} 6
	+ 2 measures	
	Vanished from my hand,	
	4 measures	
Phrase 2:	Left me blindly here to stand but still not sleeping.	} 4
	4 measures	
Phrase 3:	My weariness amazes me, I'm branded on my feet.	} 6
	+ 2 measures	
	I have no one to meet	
	4 measures	
Phrase 4:	And the ancient empty street's too dead for dreaming.	} 4

116 Chapter 7

with the chorus. Each verse begins with a 4-measure phrase that divides into two 2-measure subphrases. The music of the second subphrase (e.g., "has returned into sand") can be repeated to new words, thereby internally extending the basic length of the verse. Thus, the first verse is essentially a 16-bar form with four 4-measure phrases, but the second subphrase

of the first and third phrases is repeated (with new words) to produce a 20-bar verse.

Using similar 2-measure extensions, Dylan gradually lengthens each verse (see the Listening Guide below). The relatively simple chorus (four 4-bar phrases) is the same each time, followed by a varying number of measures of "fill" before beginning the next verse.

provides a much more detailed listening guide so that you can clearly see how the verses and choruses relate to one another. Also, there are some fairly significant differences among the verses as a result of their varying lengths due to the changing numbers of phrases—and even the lengths of those phrases—in the stanzas of Dylan's lyrics. In this particular song, even the choruses vary in length at times due to the presence (or not) of fills before the next verse begins.

Dylan tends to adhere to the relatively simple concept of strophic form, but his creativity with lyrics leads to some complex variations within the form. As a result of the influence of the folk movement, the strophic song form joined the 12-bar blues form of R&B and the AABA form of Tin Pan Alley and soft rock as relatively standardized forms used by rock musicians. The through-composed song, as exemplified by some Beatles songs, is much less common than these other three forms.

Listening Guide: "Mr. Tambourine Man" (Bob Dylan)

0:00–0:05	Introduction (4 bars)	Sets the accompaniment.
0:06–0:30	Chorus 1 (16 + 2 bars)	Four 4-bar phrases plus 2-bar fill between chorus and verse 1.
0:31–0:59	Verse 1 (20 bars)	Four phrases. First and third phrases are extended by 2 bars each. Second and fourth phrases are the normal 4-bar length.
1:00–1:26	Chorus 2 (16 + 3 bars)	Same as chorus 1 (except for 3-bar fill).
1:27–1:59	Verse 2 (24 bars)	Four phrases. First phrase extended by 6 bars. Third phrase extended by 4 bars. Second phrase is the normal 4 bars. Fourth phrase shortened to 2 bars.
2:00–2:26	Chorus 3 (16 + 3 bars)	Same as chorus 2.
2:27–3:02	Verse 3 (26 bars)	Four phrases. First phrase extended by 4 bars. Third phrase extended by 6 bars. Second and fourth phrases are the normal 4-bar length.
3:03–3:24	Chorus 4 (16 + 1 bar)	Same as previous choruses (1-bar fill).
3:25–4:08	Instrumental break (32 bars)	Harmonica lead. Accompaniment similar to verse progressions.
4:09–4:50	Verse 4 (32 bars)	Four phrases. First phrase extended by 10 bars. Second phrase shortened to 2 bars. Third phrase extended by 8 bars. Fourth phrase is the normal 4-bar length.
4:51–5:12	Chorus 5 (16 bars)	Same as chorus 4.
5:13–5:28	Coda	Fade out with harmonica lead.

BECOME AN ACTIVE LISTENER: SEARCHING FOR COMMON MUSICAL FORMS

One of the significant differences between the learning experience you are having here in comparison to many other books on the history of rock music is that you are gaining significant experience developing your listening skills *in addition to* learning about the biographies of rock artists and the socio-political developments that impacted the evolution of various subgenres of music. In this section, you will be asked to listen carefully to some of the music you enjoy and to identify songs that incorporate some of the common forms discussed in this chapter.

1. Strophic form: Find examples of these song forms in the music that you enjoy.
2. Variations on strophic form (note the manner in which the form is varied)
3. Verse-and-chorus form

7.4: The Byrds

OBJECTIVE: Describe the role of the Byrds in establishing the foundation of folk rock

The story of the Byrds is one of remarkable and unfulfilled potential. With creativity and musicianship that rivaled those of the Beach Boys, Dylan, and maybe even the Beatles, the Byrds were nonetheless undone by constant personnel changes that undermined their popularity and changed the chemistry between group members. Even so, they managed to have a significant, though brief, impact on the history of rock.

The Byrds, c. 1964
SOURCE: Pictorial Press Ltd/Alamy Stock Photo

The central figure in the Byrds was Jim McGuinn. Born in Chicago, McGuinn had a background in folk music. In 1964, McGuinn met Gene Clark of Missouri and David Crosby from Los Angeles, both folk singers. Chris Hillman, also from Los Angeles, played a bluegrass-style mandolin in his own group, the Hillmen. Crosby introduced the group to a drummer from New York named Mike Clarke. By 1964, the quintet was formed.

7.4.1: Musical and Personnel Changes

The Byrds were one of the most important bands in the era leading to folk rock. Their use of electric instruments as opposed to the traditional acoustic sounds changed the sound of the music itself. At the time when Bob Dylan was making the transition from acoustic to electric, Jim McGuinn and his bandmates were already there.

7.4.2: Country Rock Style

After more personnel changes, including the addition of country rock musician Gram Parsons, the Byrds released *Sweetheart of the Rodeo.* Here, the country rock style

Chronicle of The Byrds

The Byrds were one of the most important bands associated with the emergence of folk rock. This section provides information about the early years of the band.

"Mr. Tambourine Man"—Their first Columbia album contained four songs by Bob Dylan, including "Mr. Tambourine Man," which became a hit, and, as we mentioned previously, helped establish the new folk rock style.

Turn, Turn, Turn—Using some original material and two more Dylan songs, the Byrds recorded their second album, *Turn, Turn, Turn.* Folk singer Pete Seeger had composed the title song by adapting the words from the biblical book of Ecclesiastes and setting them to music. This song reached number 1 in December 1965.

Fifth Dimension—In early 1966, Gene Clark left the group. Deciding to become a quartet rather than replacing the lost member, the Byrds prepared their third album, *Fifth Dimension.* This album produced their third (and most controversial) hit, "Eight Miles High" (number 14). Musically, the song is quite adventuresome for mid-1966, paralleling some of the things the Beatles were doing at this same time. There are unusual chord progressions and use of the Dorian mode (like a minor scale but with its sixth note raised one-half step). It was widely believed that the lyrics referred to the effects of LSD, but the Byrds claimed the song was about flying in an airplane (remember the pre-1967 "double entendre" rationale?).

Younger Than Yesterday—The music of the Byrds became even more musically sophisticated on their next album, *Younger* *Than Yesterday.* However, before 1967 was over, Crosby left (later to form Crosby, Stills & Nash).

The Notorious Byrd Brothers—The remaining trio (McGuinn, Hillman, and Clarke), plus various outside musicians, created *The Notorious Byrd Brothers* (1968), possibly the most interesting album of the Byrds' career. Certainly, it is an eclectic album. There is "Artificial Energy," with its amphetamine references and electronically modified brass sounds; there are the folk rock sounds of "Goin' Back," with its reminiscences of childhood, and "Draft Morning," an effective protest song. The latter contains some particularly effective lyrics. Note also the mixed-in sound effects (war sounds) and a military-like trumpet call. The trumpet call is an effective touch per se, but its effect is enhanced because its notes are dissonant against the prevailing harmonies, nicely reinforcing the message that the military concept is in conflict with the Byrds' anti-draft sentiments. There are several songs on *The Notorious Byrd Brothers* that have a country sound (e.g., "Change Is Now," "Wasn't Born to Follow," and "Old John Robertson"). The result began to be called country rock, a style that the Byrds would develop further on their next album.

The Notorious Byrd Brothers also contains experiments in meter, such as "Get to You," which alternates sections with five beats per measure and sections with six beats per measure. Similarly, "Tribal Gathering" moves from a very jazz-like quintuple meter to a more common quadruple meter. Strings are used in various spots throughout the album, often subjected to electronic modification, such as filtering (e.g., "Natural Harmony") and phase shifting (e.g., "Old John Robertson"; note also the polyphonic texture in parts of this latter song). Phase shifting, or *phasing*, is an electronic manipulation that modifies the timbre of the original sound, creating a "swooshing" effect.

dominated and became a prototype for later country-oriented rock groups. The personnel problem hit dead bottom in mid-1968, when Parsons and Hillman left to form the Flying Burrito Brothers. This left McGuinn as the only remaining member of the original Byrds. He continued to release Byrds albums using a variety of players, but these simply did not measure up to the 1965 to 1968 recordings. In 1973, McGuinn finally disbanded the Byrds. Ironically, the five original members got together one last time that same year to record a reunion album: *Byrds* (number 20).

There is little doubt that the recordings released between 1965 and 1968 by the Byrds exhibited a high level of talent and creativity. They were cofounders of folk rock (with Dylan), and they led the way to the country rock sound that became popular in the 1970s. "Eight Miles High" has the questionable distinction of being one of the first drug-related songs in rock, and the Byrds were certainly one of the most innovative groups of their time regarding the use of electronic sound manipulation. One wonders what their position in rock history would have been had the original five members stayed together for 8 to 10 years.

7.5: Other Folk Rockers

OBJECTIVE: Compare the significant contributions of other folk musicians of the 1960s

To accommodate the wide variety of post-1965 folk rockers, the definition of the term *folk rock* must be very general indeed. After all, these artists do not sound alike. Each artist who melded the lyrical profundities and tunefulness of folk music with the electrification, bass line, and hard beat of rock discovered a unique recipe to achieve the combination. As always, the purists on both sides were

righteously indignant. The pure folkies felt that their music had been corrupted by the crass commercialization and mindless noise of rock; the pure rockers resented the invasion of their basic good-time music by the self-conscious lyrics of the folkies. In between, a vast new audience relished the opportunity to have more thought-provoking and intelligent lyrics served up to them in a musical context they enjoyed.

7.5.1: The Mamas and the Papas

Following the example set by the Byrds and Bob Dylan, numerous folk rock groups suddenly appeared. For the most part, these groups were formed by the folkies of the early 1960s, but now they added drums and converted to electric guitars, calling themselves folk rockers. One of the most successful of these groups was the Mamas and the Papas. Whereas the Byrds had blended the folk style with a harder rock sound, the Mamas and the Papas tended toward a softer rock style. In the two-year period from early 1966 through late 1967, they placed nine singles in the Top 40, including six Top 10 hits.

The Mamas and the Papas

SOURCE: Pictorial Press Ltd/Alamy Stock Photo

Musical Career of the Mamas and the Papas

The Mamas and the Papas were a highly successful folk rock group. Their album sales were impressive and several hit singles reached the Top 10.

John Phillips was from South Carolina; he had followed a fairly typical folk music path, having performed in Greenwich Village with several groups. Cass Elliot (her real name was Ellen Cohen) was from Baltimore, Maryland. In 1965, Elliot, Phillips, Michelle Phillips (John's wife), and a musician named Denny Doherty moved to Los Angeles and obtained a contract with Dunhill Records. Calling themselves the Mamas and the Papas, they adopted the popular new folk rock sound, releasing their first album, *If You Can Believe Your Eyes and Ears,* in early 1966.

The album zoomed to number 1, and two singles, "California Dreamin'" and "Monday, Monday," hit the Top 10 (the latter song became their only number 1 song). Some of their success was probably due to the general rage for the new folk rock style, but, beyond that, the Mamas and the Papas had an appealing sound. John Phillips was a talented writer and arranger, and their four-part vocal harmonies were absolutely solid and musical. The technical production and instrumental backup were first rate. A second album, *The Mamas and the Papas* (issued in late 1966), was another success, yielding two Top 10 singles: "I Saw Her Again" and "Words of Love."

The successes continued in 1967 with two more albums and three singles: "Dedicated to the One I Love" (a cover of a 1961 hit by the Shirelles), "Creeque Alley" (a clever autobiography of the group), and "Twelve-Thirty (Young Girls Are Coming to the Canyon)." Also in 1967, John Phillips and Lou Adler organized the Monterey International Pop Festival, an early example of the type of rock festival that would become so popular in the later 1960s (and beyond). Among the future stars presented at Monterey were Jimi Hendrix, Janis Joplin, and The Who.

The year 1968 was the beginning of the end for the Mamas and the Papas. "Glad to Be Happy" went only as high as number 26 and became the group's last Top 40 hit. By mid-1968, the Mamas and the Papas had disbanded.

Cass Elliot (Mama Cass) went on to moderate success as a solo act and television performer, though she died tragically in 1974. John and Michelle Phillips divorced in 1970. John briefly attempted a solo career but succumbed to an increasingly serious drug habit. Recovered from his addiction, he and his daughter from a previous marriage, Mackenzie Phillips, toured the country in the mid-1980s, promoting an antidrug message. John died in 2001. Michelle Phillips turned to a moderately successful acting career.

The strength of the band's music was their solid and effective vocal harmonies. With echo and some overdubbing, the quartet could sound like a full chorus. The folk aspect of their folk rock blend was derived more from their image than from anything else. They rarely engaged in protest songs, but they dressed and looked like soft-core folkniks (hippies). The rock side of their folk rock blend was a softer style of rock. Lacking the harshness of Dylan or the hard beat and electric guitar work of the Byrds, the Mamas and the Papas created a pleasing, commercial version of folk rock.

7.5.2: Simon and Garfunkel

In 1957, two 15-year-old school friends, modeling themselves after the Everly Brothers, recorded a song called "Hey Schoolgirl." The song peaked at number 49 and secured them an appearance on *American Bandstand.* Using the pseudonyms Tom and Jerry, they released several more singles (that flopped) before giving up on show business and returning to school. The boys' real names were Paul Simon and Art Garfunkel, and they had met at age 11 in school in Forest Hills, New York. After college, they pursued separate careers in the music business, then joined forces again and auditioned for Columbia Records as a folk-singing duo. In late 1964, they released their first album, *Wednesday Morning 3 A.M.* The album contained some Dylan songs, a few traditional folk songs, and some original Paul Simon songs, including "The Sound of Silence," accompanied by acoustic instruments. The album went nowhere, and so the discouraged duo again went their separate ways.

Shortly after their separation, the folk rock revolution of mid-1965 happened. Tom Wilson, the Columbia producer of *Wednesday Morning,* went back to "The Sound of Silence" tape and remixed it with electric bass, electric

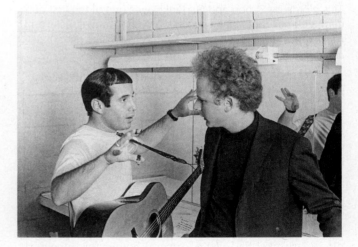

Simon and Garfunkel, 1967.

SOURCE: Pictorial Press Ltd/Alamy Stock Photo

guitars, and drums. The result (as you have learned): folk rock. In this new version of the recording, "The Sound of Silence" skyrocketed to number 1 on New Year's Day, 1966. There is no clearer demonstration of the shift from folk to folk rock than to compare the two versions of the song. The voice tracks are the same; the difference lies in the **rhythm section** tracks: the bass line, the drum beat, and the electric guitar accompaniment.

NEW FOLK ROCK ALBUM Quickly, a new folk rock album was recorded and released (*Sounds of Silence*), which included the title song plus another Top 10 hit, "I Am a Rock." The latter song has a typical folk rock sound, and the lyrics are about a loner who refuses to risk contact with others. It was a logical follow-up to "The Sound of Silence," also a song about loneliness. Simon's ability to write lyrics appropriate to the Dylan-inspired folk rock movement is evident.

In late 1966, *Parsley, Sage, Rosemary and Thyme* was released and contained yet another Top 10 hit, "Homeward Bound." A series of singles in 1966 and 1967 seemed to indicate a slight erosion in Simon and Garfunkel's popularity, but the tremendously successful film *The Graduate*, with a soundtrack featuring both their earlier hits and new songs, propelled the duo back into the limelight. The soundtrack album held the number 1 position for nine weeks. It contained the folk-like "Scarborough Fair/Canticle," "The Sound of Silence," and "Mrs. Robinson." This last song, with its sarcastic portrait of the movie's Mrs. Robinson, became the duo's first number 1 single since "The Sound of Silence."

BOOKENDS The 1968 album *Bookends* shows the effects of *Sgt. Pepper*. Like *Sgt. Pepper*, *Bookends* includes the complete lyrics on the back cover of the album and is, in part, a concept album.

The Bookends Album

This album by Simon and Garfunkel was one of the first concept albums, containing several highly innovative tracks and providing a sense of unity through the use of the recurring "bookends" theme.

Side 1—It opens with an instrumental song that is heard again at the end of the first side, with vocals added. The concept deals with time and the various stages of human life. Thus, the opening song refers to a child who is threatening to commit suicide by jumping from a building's ledge. "America" seems to be about a young couple who set out together to tour the country. "Overs" seems to be about a married couple for whom life together has become dull and routine.

A particularly remarkable track is "Voices of Old People." Garfunkel had visited several homes for the elderly and recorded segments of the numerous conversations he had with residents. Excerpts of these are combined into a montage that provides effective insights into loneliness and the problems associated with old age. This montage is followed by "Old Friends," a song that reflects on the desperately solitary existence of many senior citizens, in which the lyrics provide sobering reminders to the "don't trust anyone over 30" generation. After all, youth doesn't last forever.

Side 1 ends with the song "Bookends Theme," a wistful commentary on the inevitable passage of time. The symbolism of bookends is effectively carried out by references to the theme positioned at both "ends" of side 1, by the image of the old people on opposite ends of the park bench, and by the allusion to our life cycle, with its remarkable similarities between infancy and old age.

Side 2—The album's second side includes "Mrs. Robinson" and a strong folk rock tune, "A Hazy Shade of Winter" (number 13). Overall, the album shows the new freedom creative artists were experiencing in the post–*Sgt. Pepper* era. For example, neither "Voices of Old People" nor "Old Friends" shows any relation to rock. (The latter is accompanied by a large orchestra that builds to a climax near the end—reminiscent in concept to "A Day in the Life" from *Sgt. Pepper*.) The old rules were gone; the more creative artists were free to ignore the old formulas and express themselves with whatever musical means proved most effective.

DAWN OF THE 1970s Simon and Garfunkel lost none of their appeal as the decade of the 1970s dawned. *Bridge over Troubled Water* (1970) yielded three Top 10 singles: "The Boxer" (number 7), the title track (number 1), and "Cecilia" (number 4). Rather surprisingly, the duo then decided to go their separate ways. Paul Simon, who had done most of the songwriting for the team, had continued success as a solo artist through the 1970s, with albums and singles consistently hitting the Top 10, but then his career faded. In the mid-1980s, he made a comeback to the charts by recording an album of songs with musicians primarily from South Africa (*Graceland*) followed by an album focusing on Brazilian musical styles (*Rhythm of the Saints*). He has continued to record and tour, producing three Top 20 albums since the beginning of the new century: *You're the One* (2000), *Surprise* (2006), and *So Beautiful or So What* (2011). In 2016, he released his 13th solo album, *Stranger to Stranger*.

Art Garfunkel's solo career has been less illustrious than Simon's. Several early albums and one single fared well, but subsequent albums were less successful. The duo reunited for a highly successful concert in Central Park in September 1981. The resulting album reached number 6 in 1982 and contained a moderate hit, "Wake Up Little Susie," originally recorded by Tom and Jerry's role models, the Everly Brothers.

Simon and Garfunkel's success stemmed largely from Paul Simon's undeniable skills at lyric and tune writing. Just for fun, listen to "A Simple Desultory Philippic" from *Parsley, Sage, Rosemary and Thyme*. It pokes gentle fun at Dylan, folk rock, and even Simon and Garfunkel themselves. If you can identify every name and reference contained in this song, you score an A+ for your knowledge of the 1960s.

7.5.3: Joan Baez and Judy Collins

Joan Baez held out against folk rock as long as possible. She appeared at the 1959 Newport Folk Festival and soon became a well-known figure in the early 1960s folk scene. Her first album, *Joan Baez* (1960), set a pattern that would hold for over a decade. The album contained traditional American and English folk songs sung in a clear voice with perfect pitch and excellent enunciation. It sold well but contained no hit singles. Such was to be her fate throughout the 1960s. When Dylan turned to folk rock in mid-1965, Baez, a close friend of Dylan's, refused to go along. Instead, she stayed with her pure acoustic, socially-oriented style. Her social involvement was not only musical; she often marched and sang at civil rights demonstrations and student protest meetings.

It was not until the 1970s that Baez finally relented to the pressures of musical style by softening her approach and adding the electric sound of folk rock. She found considerable success writing her own songs. *Diamonds and Rust* (1975) was a huge album commercially and musically. The title song—her second of only two Top 40 hits—is a rather bitter complaint about a certain "legend" (a reference to Dylan). She takes another shot at Dylan in her version of his "Simple Twist of Fate," in which she does a perfect imitation of his unique, off-pitch vocal style. Baez continues to be productive into the new millennium, releasing *Folk is the New Black* (2006), including "Danger Danger," a poignant response to political developments at that time. In 2017, she was inducted into the Rock & Roll Hall of Fame.

The central position of Joan Baez in the 1960s folk music scene inspired other female vocalists to follow. Judy Collins's first two albums contained standard folk material, but, beginning with her third album, she joined the Baez-Dylan trend of contemporary protest songs. Like Baez, her albums sold well enough, but there were few hit singles. Her most enduring hit was Stephen Sondheim's "Send in the Clowns," which was number 36 in 1975 and returned to the Hot 100 in 1977 (number 19). Yet another female singer to follow the Baez-Collins lead was Joni Mitchell. Because Mitchell's primary impact was in the 1970s, a full discussion of this artist will come later in the text.

7.5.4: Sonny and Cher

Sonny and Cher began their career associated with the folk rock trend of the late 1960s. Indeed, Cher's first hit, "All I Really Want to Do" (number 15 in 1965), was a Dylan song. Salvatore "Sonny" Bono and Cher(ilyn) Sarkisian were married in 1963 and began recording as Caesar and Cleo, eventually changing their performance identity to Sonny and Cher. They produced a number of hits as a duo from 1965 through 1972 but also released solo recordings. Cher, whose solo success was the greater of the duo, eventually charted some 22 Top 40 hits, including four number 1 songs. The last ("Believe" in 1999), remained on the chart for 31 weeks, double the length of any of her previous hits. In the early 1970s, Sonny and Cher became major television personalities, thanks to their own CBS series. In spite (or because) of Cher's risqué clothing styles, the pair found a wider audience and gradually lost their folk rock identification. Sonny Bono died in a 1998 ski accident, while he was serving his second term as a member of the U.S. House of Representatives from California.

7.5.5: Buffalo Springfield

Stylistic labels such as "folk rock" are often inadequate indicators of a group's actual array of musical styles. Such is the case with Buffalo Springfield, a quintet consisting of Stephen Stills, Neil Young, Richard Furay, Dewey Martin, and Bruce Palmer. They first gained national attention in early 1967 with a song that was in the folk protest vein, "For What It's Worth" (number 7 in 1967; their only Top 40 hit), and were immediately typed as another folk rock group. In fact, Buffalo Springfield covered a wide stylistic range. Most of the members had experience in folk-oriented groups. Their first album, *Buffalo Springfield* (early 1967), revealed the versatility and solid musicianship of the quintet. Using material written by Stills and Young, the album contained strong rock songs like "Sit Down, I Think I Love You" and a prototype of the country rock style developed later by the Byrds, Dylan, and others, "Go and Say Goodbye."

Released in late 1967, *Buffalo Springfield Again* revealed a somewhat harder sound in songs such as the psychedelic "Mr. Soul" (note the "Satisfaction"-like guitar riff), "Bluebird" (complete with shouting vocal style and hard guitar solos), and "Hung Upside Down" (listen to the guitar solo in the middle). There is still a touch of country in Richie Furay's "A Child's Claim to Fame," and a more elaborate experimental song called "Broken Arrow," which alternates between triple and quadruple meters, adds external sound effects, and ends with a very impressive jazz piano solo. The folk rock style was virtually gone by the time of the second album. Jim Messina began working with the band at this time as a recording engineer, then evolved to an engineer, and eventually replaced Bruce Palmer on bass.

The third and last album (excluding compilations) was *Last Time Around* (1968). The country sound continued with "Kind Woman," a light Latin influence can be felt on "Pretty Girl Why" and "Uno Mundo," and straight-ahead rock is heard in "Special Care" and "Questions."

In 1968, Jim Messina and Furay left to form a country rock band named Poco. Stills joined with David Crosby (the Byrds) and Graham Nash (the Hollies) to form Crosby, Stills & Nash. They were soon joined by Neil Young, thus reuniting two members of the defunct Buffalo Springfield. Several ex-Springfield members eventually found their way into later groups such as the Southern-Hillman-Furay Band and Loggins and Messina. Over four decades after the band broke up, several members (Furay, Stills, and Young) reunited for a benefit performance in 2010 and then came together again in 2011 to play six West Coast dates and, then, the Bonnaroo festival. Rumors of a 30-date North American tour were never realized.

7.5.6: Donovan

Another artist whose original identification was with the folk style but who moved on to other things is Donovan Leitch. Born in Glasgow, Scotland, Donovan seemed like a British Bob Dylan. Indeed, he wore a denim cap, played harmonica and acoustic guitar, and sang folk-influenced songs. His first single, "Catch the Wind," managed to achieve the number 23 position on the U.S. Hot 100. However, his early 1966 tour to America was relatively unsuccessful.

Returning to England, Donovan underwent a dramatic change of image and sound. His next single, "Sunshine Superman," was a smash hit, rising to the number 1 position. Following quickly with the number 2 hit "Mellow Yellow," Donovan returned to the United States as a flower-bedecked hippie. The new psychedelic image sold well; his *Sunshine Superman* album (number 11) contained the hard-rocking "Season of the Witch." After a

series of moderate hits in 1968, Donovan made the Top 5 again with "Hurdy Gurdy Man," a good example of late-1960s psychedelia, with its electronically modified vocal track and its heavily distorted guitar solo. His last Top 40 hit was "Goo Goo Barabajagal (Love is Hot)," performed with the Jeff Beck Group.

JOURNAL

Folk Music vs. Folk Rock

Listen to both versions of Simon and Garfunkel's "The Sound of Silence," the acoustic version that appears on *Wednesday Morning 3 A.M.* and the folk rock version created later by producer Tom Wilson. This pair of recordings provides one of the clearest examples in existence of a song bridging the gap between folk music and folk rock. Carefully compare the sound of the two recordings, focusing especially on the differences in rhythm section instrumentation and its impact on your response to the music. In a paragraph, write down how you respond emotionally to the acoustic version and then do the same for the folk rock version. Which one do you like better? Write a second paragraph providing a detailed explanation of the reasons you prefer one over the other. Don't forget to focus on the musical elements, using your expanding musical vocabulary.

 The response entered here will appear in the performance dashboard and can be viewed by your instructor.

Submit

Summary: Folk Music and Folk Rock

By 1968, the folk rock explosion had fizzled. Dylan was recuperating from his motorcycle accident, the Byrds were turning toward country rock, the Mamas and the Papas were disbanding, Buffalo Springfield had moved away from folk rock before disbanding, Donovan had gone psychedelic, and Sonny and Cher had turned more toward commercial pop rock. Only the sounds of Simon and Garfunkel lingered on, but in its two- to three-year heyday, folk rock had brought together two important and seemingly antithetical styles of music. Some excellent new music had been produced, and from these beginnings some important trends would grow in the subsequent decade; namely, the singer-songwriter and country rock trends.

In addition to these musical influences on future rock subgenres, it is clear that another critically important capability of popular music realized during the 1960s is the fact that it could be used effectively as a form of protest. Many of the artists described in this chapter were integral to the broad acceptance of the tenets of the civil rights movement and other forms of important social change. At the time of this publication, following the 2016 U.S. election, many members of American society are feeling a level of disillusionment similar to that which emerged in the mid- to late 1960s. Mainstream rock musicians, by and large, have

chosen not to engage in such political and social issues, returning to a focus on music as entertainment. This is, of course, not true for all artists, but, in comparison to the active role of the folk artists, the percentage of those actively involved is significantly lower.

During the 2016 election, both throughout the campaign and in its aftermath, artists once again began to take a stand. There are a number of long-time activists like Neil Young and David Crosby who have spoken out against injustice consistently since the 1960s. Joining them, however, is a new generation of artists, including some who have been around a while but chose not to take a position until more recently (Bruce Springsteen and Green Day), and others who felt they could no longer remain silent (Rihanna, Katy Perry, Madonna, Miley Cyrus, and John Legend). Then, there are others who have been shouting their beliefs all along, like Rage Against the Machine (including Tom Morello). Recent releases that exemplify these statements of protest include Billy Bragg's "The Times They Are A-Changing Back," Carole King's "One Small Voice," YG's "FDT," Loudon Wainwright III's "I Had a Dream," and Fiona Apple's "Tiny Hands." Music is a powerful tool for change. It is good to see that some contemporary artists remain willing to answer the call.

Take Note: Folk Music and Folk Rock

- *What were the major changes between the 1950s and the 1960s teen culture?*—The decade of the 1950s was a period of social conservatism and conformity. The following decade was dominated by social change and unrest. Change was coming, symbolized by the civil rights movement, a new consciousness of the importance of protecting the environment, the use of mind-altering drugs, and the sexual revolution. All of this turbulence was reflected in music of the era.

- *How did Bob Dylan revolutionize folk music?*—In his early songs, Bob Dylan built on the tradition of social-protest music, addressing segregation and antiwar sentiments through his lyrics. However, within a few years he was pursuing a more personal message, leading to a new musical style called folk rock. This music wed electric instrumentation with the thoughtful lyrics of folk songs. The sophistication of Dylan's lyrics brought an enhanced level of artistry to rock and roll.

- *Who were the leading innovators in the folk rock movement?*—One of the first groups to embrace folk rock was the Byrds, scoring number 1 hits with covers of songs by Bob Dylan and Pete Seeger. Their folk-influenced vocal harmonies became another key element of the style that was emulated by many others. The Mamas and the Papas took folk rock to California, wedding the sound of folk with the sunny harmonies of groups like the Beach Boys, creating a pop-oriented style that resulted in an impressive series of hits. Simon & Garfunkel combined the craftsmanship (and wit) of Paul Simon's songwriting with the beautiful harmony of Art Garfunkel's vocal performances. Other folk rockers followed in Dylan's singer-songwriter footsteps.

SHARED WRITING

Composing Lyrics to a Contemporary Protest Song

Locate a current-events article that addresses a societal issue that you consider critically important. Using the topic of the article as a basis, compose three or four stanzas of lyrics for a protest song. As you begin, it is important to have an organizational structure in mind, so use the strophic form described in this chapter to determine the number of lines contained in each stanza, the number of syllables to be used in each line, and the desired microform (e.g., aabc); this structure should remain relatively consistent from stanza to stanza. Once you have completed this portion of the assignment, share your article and lyrics with two or three of your classmates, requesting their suggestions for improvement and integrating those you find most helpful. If you are fortunate enough to have classmates (or an instructor) with musical ability, have them set these lyrics to music and perform them for you. There is nothing that compares to hearing your own words set to music!

 A minimum number of characters is required to post and earn points. After posting, your response can be viewed by your class and instructor, and you can participate in the class discussion.

Post

0 characters | 140 minimum

Chapter 8
Soul and Motown

 Learning Objectives

8.1 Define soul music

8.2 Summarize the influence of recording studios on soul music

8.3 Describe the wide variety of vocal styles represented in soul recordings

8.4 Explain how soul music allows for freedom of expression using the elements of music

8.5 Summarize the Motown musical style

From the earliest days of rock and roll, the music of black musicians provided a primary, foundational influence. Though there were important exceptions (e.g., Nat "King" Cole, Chuck Berry, and others), the genre had been largely dominated by white musicians performing in the style of, or in styles heavily influenced by, the music of these important black musicians. During the 1960s, black musicians, producers, and record companies were given their due … actually, it would be more accurate to say, given their *long overdue*!

8.1: The History of Soul Music

OBJECTIVE: Define soul music

Soul in music is like love: You know when it is there and when it is not; but soul, as a musical genre, defies accurate definition. As Arnold Shaw has written (1982, 365), "Soul has almost as many strains in it as there are artists." Some of the biggest names in soul music have tried to define it, but their definitions do not provide much clarification (Hirshey 1984, 51, 339, 77, 228):

Soul ain't nothin' but a feelin'.

—Wilson Pickett

For a singer, soul is total vocal freedom.

—Don Covay

I am not a blues singer or an R&B singer, I'm a soul singer. We go into the studio without anything prepared, just record what come out. That's soul—the way you feel.

—Otis Redding

(Soul) is what comes from within; it's what happens when the inner part of you comes out. It's the part of playing you can't get out of the books and studies. In my case, I believe that what I heard and felt in the music of my church … was the most powerful influence on my musical career. Everyone wants to know where I got that funky style. Well, it comes from the church. The music I heard was open, relaxed, impromptu—soul music.

—Milt Jackson

Soul to me is a feeling, a lot of depth and being able to bring to the surface that which is happening inside…. It's just the emotion, the way it affects other people.

—Aretha Franklin

The first three "definitions" imply that soul has something to do with the free expression of feelings, but that could apply to a number of musical styles. Milt Jackson's comments provide a useful hint: there is a relationship between soul music and black church music. As Aretha Franklin said, "Soul came up from gospel and blues. That much you can write down" (Hirshey 1984, xiii). We know that the blues has some very definite musical characteristics, and we can identify some specific characteristics of gospel music (especially its vocal style). So if a performer combines the characteristics of R&B and gospel and uses these elements freely and expressively, he or she could be called a soul singer. In this chapter's Musical Close-Up, we will look more closely at how the vocal style of gospel music is carried over into the soul singer's style.

8.1.1: The Roots of Soul Music

Blues, gospel, jazz, R&B, and rock and roll all have their roots in the South. Soul artists derived their inspiration, to varying degrees, from each of these earlier musical styles. However, one aspect that was common to almost all soul singers was the influence of music in the church, including early opportunities to develop their musical abilities by performing in this religious context. As it evolved, soul music allowed that same level of musical passion and divine inspiration to be applied to secular—as well as downright sexual—topics.

8.1.2: Soul Music Groups

Groups like the Dominoes and the Drifters gathered, rehearsed, and performed in the streets. Often, they started as church groups and could be found singing in front of stores or local Baptist churches. Their vocal roots emerged from the close harmony gospel quartets of the 1930s and 1940s, possibly with the additional influence of Pop groups such as the Ink Spots and the Mills Brothers.

Influential Icons of Soul Music

As soul music evolved, several artists emerged from the crowd as performers who seemed to have it all. This section will briefly discuss two of the most important: Sam Cooke and Ray Charles.

Soul Stirrers—Certainly one of the most influential of these groups was the Soul Stirrers. Formed in Texas in the 1930s by R. H. Harris, the Soul Stirrers were a quartet, traveling all over the country. When Harris retired in 1950, 19-year-old Sam Cooke became the lead singer. As author Gerri Hirshey wrote (1984, 47), "His voice transfigured the sound of quartet gospel and, as early as 1950, in his gospel work,

---

Origin of Soul Music

To understand where soul music originated, we must start in the black southern church.

At the same time that the sacred and the secular were pulling black music in opposing directions, they were concurrently blending, as contradictory as that might seem. A gospel song and shouting blues may be musically identical, except that in one case the lyrics say "love my Jesus!" and in the other, "love that woman!" These musical styles both expanded northward: blues from the Mississippi Delta area and gospel from the black southern, usually Baptist, church.

For blues, this started in the 1920s, with the widespread migration of southern blacks northward to look for jobs in the industrial Northeast and Midwest. Various sub-styles of black music developed, including electric blues, urban blues, and, of course, Rhythm & Blues. In the 1940s, the new sound of blues was almost a happy sound; it was uptempo, aggressive, and electrified. Performers like B. B. King, Muddy Waters, and Howlin' Wolf represented this new *urban* or *electric blues*.

Gospel music also moved northward during this time. Gospel singers, like Sister Rosetta Tharpe, came from Arkansas to Chicago and eventually to Harlem, in New York City. Mahalia Jackson, born in New Orleans but transplanted to Chicago, popularized gospel among blacks and whites alike. Thomas Dorsey was one of the biggest names in gospel. A composer and performer, his gospel work dates back to the 1920s. When the word *soul* was appropriated by the 1960s black generation, Dorsey noted that it was really nothing new:

> It was first in the Negro church. When I was a little boy, the churches couldn't afford an organ and the sisters sat in the amen corner and kept rhythm by clapping their hands. There is no need for some fellow born yesterday to come up and tell me now that soul is something new. (Hirshey 1984, 27)

In the 1940s, a number of independent record companies were formed to popularize black blues and gospel, including Savoy and Apollo (both formed circa 1942), Specialty (1945), Chess (1947), Atlantic (1948), Peacock (1949), and Vee Jay (1953).

The expansion of black music into the white market began in the 1950s, a transition discussed elsewhere in this course. Cleveland-based deejay/concert promoter Alan Freed was an influential champion of black music. By 1951, Freed was playing R&B over the airwaves in a white radio market. He sponsored citywide dances in Cleveland that featured an all-black roster of entertainers.

Meanwhile, youngsters formed singing groups in the black areas of Detroit, Cincinnati, Chicago, Cleveland, Philadelphia, and New York City (Harlem). Gospel coaches like Billy Ward in New York City worked with them, teaching them the finest nuances of gospel and R&B singing. From his knowledge of these young singers, around 1950, Ward pulled the cream of the crop together into a group called the Dominoes. For a lead singer, he tapped a 17-year-old named Clyde McPhatter (originally from Durham, North Carolina). After McPhatter left the group in 1953, he went on to a recording contract with Atlantic Records and formed his own group, the Drifters. In 1959, after McPhatter left, the Drifters reorganized with a new lead singer, Ben E. King. They scored a number 2 hit in 1959 with a Leiber and Stoller song, "There Goes My Baby." In 1960, they had hits with "This Magic Moment" and "Save the Last Dance for Me" (their only number 1 hit). The Drifters continued to have hits through the mid-1960s.

heralded the sound of soul." Cooke's move to the Pop side with "You Send Me" (number 1 in 1957) became a model for other gospel singers to cross over to the white market. After all, R&B, through its offspring rock and roll, had proven successful with whites. By the late 1950s, other gospel artists rushed to copy Cooke's crossover success.

Ray Charles—Ray Charles was another model for the wannabe crossover artist. Charles said of his early years in Florida, "You went to church every Sunday. So naturally I was around church music. The preacher would say a couple of lines and then the church would sing what he said. It was very ad-lib" (Hirshey 1984, 49). In Charles's early recording sessions, he simply ad-libbed secular words to familiar gospel songs, often a bit of jazz and blues got mixed in as well. "I Got a Woman," his 1954 hit for Atlantic, combines the heavy chords of church piano, a strong R&B-oriented band, and, as Hirshey so aptly says (1984, 50), "a vocal that bounced between the bedroom and the blessed." That blues and gospel mix, the secular–sacred dichotomy, was evident in his no-holds-barred falsetto shrieks and vocal groans. When "What'd I Say" hit the Top 10 in 1959, with Charles's call-and-response moans and verbal interactions with the Raelettes (his female backup vocal group), he successfully brought the fiery combination of gospel and R&B to the national market … soul music.

This new success for black music led to a new kind of black pride and an interest in black roots. At first, the elusive quality of this music was called **funk**. But the term "soul" also began to be applied to much the same quality. Thus, there was "A Bit of Soul" in 1955 and "Hornful of Soul" in 1957, both by Ray Charles. Milt Jackson recorded "Plenty, Plenty Soul" in 1957, and Charles and Jackson combined on a 1957 album called *Soul Brothers*.

JOURNAL

Gospel Influences in the Music of Ray Charles

Using your favorite streaming service or YouTube, listen to several gospel recordings by Sister Rosetta Stone, Thomas Dorsey, and/or Mahalia Jackson. Then listen to Ray Charles's "What'd I Say." What specific gospel influences do you hear in Charles's performance on this recording? What are some decidedly non-religious aspects of the song? Identify at least one artist of the new millennium, one who is not associated with the contemporary Christian subgenre of popular music, in whose music you can discern gospel influence. In one or two sentences, describe clearly the musical elements that are similar between the gospel recordings and those of the chosen contemporary artist.

▶ The response entered here will appear in the performance dashboard and can be viewed by your instructor.

Submit

8.2: Atlantic and Stax

OBJECTIVE: Summarize the influence of recording studios on soul music

As the 1960s dawned, the southern-rooted suffering and pain of the blues had joined with the joyful and unrestrained celebration of gospel, but soul music might be merely a footnote to rock history if it had not been for one record company, which, by the end of the decade, would be almost synonymous with the style. We need to discuss Atlantic Records and meet two influential men: Ahmet Ertegun and Jerry Wexler.

8.2.1: Atlantic Records

Ahmet Ertegun, the son of a Turkish ambassador to the United States, was enthralled with the music of black America. In 1947, he and Herb Abramson formed a small company dedicated to black music—primarily R&B—called Atlantic Records.

8.2.2: Stax Records

A fortuitous outcome of Wexler's travels to the South was the relationship established with a Memphis recording company called Stax Records. If Motown developed a reputation as "Hitsville, U.S.A.," Stax could legitimately claim the name "Soulsville, U.S.A."

In 1959, Jim Stewart and Estelle Axton started a small record company they named Satellite Records. By 1961, they had changed the company's name to Stax and signed a distribution agreement with Atlantic Records. For the next few years, the Atlantic-Stax partnership flourished. Between Stax's own artists and the Atlantic artists who recorded there, a distinctively identifiable sound of southern soul emerged.

The early 1970s were tough times for Stax. The same year that Otis Redding died, Stax's agreement with Atlantic ended. The cooperation had already soured by 1966; then, Stax closed its doors to outside producers. Finally, in 1975, Stax filed for bankruptcy.

By the mid-1970s, soul music, as a distinct subgenre of rock and roll, had largely run its course. Stax was gone, a primary R&B label (Chess) had folded in 1968, Motown moved to Los Angeles in 1971, Otis Redding was dead, and the commercial impact of other major soul stars had declined. Jerry Wexler left Atlantic in 1975 to become a vice president of Warner Brothers. Ahmet Ertegun retreated to Atlantic's administrative boardroom. For the time being, the future of soul music appeared dim. However, it proved to be a highly influential factor in the resurgence of R&B to evolve over the next couple of decades.

The Atlantic Records' Journey to Success

The role of record labels and studios has proven to be critically important to the evolution of certain styles of music. Concerning the emergence of rock, in this course, we have already stressed the significance of Sun Records in Memphis. For soul music, the synergy between Atlantic Records and Stax (discussed later in this chapter) was crucial.

In the beginning, Ertegun wrote most of the songs for these artists. The first hit for the fledgling company came in 1948 with "Drinking Wine, Spo-Dee-O-Dee" by Stick McGhee.

By 1950, Atlantic had placed only three songs in the R&B Top 10, but—thanks to hits by Clyde McPhatter, Ray Charles, La Vern Baker, and Chuck Willis—by 1956, Atlantic claimed 17 out of that year's 81 Top 10 hits. Some of these hits were finding success in the Pop market via cover versions, as described below. Atlantic's growing success was partially due to the addition of a talented producer named Jerry Wexler, who had joined Atlantic in 1953.

The crossover phenomenon of the mid-1950s significantly benefited Atlantic Records and its hopeful young stars. La Vern Baker's "Tweedle Dee" hit number 14 on the Pop chart in 1955; in 1959, she hit the Top 10 again with "I Cried a Tear." McPhatter had three moderate Pop chart hits before "A Lover's Question" reached the Top 10 in late 1958. Chuck Willis's "C. C. Rider" rose to number 12 in 1957, and his "What Am I Living For" made the Top 10 in 1958. Ertegun also signed Bobby Darin, a white artist, to a contract and was rewarded with a long string of major hits through 1962 on the subsidiary Atco label. Further success came through the popularity of the Coasters and the songwriting talents of Jerry Leiber and Mike Stoller. By the end of the 1950s, Atlantic had moved from a small indie with moderate R&B success to a very successful independent in the Pop market. In the 1960s, Jerry Wexler steered the label in the direction of soul music, resulting in even greater success. Thanks to the soul movement, Atlantic would become a major label by the late 1960s.

Soul singer Wilson Pickett had his own description of how he achieved his sound:

> You harmonize; then you customize.... You look around for a good, solid used chassis. This be your 12-bar blues. R&B ain't nothin' if it ain't the 12-bar blues. Then you look around for what else you got. And if you come up like most of us, that would be gospel. (Hirshey 1984, 46)

Pickett combined his blues and gospel into an R&B hit in 1962: "I Found a Love." But his greatest success came a few years later, when Jerry Wexler took him back down south to record in Memphis and Muscle Shoals, Alabama. In 1966, Pickett had his biggest hit, "Land of 1,000 Dances" (number 1 R&B and number 6 on the Pop chart), with its listing of previous songs and dances and its "na-na-na-na-na" chorus. The idea of recording down south proved successful in more ways than one. Wexler discovered that by returning to southern recording studios he found an unusual blend of blues, gospel, and C&W in the racially mixed studio bands. Some of Atlantic's finest recordings, with artists like Pickett and Aretha Franklin, were made in these southern studios.

Stax Artists

In addition to the Atlantic artists mentioned earlier, there were Stax (and its subsidiary, Volt) artists like Otis Redding, Sam and Dave, and Isaac Hayes.

Otis Redding was born in Little Richard's hometown of Macon, Georgia in 1941. He absorbed many musical influences, from the country sounds of his favorites Eddy Arnold and Hank Williams to the R&B-oriented rock and roll of hometown hero Little Richard. Otis sang in the choir at the Mount Ivy Baptist Church, where his father preached to the congregation. So all of the pieces of the musical puzzle were in place. Like so many gospel and soul singers, he particularly admired Sam Cooke. In 1965, he hit the Pop chart with a song cowritten with Jerry Butler, "I've Been Loving You Too Long (to Stop Now)" (number 21). He followed up with another of his own songs, "Respect," which did very well on the R&B chart but barely made it into the Top 40 (number 35). Redding's performance of his unique blend of blues, gospel, rock, country, and Pop made a tremendous impact at the 1967 Monterey International Pop Festival. Unfortunately, Redding was killed on December 10, 1967, in an airplane crash. In early 1968, his single "(Sittin' on) The Dock of the Bay" was released posthumously, becoming his only song to reach the top of the Pop chart.

Sam Moore and Dave Prater recorded one of the soul anthems of the 1960s: "Soul Man" (number 2 in 1967), composed by Isaac Hayes. Moore was a gospel-trained deacon's son and the grandson of a Baptist preacher; Prater was from Ocilla, Georgia. After signing with Atlantic, Moore and Prater were sent by Jerry Wexler to Memphis to record for Stax. "Soul Man" was followed by another Top 10 hit, "I Thank You."

Isaac Hayes represents Stax's final years of success. After several moderate hits, he composed the score for a motion picture and the title track, "Theme from *Shaft*," reached number 1 in 1971 and also won an Oscar. However, after the success of "*Shaft*," things changed. As Hayes says, "Life got beautiful. And then it got weird" (Hirshey 1984, 355). Somewhere, the soul sound was lost. The catchy wah-wah guitar effects in "*Shaft*" and the simple, repetitive, insistent dance beat evolved into disco (Hayes is sometimes called the father of disco). He left Stax in 1974; his first post-Stax album was called *Disco Connection* (1976). Although Hayes continued to release new music into the 1990s, he is probably best known to recent generations as the voice of Chef on the animated television series *South Park*.

JOURNAL

The "Sound" of a Recording Studio

The equipment in and the spatial arrangement of a recording studio or the feeling it provides musicians as they record (sometimes referred to as "the vibe") can have a significant impact on the sound of recordings generated. Pick one of the two primary studios mentioned in the previous section (Stax or Muscle Shoals) and perform some online research to determine which artists and/or groups recorded there between the mid-60s and mid-70s. Using your own past knowledge or, if the bands are unfamiliar to you, by listening to some recorded examples via YouTube, what similarities can you identify in the sounds of recordings made by different musicians in that same space during this era? [Note: if you would like to dig a little deeper into this topic, I highly recommend that you watch one or more of these documentaries: *Sound City* (2013), *Sonic Highways* (2015; both by Dave Grohl and the Foo Fighters) and *Muscle Shoals* (2013).]

▶ The response entered here will appear in the performance dashboard and can be viewed by your instructor.

Submit

8.3: Soul Artists

OBJECTIVE: Describe the wide variety of vocal styles represented in soul recordings

As we dig deeper into the story of soul, we must take a close look at two of its most dominant personalities: Aretha Franklin and James Brown. As noted earlier, the term "soul music" includes a wide variety of styles. This becomes particularly evident when one considers that the two most prominent representatives of soul music were as different as night and day. Aretha Franklin ("Lady Soul") was the model for a female soul singer. James Brown ("the Godfather of Soul," "Soul Brother Number 1," "Mr. Dynamite," "the Hardest Working Man in Show Business," or "Mr. Sex Machine") was the model for a male soul singer. Yet these two leading soul singers seem to be almost exact opposites. Franklin has total vocal control, allowing her to execute intricate melodic and rhythmic nuances with precise control of pitch and timbre. Her voice is clear and strong; she has a remarkable range and uses it to express a wide spectrum of emotions. Brown's voice was raspy; he typically shouted a raw and basic vocal line with a significant amount of emotive **improvisation** and **vocal interpolation**. Franklin's arrangements are often quite complex and sophisticated; Brown's songs are among the simplest and most basic in all of popular music. Franklin is rather shy and introverted; Brown was flamboyant, egotistical, and aggressive.

8.3.1: Aretha Franklin

Aretha Franklin was born in Memphis in 1942; her father, the Reverend C. L. Franklin, moved his family to Detroit soon after her birth to become pastor of a church there.

Franklin frequently heard gospel singers like Clara Ward and Mahalia Jackson perform at her father's church. Noting Sam Cooke's success in crossing over from gospel style to the national Pop market, the 17-year-old Franklin recorded some demo records of her own.

Aretha Franklin, 1977.

SOURCE: CSU Archives/Everett Collection/Alamy Stock Photo

Columbia Records' John Hammond heard Franklin sing and decided that she could follow Cooke's path into the Pop market. Hammond had a knack for spotting raw talent and for converting it into a commercially successful product. He had been instrumental in the recording careers of blues singers Bessie Smith and Billie Holiday and would discover Bob Dylan as has been noted elsewhere in this course. For six years, in the early 1960s, Franklin recorded with Columbia Records, where industry executives considered her a Pop singer. She sang show tunes and jazz-flavored commercial Pop, but her four Columbia albums fared poorly from a commercial perspective.

8.3.2: James Brown

James Brown's style has been called southern soul. Many soul singers, although their roots may have been in the South, developed in the major cities of the Midwest and Northeast, but James Brown remained deeply and loyally southern. Among the record companies identified with soul music, possibly the most strongly connected with pure southern soul was King Records in Cincinnati. In Gerri Hirshey's words (1984, 260), "From 1956 to 1971, King served as a pipeline for the loudest, the rawest, the most fundamental in-your-face soul ever pumped up from the green hills of Georgia." And that describes James Brown.

Aretha's Journey with Atlantic Records

Following a rather tepid beginning with recordings focused on jazz, show tunes, and Pop, Aretha's career took off when she joined the Atlantic Records label and began to earn the title "Lady Soul."

Atlantic's Jerry Wexler had long wanted to develop Franklin into a soul singer, so when her Columbia contract expired, Wexler signed her to Atlantic Records (1967) and took her to Muscle Shoals, Alabama, to record. The result was dynamite. The first Atlantic album, *I Never Loved a Man the Way I Love You,* went to number 2 on the album chart. The title song became a Top 10 hit, and "Respect," an Otis Redding song, became Franklin's first (and only) solo number 1 song; she did reach the top of the Hot 100 one more time with a George Michael duet in 1987, "I Knew You Were Waiting (For Me)." Lady Soul was finally on her way. Franklin placed seven more songs in the Top 10 before the end of 1968 and won Grammy awards for Best R&B Performance by a Female Artist eight years in a row.

If Atlantic was the soul label, Franklin was surely that label's top artist, finding consistent success with both black and white audiences while retaining her gospel/soul sound. Franklin performed songs by some of the finest songwriters, soul and otherwise: "Respect" (Otis Redding), "Spanish Harlem" (Jerry Leiber and Phil Spector), "Eleanor Rigby" (Lennon/McCartney), "Bridge over Troubled Water" (Paul Simon), "Say a Little Prayer" (Burt Bacharach and Hal David), "Chain of Fools" (Don Covay), and "A Natural Woman" (Carole King and Gerry Goffin).

In 1972, Aretha released a fascinating album, *Amazing Grace,* which returned to her pure gospel roots. Atlantic set up their recording equipment in the New Temple Missionary Baptist Church in Los Angeles. Joined by Reverend James Cleveland and his Southern California Community Choir, plus a live congregation on two successive nights, Franklin sang traditional songs like "What a Friend We Have in Jesus" and the title song (a truly remarkable version of this composition, extending to almost 11 minutes in length). Particularly interesting is the combination of two songs into one arrangement: Thomas Dorsey's "Precious Lord, Take My Hand" and Carole King's "You've Got a Friend," providing a new context for the meaning of the latter.

As is often the case with superior musical talents, Franklin was anxious to adapt her abilities to a variety of musical styles. Often, such artists are accused of "selling out," of being inconsistent or uncommitted, or "going commercial." But it seems only natural that talented musicians should be interested in applying their talents to a variety of good songs, no matter what the stylistic point of origin. When Franklin sings a song, whether a traditional gospel song or a tune by Broadway's Rodgers and Hammerstein, the song becomes her own. This practice does not suggest a weak musical identity but, quite the contrary, a strong identity that can be applied to almost any song.

With Jerry Wexler gone and disco and harder rock styles dominating in the last half of the 1970s, Franklin left Atlantic Records to sign with Arista Records in 1979. She is regarded as one of the most influential artists of the era and continued to release recordings and perform into the new millennium, although her 2010 tour was canceled as the result of health issues. In 2001, *Woman Falling Out of Love* reached number 54 on the Pop chart, and, in 2014, she released *Aretha Sings the Great Diva Classics,* including covers of songs written and/or recorded by other artists, including Adele, Alicia Keys, The Supremes (composed by Holland-Dozier-Holland), and Sinead O'Conner (composed by Prince).

James Brown performing in England in 1966.

Brown was born on May 3, 1933, in Augusta, Georgia. He was musical from an early age, teaching himself keyboards, drums, and bass. He got into trouble—in 1949, he was arrested and sent to jail for three and a half years for breaking into automobiles—but by the early 1950s, he had also realized his interest in music. He formed a small gospel group. With R&B sounds beginning to cross over to national popularity, the group moved toward R&B and called themselves the Famous Flames. They recorded a demo called "Please, Please, Please." King Records liked the sound and signed them to a contract. The song was rerecorded and released on King's subsidiary label, Federal, in 1956 and became a regional R&B hit (number 6). A 1958 follow-up hit, "Try Me (I Need You)," actually went to number 48 on the Hot 100 chart and reached the top of the R&B chart. These songs were not far from the sound of doo-wop vocal groups; the newly popular rock and roll sound is more evident in 1959's "Good Good Lovin'" and 1960's "Think" (Brown's first Top 40 hit).

EARLY 1960S   During the early 1960s, Brown toured the country with his James Brown Revue, including 40 singers, dancers, and musicians. It was during this period that Brown developed his incredible stage act. His dancing became the model for performers from Mick Jagger to Michael Jackson, and he became known as the "Hardest Working Man in Show Business." At the end of the show, with sweat pouring off his face, he would launch into "Please, Please, Please," collapsing prostrate on the stage. Several of the Famous Flames would help him off the stage, draped in a colorful cape, but he would always return for another round of "Please, Please, Please," followed by more collapses and a return of the cape. As his boyhood friend Leon Austin tells it:

> He's not gonna come out there and be cool, and he ain't gonna have on this pretty suit that ain't gonna get dusty. He gonna wallow. He's gonna just be splittin', dancin', fallin'; he'd jump outta a air-o-plane, I swear. Mess up his knees so he can't work the next job. Or he may scream so hard he can't sing the next night. But he ain't gonna worry about that. (Hirshey 1984, 283)

MID-1960S   In the mid-1960s, Brown's voice became even rawer, with a raspier, shouting style. There were hints of the new style in his versions of "Night Train" (1962) and "Out of Sight" (1964). In 1965, the new sound took shape in two Top 10 hits based on the 12-bar blues: "Papa's Got a Brand New Bag" and, his biggest hit of all, "I Got You (I Feel Good)" (number 3). There is a choppy feeling to these songs; the horns punctuate Brown's phrases with short bursts; bass and drums play short, tightly coordinated accompanying patterns called *riffs*. In some cases, there are only two or three chords in the entire song. The band *vamps* (repeats the accompanying riff) on one chord, while Brown seemingly improvises his declamatory phrases. At a certain moment, all move to a second chord, establishing a new riff. Finally, the song returns to the original chord and riff. Listen to "There Was a Time" (1967), "Sex Machine" (1970), or "Make It Funky" (1971) for good examples of this style. This is almost as simple and repetitive as music can get. The music is more of a social experience. Brown's live performance antics and dancing were the main points. As Hirshey writes (1984, 289), "James Brown's funk works its best mojo from the neck down. You love it or hate it; it's magic or it's just screams." Certainly it is very different from the sophisticated soul of Aretha Franklin or the Pop-influenced black sound of Motown.

By 1967, Brown was at the height of his career. That year, he performed before about 3 million concertgoers and sold some 50 million records. Between 1967 and 1972, he placed 30 songs in the Top 40. Most were number 1 hits on the R&B chart but typically placed well below the Top 10 on the Hot 100.

Brown's close identification with the black cause led him into politics at times. His song "Say It Loud—I'm Black and I'm Proud" was interpreted by some as a call to black militancy, but most heard it as Brown apparently intended it—as an encouragement of black pride. In his concerts, Brown advocated a positive, nonviolent approach to racial change, with slogans like "Don't terrorize, organize!" and "Don't burn, learn!" He became renowned for this message worldwide. Leon Austin says that, in Africa, Brown and his entourage were greeted by people who emerged from their mud shacks carrying James Brown albums, even though they had no electricity and no phonograph—but they knew James Brown. Music affects behavior. One related phenomenon is the effect that entertainers have as role models. Reverend Al Sharpton, a close friend of Brown's, has remarked that "black entertainers … become substitute fathers. We learn how to dress from watchin' a star; we learn how to walk. We look at James Brown and we say, 'Hey, that's how I'm gonna be a man'" (Hirshey 1984, 277).

BROWN'S LATER CAREER   By the mid-1970s, changing styles had begun to push Brown to one side. Blacks were dancing to disco beats. These were tough years for Brown, filled with severe financial and personal problems, including the death of his son Teddy. He was also upset by the death of his friend of some 20 years, Elvis Presley. At that funeral, a teary-eyed James Brown stared into the coffin, stroked Elvis's arm, and was heard to say, "Elvis, how you let this happen? How you let it go?" (Hirshey 1984, 278). By 1978, Brown had hit bottom.

From 1975 to 1985, he had no Top 40 hits; his albums, including a disco album and several live albums, did not fare well. Then, in 1980, his appearance in the popular movie *The Blues Brothers* sparked the younger generation's interest and suggested the historically accurate connection between black R&B, gospel and soul, and the black church experience.

Throughout his career, Brown stayed with the simplified, repetitive, and percussively rhythmic style he developed in the mid-1960s. As he told *Downbeat* magazine in 1968,

> I tried the heavy approach two or three times, and every time I tried, I got stopped. Just have to keep coming back and simplifying it. It's a funny thing. You make a little three-finger chord on the guitar and they'll sell a million copies, and the minute the cat spreads his hand out across the neck, you can't give the record away. (Hirshey 1984, 289)

8.3.3: Other Soul Singers

There were many soul singers in the 1960s, each with a slightly different approach to the style. Other than Franklin and Brown, who dominated the genre, and the Atlantic-Stax artists already discussed, we now turn our focus to several other important soul performers.

Other Important Soul Performers

Jackie Wilson—Jackie Wilson was from Detroit and was the replacement for Clyde McPhatter after the latter left the Dominoes. After singing lead with the Dominoes for three years, Wilson moved on to a successful solo career. Finding himself hounded by a young songwriter named Berry Gordy, Jr., he agreed to record Gordy's songs. "To Be Loved" became Wilson's first Top 40 hit (1958), and the follow-up, "Lonely Teardrops," hit the Top 10. By the end of 1961, Wilson had charted 17 Top 40 hits. His career slowed dramatically after he was shot in a hotel room that same year. He managed to place seven more hits in the Top 40 between 1962 and 1968, before dying in 1984 at the age of 49.

Curtis Mayfield—Somewhere in the continuum between the pop commercial sound of Motown and the true soul sound was a group known as the Impressions. Formed in the late 1950s, they had their first hit in 1958 with "For Your Precious Love" (number 11). Attributed to Jerry Butler, a member of the group, the song was the work of fellow Impression Curtis Mayfield. Mayfield stayed with the Impressions throughout the 1960s and did most of the songwriting for the group. They eventually placed 17 songs in the Top 40. In the late 1960s, Mayfield songs became increasingly identified with black pride and social consciousness. Mayfield went on to a very successful solo career, culminating with the success of *Superfly*, a motion picture soundtrack and number 1 album.

Ike and Tina Turner—Ike Turner had played piano and guitar for Sam Phillips's Sun Records. He also recorded with his own group, the Kings of Rhythm, which scored an early R&B success on Chess Records with "Rocket 88" (1951). By 1957, Ike had decided to add his girlfriend to the band as lead singer. Her name was Annie Mae Bullock, who later assumed the stage name Tina Turner. Ike was from Clarksdale, Mississippi; Tina was from Brownsville, Tennessee. They married in 1958 and first hit the Top 40 with "A Fool in Love" in 1960. They developed a blatantly suggestive stage act; Turner's miniskirts were as mini as they could get. Restricted to black audiences, R&B stations, and the R&B chart, they finally broke onto the national pop scene after their appearance at Altamont with the Rolling Stones in late 1969. Their first Top 5 hit was "Proud Mary" (early 1971). The duo recorded for several labels through the 1960s and 1970s. After their divorce in 1977, Tina went on to a successful career in the 1980s, including the number 1 hit, "What's Love Got to Do with It?" While Tina became one of the hottest acts of the 1980s, Ike faded from public attention. He died in 2007.

Before we move on to discussing Motown, another important musical development during this era, let's take a moment to carefully examine the sound of soul.

JOURNAL

Soul Music: In Your Own Words

Listen to several examples of soul recordings by Aretha Franklin and James Brown. Based on that small sampling, and your previous listening to this style, if applicable, which artist's music do you prefer? Compose a paragraph describing the musical style of your selected artist, focusing on the musical elements you find most attractive. Identify two or three contemporary artists who appear to have been influenced by this sound and describe the specific influences you hear.

 The response entered here will appear in the performance dashboard and can be viewed by your instructor.

Submit

8.4: Musical Close-Up on Melody and the Soul Singer

OBJECTIVE: Explain how soul music allows for freedom of expression using the elements of music

Most descriptions of soul singing use subjective terms, like freedom, feelings, and emotion. But if we really are to understand the style, we must consider objective elements of music, such as rhythm, timbre, melody, harmony, and form. Even though the art of soul singing would seem to be an elusive phenomenon, as evident from the quotes at the beginning of this chapter, we must at least attempt to analyze, in objective musical terms, what there is about the finest soul singers that establishes their style as fitting firmly in this genre.

As noted earlier, soul singing is derived primarily from the gospel-singing tradition of the southern black church. The previous discussion indicated that many soul singers (a) were originally from the South and (b) had their earliest musical experiences as singers in the church. Quite a few (Sam Cooke, Marvin Gaye, and Aretha Franklin) were offspring of clergymen.

Following the detailed description of the musical style and artistic expression inherent in Aretha's recording of "What a Friend … " provided in the previous section, listen carefully to the entire song two or three times so that you can hear these aspects for yourself. The next section provides a listening guide to focus your ears and mind as you complete that important listening process.

After examining carefully Aretha Franklin's performance of "What a Friend … " and listening to several of her other recordings, as you have done in previous sections, begin to listen for elements of soul music in more contemporary performances. Particularly obvious examples can be found in R&B from the 1990s and from

Musical Elements of a Soul Song

This section will begin to identify defining elements of the soul style, beyond the freedom and emotion that are often cited.

Tune/Melody Perhaps, then, it would be instructive to listen to a bona fide soul singer singing gospel, which should provide some useful insights. We can find just what we are looking for on Aretha Franklin's *Amazing Grace* album. To simplify our task, let us take an uncomplicated and well-known tune: the hymn "What a Friend We Have in Jesus." Franklin turns this straightforward hymn into a gospel song.

This tune has a familiar microform: 16 measures, divided into four equal phrases, each 4 measures long. Furthermore, note that the first, second, and fourth phrases are almost alike (the familiar AABA pattern). The rhythm is quite uncomplicated. Every note is within the scale of F major, except the F# in the ninth measure. Now, let us see what Franklin does to this simple little hymn.

Click or tap the play button in the Revel course to watch a video depiction of the melody of "What a Friend We Have in Jesus."

What a Friend We Have in Jesus (melody)

Form First, there is the matter of form. Franklin turns this tune into a six-minute piece. To do this, she subdivides each of the 4-measure phrases into two halves and then elongates each half into a full 4-measure phrase of its own,

Watch the example of original form of the tune by clicking the play button in the Revel course.

Augmentation Thus, she has turned a 16-bar song into a 32-bar song. Then, she repeats the first half of the song before going on to the second half, which she also repeats. So now the 16-bar tune has become 64 bars long. But on the final occurrence of the original 15th measure, she improvises on the word "everything," repeating that measure over and over, before finally resolving on a cadence. After a short pause, Franklin hums and sings through the last half of the tune one more time, complete with the repetitive extension on the final "everything." The six-minute result begins to suggest what is meant by the word *freedom* when it is applied to the musical element of form.

Click or tap the play button in the Revel course to watch the example of the original form of the tune.

What a Friend We Have in Jesus (2 measures)

What a Friend We Have in Jesus (2 measures, augmented)

Rhythm What is even more important is how Franklin fills that elongated form with a combination of pitches and rhythms; that is, with melody. Compare the first 2 measures of the original tune with Franklin's first phrase in the first figure on the next page.

Rhythm

Pitch The basic pitches of the tune are present, but there are notes added, and the rhythms are significantly modified, with some notes falling behind where they should be and others coming ahead. Even the notation in the previous example does not exactly replicate the fine pitch or rhythmic variations of Franklin's voice (e.g., the extra pitch inflections on "have" in the second measure). The gospel/soul singer's vocal freedom is further illustrated the next time she sings these same measures.

Pitch

This is yet more different from (and more complex than) the earlier example. Again, standard notation cannot effectively capture every nuance of pitch and rhythm she sings. Note the arrow in the second measure of the foregoing example; this is a good example of a **blue note**—a pitch that is unstable, vacillating between A and A b what the blues' singers called "worrying" the pitch).

Although we cannot compare every measure of the original tune with Franklin's version, we can point out a few other places that are worthy of notice. Frequently, the gospel/soul singer adds short vocal phrases as a sort of emotive commentary on the text. For example, observe such phrases as "oh, yes we do," "oh-oh," "oh, yeah," and "let's do that one more time"—sung in the same style as the main melody. Also, there is the freedom to add words like "what a privilege (it is) to carry" or repeat words like "we often, we often, forfeit." The best examples in "What a Friend" are the extensions on "everything"—repeated for nearly one full minute, with a different melodic phrase each time. If you can listen to the entire performance while following the original tune, you will be able to see what freedom of pitch and rhythm means to the soul singer.

Melisma One of the most pronounced characteristics of the gospel/soul singer is the *melisma*: a technique in which one syllable is extended over two or more pitches. As Wilson Pickett said, soul singers "put ten, maybe twenty notes to one word" (Hirshey 1984, 51). Look back at the two immediately preceding examples and notice where words like "what" and "have" are extended over three or four notes each. Using your preferred streaming service or YouTube, locate a recording of this track on the *Amazing Grace* album and listen to it (extended to almost 11 minutes); it contains many examples of extended melismas (e.g., Franklin's repetitive melismas on the word "through," about five minutes into the song).

Vocal Timbre Finally, there is the matter of vocal timbre. The soul singer employs a wide variety of vocal timbres. These range from the shout (in "What a Friend," listen to Franklin on the words "and what needless pain," or you can hear many shouted phrases in "Amazing Grace") to a very breathy tone (listen to the second occurrence of the title line from Franklin's "I Never Loved a Man"). Other vocal timbres used in soul music include the raspiness of James Brown and the falsetto voice so often used by male backup groups. The soul singer moves with dizzying speed through a full range of such timbres.

Freedom of Expression Soul's roots in the black southern church are clear. In the context of that sacred experience, there was freedom to react vocally to the preacher's message or to an inner stirring of the spirit. Impromptu phrases were shouted out or moaned. So it is with the gospel singer. As gospel merged with R&B (both came from similar roots) and the "new kid on the block"—rock and roll—soul music was born. Although the beat got harder, the instrumentation became more electric, and the overall forms grew more formulaic, the soul singer still retained that freedom of expression—freedom of form, timbre, pitch, and rhythm—learned so long ago in a little, white, wood-framed church somewhere in the heart of the South.

Listening Guide: "What a Friend We Have in Jesus" (Aretha Franklin)

0:05–0:17	Introduction (4 bars)	Piano lead
0:18–0:44	A (8 bars)	Vocal enters ("What a friend").
0:45–1:10	A (8 bars)	Second phrase of hymn ("What a privilege").
1:11–1:37	A (8 bars)	Repeats first phrase ("What a friend") with melodic variation.
1:38–2:03	A (8 bars)	Repeats second phrase of hymn ("What a privilege") with melodic variation.
2:04–2:30	B (8 bars)	The bridge of the original hymn ("Oh, what peace").
2:31–2:56	A (8 bars)	Final phrase of the original hymn ("All because we do not carry").
2:57–3:23	B (8 bars)	Repeats the bridge ("Oh, what peace").
3:24–4:35	A (20 bars)	Repeats final phrase of original hymn ("All because we do not carry"). Extended improvisation on "everything" adds 12 bars to the original 8 bars. Beat slows to a stop at the end of this section.
4:36–5:03	B (8 bars)	Back to the bridge. Franklin hums quietly over the instrumental and choral accompaniment.
5:04–5:55	A (14 bars)	Final phrase of original hymn. Again, she adds an improvised extension (6 bars) on "everything." Builds excitement by increasing volume and adding hand claps. Beat slows to a final stop.

the early years of the new millennium, but some aspects, such as those enumerated in the next section, can be found in almost any form of popular music to which you listen.

BECOME AN ACTIVE LISTENER: ELEMENTS OF SOUL STYLE

This is your chance to identify some of the elements of soul music in music to which you listen today.

1. Find examples of these vocal techniques in the music that you enjoy:
   Shouting style
2. Blue notes
3. Melisma
4. Falsetto

8.5: Motown

OBJECTIVE: Summarize the Motown musical style

While Ahmet Ertegun was enthralled by the black musical traditions of R&B and gospel, Berry Gordy, Jr., a native-born, American black man, was rather embarrassed by it. Gordy's preference was for jazz, what he considered a far more sophisticated style of popular music, the roots of which were also black. In 1960, after his jazz-oriented

record store failed, the 31-year-old Gordy borrowed $700 and started his own record company, Tammie Records (soon changed to Tamla Records). At first, Tamla simply distributed records, such as Barrett Strong's "Money" for Gordy's sister's label, Anna. But in late 1960, Tamla released its own record, "Shop Around," by the Miracles, a group led by singer-songwriter William "Smokey" Robinson. Against all odds, the record went to number 2 on the Hot 100. What followed is an amazing story. The tiny independent label became a major power in the music industry within an incredibly short period of time. Just seven years later, Gordy's record empire, including Motown Records and subsidiary labels Tamla, Gordy, and Soul, sold more singles than any other company, independent or major. Not a bad return for an investment of $700 of borrowed money.

Motown began in a blue-trimmed, white frame house at 2648 West Grand Avenue in Gordy's hometown, Detroit. Gordy's entire family pitched in to make it as professional a facility as possible. The recording studio itself was no larger than a suburban living room. In 1960, Detroit had the fourth largest black population in the United States—over half a million. Within that population was a gold mine of talent, but if they wished to record, they had to go to Chicago, Philadelphia, or New York. With a combination of reliable musical instincts and a strong business sense, Gordy managed to attract some of that talent to his new company.

The rock and roll explosion of the mid-1950s had integrated music at a time when the rest of society remained largely segregated, but in the 1960s, even as society moved closer to real integration, the music industry moved back toward segregation. The early 1960 teen idols, the surfers, the folkies, and the British invasion groups were all white. Only the dance craze of the early 1960s kept black music on the Pop chart. The soul trend found its primary acceptance in a purely black market (the R&B chart). Typically, soul records climbed to the top of the R&B chart but wallowed in the bottom half of the Pop chart. Berry Gordy wanted to bring a style of black music to prominence in both the black and the white markets. To do this, he knew he had to have talented black musicians whose roots were in gospel, R&B, or doo-wop, but who understood that those styles had to be modified to become more commercially appealing to a wider audience. Finally, Gordy felt that to make the formula work consistently, he had to have absolute control, allowing for little or no variation from the established patterns.

8.5.1: Smokey Robinson

One of Gordy's first musical discoveries was Smokey Robinson, a talented songwriter who had started a group called the Matadors. Changing their name to the Miracles, they auditioned for Berry Gordy in the pre-Motown days. Gordy used his connections to get the Miracles a release on End Records in New York. When Gordy started Tamla, he signed the Miracles and released "Shop Around," which hit the Top 5 in early 1961 and put Tamla-Motown on the map.

Smokey Robinson became one of the important parts of the new record company. The Miracles were a consistent success throughout the 1960s, registering over two dozen Top 40 hits (including five in the Top 10). Their last Top 40 hit was "Love Machine (Part I)," which reached number 1 in early 1976; it was a disco-flavored song and was recorded by the new Miracles, without Robinson, who had left the group in 1971. Robinson's strong falsetto voice, with a smooth sound and expressiveness reminiscent of Sam Cooke, was a major asset to Motown throughout the 1960s, but, of equal importance, was Robinson's songwriting ability. In 1962, he wrote three Top 10 songs for Motown's first female star, 19-year-old Mary Wells. Later, he wrote Wells's only number 1 hit, "My Guy" (1964); Robinson also wrote major hits for other Motown stars, including the Temptations and Marvin Gaye.

8.5.2: Female Groups

Though rock and roll, including black musical styles, had been largely dominated by male performers, female groups began to break through during the Motown era.

Motown Female Groups

Along with Gordy's musical innovations and artistic control, he also proved extremely important in establishing successful groups of female artists within the Motown family. Two early examples are presented in the following section.

The Marvelettes—The Marvelettes provided a prototype for Motown female groups of the 1960s. Their song "Please Mr. Postman" became Tamla's first number 1 song, confirming that Gordy's formula could work. "Please Mr. Postman" was later recorded by the Beatles and the Carpenters, the latter version also hitting number 1 in 1975. The Marvelettes had nine more Top 40 hits for Tamla through 1968.

Martha and the Vandellas—Martha Reeves and her group, the Delphis, auditioned for Gordy's new record company but were not accepted immediately. In fact, Martha was hired as a secretary at Motown and sang various parts in recording sessions as needed. Finally, in 1962, Berry Gordy signed Martha's vocal trio (now called the Vandellas) to a recording contract; their second song, "Heat Wave," moved to the number 4 position, and the Vandellas became another successful Motown group. Recording on the Gordy label, the group (through numerous personnel changes) eventually placed a dozen hits in the Top 40 before disbanding in 1971. Their biggest hit came in 1964 with "Dancing in the Street" (number 2). As happened with a number of young Motown stars, Reeves eventually began to question the exact distribution of money from the company to the performers. Gordy perceived such questioning as disloyalty, and Reeves left Motown in 1972, recording for several other labels through the 1970s without comparable success.

8.5.3: Marvin Gaye

Another triumph of Motown's early days was Marvin Gaye. Unlike the other Motown stars, Gaye was not from Detroit but Washington, D.C. At first, Gaye was used as a session drummer on tour with the Miracles. His first solo release came in late 1962 with "Stubborn Kind of Fellow." Through the 1960s, Gaye placed 17 songs in the Top 40 and joined with four of Motown's female singers (Diana Ross, Mary Wells, Kim Weston, and Tammi Terrell) for a dozen more Top 40 hit duets. Gaye's biggest solo hit was "I Heard It Through the Grapevine" (number 1 in 1968). Gaye's 1971 album *What's Going On?* (number 6) showed him to be a talented songwriter as well as performer. The record combined concerns about the unrest in U.S. inner cities and the war in Vietnam at a time when few pop artists were addressing such sociopolitical issues.

In the late 1970s, troubled times began for Gaye. A bitter divorce from Anna Gordy Gaye (Berry Gordy's sister who was 17 years older than the singer) resulted in a strange double album called *Here, My Dear,* with songs full of irony, contradictions, and sarcasm. Following the divorce, there were problems with the IRS, involvement with drugs, and a bankruptcy action. Signing with Columbia Records, he managed a Top 5 hit in early 1983 called "Sexual Healing."

Like so many others, Gaye's career illustrates the continuing tension between the secular and the sacred in the life of black musicians. His father was a Pentecostal preacher, and Gaye's early vocals have a distinct gospel sound. But like Sam Cooke, he wished to show that the black gospel sound could be transferred to the Pop style. From the heavier sentiments of *What's Going On?* (about ecology, nuclear war, and inner-city poverty), he moved to one of Motown's most blatantly sexual albums, *Let's Get It On.* An embittered man, several of his last recordings for Columbia were quite explicit in their violent references to sex (e.g., "Masochistic Beauty"). Tragically, in 1984, he was shot and killed at the age of 44 by his own father.

8.5.4: H-D-H and the Formula for Success

Gordy struck another gold mine when he hired Eddie Holland as a songwriter and producer. Soon, Gordy added Eddie's brother Brian and singer-songwriter Lamont Dozier to the Motown staff. Between 1963 and 1967, Holland, Dozier, and Holland (H-D-H) teamed up to provide songs and production for the majority of Motown's hit singles. They were the musical creators behind numerous hits by Martha and the Vandellas, the Miracles, Marvin Gaye, the Four Tops, and the Supremes. After logging nearly 30 Top 20 hits, H-D-H demanded an accounting of their royalties, and a series of lawsuits ensued. The end came in 1972 in an out-of-court settlement. Together and separately, the songwriting team scored moderate hits throughout the 1970s for themselves and other artists.

When H-D-H stopped creating hits for Motown in 1968, morale at the record label dropped perceptibly. Most of the Motown artists were not songwriters or producers (Robinson, Gaye, and Stevie Wonder were exceptions). Without the help of Holland, Dozier, and Holland, many

Berry Gordy's Secret of Success

In a way, Berry Gordy's secret of success was also its inevitable undoing.

Gordy insisted on total control; he established a formula, saw that it worked, and then allowed little or no deviation. By sticking with a few songwriter-producers (namely, Robinson and H-D-H), he guaranteed a consistency of musical style. Although that worked beautifully, when H-D-H left, that consistency was threatened.

Gordy's rigid control was evident throughout the Motown operation. For example, he hired Cholly Atkins as choreographer. Cholly's routine was similar with all of the groups. He started rehearsals with 45 minutes of floor exercises; then, he taught the physical routines to go with each song. Once learned, the routine was never to vary. The emphasis was on synchronized precision. Contrast this with the exuberant freedom of a soul artist like James Brown. Gordy also employed an etiquette coach to teach the female performers how to get in and out of a car; how to apply makeup and style their hair; and how to walk, talk, and behave in public. There was also a vocal coach descended from the old gospel coach tradition in Harlem. The choreographer; the piano accompanists; the etiquette, makeup, and wardrobe people; and the vocal coach were all parts of the Artist Development Department. There was not to be the slightest change in any act without Gordy's approval.

He even oversaw the individual performers' finances and laid down strict rules of conduct while on tour. There would be no fraternizing with fans. The concept was that of a family: one for all and all for one. Thus, Marvin Gaye played on the Vandellas' recordings; Martha Reeves sang and clapped on Gaye's recordings; Robinson wrote songs for almost everyone; and personal relationships developed within the "family:" Smokey Robinson married Claudette Rogers of the Miracles; Marvelette Wanda Young married Miracle Bobby Rogers; Marvelette Katherine Anderson married the Temptations' road manager Joe Schaffner; and Marvin Gaye married Anna Gordy.

Gordy liked the business concept of quality control. As the decade of the 1960s progressed, his standards became more rigid. He tightened up the funkier leanings of some groups, almost purging any vestiges of gospel or true soul sound; there were no raw R&B edges left in Gordy's Motown Sound. Nothing was left to chance. His use of the same basic backup band—the Funk Brothers—on hundreds of recordings helped provide a consistency of sound. Note how many Motown recordings emphasize baritone sax, vibes, organ, and hand claps.

Through the uproarious 1960s, Motown's lyrics studiously avoided controversy and any heaviness beyond boy-girl romance. Only after about 1968 did songs like "Love Child" and "I'm Livin' in Shame" (The Supremes); "War," "Ball of Confusion," and "Don't Let the Joneses Get You Down" (The Temptations); or "Livin' in the City" (Stevie Wonder) begin to come from Motown. Some of Marvin Gaye's work in the 1970s carried Motown far beyond its previous boundaries with respect to lyrics.

were left high and dry. Typically, Eddie Holland had worked with the vocal leads in the various groups; Lamont Dozier had helped with vocal backgrounds and instrumental tracks; while Brian Holland handled overall composition and assisted with backup tracks. Without this musical foundation, sales dropped right along with morale.

8.5.5: The Four Tops and the Temptations

A second wave of major stars hit Motown in the mid-1960s. The Four Tops had sung together since the mid-1950s, recording briefly on Chess, Columbia, and Riverside Records. Gordy discovered the four Detroit natives singing in a black resort area in Michigan. Starting as a backup group, they released their first single ("Baby I Need Your Loving") in late 1964. Their fourth release, "I Can't Help Myself," hit number 1 in mid-1965. Before moving to ABC-Dunhill Records in 1972, the Tops placed 18 hits in the Top 40 for Motown. Most of these were Holland-Dozier-Holland songs, featuring the distinctive and polished sound of lead vocalist Levi Stubbs.

The most popular Motown male group of the 1960s was the Temptations. They sang well, dressed well, and danced impeccably. The dual lead singer format (Eddie Kendricks and David Ruffin) revealed the direct influence of earlier black groups like the Soul Stirrers and the Ravens. Kendricks had a strong falsetto voice, whereas Ruffin was a smooth baritone. Various members came from Alabama, Texas, and Mississippi, and they had strong gospel roots. As Ruffin said, "I heard gospel before I could think" (Hirshey 1984, 204). Their first hit was "The Way You Do the Things You Do," cowritten by Smokey Robinson and Bobby Rogers. After several moderate hits, they hit number 1 in 1965 with "My Girl" (again coauthored by Robinson, this time with Ronald White). Thereafter, the Temptations poured out a steady stream of hits through the late 1960s and mid-1970s (37 Top 40 hits, including four number 1 songs). Changes began in 1968, when David Ruffin left the group; he was replaced by Dennis Edwards (formerly with the Contours), whose less refined lead vocals fit well with the group's new direction, moving from the typical Motown style to a more modern sound established by Sly and the Family Stone. The Temptations' first hits in the new style, sometimes called **psychedelic soul**, were "Cloud Nine" and "Run Away Child, Running Wild" in 1969. Some of their early 1970s hits served as a harbinger for the disco style to emerge later that decade.

8.5.6: Gladys Knight and the Pips

Continuing in the more traditional Motown style was Gladys Knight and the Pips. Gladys (born in Atlanta in 1944) was singing gospel music as early as 1952 with a family singing group. In 1965, Gladys Knight and the Pips signed with Motown's Soul label, and, in late 1967, they hit the number 2 position with Marvin Gaye's "I Heard It Through the Grapevine" (Gaye's own recording went to number 1 a year later). Through 1973, the group scored a dozen more hits, including three more Top 10 songs. In spite of their success, Knight and the Pips felt they were not being treated as a priority Motown act, so they switched to Buddah Records in 1973. The debut Buddah album, *Imagination* (number 9 in 1973), included their first number 1 song, "Midnight Train to Georgia." After the mid-1970s, album sales declined for the group and single hits stopped; however, as a solo artist, Knight continued recording into the new millennium with numerous Top 40 singles on the R&B chart.

8.5.7: Stevie Wonder

Back in 1960, when it became known that a local man was starting a record company, Detroit parents flocked to West Grand Avenue with their "young musical geniuses" in tow, all certain that theirs would be the next Sam Cooke or Chuck Berry. Most had less of a chance than a snowball in that very hot place. However, 10-year-old Steveland Morris was an exception.

"LITTLE" Stevie Wonder, c. 1963.

SOURCE: CSU Archives/Everett Collection/Alamy Stock Photo

8.5.8: Diana Ross and the Supremes

Motown's greatest success came with Diana Ross and the Supremes. In terms of chart performance in the decade of the 1960s, this group ranks third behind the Beatles and

Stevie Wonder's Musical Career

One of the most successful Motown artists of all time is Stevie Wonder, whose phenomenal career is outlined in the following section.

Little Stevie Wonder Despite his blindness from infancy—or perhaps propelled by it into a world focused on sound—he amazed Berry Gordy by playing the piano, the organ, the drums, and anything else he could find in the small Motown studio. Young Mr. Morris was promptly signed to the Tamla label and given a new professional name: Little Stevie Wonder. His fourth release, "Fingertips—Part 2," went to the number 1 position in 1963. It was the young company's second number 1 hit, following the example set by the Marvelettes' "Please Mr. Postman." His live performances on the **Motortown Reviews** were so successful that Gordy decided to release a live recording. The live seven-minute version of "Fingertips" was too long for a single, so it was divided into two parts and released as part 1 and part 2. The first live single to hit number 1, "Fingertips" is a mainstream, rocking song, with Wonder playing solo on the first instrument he had learned as a young boy: the harmonica. Combining Wonder's 12-year-old voice and harmonica with a strong instrumental backup, the song generated excitement. It launched the career of an artist whose singles chart accomplishments would become among the most impressive in the history of rock music.

Move to Motown Although Wonder had a string of 16 Top 40 hits in the 1960s, it was not until the beginning of the 1970s that his full potential began to be realized. In 1970, he released his first self-produced album, *Signed, Sealed, and Delivered*. It was his highest-ranking album (number 25) since his initial release. Next, he turned to synthesizer and other electronic keyboards in *Where I'm Coming From*. In 1971, he turned 21 and demanded an accounting of his royalties. Wonder took $250,000 of his $1 million trust and set up his own 40-track studio. He began production of his own album, refusing to submit to Motown's control. Finally, Berry Gordy made him an unprecedented offer (for Motown): The company would distribute his album and split songwriting royalties 50-50; Wonder would do his own production and have his own publishing company. In effect, he had full artistic control.

Motown Hits The first album under this new contract was *Music of My Mind* (1972). It did well, but Stevie's next album, *Talking Book*, was a smash hit, peaking at number 3 and remaining on the chart for 109 weeks. *Talking Book* contained two number 1 hits: "Superstition" and "You Are the Sunshine of My Life." "Superstition" reflected his admiration for the psychedelic soul sound of Sly and the Family Stone, tempered by the more sophisticated style of Earth, Wind, and Fire. "You Are the Sunshine of My Life" suggested jazz-rock fusion in its harmonies and horn line.

Innervisions *Innervisions* (1973) moved to more socially conscious lyrics than had previously come from Motown (e.g., the two Top 10 hits "Higher Ground" and "Living in the City"). Mid-decade, Wonder negotiated a new contract with Motown; guaranteeing him $13 million over seven years; this contract was the biggest single artist contract in rock's first 20 years. Wonder's 1976 album *Songs in the Key of Life* became the first American album to enter the album chart at number 1. Years in preparation, *Journey Through the Secret Life of Plants* (1979) was more sophisticated than any previous Wonder album. "Send One Your Love" revealed a definite drift toward jazz-oriented harmonies and melodic concepts. The line of development that began in 1963 with "Fingertips" and culminated with the 1979 *Plants* album is one of the most impressive artistic trajectories in the history of rock music.

Wonder's Later Career As Wonder moved into his third decade in the music industry, he appeared to lose no momentum. Major hits in the 1980s came with the number 1 songs "I Just Called to Say I Love You" (1984) and, a year later, "Part Time Lover." There can be no doubt that Little Stevie is one of the giants. Although his commercial success waned and releases were less frequent during more recent decades, he scored a Top 10 album in 2005 with *A Time to Love*, though the hit single "So What the Fuss" barely made the Hot 100 and remained there only a single week.

The Supremes, c. 1966.

Elvis Presley. From 1964 to 1969, they amassed 12 number 1 hits plus 13 other Top 40 hits.

While in high school, Diana Ross joined a female vocal group, the Primettes, which would be a sister group to the Primes. As the Primes evolved into the Temptations, the Primettes evolved into the Supremes. While still the Primettes, Diana Ross, along with singers Florence Ballard and Mary Wilson (originally from Mississippi), won a high school talent contest and began pestering Berry Gordy, Jr., for an audition with his new record company. Finally, a former neighbor of Ross's, Smokey Robinson, arranged for their audition. They signed with Motown in 1962 and began recording as the Supremes. They endured several flops before Gordy put H-D-H on the case.

Musical Journey of the Supremes

The Supremes were the most successful of the Motown female groups. In fact, without qualification, they were one of the most successful recording groups of the 1960s.

"When the Lovelight Starts Shining Through His Eyes" rose to number 23 in early 1964. The Supremes started the Dick Clark Cavalcade of Stars tour as the opening act, but during the tour, "Where Did Our Love Go" was released and moved up the chart to number 1. By the end of the tour, they had the prestigious closing spot on the show. Before 1965 was over, the Supremes had registered six number 1 songs ("Where Did Our Love Go," "Baby Love," "Come See About Me," "Stop! In the Name of Love," "Back in My Arms Again," and "I Hear a Symphony") and one number 11 hit ("Nothing But Heartaches"). All were H-D-H compositions.

By the mid-1960s, the Supremes were Motown's biggest act. Naturally, they received the whole quality control treatment. Compared to some of the male groups, the Supremes' stage act was less athletic; for them, choreographer Cholly Atkins designed graceful and (of course) precisely synchronized hand movements.

The series of hits continued unabated in 1966. But problems began to arise. Some say the problems began when Diana Ross started showing up at social functions arm in arm with Berry Gordy. Gradually, she was becoming "the act," with Ballard and Wilson serving as backup vocalists. After 1967 began with another number 1 hit ("Love Is Here and Now You're Gone"), things changed. Released that summer, "Reflections" (number 2) was credited to "Diana Ross and the Supremes." Ballard began missing performances because of so-called illness. Although the exact circumstances have never been clarified, she either left the group or was expelled in 1967 (replaced by Cindy Birdsong). Ballard tried to make it as a solo act on ABC Records but had no luck. She endured a bewildering series of personal and professional disasters through the 1970s and died of cardiac arrest in 1976 at the age of 32.

The Supremes' hits continued through 1969. Finally, Diana Ross, with Gordy's encouragement, left the group to begin her career as a solo performer. Ironically, "Someday We'll Be Together" was Ross's last recording with the Supremes, becoming the group's final number 1 hit. Ross was replaced by Jean Terrell, and the group endured numerous personnel changes throughout the 1970s, but managed to produce seven more Top 40 hits after Ross's departure.

Mary Wilson was the only constant member of the Supremes from the beginning until they faded from sight in the late 1970s. As Ballard had done earlier, Wilson sued Motown in 1977 for money she felt she was owed from the early days. Eventually, she received 50 percent usage and interest in the name "Supremes." Wilson eventually published a biography of her life with Motown.

Diana Ross went on to become a major figure in the music industry and a successful star on television, in Las Vegas, and in films, such as *Lady Sings the Blues, Mahogany,* and *The Wiz.* She left Motown in 1981 for what was reported to be a $20 million contract with RCA. In 1983, she reunited with ex-Supremes Mary Wilson and Cindy Birdsong for the finale of a two-hour television special saluting Motown's 25th anniversary.

The music of the 1960s Supremes typifies the Motown sound. There is the lead singer with vocal backup; there is the strong professional orchestration, using strings, brass, sax, keyboards, and percussion. Note especially the frequent reliance on baritone saxophone (doubling the bass line and providing solo breaks) and vibraphone (listen to "My World Is Empty Without You Babe"). The beat is always strong, with a heavy backbeat, often reinforced by hand claps. A trademark is the rather predictable modulation (change of key) that occurs about two-thirds to three-quarters of the way through the song. The music abruptly shifts from one key (e.g., C major) to a key one-half step higher (e.g., D-flat major); for an obvious example, listen to "Baby Love" (the modulation occurs about 1 minute and 35 seconds into the song). These were all elements in the formula; millions of record sales proved it worked.

JOURNAL

Berry Gordy's Control at Motown

In this chapter, you learned about the level of control Berry Gordy exerted on Motown artists. While this proved to be a highly successful business decision, take a moment to reflect on how you would feel if you were one of those artists. Would you have been willing to sacrifice artistic freedom to an extent that you could simply follow the instructions exactly as you were told? Would you have gone along with that proven formula, or would you have preferred to look for success elsewhere, knowing it might never come? Determine whether you support Berry's approach or not, then write a paragraph presenting your rationales for this position.

 The response entered here will appear in the performance dashboard and can be viewed by your instructor.

Submit

Summary: Soul and Motown

Soul Summary

Soul music became popular in large part because it tapped the expressiveness and creative freedom of gospel and inserted it into a secular market. Yet, despite its popularity, most authentic soul music flourished within an all-black market. Many soul artists toured the so-called **chitlin' circuit** of southern black concert sites and inner cities, and their greatest commercial successes were on the R&B chart. There were occasional breakthroughs by James Brown, Otis Redding, Sam and Dave, Wilson Pickett, and, most notably, Aretha Franklin, but the most overwhelming commercial success on the Pop chart was reserved for a small company that grew into a monster: Motown.

Motown Summary

The meteoric trajectory of Motown's success is truly remarkable. Berry Gordy's ability to spot and make use of talents explains a large measure of his success. Remember how the word *freedom* came up in almost every definition of soul? Motown's 1960s style was anything but free. It was slick, professional, polished, and precisely coordinated. The sound was popular with blacks and whites, but it should not be confused with authentic soul music.

Gordy's absolute control led to both success and problems. Although many Motown artists were grateful for Gordy's formula, they also resisted it at various points. As mentioned, those who left the Motown family included some big names: Holland, Dozier, and Holland; the Miracles; the Contours; the Spinners; Diana Ross; the Isley Brothers; Martha Reeves; Gladys Knight and the Pips; and the Four Tops. (In some cases, Motown owned the group names, so when the individuals left, Gordy simply trotted out some new members under the old name.)

Motown Records left Detroit in 1971 for a high-rise building on Sunset Boulevard in Los Angeles. Motown's success continued with names like the Jackson Five, the Commodores, Stevie Wonder, and Diana Ross. Berry Gordy, Jr., was still the kingpin, and millionaire vice president Smokey Robinson divided his time between the company and his family, consisting of former Miracle Claudette and their two children, Tamla and Gordy. In June 1988, Motown was purchased by MCA Records, bringing to an end its distinction as the largest, black-owned and operated company in America.

Take Note: Soul and Motown

- *How would you define soul music, and what is its history?*—Soul music evolved as traditional gospel music and R&B styles merged. Soul's vocal style—showing great intensity and depth of feeling—is particularly influenced by the music of the traditional church. The popularity of gospel quartets, doo-wop groups, and singers like Ray Charles all fed into the developing style.
- *What roles did the Atlantic and Stax labels play in the popularization of soul music?*—Atlantic and Stax were both leaders in producing R&B and soul music in the 1950s and 1960s. Atlantic nurtured a number of artists, including La Vern Baker, the Coasters, and soul singers Wilson Pickett and Aretha Franklin. Stax was founded in Memphis, Tennessee, and produced artists like Sam and Dave and Isaac Hayes.
- *Why was Aretha Franklin known as Lady Soul?*—Under the guidance of Atlantic producer Jerry Wexler, Aretha Franklin recorded a string of soul hits in the late 1960s and early 1970s that have become classics, beginning with a powerful cover of Otis Redding's song "Respect" through "Chain of Fools" and "A Natural Woman." Gaining experience and significant aspects of her vocal style from singing in the church, she was a standout soul artist.
- *Why was James Brown known as "the Godfather of Soul"?*—Brown is known as the Godfather of Soul because of his powerful, raspy, shouting vocal style; highly rhythmic music; and powerful stage presence, which served as a model for both Mick Jagger and Michael Jackson. He earned the nickname the "Hardest Working Man in Show Business" through his energetic stage movements, intense singing, and eye-catching costumes. Brown pioneered funk in songs like "Papa's Got A Brand New Bag" and "I Got You (I Feel Good)," both based on catchy repetitive riffs.
- *How did Motown and its artists differ from soul music?*—While R&B and soul artists reflected African-American vocal styles and rhythms, Motown aimed at creating powerful Pop-influenced hits that would appeal to a broad audience. With a stable of talented musicians and songwriters, the label churned out hits through the 1960s and 1970s with its carefully groomed groups designed to appeal to the teen market. Motown stars included Smokey Robinson and the Miracles, Marvin Gaye, the Four Tops, the Temptations, Gladys Knight and the Pips, Stevie Wonder, and the biggest hit makers of them all, Diana Ross and the Supremes. Unlike soul music, the Motown style was carefully controlled. Artists were rarely given the freedom to improvise or vary from the predetermined arrangements.
- *Why were Diana Ross and the Supremes among the most successful Pop-influenced groups of the 1960s?*—Diana Ross and the Supremes were the ultimate achievement of the Motown machine. Ross was carefully groomed to be an attractive, stylish lead singer. The writing trio of Holland-Dozier-Holland, Motown's finest, supplied a string of hit songs for the group, beginning with "Where Did Our Love Go," "Stop! In the Name of Love," and "Back in My Arms Again," all featuring catchy and memorable choruses and dramatic stage choreography. The Supremes became the model for dozens of vocal groups that followed.

SHARED WRITING

Comparing Soul and Motown

In this chapter, you learned about and listened to many soul (Ray Charles, Atlantic/Stax artists, Aretha Franklin, and James Brown) and Motown (Smokey Robinson & the Miracles, the Marvelettes, & 2nd wave artists [do NOT include later Steve Wonder recordings for this comparison]) artists. Take time to listen to a few examples of the artists you like best in both categories. On a piece of paper or in a word processing document, create two columns, one marked "similarities" and the other "differences." *Use your listening skills*, and take time to make a list of similarities and differences between these two primary styles of black music during the 1960s. By this time in the course, you should be able to effectively integrate the musical vocabulary you have developed. Once you have created your list independently, meet with two or three peers to share your responses and revise your own list based on these conversations.

A minimum number of characters is required to post and earn points. After posting, your response can be viewed by your class and instructor, and you can participate in the class discussion.

Post

0 characters | 140 minimum

Chapter 9
San Francisco

 Learning Objectives

9.1 Explain the factors that influenced the emergence of the San Francisco sound

9.2 Compare the major bands that influenced the evolution of the San Francisco sound

9.3 Identify groups outside San Francisco that influenced the development of acid rock

9.4 Explain how music is improvised

As you have learned earlier in this course, rock and roll emerged in the mid-1950s as a musical explosion, disrupting the existing three markets: Pop, C&W, and R&B. Heavily influenced by this early sound, especially that of mainstream rock, many of the most innovative rock artists of the mid-1960s were part of the British Invasion, an influx of groups from across the Atlantic. During this same period, American artists were developing folk rock, soul, and Motown. Proceeding toward the late 1960s, San Francisco became a hub of creative, musical innovation and home to the Summer of Love.

9.1: America Counters the British Invasion

OBJECTIVE: Explain the factors that influenced the emergence of the San Francisco sound

New York City has been described as America's great melting pot, but for the last half of the 1960s, this epithet seemed to better describe San Francisco. A bewildering kaleidoscope of styles, musical and cultural, blended together into an almost indescribable mixture. In the words of Jefferson Airplane guitarist Paul Kantner,

There was an interweaving of the rock and roll world and the political world, the world of labor unions and the armed forces and kids and hippies and yippies and weathermen and democrats, mods and rockers,

policemen worlds and the drug world, artists, craftsmen, Sierra Clubs and Hell's Angels, women's movements and Black Panthers, gurus, Jesus freaks, punks, lawyers, doctors, and Indians—you get the picture, I hope. (McDonough 1985, vii)

How had such an unlikely mixture transpired in San Francisco at just this time? The disillusionment of the youth movement, addressed in other parts of this course, was only deepening. Kids began "dropping out and turning on," to paraphrase the words of ex-Harvard professor Timothy Leary. Where does one go when one drops out of society? The West Coast was "new America," open to unconventional perspectives and alternative lifestyles. The University of California at Berkeley, San Francisco State University, Stanford University, Mills College, and numerous other small colleges in the area were centers of countercultural thought. In comparison, almost any other geographic area of the United States seemed to represent "the establishment."

Youth from all over the nation hitchhiked their way to San Francisco, with many arriving at the epicenter of the psychedelic-flower power world, the Haight-Ashbury neighborhood. Central to this scene were drugs, open sex, the love-peace philosophy, and music. By 1967, often referred to as the Summer of Love, that scene had reached its zenith. It has been estimated that there were as many as 1,500 local bands in the Bay Area at that time. By 1970, the wave had begun to lose its power, but, during the late 1960s, the most influential of these bands would leave their mark on the history of rock.

Coalescing Disparate Fragments of an Eclectic Society

There were several catalysts that helped to provide a sense of coherence to a society that may have seemed chaotic to many. We shall address such elements in this section: rock concert halls and FM radio.

Rock Concert Halls—To coalesce the disparate fragments of this eclectic society, several catalysts were necessary. One was the establishment of rock concert halls. The history of several of these ballroom music halls reached back to the swing era of the 1930s and early 1940s. In late 1965, concert promoter Bill Graham began presenting concerts at the Fillmore Auditorium, located in the heart of San Francisco. Graham booked hundreds of rock acts into his various sites over the next five years, both big-name acts and unknowns. By the turn of the decade, the rock festival phenomenon (including Woodstock and Altamont) had created audiences too large and unruly for these small venues that could only hold a few thousand. But for a time, Graham's concert halls in San Francisco, as well as others like the Avalon and the Longshoremen's Hall, pulled the new San Francisco youth society together to share a common musical experience.

FM Radio—A second coalescing factor was radio. For years, FM (frequency modulation, which broadcast higher quality sound than its sister method, AM, amplitude modulation) had been the home of classical music and easy listening styles. Prohibited from merely replicating AM programming, stations such as New York's WOR-FM began a so-called contemporary music format that featured album tracks, lengthy sets of recordings, and a calmer, more sophisticated style of disc jockey chatter. The format was called progressive rock and, later, **album-oriented rock (AOR)**. In 1967, a man named Tom Donahue was hired by an almost down-and-out San Francisco FM station, KMPX. He tried this new "progressive" format, and soon KMPX's advertising revenues quintupled. In 1968, Donahue moved to a station that had been broadcasting classical music, KSFR; changing its call letters to KSAN and its format to this emerging form of progressive rock, the station soon became the mainstay of the new San Francisco rock scene.

9.1.1: The San Francisco Sound

The new youth culture of San Francisco was a bewildering mixture, and this was clearly reflected in the music. Although one occasionally hears about the **San Francisco sound**, in fact, this label is almost as vague as *folk rock* or *soul*. Many of the San Francisco musicians cut their musical teeth in folk groups, and quite a few of them also admired the old R&B style. So, when the British blues-based bands, such as the Stones, landed in America with their harder mainstream rock, many of the San Francisco bands blended elements of the folk style with the R&B-derived rock style of their British counterparts. The result was a hard-driving style of rock that was really the only American style of this period that could counter the harder styles of the British bands.

9.1.2: Characteristics of the San Francisco Sound

While the sounds of the San Francisco groups of this era were quite eclectic, there are some specific musical characteristics we can identify that remained relatively consistent. However, keep in mind that this was a highly experimental and creative period in rock history, so even the musical style represented on the recordings of a single group could vary quite dramatically.

Attributes of San Francisco Bands

A few musical characteristics typify most of the San Francisco bands. The following section will reveal a number of these.

Drugs—Sometimes music of the San Francisco bands is called **acid rock** (or psychedelic rock). Certainly there had been drug references in rock music before (e.g., "Eight Miles High" and "Lucy in the Sky with Diamonds"). With the San Francisco bands, however, drugs became a dominant theme. By 1967, the necessity of the double entendre trick was discarded, and the lyrics became blatantly and explicitly drug-oriented. Beyond the lyrics, certain aspects of the music itself were identified with drugs. Long instrumental improvisations and electronic experimentation became associated with acid rock. San Francisco was considered the psychedelic capital of the nation. The bands and their fans were assumed to be stoned, freaked-out acid eaters. The whole scene was psychedelic, from the music to the clothing to the brightly painted Volkswagen minibuses. Hair was long, stringy, and greasy. Clothing ranged from Jesus look-alikes to Superman outfits—the freakier the better. Psychedelic posters advertised upcoming concerts at the Fillmore and other concert halls.

Sound—Loudness levels at live concerts reached a new high. Rock and roll had never been quiet music, but most groups had managed to get by with tinny-sounding public address systems. An explosion of sound technology innovation through the 1960s now permitted groups to amplify their sound with tremendous power. The sound at these concerts was riveting, even overwhelming. The vibrations literally could be felt in the rib cage; the ringing in the ears lasted for hours after the concert had ended.

Instrumentals—Up to this time, singers had dominated the rock scene, but the San Francisco groups often placed considerable emphasis on instrumentalists, especially the guitarists. Long improvisations, often lasting 20 to 30 minutes, were not uncommon at live concerts. Such improvisations were old hat in the jazz scene but were new to rock (except for some British blues-based bands, such as the Yardbirds). To psychedelically-oriented rock fans, such long-winded flights of fancy seemed to be musical "trips," possibly inspired by drugs.

Electronic Technology—Musicians soon learned that electronics could generate or heavily modify sound from their instruments; especially fascinating was the phenomenon of feedback. Electronically produced music had been around for several decades in the field of art music (e.g., Edgard Varèse's *Poeme électronique* [1958] or Karlheinz Stockhausen's *Kontakte* [1959–1960]), but to the acid rockers, these sounds were "far out." There was certainly an association between these freaky sounds and the drug experience.

JOURNAL

The San Francisco Sound and Your Ears

Of the three musical characteristics describing the San Francisco sound enumerated above—let's leave the element of drugs aside for the moment—which would you have found most attractive to your own ears, had you been part of the Haight-Ashbury, love-peace generation of the late 1960s? As you contemplate this question, consider the popular music of today that most appeals to you. What attracts you to this particular characteristic of musical sound? Briefly describe the music of two or three of your favorite groups, enumerating how your selected characteristic is evident in the sound of their music.

 The response entered here will appear in the performance dashboard and can be viewed by your instructor.

Submit

9.2: San Francisco Bands

OBJECTIVE: Compare the major bands that influenced the evolution of the San Francisco sound

Throughout the incredibly innovative San Francisco acid rock era, there were a number of bands that pushed the boundaries of rock and roll's musical horizons. Though one cannot speak of *a* San Francisco sound (there were many different styles), factors that remained somewhat consistent among these bands include the use of explicit lyrical references to drugs, very loud live musical performances, extended and often virtuosic performances by instrumentalists, and an increased use of technologies to alter the sound of electronic instruments. The following section will provide additional details about each of these characteristics.

Grace Slick and Jefferson Airplane at the Family Dog Ballroom, San Francisco, 1969.

SOURCE: Interfoto/Alamy Stock Photo

9.2.1: Jefferson Airplane

The first San Francisco band to get a recording contract with a major label (RCA) was Jefferson Airplane. The group had been formed in 1965 by male lead singer Marty Balin, who took over a small club on upper Fillmore Street and recruited two guitar players (Paul Kantner and Jorma Kaukonen) and vocalist Signe Toly to join him as the house band.

9.2.2: The Grateful Dead

Elvis's fans tore at his clothes, screamed and cried, and, years later, fainted as he lay in state at Graceland. Beatlemania was a kind of cultural hysteria, and there are Stones' fans who refuse to hear even the slightest criticism of their heroes. Few fans are as devoted, persevering, and tolerant, though, as the *Deadheads*—the unwaveringly loyal following of the Grateful Dead. The Dead are the archetypal San Francisco band of the late 1960s, combining all of the major characteristics of that style. Like so many others, their roots were in the folk era of the early 1960s.

Jerry Garcia was born in San Francisco in 1942. His family moved around the Bay Area a great deal, and Jerry, although unquestionably bright, never settled into a successful school routine. By 15, he was in constant trouble for fighting, drinking, and smoking marijuana. He finally dropped out of school at 17 and joined the army. Following several courts-martial and a series of AWOLs, he was discharged. Returning to civilian life, he found that folk music was the rage in San Francisco of the early 1960s. He became fascinated with bluegrass music, learned to play the five-string banjo, and began performing in San Francisco coffeehouses. Along with several other musicians, Garcia, Ron "Pigpen" McKernan, and Bob Weir formed Mother McCree's Uptown Jug

Musical Career of Jefferson Airplane

One of the earliest and most important of the San Francisco bands was Jefferson Airplane. As you will learn in this section, there were many significant "firsts" accomplished by this acid rock group.

Their first album, *Jefferson Airplane Takes Off*, did not fare well. Following the release of that album, female lead singer Signe Toly Anderson left the band to have a baby. For a new female lead singer, the band chose Grace Slick, who was a former model and a member of another local band called the Great Society. With a new lineup—Grace Slick, Jack Casady, and Spencer Dryden joining Balin, Kantner, and Kaukonen—the band recorded a second album, *Surrealistic Pillow* (1967), which reached number 3 on the album chart and yielded two hit singles, Jefferson Airplane's only Top 40 singles: "Somebody to Love" (number 5) and "White Rabbit" (number 8). The lyrics of "White Rabbit," appearing in the same powerful summer as *Sgt. Pepper*, evoke images of a psychedelic Alice in Wonderland, including the hook line "go ask Alice," which would become the title of an antidrug book and movie in 1973. Previously, female singers had been associated either with soft rock, including the doo-wop style and Motown female groups; but, with this album, Grace Slick became the first authentic female rock star.

In late 1967, Airplane issued *After Bathing at Baxter's*. Although the album reached the Top 20, there were no hit singles. This was not unusual for San Francisco groups. In fact, many of these groups were actually quite disdainful of Top 40 hits and considered chart success a rather unbecoming distinction.

Gradually, Slick and Kantner took greater control of the Airplane, reducing Balin's role. *Crown of Creation* (1968) contained an interesting variety of styles. The title song, by Kantner, was a mainstream rock song. Slick's "Lather" sounds like a latter-day folk rock song, complete with externally mixed sound effects and obscure lyrics. Of particular interest is "Chushingura," a haunting example of electronic experimentation. In addition to the natural sounds of piano and acoustic guitar on this track, there is electronic feedback and other electronically generated sounds; the asymmetric clicking sounds were reportedly made by a row of suspended steel balls, known as Newton's cradle, which can be found in just about any novelty gift shop.

After touring Europe in 1968, the group released a live album, *Bless Its Pointed Little Head*. A particularly interesting cut on this album is the live version of "Plastic Fantastic Lover," first issued on *Surrealistic Pillow*. It features a shouting vocal style and impressive instrumental improvisation. The Airplane's last 1960s album was *Volunteers,* released in 1969. It contained songs with sociopolitical messages ("We Can Be Together" and "Volunteers") and masterful vocal and instrumental work.

Personnel problems began to plague Jefferson Airplane in the early 1970s, and the band released only a few more albums before disbanding. However, from the ruins of Jefferson Airplane arose a new band. Back in 1970, *Blows Against the Empire* had been released under the name Jefferson Starship. That album was recorded by Kantner, Slick, Casady, and others (including Jerry Garcia, David Crosby, and Graham Nash). One of the more interesting additions to the personnel on that recording was that of "Papa" John Creach (born in Beaver Falls, Pennsylvania in 1917), who was a member of Jefferson Starship through the 1970s. Papa John, a black violinist, had been involved in the blues scene for decades; a true instrumental pioneer, he had amplified his violin as early as the mid-1940s. The name Jefferson Starship, updating "Airplane," was used for the release of *Blows Against the Empire* (number 20, 1970), an effort led by Paul Kantner.

Marty Balin rejoined Jefferson Starship in 1975, helping them attain their first number 1 album, *Red Octopus*, containing the hit single "Miracles" (number 3). Thereafter, Slick and Balin dropped out of the group, leaving Kantner as the only remaining original member. By 1982, however, Slick had rejoined Jefferson Starship. Several moderately successful albums emerged in 1982 and 1984. In the latter year, Paul Kantner left Jefferson Starship; as a result of his lawsuit, the band was required to drop the name Jefferson, thus becoming simply Starship. As Starship, the band enjoyed continued success into the late 1980s (including three number 1 hits). After that, there were various reunions and reformations of the group, but none had lasting commercial or significant artistic impact approaching that of their earlier recordings. Jefferson Airplane, however, remains one of the most influential bands representing the late 1960s San Francisco sound.

The Grateful Dead on stage in San Francisco in 1970.
SOURCE: Interfoto/Alamy Stock Photo

Champions. Thanks to Beatlemania of 1964, the jug band decided to go electric and play rock and roll. McKernan switched from harmonica to organ; they added drummer Bill Kreutzmann and changed their name to the Warlocks. Soon, Phil Lesh, a classically trained violinist and serious avant-garde composer, was invited to join the band.

KEN KESEY One of the more colorful characters in mid-1960s San Francisco was author Ken Kesey (*One Flew over the Cuckoo's Nest*) and his freethinking band of cohorts, the Merry Pranksters. Kesey was known for throwing wild and weird parties, which included Kesey's intellectually liberated friends, the less intellectual but equally countercultural Hell's Angels, and the Warlocks. Anything and everything went on at these freely structured "happenings" (which became known as "*Acid Tests*"). The only predictable constants were drugs (especially LSD), weird costumes, and loud rock music by the Warlocks. As Garcia later said,

> We were ... lucky enough to have experienced the Acid Test, which was one of the truly democratic art forms to appear in this century. The audience didn't come to see us; they came to experience something altogether different. So we could play – or not, ya know – so we had the luxury of being able to experiment freely in a situation that didn't require *anything* of us. It didn't require that we be good, require that we repeat a song, it didn't require that we be intelligible on any level. I mean for a musician, that's like carte blanche. That was great fun, but the Acid Test experience gave us glimpses of the form that follows chaos, ya know. You throw everything out and lose all rules and stop trying to make anything happen on any level, *other* stuff starts to happen. (*Classic Albums: Anthem to Beauty*)

In this atmosphere, the Warlocks' music got louder, harder, more improvisatory, and longer. Playing with all sorts of electronically generated sounds, from distortion to feedback, they were met with enthusiastic approval by the partygoers, but by mid-1966, the Acid Tests had ended. Kesey had been charged with drug possession and fled to Mexico.

THE GRATEFUL DEAD IN THE 1960s   Changing their name from the Warlocks to the Grateful Dead, the band moved into an old Victorian building in the Haight-Ashbury neighborhood of San Francisco. Their music at this time consisted of blues material, Motown, soul, and Dylan songs. There were extended improvisations worked into these songs and continuing experimentation with sound alterations, such as **fuzz tone**, feedback, and use of the **tremolo bar**.

In late 1966, the Dead signed a record contract with Warner Brothers. Unfamiliar with the structured environment of the recording studio, the band turned out a relatively unimpressive debut album, *The Grateful Dead*, in 1967.

Many groups say they are not seeking commercial success but then sign lucrative record contracts and do everything possible to achieve top-of-the-chart success. But the Dead seemed to practice what they preached. During the peak of their popularity (late 1960s), they did not have a Top 40 hit. Their albums sold well but not spectacularly. Their real emphasis was on live performance. They were a concert—not a studio—band. They played five-hour concerts, free concerts, and even hauled their equipment to Egypt at a cost (to them) of $500,000 to play a benefit concert at the foot of the Great Pyramids in 1978. They considered their Deadhead followers to be an extension of the Dead family.

After the release of that first album, the band added drummer Mickey Hart and lyricist Robert Hunter. The next two albums, *Anthem of the Sun* (1968) and *Aoxomoxoa* (1969), fared only moderately from the perspective of commercial success. Finally, they released a live double album, *Live/Dead*, in late 1969. Most Deadheads consider this to be the group's best album of the 1960s.

There are several standout performances on *Live/Dead*. The 23-minute version of "Dark Star" illustrates the lengthy instrumental improvisation that typified the Dead and other San Francisco groups. The Dead were known for taking a half an hour to tune up, and, indeed, the opening of "Dark Star" seems to grow from out of nowhere, as if the band were simply trying to get into a groove. However, the playing is technically proficient and musically inventive. For an example of typical San Francisco electronic experimentation, listen to "Feedback," which is exactly what the title suggests. "Saint Stephen" is a fun-loving rock song. "Turn On Your Lovelight" is a prime example of both the blues-based rock style and some very fine instrumental improvisation. To get the full late-1960s San Francisco effect of this album, be sure to turn up your stereo to a loudness level just short of blowing out the speakers.

CHANGING DIRECTION IN THE 1970s   In the early 1970s, the Dead moved toward a simplified, country-oriented sound on two outstanding albums: *Workingman's Dead* and *American Beauty* (both released in 1970). These were the Dead's first albums to reach the Top 30. Garcia had learned to play the pedal steel guitar, lending an authentic country flavor to these albums. A reliance on acoustic instruments suggested a dramatic shift away from their psychedelic rock of the late 1960s.

Blues for Allah (1975), the Dead's most successful album commercially, exhibits a touch of jazz influence. There were several personnel changes during the 1970s, but Garcia, Lesh, Weir, and Kreutzmann all remained. McKernan died in 1973 at the age of 27. Later albums revealed a variety of approaches, including the horns, strings, and vocal choruses of *Terrapin Station* (1977); the all-acoustic double album *Reckoning* (1981); and its companion electric double album *Dead Set* (1981).

The Dead's fans were a flexible and tolerant bunch, as their heroes moved through psychedelia, country rock, blues, folk, jazz, acoustic rock, electric rock, and even horns, strings, and choruses. In their free-spirited, idealistically anticommercial way, the Dead embodied the spirit of late-1960s San Francisco. The band enjoyed something of a renaissance in the late 1980s with a number 6 album (*In the Dark*) and a Top 10 single ("Touch of Grey"). The death of Jerry Garcia in August 1995 was a traumatic moment for the band and its devoted followers. Through the late 1990s and early 2000s, the remaining members of the band toured (initially called the Other Ones, then the Dead). In 2010, Lesh and Weir formed Further (without Hart and Kreutzmann), adding a singer-guitarist who had performed for over a decade in a Grateful Dead cover band. Trey Anastasio (Phish) joined the Dead for a set of historic reunion concerts at Chicago's Soldier Field during the summer of 2015, and John Mayer joined the band (Dead & Company) for a tour during fall of that same year.

9.2.3: Janis Joplin

San Francisco in the late 1960s was full of transplants and honest-to-goodness characters; Janis Joplin fit into both categories. Born in Port Arthur, Texas (1943), she grew up amid blues, gospel, and country music. A natural free spirit, Joplin left Port Arthur and headed for San Francisco to sing in a few folk clubs and bars, but then returned to Texas to attend the University of Texas at Austin. Although she remained in Texas only one year, she obtained critically important experience singing in local bars.

Janis Joplin

SOURCE: Trinity Mirror/Mirrorpix/Alamy Stock Photo

JANIS JOPLIN'S MUSICAL STYLE   Janis Joplin's musical style places her squarely in mainstream rock, but her roots in R&B and gospel are evident in almost every song. Elsewhere in this course, the Musical Close-Up focuses on the gospel-oriented soul singer, which applies directly to Joplin's version of "Summertime" on *Cheap Thrills*. Granted, Joplin is white, but her vocal style has virtually every characteristic evident in the black soul singer. Sometimes, she sings straight-ahead, blues-derived mainstream rock ("Move Over," from *Pearl*, is a powerful example), but from that same album, "My Baby" clearly shows gospel roots: the triple meter; the chord movement from I up to IV and

Musical Career of Janis Joplin

A seminal artist during the San Francisco era, Janis Joplin created her own unique style of music performance. Details about her rise and tragic end will be provided in this section.

In 1966, Chet Helms, who managed a San Francisco band called Big Brother and the Holding Company, convinced Joplin to return to San Francisco to be the band's female lead singer. Big Brother got its big break in 1967 at the Monterey International Pop Festival. Joplin's voice was already raw and strong, but faced with the necessity of overcoming the powerful rock band, she truly began to scream and shout her lyrics. The performance was greeted with high praise. Dylan's manager, Albert Grossman, became Joplin's manager, and Columbia Records offered the band a recording contract.

In 1968, Big Brother's first Columbia album, *Cheap Thrills*, rose to number 1 and stayed at the top spot for eight weeks. "Piece of My Heart" hit the Hot 100, eventually peaking at number 12. Other songs of interest on this album are Joplin's version of Big Mama Thornton's "Ball and Chain" and George Gershwin's "Summertime."

At the beginning of 1969, Joplin went solo. She felt that she was the real star and that Big Brother was holding her back (an idea not without some merit). Joplin's *I Got Dem Ol' Kozmic Blues Again* was released in mid-1969 and moved to number 5 on the album chart. The album's title song, "Kozmic Blues," is a good example of Joplin's powerful, sandpaper-raw voice; her soul-like vocal style is also evident on "Try (Just a Little Bit Harder)."

By the beginning of 1970, Joplin was busy creating a truly top-notch band that she called Full-Tilt Boogie. Since Big Brother, each of her bands had proven better than the previous one.

Full-Tilt Boogie's performance on Joplin's last album, *Pearl*, is very strong indeed. *Pearl* was recorded mostly during the late summer of 1970, but before it could be released, Joplin was found dead in her Hollywood hotel room. The victim of a heroin overdose, she was only 27 at the time of her death on October 4, 1970. *Pearl* was released posthumously, reaching number 1 and staying there for nine weeks. "Me and Bobby McGee" was released as a single, and it became Joplin's only number 1 hit, holding that position for two weeks.

on to V; the cadence on the title, which moves from IV back to I; the gospel-style acoustic piano and organ are all elements that create a gospel feeling. If Joplin had replaced the words "My Baby" with "My Sweet Lord," the latter would fit quite naturally. For a monumental example of the blues influence, listen to the live version of "Ball and Chain" on *Janis Joplin's Greatest Hits*; it is a truly remarkable performance that, in a way, tells you everything there is to know about Joplin.

Click or tap this URL to listen to Watch "Ball and Chain" by Janis Joplin

Click or tap the video title to listen to "Ball and Chain." https://www.youtube.com/watch?v=mrF_nM9pknU[*]

Janis was unique. She was a white soul singer, and she was a female mainstream rock singer (along with Grace Slick, a model for those who followed). Her sandpaper voice was like no other. Although the official medical reason for her death was a heroin overdose, one almost feels that she died of old age, having crammed at least one lifetime into her 27 years. In the words of her own song, she was determined to "Get It While You Can" (*Pearl*).

Joplin left one remarkable song that has become a classic. "Mercedes Benz" (*Pearl*) is an **a cappella** vocal solo in which Joplin puts her tongue squarely in her cheek and does a song of "great social and political import." She takes potshots at upper-class values, from color televisions to Porsches. Her cackling laughter at the end of the recording reminds us that she was truly one of a kind. In a business where everybody copies everybody, Joplin was a true original.

9.2.4: Other San Francisco Groups

The Airplane, the Dead, and Joplin—these were the most prominent artists from the late-1960s San Francisco scene, but there were many others (see Table 9.1). Several bands that formed in the late 1960s in San Francisco would have their biggest impact in the early 1970s, including the Steve Miller Band, Santana, Tower of Power, Creedence Clearwater Revival, and Sly and the Family Stone; they will be discussed later in this course.

Table 9.1 Prominent Artists from the Late 1960s

Band	Comments
Charlatans	1965 to 1968; a prototype for later San Francisco bands; repertoire of folk songs and blues; concept was more visual than musical; no hit singles, but in many ways "got the ball rolling"
Quicksilver Messenger Service	1965 to 1975; talented lead guitarist John Cipollina played lengthy improvisations, rivaling those of the Grateful Dead; series of moderately successful albums from 1968 to 1970; recommended song: "The Fool"
Country Joe McDonald and the Fish	Began in 1965 as a folk duo; overtly political protest songs; grew to a quintet and went electric; crazy costumes and humorous stage act; became known for pro-drug songs and Vietnam protest songs; major appearance at Woodstock
Moby Grape	Premiered at Fillmore in 1966; triple guitar front line; first album and five singles released in 1967; second album, *Wow*, included second disc with lengthy instrumental improvisation (with "guests" Al Kooper and Mike Bloomfield); continued into 1970s (with changing personnel), but peak of popularity had passed

*By clicking this link, you will be redirected to a third-party site.

Favorite San Francisco Band

After listening to the various styles of the primary artists described above (Jefferson Airplane, the Grateful Dead, and Janis Joplin), which of these artists do you like best? What is it *specifically* about the sound of your chosen artist(s) that you find most appealing. To what degree does your explanation relate to the characteristics of the San Francisco sound identified in this chapter?

> The response entered here will appear in the performance dashboard and can be viewed by your instructor.

Submit

9.3: Acid Rock Outside San Francisco

OBJECTIVE: Identify groups outside San Francisco that influenced the development of acid rock

San Francisco was the psychedelic center, to be sure, but there were also bands in other parts of the country that shared the characteristics of San Francisco acid rock, including the Fugs, Blues Magoos, and Vanilla Fudge. The style was also influential upon and further developed by second-wave British Invasion groups like Small Faces, Traffic, and Pink Floyd.

9.3.1: After the Summer of Love

After the Summer of Love in 1967, when the San Francisco scene hit its apex, the facade began to unravel. Crime, drugs, and racial tensions took their toll. The city government banned live performances in the Panhandle, a strip of grass and trees adjacent to Haight-Ashbury, where many concerts had been held, but the most disintegrating effect came from the new "dropouts" who flowed into the city. As *BAM* writer Blair Jackson describes it,

> Somewhere along the line ... the Haight started to lure droves of young people who were less interested in the utopian ideals that had originally been the source of the neighborhood's strength, and more focused on the idea of being able to take drugs, eat for free, listen to rock and roll, and further the sexual revolution. The Haight-Ashbury culture had encouraged young people to "drop out" of conformist society, and a regrettable by-product of that battle cry was that some people took it as their cue to drop out altogether, ceasing to offer their energy toward the furtherance of the new order. (1983, 77)

What had begun in San Francisco would have its effect well beyond these city limits. Two of the more important, non-San Francisco bands of the late 1960s were the Doors and the Jimi Hendrix Experience.

9.3.2: Jim Morrison and the Doors

Jim Morrison was born in Melbourne, Florida, in 1943. At the age of 20, he enrolled in the film department at the University of California, Los Angeles, where he met keyboard player Ray Manzarek (born in Chicago in 1943). The two formed a band with Morrison as lead singer and Manzarek playing piano, organ, marimba, and sometimes bass. They recruited two Los Angeles musicians, jazz drummer John Densmore and guitarist Robbie Krieger.

The Doors, c. 1967.

SOURCE: Pictorial Press Ltd/Alamy Stock Photo

Listen to these Doors songs on YouTube.

> **Watch "People are Strange" by The Doors.**
>
> **Click or tap the video title to listen to "People Are Strange": https://www.youtube.com/watch?v=i9oDP5WFJRc***
>
> **Watch "Riders of the Storm" by The Doors.**
>
> **Click or tap the video title to listen to "Riders on the Storm": https://www.youtube.com/watch?v=XKgA_D6V1Uk***

9.3.3: The Jimi Hendrix Experience

There are some interesting parallels between Jimi Hendrix and Bob Dylan. First, neither will be remembered primarily as a great vocalist. In fact, Hendrix had not done much singing until he heard Dylan; then he decided that if Dylan could get away with singing, so could he. Hendrix's only Top 40 hit single came in 1968 with "All Along the

Musical Journey of the Doors

Though not from San Francisco, the eclectic sounds and drug-oriented lyrics of the Doors music fit well into the category of acid rock. You will learn about their interesting road to stardom in this section.

Soon the Doors, named after an essay entitled "The Doors of Perception" by Aldous Huxley, were hired as the house band at the famous Whisky a Go-Go club. Signing with Elektra Records in 1966, they released their first album, *The Doors,* in early 1967. Broadcast primarily on the newly established AOR stations, the album was a huge success, rising to number 2. The album contained a long (nearly seven minutes) version of a song by Krieger called "Light My Fire." A shorter single version was released and became a number 1 hit by mid-1967.

The Doors' musical style can be described as blues-based, mainstream rock. Morrison's flat, baritone voice had a dark quality; his vocal lines were usually in a very narrow range and were quite repetitive, frequently emphasizing the interval between the tonic scale degree and the minor third degree. (Note the similarity between the basic melodic lines of "Light My Fire," "Love Her Madly," "Riders on the Storm," "Moonlight Drive," and "Hello, I Love You.") The minor keys used in many Doors' tunes also provide a darker musical context. Add to this the lyrics, which are often centered around death, violence, darkness, and a menacing sexuality. Musically, Manzarek's keyboard solos are the Doors' strongest point.

Their second album, *Strange Days (number 3),* was another success and contained two hit singles, "People Are Strange"

(number 12 in 1967) and "Love Me Two Times" (number 25 in early 1968). It also contained the 11-minute "When the Music's Over." *Waiting for the Sun* (1968) became the Doors' only number 1 album and contained the number 1 single "Hello, I Love You."

However, by 1969, Morrison had succumbed to alcoholism and drug abuse. His stage performances were erratic; at a concert in Miami in 1969, he allegedly exposed himself, drunkenly, to the crowd and was arrested for indecent exposure and public drunkenness. These charges were officially dropped, albeit four decades later and posthumously (for Morrison), by the governor of Florida.

The next Doors album, *The Soft Parade,* was an oddity, an acid rock group doing soft rock, complete with brass, strings, and more prominent background vocals. The album made the Top 10, and the single "Touch Me" rose to number 3. With *Morrison Hotel* (1970), the band returned to its mainstream rock sound, but there were no hit singles. Morrison's last album, *L. A. Woman* (1971), hit the Top 10 and yielded two Top 20 singles, "Love Her Madly" and "Riders on the Storm."

Beset by legal and physical problems, Morrison moved to Paris to recuperate; he died there on July 3, 1971, from a heart attack. He was 27 years old. The Doors issued several more albums before disbanding in 1973. Of particular interest among these late recordings is *An American Prayer* (1978), a poetry reading session recorded in 1970 on Morrison's 27th birthday to which the remaining Doors added musical accompaniment.

---

*By clicking this link, you will be redirected to a third-party site.

Watchtower" (number 20), a Dylan song. Also, just as Dylan almost single-handedly transformed the lyrics of rock music, so Hendrix exerted a tremendous influence on post-1968 rock guitar styles.

JIMI Hendrix with bassist Noel Redding performing in 1967.
SOURCE: Pictorial Press Ltd/Alamy Stock Photo

Jimi Hendrix was born in Seattle on November 27, 1942, into a middle-class family. He began his musical career playing backup guitar for various black artists (including Little Richard, Ike and Tina Turner, Wilson Pickett, and Jackie Wilson) on the chitlin' circuit. He arrived in New York in 1964 and formed his own band in 1965, calling it Jimmy James and the Blue Flames.

Hendrix died in London from inhalation of vomit resulting from barbiturate intoxication. An autopsy revealed 18 times the recommended dosage of Vesparax, plus tranquilizers, amphetamines, depressants, and alcohol.

Watch "Hey Joe" by Jimi Hendrix.

Click or tap the video title to listen to Jimi Hendrix singing "Hey Joe" : https://www. youtube.com/watch?v=rXwMrBb2x1Q[*]

HENDRIX'S STYLE   When listening to Hendrix, you might say, "Hey, what's the big deal? I've heard lots of recent guitarists who do all that stuff and more!" That is exactly the point. Hendrix pioneered new styles, new ways of making music with his instrument, the guitar using electronic effects to their fullest extent. Hendrix has become almost deified by later rock enthusiasts, especially guitarists. Although he belongs with the somewhat dated psychedelic or acid rock era, he is an important link in a line that runs from the 1950s mainstream rockers to the Stones

Musical Career of Jimi Hendrix

Jimi Hendrix is considered one of the most innovative guitarists in rock history. In this section you will learn about his interesting path to success and, along with Joplin and Morrison, his early demise.

Hendrix went to England in September 1966; there, he recruited British musicians Noel Redding (bass) and Mitch Mitchell (drums), forming a rock trio known as the Jimi Hendrix Experience. The group was an immediate success, scoring several major hits on the British charts ("Hey Joe," "Purple Haze," and "The Wind Cries Mary"). In those early days, Hendrix played a heavy dose of blues, some soul songs, and a few originals. He had begun to experiment with feedback, fuzz tone, and other electronically generated or modified sounds.

The Experience frizzed their hair, adopted psychedelically appropriate costumes, and prepared to invade America. Their debut was at the Monterey Pop Festival in June 1967. Hendrix played his guitar with his teeth and behind his back; he caressed his guitar and attacked it in a sexually suggestive way. After a rocking version of Dylan's "Like a Rolling Stone" and a driving version of the Troggs' "Wild Thing," he drenched his guitar in lighter fluid and set it on fire (reminiscent of Jerry Lee Lewis?). To put it mildly, he succeeded in getting America's attention.

Are You Experienced? had already been released in this country that summer and had risen to number 5. This album featured a hard, raw, blues-based style of mainstream rock. The guitar sounds were utterly unique. Hendrix was left-handed but played a right-handed guitar upside down, restrung so that the high strings and low strings were in their traditional positions. He played extremely loudly, overloading his sound system; he also used a fuzz box for distortion, a Uni-Vibe (which simulated rotating speakers), a wah-wah pedal, and the guitar's toggle switch and tremolo bar for special effects. Groups like the Grateful Dead, the Who, and the Yardbirds were using similar techniques, but Hendrix seemed to use them with more control for deliberate musical effect. A prime example of these effects can be found on this album in the song "Third Stone from the Sun."

Hendrix's most critically acclaimed album was his third release, *Electric Ladyland* (August 1968). His only number 1 album, *Electric Ladyland* included several highly experimental works, like the album's first cut, "And the Gods Made Love," which uses tape speed manipulation to create a successful, though brief, electronic composition. "Voodoo Chile" contains excellent playing by drummer Mitchell, guest organist Stevie Winwood, and Hendrix. The bluesy vocal shows the full range of Hendrix's voice, from Dylanesque delivery to a full shouting style. *Electric Ladyland* also

*By clicking this link, you will be redirected to a third-party site.

includes Hendrix's only hit single, "All Along the Watchtower," mentioned previously.

There are many delights on *Electric Ladyland* with an interesting thread of unity running through the double album, as several songs are begun on one side and reprised (returned to) on a later side. For example, the album ends with "Voodoo Child (Slight Return)," which is related to the earlier "Voodoo Chile." Also, "Rainy Day, Dream Away" begins on side 3 as a gentle rock song with a hint of jazz feeling, and returns on side 4 as "Still Raining, Still Dreaming," this time with a harder rock feeling. One can hear an old-fashioned, 12-bar blues on "Come On (Part I)" and Hendrix's infinite modifications of guitar timbres on "Gypsy Eyes."

If you listen to only one cut on *Electric Ladyland,* it should be "1983" (which imperceptibly flows into "Moon, Turn the Tides"). This long song shows all sides of Hendrix's art. There are fine solos by drummer Mitchell and bassist Redding; tasteful use of the flute (played by Chris Wood) adds to the ethereal timbre. There are moments of driving rock, countered by peaceful moments of nicely refined electronic effects. Overall, it is a classic track.

Electric Ladyland shows that Hendrix was well ahead of his time and was a far more creative musician than his reputation at the time would suggest. Indeed, Hendrix himself began to feel that his stage antics were detracting from his more serious musical abilities, but as he attempted to play it straight, many fans were dissatisfied, apparently being more impressed by theatrics than by music. Hendrix disbanded the Experience in 1969 and retreated to upstate New York (more shades of Dylan?). However, he did appear at Woodstock, providing a spectacular version of "The Star Spangled Banner" during his set.

He opened his own studio, Electric Ladyland, in New York in 1969 and began recording his next album. There were problems, however; one came in early 1970 at Madison Square Garden, where Hendrix simply stopped playing in the middle of a set. He wandered offstage, apparently lost in his own mind. In the decades since Hendrix's death, those who have managed his estate—despite significant discrepancies and legal challenges at times—have been masterful at packaging his recordings into dozens of posthumous re-releases, compilations, live albums, and box sets; over 20 of these albums reached the Billboard Hot 200 album chart. A particularly significant release was entitled *Valleys of Neptune*, a set of 12 previously unreleased Hendrix recordings from his studio sessions in late 1969 (number 4 in 2010).

and their followers, through Hendrix and the other acid rockers, and on into the harder rock and heavy metal of the 1970s and 1980s. Regrettably, some (though, thankfully, not all) of the later bands grasped only the superficial and most accessible of Hendrix's developments and left the more subtle and refined elements unused. According to music journalist John Morthland, "The Seventies heavy metal bands, with their emphasis on volume, monolithic riffs and droning guitars, owe something to Hendrix, but none have shown even a small fraction of either his finesse or imagination" (Miller 1980, 302).

JOURNAL

Jimi Hendrix as a Rock Guitar Pioneer

As noted above, much like Chuck Berry before him (but in a very different way), Jimi Hendrix was a significant influence on almost every rock guitarist who came after him. Listen carefully to several of his hit singles ("Purple Haze," "Foxey Lady," and "All Along the Watchtower"), then take time to listen to several of the more adventurous tracks mentioned in this chapter ("Third Stone from the Sun" and "And the Gods Made Love"). After listening to Chuck Berry and other mainstream rock guitarists, describe at least three ways in which Hendrix's guitar playing is different from these previous artists. Name at least one band of the new millennium in which you hear the influence of Hendrix's guitar innovations, providing a brief explanation of that influence.

▶ The response entered here will appear in the performance dashboard and can be viewed by your instructor.

Submit

9.4: Musical Close-Up on The Art of Improvisation

OBJECTIVE: Explain how music is improvised

The concept of musical improvisation has been referenced at various times throughout this course. Instrumental improvisation became an important factor in most rock styles from the 1970s on, so let us take a closer look at the practice.

Grove Music Online tells us that improvisation is "The creation of a musical work ... as it is being performed" (Nettl, 2011). Essentially, this means that a musician is improvising anytime she or he makes up something to play on the spot or spontaneously adds to or changes what was previously written or planned. This can mean anything from the most minute change all the way to an entire piece that is made up on the spot:

Continuum of Improvisation

✗—————————————————————✗

→ **Change or add a single note or rhythm.**

Make up an entire solo or piece with no preexisting structure.

9.4.1: The Improvisation Continuum

In the Western classical music tradition, a performer typically strives to reproduce, as faithfully as possible, the exact notes and rhythms conceived by the composer, as represented in musical notation. Even in classical music, however, performers sometimes add their own dynamics, phrasings, and tempo variations; these types of changes, which are usually preplanned, are considered interpretations, rather than improvisations. Gospel, C&W, rock, and every subcategory of jazz lie somewhere along our improvisational continuum. C&W, for example, has been relatively conservative; it would lie somewhere on the left end of the continuum.

On the other hand, jazz has always relied heavily on improvisation. Especially beginning in the mid-1940s, an increasing emphasis on freer improvisation was integrated into jazz. This trend reached its peak in the 1960s, when some jazz performers experimented with *free jazz*. In this style, performers simply played whatever came to mind at the moment, with little regard for traditional structure or common concepts of melodic and/or harmonic coordination with other players in the ensemble. This style comes very close to the extreme, right side of our improvisational continuum.

For the first 10 years of rock and roll's history, improvisation certainly existed, but it was rather limited. Because many of the players could not read music, the songs and arrangements were made up in their heads. Once set, there was an attempt to perform the song more or less the same way each time. Inevitably, no two performances would ever be exactly the same; performers could make small internal changes with each performance. Chuck Berry, Little Richard, and Jerry Lee Lewis were the most improvisational; the least improvisational early rock styles were the soft rock styles and, of course, Motown, but even these were, to some modest extent, improvisational.

However, with some of the British blues-based bands, such as the Yardbirds, and the psychedelic rock bands, such as the Grateful Dead, rock improvisation crosses over the imaginary center point on our continuum. When Eric Clapton took off on one of his 30-minute **rave-ups**, rock approached the level of improvisation known in jazz since the 1940s. When the Dead performed one of their 30-minute pieces without the benefit of a carefully planned arrangement, they moved to a new level of rock improvisation. On *Electric Ladyland*, Jimi Hendrix improvises extensively, at times approaching the rock equivalent of free jazz. Improvisation will become increasingly relevant to our study of rock throughout the 1970s.

One by-product of this increasing emphasis on improvisation is the enhanced status of the instrumentalist. Prior to the mid-1960s, the singer was almost always the rock star; instrumentalists were necessary, but largely expendable. Frankly, it is difficult to name many rock stars prior to 1965 whose reputations were built on playing, rather than singing. However, since the mid-1960s, the skillful instrumental improviser has gradually ascended to the level of the rock singer. Examples include guitarists such as Eric Clapton, Jimi Hendrix, Jeff Beck, John McLaughlin, Pete Townshend, and Eddie Van Halen; keyboardists such as Keith Emerson and Rick Wakeman; or drummers such as Carl Palmer, Billy Cobham, and Danny Seraphine.

9.4.2: The Organization of Improvisation

This Musical Close-Up is focused on "The Art of Improvisation." Improvisation is truly an art, and, like most arts, it involves some rather indefinable elements (sometimes called *inspiration* or *intuition*) as well as some relatively objective elements. In some ways, improvisation is the ultimate musical expression because it combines the skills of both the performer and the composer. The improviser must think (or feel) what to play and then play it, all within a split second. It is a difficult thing to do and a difficult thing to teach. Like any other skill, one can learn the objective rudiments of the skill but not be able to add the intuitive element.

9.4.3: Shaping Improvisation

Improvisation is really a rather amazing process. The effective improviser must unerringly feel the rhythm, know the chord progression (vertical thinking) and the appropriate scale (horizontal thinking), dream up something interesting that fits, and then be able to play it, all instantaneously. The best improvisers also have some overall idea about the shape of their complete solo. Is it to be a structured length (e.g., 16 bars or 32 bars), or is it open-ended ("nod when you are through")? Knowing that, what does one do within that time frame? One can start on low pitches, move to higher pitches, and then end low; or one can start low and gradually move upward toward the end in a straight line; or one can envision a series of peaks. What about dynamics? Does one start softly and build loudness to the end or start loudly, get softer in the middle, and then build to a big finish? Then, there are considerations of rhythmic activity. One can begin with sparse rhythmic activity (just a few notes per bar) and build to a flurry of notes at the end or begin with a burst, calm down in the middle, and end with another burst. Sometimes, a player will take one short

Ways of Organizing Chords and Scales

So what are the rudiments of improvisation? What do good improvisers (rock, jazz, or whatever) need to know, and what are they doing when they improvise?

Vertical Organization—First, they must have total technical mastery of their instrument (and this includes vocalists, by the way). It does no good whatsoever to have the greatest musical inspiration of all time and then not be able to perform it. Second, the improviser must have an absolutely solid feeling for rhythm. Rhythm must be internalized; that is, the improviser needs to be able to feel the rhythm inside automatically, without counting. Third, the improviser must thoroughly understand chords and scales; that is, the way musical pitches are organized vertically and horizontally. These two terms—*vertical* and *horizontal*—may be a bit confusing to the nonmusician. *Vertical organization* refers to musical sounds that occur simultaneously; that is, chords:

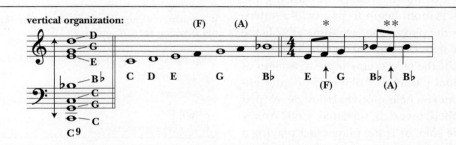

The chord shown above happens all at once; it contains five different pitches (C-D-E-G-Bb). If the improviser is thinking vertically, he or she automatically knows that those five notes will work in whatever line is improvised. The in-between notes (F and A) can work, too; for example, they could be used as passing notes between two chord tones (*) or as a neighbor to a chord tone (**). Click or tap the play button in the Revel course to watch a video demonstrating vertical organization.

Horizontal Organization—*Horizontal organization* refers to a musical line, such as a melody, that unfolds sequentially, note by note, in time. Scales organize musical pitch material in a horizontal way:

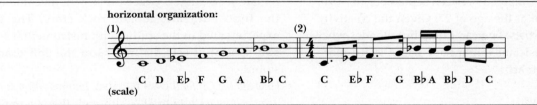

Thus, if an improviser knows that the horizontal collection of pitches shown in measure one of the musical notation example above is the scale used for a certain song, he or she is fairly safe creating an improvisational line using those pitches (such as the line in measure two). Even so, the improviser needs to be thinking vertically and rhythmically because how those notes are placed within the measure can determine whether they sound right against the prevailing chord. Click or tap the play button in the Revel course to watch a video demonstrating horizontal organization.

Styles in improvisation change over time just like almost everything else in music. In some styles, vertical thinking predominates; players primarily think in terms of chords and shaped improvisational lines to fit chords. At other times, players lean toward the horizontal (or *linear*) approach, thus allowing the scale and melodic line to take precedence over the chord. The latter approach often leads to a more dissonant sound because the horizontally conceived line may take the player outside of the notes of the prevailing chord (into a different tonal area).

musical idea (called a **motive**) and work it over and over, playing it on different pitches, fragmenting it, extending it, changing its rhythm or accents, or even inverting it (changing the direction of the notes).

Shaping one's improvisation is as important as playing the right scale or chord or rhythm. Nothing is worse than a solo that goes nowhere—one that aimlessly wanders from beginning to end, with a lot of meaningless notes in between, even if "correct" within the chord structure. Far too many rock fans tune in to the singer and the lyrics and tune out during the instrumental break; but in a good band, some of the most exciting music happens not during the vocals, but during the instrumental improvisation. Begin to pay careful attention to such solos. Is the player "on" rhythmically? Is the soloist really in sync with the chordal harmonies the others are playing? Or, if the solo seems to be dissonant at times, is it intentional ("outside" playing) or unintentional (mistakes)? Can you hear motives being developed (sequenced, fragmented, inverted, repeated, etc.)? And is there direction to the solo, or is the player just playing a wandering series of notes? Improvisation is an art. Most improvisers live for their creative moment in the spotlight—their solo. Perceptive listening is almost as difficult as good improvising. It takes practice, but if you try, you will be surprised at how rewarding it is to really appreciate a great improvisation.

BECOME AN ACTIVE LISTENER: EXAMPLES OF IMPROVISATION

It is time to put your ears to the test again. For each of the items in the following section,

Find examples of improvisation in these musical styles:

1. Traditional jazz
2. Jazz rock
3. Acid rock
4. Your favorite musical style

Summary: San Francisco

After the imaginative innovations of the Beach Boys and the Beatles in the mid-1960s, San Francisco acid rock stretched the boundaries of rock even farther through electronic experimentation and instrumental improvisation. Accompanying the high level of creativity, there were some undeniable lows that occurred. Tragically, the three *J*s—Jimi, Janis, and Jim—all died between September 18, 1970, and July 3, 1971, all at the age of 27. Given the creativity inherent in these artists, one can't help but wonder what influence these musicians might have had if given more time to develop their art.

Take Note: San Francisco

- *What was the San Francisco sound?*—In the late 1960s, San Francisco was a magnet for youth from all over the country, who converged on the city to create an alternate society based on peace, love, and hallucinogenic drugs. The San Francisco sound was an outgrowth of this movement. The music—known as psychedelic rock or acid rock—sought to mirror the drug-induced state of mind through long instrumental improvisations and electronic effects. It was louder and more aggressive than earlier rock. Less emphasis was put on the vocalist and more on virtuoso instrumentalists. Instrumental sounds were often dominated by special effects to give them a "freaky" or "far out" quality.

- *Why was Jefferson Airplane an important band in the development of the San Francisco sound?*—Jefferson Airplane was the first San Francisco band to land a national recording contract and among the first to have major hits with "Somebody to Love" and "White Rabbit." They also were noteworthy for featuring a female lead singer, Grace Slick, who became one of the first, authentic female rock stars. The group experimented in the studio with instrumental sounds and special effects, hallmarks of the San Francisco sound.

- *How did the Grateful Dead introduce improvisation and other new techniques into rock?*—Although they were not the first band to incorporate improvisation into rock music, the Grateful Dead made it central to their performances. They were closely associated with the Acid Tests of the mid-1960s, events in which partygoers experimented with LSD as a means of "expanding their minds." They considered themselves primarily a live band and prided themselves on their ability to **jam** for long periods, extending their songs well beyond the typical three-minute hit single limit. Lead guitarist Jerry Garcia demonstrated a mastery of electronic effects and creative improvisatory skills.

- *What was the impact of Janis Joplin on the development of rock music?*—Joplin was among the first white female rock stars to capture the power and intensity of R&B in her vocal style. She was a dynamo on stage, whose vocal style ranged from a dramatic raspy whisper to out-and-out screams. After Grace Slick, she became the leading female rock star, but her career was tragically cut short by death in 1970, the result of a drug overdose.

- *What groups and individuals outside of San Francisco played a role in the development of acid rock?*—Psychedelic rock spread well beyond San Francisco. The Doors (from Los Angeles) combined instrumental improvisation with the dark lead vocals of Jim Morrison. The group's first major hit, "Light My Fire," reflects these two elements; on the album version, there are lengthy organ and guitar solos that constitute the middle section of the song, framed by Morrison's lead vocal. The foremost guitarist in psychedelic rock was the highly innovative Jimi Hendrix, who created his own power trio, The Jimi Hendrix Experience, scoring hits with songs that have become rock classics ("Purple Haze" and "Hey Joe"). The group's U.S. debut at the Monterey Pop Festival was caught on film, including the dramatic culminating moments of Hendrix's performance, when he set his guitar on fire. By the time of Woodstock in 1969, he had gained such notoriety that he served as the festival's headlining act, concluding the three-day lineup of music; during this set, he performed his well-known version of the "Star Spangled Banner."

SHARED WRITING

All Along the Watchtower

Using a streaming service, listen to Bob Dylan's original version of "All Along the Watchtower" from *John Wesley Harding*, then listen to Jimi Hendrix's version on *Electric Ladyland*. Write a paragraph describing what you perceive as innovative elements of Hendrix's cover version of this song. You will want to focus on the various musical elements discussed earlier in this course, as well as vocal timbre, singing quality, instrumentation, guitar performance style, and overall sound. Does the musical setting have an effect on your interpretation of the meaning of the lyrics? What would you consider to be the most prominent musical feature of each recording? Share your paragraph with two or three other students as you review their comments. Revise your paragraph, integrating any aspects you would like to adopt from these peer responses. Compose a second paragraph in which you identify your preference for either the Dylan or Hendrix version, providing clear rationales for this decision.

A minimum number of characters is required to post and earn points. After posting, your response can be viewed by your class and instructor, and you can participate in the class discussion.

Post

0 characters | 140 minimum

Chapter 10
Jazz Rock

Learning Objectives

10.1 Explain how jazz rock music emerged

10.2 Explain how Blood, Sweat & Tears influenced the evolution of jazz rock

10.3 Analyze the Blood, Sweat & Tears transformation of "Sympathy for the Devil"

10.4 Describe the impact of Chicago on jazz rock

10.5 Summarize the contributions of jazz rock groups to the evolution of rock

Our study of rock history in this course so far has involved a discussion of the styles leading to the emergence of rock in the mid-1950s, evolving from existing musical styles at the time and settling into three primary subgenres by the late 1950s. A number of varying musical styles emerged during the transition to the 1960s and, in conjunction with the British Invasion (and especially with the musical innovations represented by the Beach Boys and the Beatles), led to the substantial amount of experimentation engendered in the music of the San Francisco bands. In this chapter, we turn to a style of music that involves the integration of extremely precise and highly technical musicianship, aspects that had not often been a core component of earlier rock music, though one can certainly point to virtuosic performers (e.g., Jimi Hendrix). At this time, we will turn our attention to the merging of two truly American forms of popular music and the initiation of their fusion.

10.1: A Tale of Sibling Rivalry and Its Resolution

OBJECTIVE: Explain how jazz rock music emerged

Imagine a small family consisting of a mother, a father, and a teenager named Fred. Fred has been the pride and joy of his family for some 13 years and is quite a sophisticated, intelligent, and "cool" kid.

Then, one day, a newcomer appears on the scene: a cute, cuddly baby sister. Suddenly, Fred is no longer the center of attention. Everyone devotes more time and attention to baby Susie, which makes Fred very jealous. After all, this gurgling little brat does not have one-tenth of Fred's intelligence, sophistication, or coolness!

Yet some years later, perhaps because Fred and Susie both come from the same roots, they find that they have much in common. In fact, as they become young adults, they find that they have much to share with each other.

No analogy is perfect, but Fred and Susie are a lot like jazz and rock. Both jazz and rock have a similar heritage in black music. Jazz—or at least its forerunner, the blues—is half a century older than rock but went through the same growing pains. By the time rock was born, jazz was considered a more sophisticated style of music. Rock and roll, in its infancy, was starting all over again, with 12-bar blues, simple and basic rhythms, and musicians for whom formal musical training was the exception rather than the rule. Yet it was getting all of the attention, shoving jazz off the radio and out of the record stores.

The typical jazz player of the mid-1950s resented rock for two basic reasons: one musical and one financial. First, compared with jazz, rock was a musical infant. Jazz players were often superb technicians on their instruments; most early rock tunes rarely extended beyond three chords. Jazz rhythms, harmonic structures, improvisations, and forms had evolved to a high level of sophistication; rock was basic, simple, and musically mundane in a comparative sense. To add insult to injury, rock and roll was lifting money right out of the pockets of jazz musicians. More and more, paid musical work at schools, country clubs, and in recording studios went to youngsters who could play what was selling: rock and roll. And rockers had little interest in jazz. Rock was easier and more fun to play and to listen to; besides, it was the big money-maker—and so, for the time being, the two siblings split. It would be some years later that they would realize a mutual alliance.

10.1.1: Blending Jazz and Rock

By the late 1960s, a new, young generation of musicians was hitting the scene. Typically, they had been born in the mid- to late 1940s, and they had grown up with rock. However, their musical appetites yearned for new, more challenging sounds and more sophisticated demands on their musicianship, yet still in a style closely related to rock. They found an answer by blending features of jazz and rock.

Progenitors of the Jazz Rock Style

The blending of jazz and rock elements was a very exciting development in rock and roll. Some of the earliest pioneers in this subgenre will be discussed in the following section.

The Paul Butterfield Blues Band and Electric Flag— Beginning around 1966, several bands appeared that mixed the sounds of rock with an older, blues-oriented style that featured horns; some examples include the Blues Project, the Paul Butterfield Blues Band, and the Barry Goldberg Blues Band. Typically, these bands added a horn line (trumpets and saxes) that played riffs, patterns, and interludes drawn from the style of black bands from the 1940s and 1950s. These early bands were the progenitors of a new subgenre: jazz rock.

In their third album, *Resurrection of Pigboy Crabshaw* (1967), the Butterfield Blues Band included horns (trumpets and saxes). One member of the Butterfield band, guitarist Mike Bloomfield, went on to the Electric Flag, another early model of the jazz rock band. Electric Flag had evolved from the earlier Barry Goldberg Band and consisted of Goldberg, Bloomfield, drummer Buddy Miles, and a changing membership that totaled between 8 and 10 players, including three horns. The Flag lasted only a year and a half. Their second album, *A Long Time Comin'* (1968), provides a perfect example of their sound. Listen to "Killing Floor" from that album; it is a 12-bar blues and illustrates how the horns were integrated into the fabric of the song.

*The Blues Project—*Of more long-lasting importance to jazz rock was the Blues Project. Perhaps surprisingly, given the eventual sound of the group, the band emerged out of the folk music scene in Greenwich Village. As was the rage in 1965, the band turned electric and represented the new folk rock sound, but they also played an electrified blues style. Membership in the Project vacillated from their beginning in 1965 through 1968, while they released several moderately successful albums. Along with the usual instrumentation, the Project included flute and saxophone. Two of its members, Al Kooper (keyboards) and Steve Katz (guitar), recruited two colleagues from a recent jam session at Café Au Go-Go in New York City—drummer Bobby Colomby and bassist Jim Fielder—and formed a new band. They added four horn players and called their new band Blood, Sweat & Tears (BS&T), the band to which we turn next.

10.2: Blood, Sweat & Tears

OBJECTIVE: Explain how Blood, Sweat & Tears influenced the evolution of jazz rock

Blood, Sweat & Tears (BS&T), beginning with the personnel enumerated in the previous section, emerged as one of the most successful early jazz rock groups. Al Kooper was no newcomer to the music business. At 13, he had been a member of the Royal Teens when they recorded the novelty hit "Short Shorts" (number 3, 1958). He re-emerged as coauthor of a number 1 song in early 1965: "This Diamond Ring," recorded by Gary Lewis and the Playboys. Kooper also played organ on Bob Dylan's "Like a Rolling Stone," creating one of the most memorable keyboard riffs in rock.

Blood, Sweat & Tears, 1969.

SOURCE: Pictorial Press Ltd/Alamy Stock Photo

Drummer Bobby Colomby had played both jazz and rock drums. Jim Fielder played briefly with Frank Zappa's

Mothers of Invention and Buffalo Springfield before joining BS&T. For the horn lineup, the first recruit was Fred Lipsius, who, in addition to alto sax and clarinet, played piano and arranged instrumental parts, having studied at Boston's Berklee College of Music. Dick Halligan was hired as a trombone player but later proved invaluable on flute, keyboards, and as an arranger. He had earned a master of arts degree from the Manhattan School of Music and was oriented more toward classical and jazz styles. Randy Brecker and Jerry Weiss, both trumpeters, rounded out the original eight-man lineup.

10.2.1: Personnel Changes and Musical Style

Consisting of highly trained and technically skilled musicians, BS&T produced some truly groundbreaking recordings, evincing a high level of musical creativity. For a variety of reasons, the group was plagued by frequent personnel changes.

Musical Journey of BS&T

The following section will provide details about BS&T's earliest recordings and the impressive contributions of this band to jazz rock.

The First Album: Child Is Father to the Man—Appearing at the Café Au Go-Go in Greenwich Village, the new BS&T met with immediate critical and popular approval around New York City. Their first album, *Child Is Father to the Man* (1968), had moments of brilliance that foreshadowed subsequent sounds, but the quality of the tracks was uneven, revealing the tensions already present between those in the band who favored rock and those who leaned more toward jazz. Two of the album's better cuts are Kooper's "My Days Are Numbered" and Randy Newman's "Just One Smile." Near the end of the latter song, the band breaks into a genuine polyphonic texture that nicely offsets the melody-and-accompaniment texture of the balance of the song. More bluesy singing by Kooper may be heard in "Somethin's Goin' On" (which also includes some fine, growling sax work by Lipsius). The strains of the "Overture" return at the end of the album, now titled "Underture."

The group's first album rose to number 47 on the album chart but contained no Top 40 hits.

The Second Album: Blood, Sweat & Tears—The conflicts within the group culminated in the departure of Kooper, Brecker, and Weiss. The rest of the band decided to try again, with new personnel. To replace Weiss and Brecker, Lew Soloff and Chuck Winfield were added. Soloff had earned his bachelor's degree from the Eastman School of Music. Winfield received his bachelor's and master's degrees from the Juilliard School of Music. Both trumpeters were steeped in a classical background. Notice

that this is the first time in this course that graduate degrees, or any degree for that matter, have been mentioned. To replace Kooper, David Clayton-Thomas, a Canadian singer, joined as lead vocalist in 1968. Their next album, *Blood, Sweat & Tears,* exploded to the number 1 position in early 1969. Three hits came from the album—"You've Made Me So Very Happy," "And When I Die," and "Spinning Wheel"—all reaching the number 2 position. BS&T received an unprecedented, at the time, 10 Grammy nominations, winning three awards.

"Spinning Wheel," by Clayton-Thomas, the album's biggest hit, reveals a bit of what jazz rock was about. It begins with a distinctive jazz chord (an augmented ninth chord). Out of that chord comes a gentle rock song, but at the instrumental break, the rock beat gives way to a jazz feel, complete with a jazz walking bass (usually, one bass note per beat) and Lew Soloff's jazz-style solo. (*Make sure to listen to the original album version of the song, since this section was eliminated from the single, the version found on their greatest hits recording.*) The rock beat returns as Clayton-Thomas re-enters. The song fades on a curious calliope-like sound over an accompanying vamp that alternates 9/8 and 6/8 meters.

The Third Album: Blood, Sweat & Tears 3—*Blood, Sweat & Tears 3* (1970) revealed no lessening of quality in comparison to its predecessor. It yielded two more hits: "Hi-De-Ho," by Gerry Goffin and Carole King, and "Lucretia MacEvil," by Clayton-Thomas. The latter is a strong rock piece flavored with jazz harmonies. It is followed by "Lucretia's Reprise," which begins with a jazz rock vamp based on the previous song's chord progression; Clayton-Thomas shouts a vocal improvisation before Lew Soloff enters with a particularly impressive trumpet solo. There is an effective version of James Taylor's "Fire and Rain" and a creative arrangement by Lipsius and Colomby of "Forty Thousand

Headmen," a song composed by Traffic's Steve Winwood and Jim Capaldi. In the latter song, themes by classical composers Bartók ("Ballad" from *Fifteen Hungarian Peasant Songs*) and Prokofiev (*Lieutenant Kijè Suite*) and jazz pianist Thelonious Monk ("I Mean You") are artfully interwoven. Clayton-Thomas's vocal versatility is best shown in "Lonesome Suzie" as he covers the range from a soft, tender timbre (including falsetto) to a full shouting style. "Somethin' Comin' On" provides a forum for Fred Lipsius's fascinating sax solo; notice the effective transition to Halligan's organ solo.

A masterpiece found on *Blood, Sweat & Tears 3* is "Symphony for the Devil/Sympathy for the Devil," a stunningly creative arrangement of the Rolling Stone song composed by Mick Jagger and Keith Richard, which will be the subject of the Musical Close-Up in this chapter.

The Fourth Album: Blood, Sweat & Tears 4—There was one personnel change prior to *Blood, Sweat & Tears 4* (1971): Jerry Hyman was replaced by Dave Bargeron, who played low brass instruments (trombone, bass trombone, tuba, and baritone). Bargeron holds a degree in music education from Boston University. The only Top 40 hit from this album is the hard-rocking "Go Down Gamblin'." Ever since the late 1940s, jazz players had been extending the upper range of their horns, so, of course, the jazz rock horn lines followed suit with upper-range playing. Note the trumpet break on "Go Down Gamblin'," as the top note reaches above high C. Another particularly impressive example of upper-range playing is Dave Bargeron's solo on "Redemption." Beginning a short motive near the bottom of the trombone range, he moves it up octave by octave until he reaches the upper end of the trumpet's range (on the trombone, mind you), reaching high C above the treble clef. Granted, it is virtually a squeal, but it is typical of jazz players' fascination with the upper range of brass instruments.

As we discovered with the most creative rock groups, such as the Beach Boys, the Beatles, and the Byrds, there are often small creative ideas worked into songs with such subtlety that one hardly notices. For example, on "Lisa, Listen to Me," as the instrumental break ends, Clayton-Thomas returns to the chorus, but as he sings the vocal line, the horn line imitates what he sang in the vocal part two beats earlier; the result is a brief but effective imitative polyphony between the two lines. BS&T could have simply used the same accompaniment they had used on the first two choruses, but this modest change represents the creative mind at work.

BS&T Disbands—The bottom fell out for the group in 1971. Clayton-Thomas left in hopes of establishing a solo career. Having little success, he returned to the band in the mid-1970s, but by then, it was too late. Lipsius and Halligan, the band's most talented arrangers, had also left, and, by 1973, Katz and Winfield departed. Through the 1970s, there were several lead singers and a dizzying number of changes of instrumental personnel. The band swung like a pendulum between a more progressive jazz style and a heavier rock style. Album sales plummeted; the group's identity—and their magic—had dissipated. Remnants of the band continued to tour into the new millennium, and the horn section has recorded with other artists, including Jeff Lorber (*He Had a Hat*, 2007, and *Now Is the Time*, 2010).

10.2.2: The Musical Characteristics of Blood, Sweat & Tears

While BS&T recorded many tracks worthy of significant attention, perhaps their most impressive cut, found on *Blood, Sweat & Tears*, is "Blues—Part II," essentially an introduction to the band that features solos by various members. This composition, which lasts well over 10 minutes, provides a good example of a *through-composed* form, meaning that each section of the piece is new; none of the earlier sections is repeated. The piece begins with an organ solo that is an impressive working out of a motive stated at the outset: a series of rising perfect fourths (an interval created by playing a note, such as C, skipping two notes of the underlying scale of the key [D and E], and then playing the next note [F]). Dick Halligan develops the **quartal** motive by transposing, fragmenting, extending, and inverting it. As the Listening Guide provided below reveals, "Blues—Part II" then proceeds through a series of sections featuring a sequence of soloists and styles.

Odd meters (five beats, seven beats, etc.) and **changing meters** had been a part of jazz since the 1950s. Except for a few experiments by the Beatles and the Byrds, such metrical experiments were uncommon in rock. However, jazz rock groups helped bring them into mainstream popular music. Steve Katz's "Sometimes in Winter" is basically in quadruple meter, but at the bridge section, the meter changes to 9/8 (in effect doubling the speed of the beat and establishing nine beats per measure), then back to quadruple, then again back to 9/8, followed by a measure of triple meter (3/4), before finally returning to 4/4. The horns join in a brief chorale at this point, accompanied by a running bass line; the chorale ends in a five-beat measure on another jazz harmony (a major ninth chord with a lowered fifth). Can you clearly sense the rise of musical complexity that has arrived with the jazz rock style?

All in all, *Blood, Sweat & Tears* is an exceptionally strong album, but some hard rock purists felt that the jazz rock fusion was too cerebral, too tight, and too sophisticated to be "real rock." However, BS&T opened up a whole new audience for rock. Jazz fans and some of the more open-minded classical listeners could find music to respect and enjoy in BS&T. Those rock fans who were willing to listen (fortunately, record sales suggest there were many) discovered that they could enjoy a well-played, technically more sophisticated style of rock. In late 1969, BS&T undertook a major tour that included 55 performances in nearly every major U.S. city and at many colleges and universities. Among the dates on this tour was a precedent-setting engagement at Caesar's Palace on the Las Vegas strip. The big Vegas hotels had avoided rock acts until earlier in 1969,

Listening Guide: "Blues—Part II" (Blood, Sweat & Tears)

0:00–1:56	Section A: part 1	Organ solo. Statement of *quartal* (built in fourths) motive; sequenced five steps lower. Extended by improvisation based on the quartal motive.
1:57–2:36	Section A: part 2	Rhythmic quartal chords; motive sequenced.
2:37–3:30	Section B	Rhythmic pattern on quartal chords (organ). Horn line enters (briefly). Bass solo (light drum accompaniment) in jazz style.
3:31–4:22	Section C	Drum solo (jazz style).
4:23–6:31	Section D: part 1	After a brief transition by the band, jazzy sax solo over rock-style bass riff and light drums. **Ritard** at end.
6:32–7:53	Section D: part 2	Sax solo continues, but in a slower, softer jazz style; accompanied by bass, guitar, and drums.
7:54–8:46	Section E	Bass states familiar blues-rock riff (similar to earlier riffs by Cream and Iron Butterfly) four times; horn line harmonizes the riff, which becomes the accompaniment to a rock-style sax solo.
8:47–10:08	Section F: part 1	Short transition leads to vocal entry. Style is extremely relaxed at beginning (to allow for an increase in tension to climax in next part).
10:09–11:45	Section F: part 2	New, two-bar ascending scalar riff in organ and bass; vocal intensifies. Horn line joins the riff; as vocal moves to shouting, brass moves riff to high range. As climax is reached, recording fades to segue to next track on album.

when the International Hotel had booked Elvis Presley. BS&T's three-day engagement at Caesar's Palace broke the house attendance record set by Frank Sinatra, but the hardcore rock counterculture was aghast that a rock band would stoop to play to such an overtly upper-crust audience (the Beatles' 1963 Royal Command Performance had apparently slipped their minds). The reaction reveals that these so-called rock fans were not really viewing rock as music but as a socio-cultural symbol. As Clayton-Thomas put it, "We didn't change our show for [the Las Vegas audience]. We're playing our music the same way. It's not diluted one bit from the early days at the Café Au Go-Go or the early days of the Fillmore East or West" (Wise 1971). Nevertheless, some of the same people who had applauded BS&T earlier now howled in derision, even though the music had not changed.

JOURNAL

Rock and Jazz Elements in "Spinning Wheel"

Listen carefully to "Spinning Wheel" by Blood, Sweat & Tears (the album version, which is just over four minutes long, not the edited single version that is found on the *Greatest Hits* compilation). Before you begin to reflect on the piece, listen to it three or four times. After doing so, start playback of the recording about a minute-and-a-half into the track (the beginning of a verse). Pay careful attention to the dramatic musical change that occurs at around the two-minute mark, when the trumpet solo begins. The rock beat returns about 40 seconds later, at the conclusion of the solo. Write a few sentences describing the differences you hear in the music when comparing the rock sections to the jazz-influenced solo. Use your developing musical vocabulary to address specific musical elements that differentiate the two styles, both of which are integral to jazz rock. This tune provides an exemplary opportunity to hear both the rock sound and jazz sound that fused into jazz rock.

> The response entered here will appear in the performance dashboard and can be viewed by your instructor.

Submit

10.3: Musical Close-Up on the Analysis of "Symphony for the Devil/Sympathy for the Devil" (Blood, Sweat & Tears)

OBJECTIVE: Analyze the Blood, Sweat & Tears transformation of "Sympathy for the Devil"

In a Musical Close-Up earlier in this course, we analyzed a song by the Rolling Stones called "Sympathy for the Devil." It is an interesting rock song, but it is relatively simple musically. The entire six-minute song consists harmonically of only four chords; the form was simple and repetitive; there was little or no change in the meter, beat, or rhythmic texture; there were only a few changes in timbre, and no key changes; and the melody was simple and repetitive.

On *Blood, Sweat & Tears 3*, there is an arrangement of "Sympathy for the Devil" that so utterly transforms the original song that, for all practical purposes, a new composition has been created. Dick Halligan's arrangement, in fact, seems to require a new title—hence the change to "Symphony for the Devil/Sympathy for the Devil." To help you understand what a talented arranger can do to transform a rather simple song into a creative landmark, a rather thorough analysis of the BS&T version of "Sympathy" will be undertaken.

The BS&T version is nearly eight minutes long and is in three major sections, entitled "Emergence," "Devil's Game," and "Submergence." The Rolling Stones tune actually appears only in the "Devil's Game" section. "Emergence" and "Submergence" consist of entirely new material. The Listening Guide provides a useful tool for understanding the BS&T composition.

Listening Guide: "Symphony for the Devil/Sympathy for the Devil" (Blood, Sweat & Tears)

0:00–1:10	Emergence: Theme A	Theme A*.
1:11–1:23	Emergence: Fanfare	Series of drum rolls leads to a dissonant brass fanfare.
1:24–2:03	Devil's Game: Labyrinth Chorus I (Theme B)	Theme B is the original Rolling Stones tune; six phrases*. Transition from sixth phrase to Chorus II (organ) based on notes 2–6 of Theme A.
2:04–2:40	Devil's Game: Labyrinth Chorus II (Theme B)	Chorus II has different accompaniment*. Transition from sixth phrase to Chorus III (horn line) based on notes 2–16 of Theme A.
2:41–3:18	Devil's Game: Labyrinth Chorus III (Theme B)	Chorus III uses another new accompaniment*. Note the transition between fifth and sixth phrases (notes 2–9 of Theme A). Last phrase is *a cappella*.
3:19–4:05	Devil's Game: Satan's Dance (Part 1)	Part 1 is a polyphonic section based on fragments of Theme A*.
4:06–4:52	Devil's Game: Satan's Dance (Part 2)	Improvised sax solo accompanied by drums and dissonant brass chords.
4:53–5:37	Devil's Game: Satan's Dance (Part 3)	Fugue section*.
5:38–6:32	Devil's Game: The Demand (Chorus IV)	Chorus IV based on Rolling Stone lyrics. Creates an overall arch in dynamics by beginning with whispers, increasing volume and intensity, and then decreasing instrumentation down to solo bass*. Notes 1–12 of Theme A accompany the spoken lyrics.
6:33–7:04	Submergence: Contemplation	Theme A returns (notes 1–15) in piano.
7:05–7:44	Submergence: Return	Theme A, played backwards. Begun by celesta; completed by piano, bass, trombone (like at the beginning of the track).

For a detailed discussion of all items marked with * see the section following.

10.3.1: "Emergence"

In "Emergence," we are presented with a 20-note musical theme that we shall call "Theme A."

Watch THEME A

This 20-note musical theme serves as such a critically important organizational element for this innovative version of the Rolling Stones song upon which it is based that it is essential that you have an understanding of this interesting—and, perhaps, unfamiliar sounding—series of pitches. It will serve you well to listen many times to this example. I strongly recommend, when considering this particular composition, that you return to this listening example frequently to "keep it in your ears."

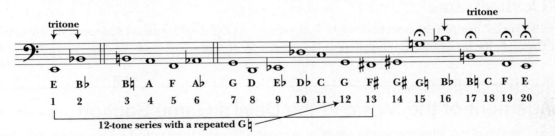

Arrangement of the Music in the Emergence Section

The following section provides a guided tour through the opening section of this composition. Along with "Karn Evil 9" by Emerson, Lake & Palmer, you may consider this one of the most challenging pieces presented in this book. I encourage you to take on this challenge boldly, as it will expand the horizons of your music listening.

Theme A emerges from the dark, low range of the trombone, bass guitar, and piano (as if the devil were hesitantly crawling out of some trapdoor from hell). First, we hear notes 1 and 2 of Theme A. These two notes are significant. The interval between E and B♭ (notes 1 and 2) is a **tritone**; that is, it consists of three whole steps. Because the tritone has some unique acoustic characteristics, it was nicknamed many centuries ago *diabolus in musica*—"the devil in music." What better way to begin a song about the devil than with the tritone?

After notes 1 and 2, Theme A starts over, giving us notes 1–6; then, it starts over again, this time rushing, with no regular beat, from note 1 to note 15. There is a pause before moving to notes 16–20 (with some more pauses). Theme A ends where it began, on E.

Throughout this century, some classical composers have sought to avoid **key centers**. One way to achieve this goal is to compose a series of pitches in which all 12 different notes are used with no repetition (thus avoiding emphasis on any single note), a technique referred to as *12-tone composition* and credited to composer Arnold Schoenberg and other members of the Second Viennese School in the early twentieth century. Once devised, this series of pitches was used over and over to generate the balance of the composition. Theme A has 11 different pitches before it repeats G (which appears as both notes 7 and 12 in the theme); the very next note (F#) would be the 12th different pitch. Thus, the first 13 notes of Theme A are like a 12-note series with only one repeated note; notes 14–20 are not composed by any system, but are simply the result of Halligan's musical intuition. Interestingly, the highest note in Theme A is B♭; from it, Theme A descends to the final note, E, thus outlining another B♭ to E tritone, extended across a wider pitch range.

After this darkly ominous presentation of Theme A, the celesta plays a sequence that repeats notes 2–6 and ends on notes 7 and 8 (transposed to fit the last part of the sequence), as shown in the figure below.

 Click or tap the play button in the Revel course to watch a video presenting Theme A as performed on the celesta.

Theme A (performed on the celesta)

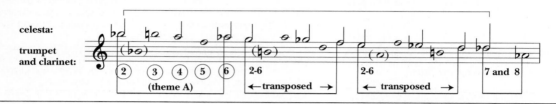

 Notice that the celesta sequence is accompanied by accented notes at the beginning of each pattern (trumpets and clarinet); these notes are B♭, B#, and A—notes 2–4 of theme A. Returning to the low register, the trombone, bass, piano, and trumpet finish Theme A from notes 9–20 (untransposed). As the last note (E) is held in the bass, various pitches are added, creating a rather dissonant chord, but the pitches are not random; they are notes 1–8 of Theme A.

As this chord releases, a series of four drumrolls enters. As they increase in loudness, the devil prepares to speak. A brass fanfare is appropriate, but it is not a "pretty" one. Instead, the brass play a brief but dissonant fanfare, the notes of which are drawn from Theme A (notes 1–15).

10.3.2: "Devil's Game"

Part 2, "Devil's Game," begins with a section called "Labyrinth." As the devil introduces himself, we are exposed for the first time to Theme B, the tune of the Rolling Stones' "Sympathy for the Devil."

Arrangement of the Music in the Devil's Game Section

The second section of this adventurous piece is likely to sound a bit more familiar than the opening section, especially if you have previously read the portion of this course on the British Invasion, which includes a discussion of the Rolling Stones' "Sympathy for the Devil." A detailed discussion of BS&T's adaptation of this song is provided here.

As we discussed earlier in this course, there are six phrases in each chorus of the original song. "Labyrinth" begins with the first chorus, but instead of using the same accompaniment throughout, as the Rolling Stones had done, BS&T devised a slightly different accompaniment for each phrase:

Chorus I:

Phrase 1: "please allow me"—voice; guitar on first beat of each bar

Phrase 2: "I've been around"—add piano (E) on third beat of each bar

Phrase 3: "I was around"—add syncopated bass guitar

Phrase 4: "made damn sure"—add syncopated drum notes

Phrase 5: "pleased to meet you"—full beat and accompaniment

Phrase 6: "what's confusing you"—suspend accompaniment in second bar

The second chorus is not set in the same way as the first chorus. For example, the phrase 1 accompaniment includes organ chords; phrase 2 adds brass chords, each of which starts softly and gets louder; and the bass line falls an octave as phrase 3 begins.

The third chorus is accompanied by an interesting interplay between the horn line and the electric guitar. The horns play a chord at the beginning of each measure; even though the chords descend within each phrase, the overall pattern rises in pitch from phrase to phrase. The guitar is also gradually working up to a high note near the end of the fourth phrase.

"Satan's Dance" is, in effect, an instrumental break midway through the piece. It consists of three internal sections: (a) a polyphonic section based on fragments of Theme A, (b) a sax solo, and (c) a brief *fugue*—a polyphonic technique in which a theme (called a subject) is first presented alone and is then imitated successively by other voices or instruments at different pitch levels. The subject of this fugue is based on Theme A. The opening polyphonic section begins with a five-note motive derived from Theme A, as shown in the figure below. For ease of reference, we will call this motive (notes 2–6 of Theme A) "Motive S" (for "Sympathy").

Click or tap the play button in the Revel course to watch the video demonstrating Motive S.

MS

After Motive S is introduced, it generates a falling sequence that is imitated at a delay of one beat (by keyboards). Then, the same thing is done again, but by two muted trumpets and trombone, creating a three-way descending imitative polyphonic sequence. Next, the piano plays a short interlude based on notes 12–15 of Theme A.

Click or tap the play button in the Revel course to watch the video of the piano interlude.

Piano Interlude (notes 12-15)

This is followed by a rising sequence, again with imitation, accompanied by rising chords in the horns. At the top of this rising pattern, Motive S returns. Finally, Halligan inverts Motive S; that is, where the notes of the original motive go up, the notes of the inverted motive go down, and vice versa. Using inverted Motive S, Halligan creates another rising sequence, played in imitation (delayed by one beat) on keyboards. This leads to an improvised sax solo, which is accompanied by wild-sounding drums and dissonant brass chords. The horn players produce a series of squeals as the solo comes to an end.

Click or tap the play button in the Revel course to watch the video of Motive S.

Motive S

Click or tap the play button in the Revel course to watch the video of the Motive S (original).

Motive S (original)

Click or tap the play button in the Revel course to watch the video of Motive S (inversion).

Motive S (inversion)

inverted motive S:

"Satan's Dance" ends in a fugue. This little fugue begins with Theme A (notes 1–15), but not at its original pitch level; interestingly, it is transposed up a tritone (the devil again!).

This subject (played by low brass) is imitated, beginning in the sixth measure, by trumpet. This is accompanied by the continuation of the lower brass line, creating a two-part (and eventually, a three-part) non-imitative polyphonic texture.

Click or tap the play button in the Revel course to watch the video of Satan's dance (fugue).

Satan's Dance (fugue)

Finally, in the 11th measure of the fugue, the second occurrence of the subject (in trumpet) ends, and the third entry occurs, this time in the low range of the piano and bass; the occurrences of the three subject entries (low brass, trumpet, then piano/bass) sequentially constitute imitative polyphonic texture. Here, the subject is extended to become the full Theme A and is played at its original pitch, as shown in the video below.

Click or tap the play button in the Revel course to watch the video of Satan's dance (fugue, low brass).

Over this bass presentation of Theme A, the upper lines continue playing countermelodies.

Satan's Dance (fugue, low brass)

As Theme A reaches notes 16–20, the rhythmic values are lengthened (this is called *augmentation*); the beat slows down (*ritard*). As note 20 is reached, a gong is struck. The fourth chorus is set still differently from the earlier choruses. The lyrics begin in a whisper; the organ accompanies these whispers by building up a huge chord one note at a time. The notes of this chord, beginning with the low E, consist of notes 1–12 of Theme A. As the chord gets louder and more dissonant with each added note, the whispers increase in volume, finally reaching a loud, full voice as the devil demands sympathy and courtesy or he will "lay your soul to waste."

The climax of the fourth chorus is reached as the organ chord and the spoken lyrics reach their highest volume; suddenly, they stop, and the devil sarcastically says, "Pleased to meet you!" As the accompaniment re-enters (on "hope you guess my name"), the instruments begin dropping out successively, until nothing is left but the bass. The fourth chorus has created its own little arch, beginning with one bass note, then whispers building to a climax, and ending with a solo bass line.

10.3.3: "Submergence"

It is time for the devil to return; "Submergence" depicts this narrative action. First, there is "Contemplation." We hear Theme A much as we did in the beginning (though played on the piano this time), starting with notes 1 and 2, then notes 1–6, and finally, notes 1–15. However, Theme A stops on note 15; then, there is a free-spinning around and around (notes 13–15), as they get louder and faster, then softer and slower (a mini-arch). The piano's damper pedal is held down throughout "Contemplation," creating a kind of blur as the notes sustain. If the devil emerged to the sounds of Theme A played forward, it is only reasonable that he submerge while Theme A is played backwards. Thus, in "Return," Theme A begins on note 15 and moves backwards to note 1 (played by celesta). Trombone, bass, and piano play notes 6–1, then notes 2 and 1 (the tritone again). Finally, after a pause, the devil shuts the trap door to hell behind him as note 1 of Theme A sounds one last time.

Arranger Halligan has illustrated creative use of every parameter of music: form, timbre, harmony, rhythm, melody, loudness, and texture. Although this version is based on the Stones' original material and must, therefore, be considered an arrangement, I trust, after reading the detailed description above, that you will agree it is virtually a new composition. To compare the original version with the BS&T version would be like comparing the most sophisticated jet engine with a paper airplane; each has its place, and we may use and enjoy both, but let us understand and appreciate the differences.

I hope that this detailed analysis of "Symphony for the Devil/Sympathy for the Devil" has made clear the musical innovation inherent in this unique arrangement/recomposition of a song by the Rolling Stones. BS&T's music was both commercially and critically successful. In fact, in acknowledgment of the group's artistic innovation, they received *Billboard*'s Trendsetter Award for 1970 for *Blood, Sweat & Tears* (the band's second album). It was an appropriate award, since BS&T did indeed set a trend that persisted through the 1970s, into the 1980s, and beyond.

10.4: Chicago

OBJECTIVE: Describe the impact of Chicago on jazz rock

In the beginning, most jazz rock bands were simply variations on the BS&T format, but one of these groups proved to have staying power long after BS&T and the other jazz rock groups had fallen by the wayside. Chicago's continuing popularity is matched only by a handful of performers in the history of rock. They had at least one Top 40 hit every year in the 1970s and 12 more during the 1980s. By 2011, Chicago could claim 5 gold albums, 10 platinum albums,

and 8 multi-platinum albums; from those albums came 20 Top 10 singles, including three that reached number 1. Few rock groups can claim that kind of success for more than three decades.

Chicago

SOURCE: Pictorial Press Ltd/Alamy Stock Photo

10.4.1: Chicago's Beginnings

The seven founding members of Chicago were all natives of the Windy City, except for Robert Lamm who moved there as a teenager. They formed their first group in 1967, the Missing Links (later the Big Thing), and began playing in clubs throughout the Midwest. A college friend, James William Guercio, had moved to Los Angeles where he became a record producer for Columbia Records. Following his successful work with BS&T, he summoned his Chicago friends to Los Angeles. They became the house band at the trendy Whisky a Go-Go club and signed a Columbia contract under the name Chicago Transit Authority (CTA). The original CTA lineup included Lamm on keyboards, Peter Cetera on bass, Terry Kath on guitar, and Danny Seraphine on drums; the horn line consisted of Lee Loughnane on trumpet, James Pankow on trombone, and Walter Parazaider on flute and saxophones. Cetera, Kath, and Lamm alternated as lead singers.

Columbia released *Chicago Transit Authority* in the spring of 1969. Several songs ("Questions 67 and 68," "Beginnings," and "Does Anybody Really Know What Time It Is?") were not immediate successes, but made the Top 30 later (1971). *Chicago Transit Authority* is a double album (unusual for a debut rock album). The opening cut, "Introduction," is similar in concept to "Blues—Part II" by BS&T, in that it serves as an introduction to the group. Beginning with a strong vocal and instrumental ensemble in a driving quadruple meter, it moves to a rapid-fire series of changing meters one minute and 15 seconds into the track.

Introduction to Changing Meters

The level of metrical complexity evident in some jazz rock tracks extends significantly beyond what was common in rock and roll of the era and equals the level of creative innovation apparent in even the most advanced examples by the Beatles.

The sound files included in the following sections (with accompanying animations) in the Revel will assist you in perceiving and better understanding these metrical and rhythmic aspects of jazz rock.

Click or tap the play button in the Revel course to watch a video demonstrating the introduction changing meters.

An example of changing meters

$$| \frac{4}{4} | \frac{6}{8} | \frac{7}{8} | \frac{6}{8} | \frac{6}{8} | \frac{7}{8} | \frac{6}{8} | \frac{6}{8} | \frac{7}{8} | \frac{6}{8} | \frac{3}{4} |$$

This example changes meter with almost every measure; and, even where it does not change meter (the two consecutive 6/8 measures), the feel changes due to a change in the subdivision of the beat into triple or duple groupings. Not only is the tempo fast, but the 6/8 measures alternate between a feeling of 3 + 3 (triple subdivision) and 2 + 2 + 2 (duple subdivision), further obscuring the meter.

See if you can follow along with this very complex metrical example, listening carefully for the accented notes performed as a rim shot on the snare drum. Be aware that it is likely to require listening intently many times to get it right. Here is the exact sequence of beat subdivisions for the complete audio example:

| 2 + 2 + 2 + 2 | 3 + 3 | 2 + 2 + 3 | 2 + 2 + 2 | 3 + 3 | 2 + 2 + 3 | 2 + 2 + 2 | 3 + 3 | 2 + 2 + 3 | 2 + 2 + 2 | 2 + 2 + 2 |

The following example demonstrates how the metrical feel of the same meter (i.e., 6/8; in which an eighth note gets a beat and there are six within a measure) can change significantly by simply arranging the accents differently. In this particular case, though the tempo remains the same, the first measure is divided into two subgroups of three eighth notes, while, the second measure, is divided into three subgroups of two eighth notes. Note that both consist of a total of six eighth notes (2 × 3 or 3 × 2), so fit appropriately within the same 6/8 meter. The two-measure sequence is repeated four times, so that you can hear the difference in an alternating example. I recommend listening a number of times

until you can clearly hear the change and even follow along comfortably tapping your finger or foot along with the accented notes.

Click or tap the play button in the Revel course to listen to the example while observing an animation that shows this alternation of two alternating versions of 6/8 meter.

6/8 meter (alternating between triple and duple subdivision)

$$| \frac{6}{8} | \frac{6}{8} |$$
$$\quad 3 + 3 \quad\quad 2 + 2 + 2$$

Now that you have listened to the alternating example in which the two versions of 6/8 meter are played consecutively, listen closely to just the first measure (two groups of three eighth notes) several times until the sound and feel are very familiar to you.

Click or tap the play button in the Revel course to watch a video showing the first version of 6/8 meter you experienced in the 6/8 meter (alternating between triple and duple subdivision) example.

6/8 meter (triple subdivision)

$$| \frac{6}{8} |$$
$$3 + 3$$

The following figure shows an example of the second measure (three subgroups of two eighth notes) in isolation; like you did in the previous example, listen closely to this example several times until the sound and feel are familiar to you. Once you are comfortable with both examples of the two measures in isolation, I encourage you to return to the example of changing meters and listen again—with more informed ears—to the example that alternates between the two. Developing a clear understanding of meter will greatly enhance your ability to differentiate various styles of music and to appreciate more complex music.

Click or tap the play button in the Revel course to watch a video showing the second version of 6/8 meter you experienced in the 6/8 meter (alternating between triple and duple subdivision) example.

6/8 meter (duple subdivision)

$$| \frac{6}{8} |$$
$$2 + 2 + 2$$

The original key of G minor is lost as a series of sequences moves through several implied keys, before finally settling back into G minor for a trombone solo by Pankow. Loughnane follows with a trumpet solo in G major, complete with jazz-oriented harmonies. A guitar solo brings back both G minor and the rock feeling; the horn line returns to lead to the closing vocal. No blended form can ever land directly in the middle between two styles. If push came to shove, it would probably be accurate to state that BS&T landed slightly on the "jazz

side" of jazz rock, whereas Chicago lay more on the "rock side."

When Chicago mayor Richard Daley initiated a lawsuit over the band's use of the name of the city's transportation department (Chicago Transit Authority), the band shortened its name to Chicago. *Chicago II* was released in early 1970 and contained two Top 10 singles, "Make Me Smile" and "25 or 6 to 4." "Colour My World," a plaintively simply but truly beautiful song, featuring a flute solo by Parazaider, was released in 1971 on the flip side of

Album Chicago VII

Perhaps the most interesting of the group's albums is *Chicago VII*, because it diverges at times from the typical Chicago sound. Appearing on this album were producer Guercio (acoustic guitar and bass); the Pointer Sisters; and Beach Boys Carl Wilson, Dennis Wilson, and Al Jardine.

The album also explores (lightly) electronic keyboards, including the ARP synthesizer and the Mellotron. The different sounds of *Chicago VII* are heard in the opening tracks. "Prelude to Aire" begins with bongos and tom-toms; Parazaider's rhythmically complex solo is accompanied by increasingly sophisticated cross-rhythms in percussion and the sounds of a Mellotron. "Aire" features the more typical Chicago horn line, but in a fast 7/8 meter, complete with syncopations; at the guitar solo, the meter changes to 7/4 (half as fast as 7/8). The song ends with complicated ensemble patterns back in 7/8 meter.

"Devil's Sweet" opens with soprano sax improvisations over quartal chords (built in perfect fourths). After some rather ethereal sounds on percussion, there is a lovely duet for flügelhorn and soprano sax. The 6/8 meter is full of syncopation. A delicate solo on drums, using wire brushes, provides a transition to the next section, written in duple meter (the 2/4 meter is reinforced by Seraphine) but with its bass line and horn ensemble in triple meter (3/4). Finally, a somewhat more normal rock sound emerges, featuring guitar and synthesizer; a drum solo leads back to the earlier soprano sax improvisations and the opening soprano sax–flügelhorn duet. All in all, the opening tracks of *Chicago VII* are the most adventurous and complex music on any of Chicago's recordings.

The following songs continue the experimentation of the opening. "Italian from New York" begins with bongos and ARP synthesizer (set in a sequencer pattern); quartal chords are set into an accompanying vamp with five beats per measure. "Hanky Panky," after a syncopated introduction, settles into a pure jazz trombone solo by Pankow. The album begins to return to normalcy with "Lifesaver"; it has a pounding piano beat (in 4/4 meter) and more typical Chicago horn parts. It also provides the album's first vocals. The true Chicago fan must have breathed a massive sigh of relief as the last cut on side 2, "Happy Man," began. Peter Cetera's vocal over a bossa nova–style beat is a far cry from hard rock, but at least it approached the more familiar Chicago style.

The last half of *Chicago VII* settles down to the more familiar Chicago sound. "(I've Been) Searchin' So Long" is one of Chicago's finest songs, starting calmly but building to a big finish, with Cetera's shouting vocal improvisations, active string lines, powerful bass lines, and high brass. "Mongonucleosis" is a strong Latin rock piece that may remind us of Buffalo Springfield songs, like "Uno Mundo," and, of course, Santana. "Wishing You Were Here" is a beautiful song, profiting from the instantly recognizable Beach Boys harmonies. "Call on Me" is absolutely dead center, typical Chicago in every way (it was the biggest hit on this album). In all, *Chicago VII* is a strong album, revealing the real versatility, creativity, and technical mastery of this band.

"Beginnings" and became popular in its own right. *Chicago III* (early 1971) was the band's third consecutive double album; it rose to number 2 and contained the hit singles "Free" and "Lowdown."

Chicago IV (number 3, late 1971) was a four-record boxed set containing live recordings from the band's concert at Carnegie Hall. What followed was an amazing string of five consecutive number 1 albums, beginning in 1972 with *Chicago V* and going through 1975 with *Chicago IX*, a multi-platinum greatest hits album. All told, *Chicago V* through *VIII* contained nine Top 30 hits, including six in the Top 10. During this period, the band's sound was very consistent. The only personnel change was a single addition—Brazilian percussionist Laudir de Oliveira in 1974 (on *Chicago VII* and subsequent albums).

10.4.2: Chicago's Longevity

There was a momentary dip in Chicago's popularity at the turn of the 1980s. *Chicago XIV* and *XV* (a greatest hits album) failed to make the Top 30, but with *Chicago 16*, the band regained its former strength with "Hard to Say I'm Sorry," which became a number 1 single (their only previous number 1 hit had been "If You Leave Me Now" from *Chicago X*). The albums *Chicago 17, 18,* and *19* (1984, 1986, and 1989, respectively), along with *Greatest Hits 1982–1989* (1989), sustained the group's popularity and moved away from the jazz rock style toward a purer mainstream rock style. The band continued to record well into the new millennium; *Chicago XXX* (2006) nearly cracked the Top 40, while *Chicago XXXII: Stone of Sisyphus* (2008) and *O Christmas Three* (2011) didn't crack the Top 100. Peter Cetera released a solo album in 1981 and left the band in 1985, replaced by Jason Scheff (the son of Elvis's bass player). Cetera's solo career looked promising initially, resulting in four Top 10 hits during the late 1980s; however, only one of his solo albums, *Solitude/Solitaire*, placed in the Top 30.

Probably a central reason for Chicago's remarkable longevity was the stability of its personnel. Six of the original seven members were still with the band as of 1986 (Terry Kath died from an accidental gunshot wound in January 1978); although there had been additions and guest artists (e.g., the Beach Boys, the Pointer Sisters, and

Maynard Ferguson), the basic nucleus remained intact. Of all of the jazz rock bands of the late 1960s to early 1970s, Chicago alone survived into the 1990s, with four of the original members still performing together.

10.5: Other Jazz Rock Groups

OBJECTIVE: Summarize the contributions of jazz rock groups to the evolution of rock

Following in the footsteps of BS&T and Chicago were many bands that combined basic rock instrumentation with horn lines of varying descriptions. Most failed to achieve significant commercial success, but one that did find its way onto the charts was Chase. Bill Chase had played lead trumpet with Woody Herman's big band for a few years before organizing his own jazz rock band. The nine-man band, Chase, took a slightly different approach to the typical jazz rock horn line: it consisted of four trumpets. This emphasis on trumpets—especially in the high range—gave Chase a distinctive sound. Their first album, *Chase,* was released in 1971 and yielded the hit single "Get It On," a hard-rocking tune similar to the best of BS&T and Chicago. On another of this album's songs, "Reflections," Chase used a tape delay echo effect on his trumpet solo; the timing of the delay was such that he ended up playing a polyphonic duet with himself.

By the time of their third album, *Pure Music* (1974), the band contained only one original member—Bill Chase himself. It was more jazz-influenced jazz rock fusion, with little of the strong rock feeling of some of the earlier Chase cuts. Tragically, on August 9, 1974, Chase and three other band members were killed in a plane crash.

Other bands to follow the lead of Blood, Sweat & Tears and Chicago were Dreams (which included original BS&T member Randy Brecker and his brother Mike on tenor sax), White Elephant (a 17-member band that also included both Breckers), and Symphonic Metamorphosis (a band made up of eight members of the Detroit Symphony).

As discussed in another part of this course, jazz rock evolves into fusion during the 1970s. Fusion artists included some of the most important jazz musicians of the era (e.g., Miles Davis, Herbie Hancock, and Chick Corea) as well as new artists influenced to varying degrees by jazz and rock. Instrumental virtuosity was clearly on display in the recordings of guitarists like John McLaughlin and Jeff Beck. Some of the most important fusion groups of that slightly later era include both those whose roots in jazz went very deep (e.g., Weather Report) and other groups whose roots were primarily in the rock and popular music genres, like Tower of Power and Earth, Wind & Fire. We will return to these groups in much greater detail in a future section of this course.

BECOME AN ACTIVE LISTENER: FINDING JAZZ ELEMENTS IN ROCK

It is time, again, to apply your developing listening skills outside the content of these course materials.

Find examples of the following in music that you listen to:

1. Jazz instrumentation (e.g., use of a horn section)
2. Jazz-influenced improvisation
3. Odd meters
4. Changing meters

Summary: Jazz Rock

By about 1972, the first phase of jazz rock was over (except for Chicago, as you now know). But the jazz influence had added new concepts to rock and reinforced a few previous ideas. Jazz brought with it a set of more complex chords, odd and changing meters, complex superimposed rhythms and syncopations, and new levels of complexity. It reinforced the concept of the lengthy and complex instrumental improvisation and added new musical sophistication. Finally, most previous rock groups had considered horns representative of "old" music and, if used at all, were better reserved for background chords or intermittent punctuations. With jazz rock, it became more evident that horns could take their place on the front lines with the lead guitar. Sometimes, the jazz rock groups would move smoothly between a rock style and a jazz style; at other times, the rock beat and bass line would underlie a jazz-style solo.

Just as it had done with folk and gospel influences earlier, rock absorbed the new jazz influence and broadened as a style. Although such external influences are sometimes decried by rock purists, rock's ability to integrate stylistic devices from coexisting sources is one of its strengths—and a primary reason why it continues to be a living, evolving, and dynamically vital style of music.

Take Note: Jazz Rock

- *What is jazz rock and when did it first emerge?*—By the late 1960s, a new, young generation of musicians was hitting the scene. Typically, they had been born in the mid- to late 1940s, and they had grown up with rock. However, their musical appetites yearned for new, more challenging sounds and more sophisticated technical demands, yet still in a style closely related to rock. Blending the best of jazz and rock, groups like Blood, Sweat & Tears and Chicago were among the most popular to arise and meet this challenge.

- *Why was Blood, Sweat & Tears a key jazz rock ensemble?*—Blood, Sweat & Tears achieved mainstream success with a number of hits in 1968. Their biggest hit, "Spinning Wheel," incorporated jazz harmonies and rhythms (particularly in the instrumental break) into a pop-rock song. The band incorporated unusual rhythms, jazz harmonies, and jazz instrumentation into a rock format. Their success built a new audience for the musical style.

- *How did Chicago change the jazz rock style?*—Chicago built on the Blood, Sweat & Tears style and instrumentation on their initial releases, gaining success with hits like "Does Anybody Really Know What Time It Is?" and "25 or 6 to 4." They ruled the charts in the early '70s, with a series of five number 1 albums and nine Top 30 hits. The group continued to experiment with different sounds and rhythms, incorporating synthesizers and Latin elements into the jazz rock mix.

- *What other groups were influential in the development of jazz rock?*—Chase, led by trumpeter Bill Chase, emphasized its four-trumpet lead lineup to create a distinctive sound. The group had a hit single with "Get It On" in 1971. There were a few other successful jazz rock ensembles, but the style had largely run its course as a primary rock subgenre by the early 1970s, when it formed the basis for fusion (discussed elsewhere in this course).

SHARED WRITING

Comparing Chicago's Early and Late Styles

Compare the stylistic elements of the early and late music of Chicago, one of the primary groups presented in this chapter. Listen to "Make Me Smile" (1970); then, listen to "Along Comes a Woman" (1985). Focusing on the elements of rhythm, vocal style, instrumentation, complexity, use of improvisation, and intended audience, discuss the ways in which the band's music changed between their early and late periods. Share your response with two or three of your peers. Which of these styles (early Chicago or later recordings) do you and your friends prefer? Provide a clear rationale for this decision, using your musical vocabulary and specific musical elements as a basis.

 A minimum number of characters is required to post and earn points. After posting, your response can be viewed by your class and instructor, and you can participate in the class discussion.

Post

0 characters | 140 minimum

Chapter 11
Art Rock

 Learning Objectives

11.1 Summarize ways that rock integrated elements of classical music

11.2 Explain how some art rock groups presented a series of related songs as a rock opera

11.3 Summarize the reasons that rock bands began playing with orchestral accompaniment

11.4 Identify some of the most important art rock groups

11.5 Analyze Emerson, Lake & Palmer's artistic approach to *Karn Evil 9*

As an art form, rock and roll varies significantly in its level of complexity. Much of early rock and roll, as a result of its R&B or C&W heritage, was far toward the "less complex" side of this continuum, often basing an entire song on three chords and repetitive rhythmic patterns. As we explored the music of some artists (e.g., the Beatles and the Beach Boys), we discovered that some other forms of rock evolved into impressively complex examples. In this chapter, we will go even farther to the "complex" side of the continuum, as we begin to examine the emergence of art rock in the late 1960s.

11.1: Rock as a "Legitimate" Musical Vocabulary

OBJECTIVE: Summarize ways that rock integrated elements of classical music

Prior to the mid-1960s, rock and roll was generally considered a simple and musically inconsequential style that appealed almost exclusively to teenagers. But then the Beach Boys, the Beatles, and others demonstrated that rock could be something more, … substantially more. After all, rock and roll is a musical language; like all languages, it can be used to articulate substantive ideas as well as lighter subjects.

In the late 1960s, some rock artists began to explore folk styles, some moved toward country, and others ventured into jazz and new electronic techniques. In each of these cases, the genre of rock music was enriched. There was an exciting realization that rock, as a musical language, was flexible and could be enhanced by absorbing from and fusing with other musical styles. Rock was not limited to two and a half minutes of clichéd lyrics over three basic chords.

11.1.1: Six Approaches to Combining Rock with Classical Music

Earlier in this course, we met some rock and roll pioneers: the Beach Boys, the Beatles, the Byrds, Bob Dylan, Aretha Franklin, Jimi Hendrix, and Blood, Sweat & Tears. To some musicians, the question was, "Just how far can rock really go?" Can the musical language of rock be used to create major works of art, comparable to those of the classical tradition? Why not? After all, symphonies consist of melodies, rhythms, chords, timbres, textures, and forms; why couldn't rock-style versions of these elements be used to create works of similar complexity? It was just a matter of time before creative musical minds would answer that question.

The attempts to combine rock with classical music brought a storm of criticism. Calling this new style "self-conscious" and "pretentious," critics seemed to assume the worst motives on the part of the new musical explorers, accusing them of "lame affectations of a cultured sensibility" and of seeking "to dignify their work, to make it acceptable for upper-class approbation" (Miller 1980, 347–48). The rock musicians who explored the new ground of "art rock" (or "classical rock," as it was sometimes known) were risking condemnation by the hard-core rock establishment. Surprisingly, that establishment, which prided itself on its rebelliousness, could be quite intolerant when some rock musicians ventured into previously unexplored areas.

Approaches to Combining Classical Elements and Rock Elements

There were six typical approaches to combining classical elements and rock elements:

Quote a classical excerpt in the midst of a rock song.— Cute, but this approach is often simplistic and hardly constitutes a true blending of styles.

Use a melody as the basis of a rock song.—Again, no real stylistic blending takes place; the result is simply a rock song with a borrowed tune.

Create a series of rock songs conceived of as units in a larger form.—Such attempts are often called **suites** or **song cycles**. If the songs are not unified in some way, this can, in fact, merely be a pretense of classicism. However, if there is some discernible thematic unity or development within the set, the results can be satisfying.

Adapt a full classical work to a rock-style performance.— Here, a greater part of the classical work is borrowed: the form, the chords, the melodies, and the internal development, largely as the classical composer originally intended it. These elements are then transformed by rock instrumentation, texture, and rhythmic interpretation. If done well, this method can offer a true mixture of styles.

Create a work for rock group and classical ensemble.— This, too, can be quite successful. Here a rock group performs as a partner with a symphony orchestra or other classically-oriented ensemble. Often, musical material is presented in a straight version by the orchestra and is then used as the basis of further elaboration, in a rock style, by the rock group. Sometimes, the two units come together to create a true blend of genres.

Using the musical language of rock, create an extended work modeled after a classical form.—This is the most challenging approach but one that has the potential to be the most successful. Length is not the criterion. A long rock piece is just that—a long rock piece. If there is thematic development and purposeful structure, though, the result can indeed be comparable to classical models, simply using a different musical language: rock. The most impressive achievements in the subgenre of art rock lie within this

category. In this chapter, we will concentrate on the fifth and sixth approaches, with occasional references to the fourth.

11.2: Rock with Orchestra

OBJECTIVE: Explain how some art rock groups present a series of related songs as rock operas

Of the six approaches to art rock enumerated previously, one involved adding symphonic instrumentation (i.e., an orchestra) to the core rock instrumentation of guitar, bass, drums, keyboard, and lead vocal. The extent to which the orchestral instruments are truly integrated into the rock ensemble can vary widely. Sometimes, the orchestra provides little more than instrumental support for existing rock music (perhaps even music that has been previously recorded) while, at other times, the orchestra can serve the limited purpose of providing instrumental interludes between a series of more traditional rock songs that use, almost exclusively, the traditional rock instrumentation. In other cases, as you will experience in this chapter, music is composed specifically to take advantage of both sets of instruments in a more egalitarian manner. Each of these options expands the timbral palette of musical sound in rock music and forms the base for the rock subgenre known as art rock.

11.2.1: The Moody Blues

Most early art rock explorations are found on recordings by British bands. The first major effort was by the Moody Blues, a group formed around 1964 as a blues-based band.

11.2.2: Deep Purple

The next significant effort in the direction of rock with orchestra came from a second-wave British invasion band whose hard-rock style would come to be called **heavy metal**.

Musical Career of the Moody Blues

The following section provides information about the Moody Blues, one of the earliest examples of art rock music.

Composition of the Band—After an early blues-oriented hit, "Go Now!" (number 10, 1965), two of the original members departed. With the addition of Justin Hayward and John Lodge, the band purchased a **Mellotron** and changed musical directions.

First Successful Album—They released *Days of Future Passed* in mid-1968; it became their first successful album in the United States, rising to number 3. "Tuesday Afternoon (Forever Afternoon)" hit the U.S. Hot 100 (number 24), as did "Nights in White Satin" when it was reissued in 1972 (number 2).

Days of Future Passed was recorded with the London Symphony Orchestra and was a **concept album**. Although important as a prototype, the album was a pleasant but rather superficial attempt at a rock-classical confluence. There is no significant simultaneous interaction between the orchestra and the band and no real blending of styles. The orchestra provides an overture-like beginning and then provides transitions between the band's songs. At times, the Mellotron provides an orchestra-like accompaniment for the band, rather than using the string, wind, and brass instruments of the orchestra.

Musical Style—Most of the rock songs are reminiscent of the soft rock style, except for "Peak Hour." The orchestra's music, though impressively orchestrated, adheres to a late nineteenth-century style, one of the pitfalls of many rock-with-orchestra experiments; often, the rock musician's idea of classical music refers to styles that were prominent during the eighteenth and nineteenth centuries, so the result is a curiously anachronistic blend between up-to-date rock and an out-of-date classical style.

Popularity—The Moody Blues' popularity ebbed and flowed throughout the 1970s and into the 1980s. They enjoyed peak popularity in the early 1970s with albums like *A Question of Balance* (number 3, 1970), *Every Good Boy Deserves Favour* (number 2, 1971), and *Seventh Sojourn* (number 1, 1972), and again in 1981 with *Long Distance Voyager* (number 1). Their use of the Mellotron became an identifying feature, as did their sophisticated melodies, harmonies, and vocals.

The Journey of Deep Purple

Though known by many as a hard rock band, Deep Purple had a highly artistic streak and contributed some impressive large-scale works to art rock, as described in the following section.

Early Career—Deep Purple was founded by guitarist Ritchie Blackmore in 1968. While living in Hamburg, Blackmore recruited four other British rockers for his new band. Their first single, a hard-rocking song called "Hush," hit the number 4 position on the U.S. Hot 100. Their first two albums, *Shades of Deep Purple* and *The Book of Taliesyn,* also sold well.

Deep Purple

Lord's Concerto—In September 1969, Deep Purple (now consisting of Blackmore, keyboardist Jon Lord, vocalist Ian Gillan, bassist Roger Glover, and drummer Ian Paice) gathered to perform Lord's *Concerto for Group and Orchestra* with the Royal Philharmonic Orchestra, conducted by Malcolm Arnold. The live recording, made in Royal Albert Hall, was released as Deep Purple's fourth album.

Lord's concerto is in three large movements (fast, slow, fast), as is typical of the classical concerto. The orchestral style is more contemporary than that of the Moody Blues' orchestra but still seems to be a compendium of early twentieth-century idioms. There are even *cadenzas*—virtuoso solos (often improvised) that are also common to the classical concerto. The second movement includes voice—rather unusual for a concerto—which is almost exclusively an instrumental form. For the most part, Lord's themes are presented by the orchestra in a straight style and are then interpreted by the band in a rock style. The third movement is by far the most successful musically, because the two ensembles and styles begin to mesh, approaching a real rock-classical fusion.

Gemini Suite—In 1970, Lord fulfilled a BBC commission to write another work for rock group and orchestra. Beginning as a Deep Purple project, it soon grew beyond that. The resulting *Gemini Suite* is a six-movement work for rock soloists and orchestra. Each movement is centered on a different soloist, three of whom—Lord, Glover, and Paice—were members of Deep Purple; the other three soloists were guitarist Albert Lee and vocalists Tony Ashton and Yvonne Elliman. In *Gemini Suite,* Lord's orchestral writing is more sophisticated than in his concerto, and there is some excellent rock virtuosity. There is a closer interaction between the soloists and the orchestra, at times, providing a very effective partnership. Overall, *Gemini Suite* is a successful step in the direction of rock-classical integration.

A brief description of the suite's six movements can be found in the table below.

Suite's Six Movements

1st movement	Guitar	Based on an ascending third motive (C to E♭) and an ascending major triad; these motives are developed throughout the movement.
2nd movement	Piano	Elements of classical, rock, and jazz.
3rd movement	Drums	Features tight coordination between the drums and orchestra; following an extended drum solo, the orchestra returns with a march-like section.
4th movement	Voice	Begins with lyrical string melody; female vocalist sings two solo verses (accompanied by orchestra); following a short orchestral interlude, male vocalist enters; a male-female vocal duet based on the earlier female melody closes the movement.
5th movement	Bass guitar	Bass underlies the orchestra before entering a solo cadenza; orchestra reenters for a brief dialogue; the movement ends quietly.
6th movement	Organ	The orchestral writing in this movement is more contemporary in style; interaction between organ (accompanied by bass and drums) and the orchestra involves trade-off passages.

Impact and Personnel Changes—Deep Purple's primary commercial impact came in the early 1970s with albums like *Fireball* (1971), *Machine Head* (1972), *Who Do We Think We Are* (1973), *Made in Japan* (1973), *Burn* (1974), and *Stormbringer* (1974). Their biggest single hit, "Smoke on the Water" (the live version hit number 4 in 1973), was an early classic of the hard rock, heavy metal trend of the 1970s. From mid-1973 onward, a series of personnel changes impacted the band, and their popularity waned. The group disbanded in 1976 but reunited in 1984 to produce a number 17 album *Perfect Strangers*, producing only one single that broke the Hot 100 ("Knocking at Your Backdoor," number 61). Since the mid-1980s, there have been more personnel changes, several tours, and occasional recorded albums. In 1999, they recreated Lord's *Concerto for Group and Orchestra* in a Royal Albert Hall concert with the London Symphony Orchestra.

11.2.3: Procol Harum

Formed in 1962 as the Paramounts, a blues-based band from London, Procol Harum's first single "A Whiter Shade of Pale" (1967) reached number 5 in the United States. After several personnel changes, there was a series of successful albums in the late 1960s and early 1970s. Their album *Live in Concert with the Edmonton Symphony Orchestra* (1972) became the group's highest-ranking album (number 5) and their only gold album.

For the Edmonton performance (November, 1971), the band drew on songs released on earlier albums; the songs were orchestrated and given a larger orchestral context. The most ambitious effort was "In Held 'Twas In I," a 19-minute work that had first appeared on the *Shine On Brightly* album. In this extended song, lyricist Keith Reid takes us on a journey from self-pity and depression through madness to an exalted reaffirmation of faith. The orchestra basically provides accompaniment with symphonic instrumentation for the series of songs in the set. Certainly the orchestral style is not as contemporary as the best moments of *Gemini Suite,* nor is the band as hard-rocking as Deep Purple. Nevertheless, "In Held 'Twas In I" is a thought-provoking sample of early 1970s art rock.

There were others who explored the rock-with-orchestra format, such as the New York Rock Ensemble, the Electric Light Orchestra, Frank Zappa's Mothers of Invention, and Emerson, Lake & Palmer, some of whom we will discuss later in the chapter.

JOURNAL

Deep Purple's Impressive Versatility

Deep Purple is known as a seminal band that provided inspiration for many future heavy metal bands. Lesser known are their more progressive recordings. Listen to their well-known hit "Smoke on the Water" and then listen to the "Organ" movement of Jon Lord's *Gemini Suite*. Using your developing musical vocabulary and focusing specifically on musical elements, identify five differences between the performance style of these two compositions. Write two or three sentences stating your preference and a clear rationale for why you like one of these recordings more than the other. [Optional post-assignment challenge: Our preferences are often heavily influenced by familiarity. Take time to listen to the entire *Gemini Suite* at least three times over a one-week period; then reconsider your response to this Journal item.]

 The response entered here will appear in the performance dashboard and can be viewed by your instructor.

Submit

11.3: Rock Operas and Theatrical Works

OBJECTIVE: Summarize the reasons that rock bands began playing with orchestral accompaniment

During late 1960s and early 1970s, rock musicians also created music with a theatrical aspect. Works that include acting, costuming, and scenery can be described as **rock operas**. In some cases, the intent is a concert presentation rather than a staged presentation—but still with the elements of specific characters, represented by soloists or a chorus and a developing story line. In those cases, we will still use the term "rock opera," acknowledging that this application of the term is somewhat loose.

In 1967, the relatively conservative world of Broadway was stunned by a rock musical called *Hair*. With music by Galt MacDermot, *Hair* was a celebration of the new Aquarian Age and the revolutionary freedom of the psychedelic, hippie generation. The popularity of *Hair* (it ran on Broadway for 1,729 performances) was admittedly enhanced to some degree by the notoriety it gained as a result of a nude scene enacted on stage. The rock music of *Hair* was in a soft rock style but was certainly revolutionary enough for Broadway. A song from the show, "Aquarius/Let the Sunshine In," became a number 1 hit in 1969 when it was covered by the Fifth Dimension.

Although opera is generally considered a classical form, there is nothing in its definition that dictates a particular musical style. In the simplest terms, an *opera* is just a play in which most or all of the dialogue is sung instead

of spoken. Early in the twentieth century, ragtime pianist-composer Scott Joplin had composed several operas using ragtime as the predominant musical style (e.g., *Treemonisha*). In 1935, George Gershwin used jazz as the basis for his opera *Porgy and Bess*. It seemed only a matter of time before someone used rock as the musical basis of an opera.

11.3.1: The Who

In the late 1950s, Pete Townshend and classically trained John Entwistle got together with guitarist-singer Roger Daltrey, calling themselves the Detours at first and then the Who. Soon they replaced their original drummer with Keith Moon, a former member of a British surf music group. They adopted a "mod" image, a new name (the High Numbers), and identified with the same blues-based milieu that produced the Rolling Stones and the Yardbirds. After their first release flopped, they returned to the earlier name, the Who, and cultivated their mod image with flashy new clothes.

Musical Career of The Who

The Who was one of the first rock bands to explore the theatrical possibilities of rock music. The following section outlines their rise to prominence.

Popularity in England—The Who gained major popularity in England during 1965 and 1966, placing four singles in the British Top 10. One of these, "My Generation," used a stuttering vocal in the opening phrase of the song to enunciate a rebellious teenage theme.

Their antiestablishment image was enhanced quite by accident when, at a 1965 performance, Townshend inadvertently broke the neck of his guitar on a low ceiling, and then he lost his temper and smashed it to pieces. Keith Moon followed suit by busting up his drum set. Noting the frenzied crowd reaction, they decided to keep the instrument-smashing routine as the climax of their act.

Debut Album—The Who's debut album, *The Who Sing My Generation* (1966), contained the title hit plus several rather derivative works, including James Brown's "Please, Please, Please" and a Beatle-like follow-up to "My Generation" called "The Kids Are Alright." There was also a very strong instrumental called "The Ox," which featured excellent rock drums, piano, and guitar (including an early experiment with feedback). To fill up space on their second album, *Happy Jack* (1967), Townshend composed a long song with a story line and characters. He called the resulting "A Quick One While He's Away" a "mini-opera."

American Breakthrough—Although the Who had been popular in England since 1965, they had failed to make the first British invasion of America. Their American breakthrough came in June 1967 at the Monterey Pop Festival. Their next release following that performance, the psychedelic "I Can See for Miles," made the

Top 10 in the United States. *The Who Sell Out* (1968), a concept album released shortly after their success in Monterey, ended with another mini-opera called "Rael."

British Mainstream—By 1969, the Who had established themselves as an important British mainstream rock band, but rather undistinguished from all the others, except for their flamboyant stage act. However, that was about to change—in 1969, the Who released *Tommy,* a 90-minute rock opera. It was composed primarily by Townshend, with some material by Moon and Entwistle. Destined to become one of the most acclaimed rock albums since *Sgt. Pepper*, *Tommy* rose to number 4, initiating a series of nine Top 10 albums for the band between 1969 and 1982.

Pete Townshend of the Who leaps while playing the guitar, c. 1969.
SOURCE: David Hickes/Alamy Stock Photo

"Tommy"—*Tommy* presents the story of a "deaf, dumb, and blind kid" who triumphs by virtue of his incredible ability as a pinball "wizard." Brock Helander (1982, 625) calls the plot "a bizarre and elaborate tale of lost innocence, redemption, and contrition." Writer Dave Marsh calls it "skimpy, muddled, silly" (Miller 1980, 290). The music is certainly more restrained and sophisticated than the Who's previous music, certainly bearing no resemblance to classical music. Musically, *Tommy* does not go beyond earlier adventures by groups such as the Byrds, the Beach Boys, Hendrix, and the Beatles. Nevertheless, the concept itself—a 90-minute theatrical presentation that develops a story line (however vaguely) through the use of characters, based on a rock musical style—was innovative. *Tommy* captured the imagination of critics and fans alike. It was performed in its entirety in London and New York (at the Metropolitan Opera House, no less). There was a symphonic version, a stage production, a ballet performance, a brass band version, and, eventually, a film version and a Broadway musical; *Tommy* is the Who's most well-known work.

Lifehouse Project—Eager to follow up on *Tommy*, Townshend began a new project called "Lifehouse," based on a science fiction theme. Although Lifehouse was abandoned, several songs for the project were included on the album *Who's Next* (1971). Possibly the Who's strongest non-rock opera album, this recording contains consistently excellent mainstream rock singing and playing, including well-integrated electronic sounds (the latter resulting from Townshend's new fascination with the **synthesizer** and **step sequencer**).

"Quadrophenia"—In 1973, *Quadrophenia* was released as Townshend's second full-length rock opera. "Schizophrenia" refers to a double personality, while "quadrophenia" refers to a four-way split. Apparently, the reference was to the four very different personalities within the Who, and the four musical themes of *Quadrophenia's* four album "sides" seem to reflect this disparate foursome. The plot, if one can call it that, is even more obscure than *Tommy'*, but the music is more mature. *Quadrophenia* reached number 2 on the album chart in 1973.

Solo Projects and Reunions—Severe problems and misfortune overtook the band by the end of the decade. In 1978, years of alcoholism and drug abuse caught up with Keith Moon; he died of an overdose on September 7, 1978. At a performance at Cincinnati's Riverfront Stadium on December 3, 1979, eleven people were killed in the crush of fans outside of the stadium. Townshend managed to keep the Who together, although each remaining member pursued individual projects. Despite these external efforts, The Who's *Face Dances* (1981) hit the Top 5, and *It's Hard* (1982) made the Top 10. After disbanding and reuniting several times during the 1980s and 1990s, the Who considered returning to the studio to create a new album. Entwistle's death in 2002 delayed the project, but Townshend and Daltrey released *Endless Wire* in 2006, which climbed to number 7. In 2009, The Who initiated a six-month tour of *Quadrophenia*, and, in 2010, the band played, surprisingly unimpressively, as featured artists for the Super Bowl halftime show.

JOURNAL

An Assessment of Rock Opera

Though opera came into existence in the late sixteenth century, the idea of a rock opera, building on but extending significantly the concept album, did not emerge fully formed until The Who's *Tommy* (1969). Townshend's initial foray into this realm began as a frantic effort to fill up 10 minutes of space on *Happy Jack*. Listen to the resulting "mini-opera" entitled "A Quick One While He's Away." In a paragraph, provide your evaluation of the dramatic and theatrical elements of this track. Does the narrative hold together in a sensible way? Is the story clearly communicated? Do you think that the music assists in moving the narrative forward effectively and/or clarifying the message? What is your overall assessment of this early attempt at an "operatic" presentation of rock? Be specific as you communicate both positive and negative aspects of your evaluation.

 The response entered here will appear in the performance dashboard and can be viewed by your instructor.

Submit

11.3.2: Other Rock Operas and Musicals

Another major rock opera of the early 1970s was *Jesus Christ Superstar*. With lyrics by Tim Rice and music by Andrew Lloyd Webber, *Superstar* opened in New York in October 1971 and ran for 720 performances. Centering on the last week of Jesus' life, the plot was familiar and the music was strong. The "Overture" presented many of the opera's themes; the individual songs varied from the lovely ballad "I Don't Know How to Love Him" (a Top 10 hit for Yvonne Elliman [Mary Magdalene]) to the mainstream rock song "Superstar" (a Top 20 hit for Murray Head [Judas]). In between were powerful songs, like "Gethsemane (I Only Want to Say)," and humorous songs, like "King Herod's Song." Virtually all of the dialogue was sung, often to very effective music. A revival "arena tour" of *Superstar* was released on DVD in 2012 and live performances were planned for 2014, but the tour was abruptly canceled less than two weeks before it was set to begin, without explanation.

Other rock musicals and rock operas include *Godspell* (1971), *Joseph and the Amazing Technicolor Dreamcoat* (1971), *The Wiz* (1975), *Rocky Horror Picture Show* (1975), *Evita* (1978), and *Grease* (1972). The primary distinction between rock operas and rock musicals is that the former are set to music from beginning to end, while the latter includes spoken dialogue between songs. *Grease,* when it closed in April 1980, was the longest-running Broadway show to that time, with a total of 3,388 performances ... a record that has since been surpassed over a dozen times. During the 1990s and early 2000s, there was a resurgence of interest in rock musicals, including *Rent* (1996), *Hedwig and the*

Angry Inch (1998), *Mamma Mia!* (2001; based on music by Abba), and *Spring Awakening* (2006). The appearance of *Rock of Ages* (2009), a collection of classic rock tunes by artists, including Journey, Styx, Pat Benatar, Bon Jovi, Poison, and Twisted Sister, seemed to prepare the way for a series of shows based on the music of rock artists: *American Idiot* (2010; based on the album by Green Day), *A Night with Janis!* (2013; the life and music of Janis Joplin), *Motown* (2013; based on Berry Gordy's musical journey with the music of numerous Motown artists), *Beautiful: The Carole King Musical* (2014), and *Springsteen on Broadway* (2017, intimate musical performances by The Boss himself who also read excerpts from his autobiography).

Broadway also provided an outlet for the artistry of numerous successful artists and an opportunity to apply their craft beyond the world of hit singles. Elton John composed original songs in collaboration with lyricist Tim Rice for *The Lion King* (1997) and *Billy Elliot: The Musical* (2008). U2's Bono and the Edge composed the music for *Spider-Man: Turn Off the Dark* (2011), and Cyndi Lauper composed music for *Kinky Boots* (2013). In 2015, hip-hop lit up Broadway with the smash hit *Hamilton*, based on the life of one of the Founding Fathers of the United States of America.

11.3.3: Rick Wakeman and Yes

Yes was formed in 1968 by vocalist Jon Anderson and bassist Chris Squire. When keyboardist Rick Wakeman joined in 1971, he introduced multiple keyboards (acoustic piano, electric piano, organ, Mellotron, clavinet, harpsichord, and synthesizer) to the band's sound. Yes had already become known for its long, complex instrumental cuts, and, with Wakeman's influence, the band's reputation for progressive rock grew even stronger. The next album, *Fragile* (number 4, 1972), yielded the group's only Top 20 hit of the 1970s, "Roundabout."

Anderson's clear, high voice, Wakeman's exemplary keyboard work, and solid musicianship by Squire, guitarist Steve Howe, and drummer Alan White made Yes one of the most technically impressive and musically appealing rock bands of the 1970s. Four of the five members of Yes had at least some classical training (all except Anderson). *Close to the Edge* (number 3, 1973) contained only three songs, one of which consumed half of the album. The live triple album, *Yessongs* (1973), was elaborately packaged and adorned with otherworldly cover art by Roger Dean. For *Tales from Topographic Oceans* (number 6, 1974), Anderson and Howe based their lyrics on the shastric scriptures by guru Paramhansa Yogananda. This rather experimental album continued Yes's consistent ability to sell albums, but shortly after the release of the album, Wakeman left the group to pursue solo projects.

Rick Wakeman at the keyboard.

Wakeman's Solo Projects

Rick Wakeman is a highly trained keyboard player who was also a pioneer in exploring the use of synthesizers. After his time with the art rock group Yes, he released some very impressive solo recordings, some of which incorporated a full symphony orchestra and choir.

The Six Wives of Henry VIII—In 1972 to 1973, using various backup musicians, Wakeman produced an album called *The Six Wives of Henry VIII*, which featured his multi-keyboard work. The nine keyboards—two Mellotrons, two Minimoog synthesizers, organ, acoustic piano, electric piano harpsichord, acoustic harpsichord, and ARP synthesizer—were further modified with other electronic devices (e.g., fuzz, wah-wah pedals, and echo units).

Journey to the Centre of the Earth—Wakeman's most ambitious work came with *Journey to the Centre of the Earth* (number 3, 1974). Performed live at London's Royal Festival Hall, the production included the London Symphony Orchestra, the English Chamber Choir, a narrator, and, of course, a rock band. Based on the Jules Verne classic, the text is shared by a narrator, a chorus, and two vocalists. A symphonic introduction opens the first part, called "The Journey." The bulk of the work consists of soft rock songs and instrumentals with interspersed narration, which continues until the final song, "The Forest." A brief segment of classical Norwegian composer Edvard Grieg's familiar "In the Hall of the Mountain King" is interjected before the work comes to a Hollywood-style closing.

The Myths and Legends of King Arthur and the Knights of the Round Table—In 1975, Wakeman followed *Journey to the Centre of the Earth* with another similarly epic musical narrative, *The Myths and Legends of King Arthur and the Knights of the Round Table* (which premiered as a pageant on ice). *King Arthur* is generally less prone to slip into naive clichés and involves moments of more authentic rock style. "Sir Lancelot and the Black Knight" is an interesting combination of shouting vocal, rock, chorus, synthesizer, and orchestra; it may be the best achievement in either of Wakeman's two major works, although "Merlin the Magician" is also a fascinating blend of many diverse elements. Overall, *King Arthur* is a significant advance in the integration of musical styles and media, compared to *Journey*. *Journey* and *King Arthur* are not operas, but they are a type of musical theater, telling stories and involving characters through a variety of performance forces. In the classical tradition, narrative stories could be staged (opera) or presented as concert performances (oratorio). This is true of rock operas and rock musicals as well. Wakeman's performances were of the unstaged, concert performance type.

Wakeman and Anderson both left Yes by 1980, although Anderson returned for the 1983 album *90125*. Yes's biggest hit, "Owner of a Lonely Heart" (number 1), came in 1984. Members of the band, in various permutations and reunions, continued to tour and record into the new millennium. Replacing vocalist Jon Anderson with Benoit David, recruited from a Yes tribute band named Close to the Edge, the band—Steve Howe (guitar), Chris Squire (bass), Alan White (drums), and Geoff Downs (keyboards)—released *Fly from Here* (number 36 in 2011).

11.3.4: Genesis

Genesis began in 1967 as a songwriter's collective of four students at England's Charterhouse School. By 1971, the band had grown to a quintet that included singer Peter Gabriel and drummer Phil Collins. Building a reputation as a progressive rock band in England, the band used the Mellotron and other electronic keyboards as well as multimedia visuals and highly theatrical elements in live performance.

In 1974, they released the double album *The Lamb Lies Down on Broadway*, a surrealistic description of the adventures of Rael as he confronts the modern civilization of New York City. The story unfolds in a series of songs, all performed by the band alone (no orchestra, chorus, or narrator), in a sophisticated rock style that involves heavy use of electronics. However, the concept is theatrical; it develops a story with characters and commentary. On tours, they performed the album live, with Gabriel portraying Rael.

Peter Gabriel left the band in mid-1975, and Phil Collins assumed the role of lead singer. Eventually reduced to a trio, the group achieved its greatest commercial success in the 1980s with 4 Top 10 albums and 11 Top 40 hits (5 in the Top 5). Both Gabriel and Collins went on to have highly successful solo careers. While Gabriel had separated from Genesis, Collins continued to balance his career between the group and his solo efforts until 1995. While Gabriel has earned more critical acclaim for his work, has pursued numerous world music projects, and has even participated in musical experimentation with animals to gain a greater understanding of their cognitive capabilities, the commercial success of Collins's solo work is undeniable. In comparison to Gabriel's five Top 40 hits, Collins earned 21, including seven number 1 songs (including "Against All Odds (Take a Look at Me Now)," "Sussudio," and "Groovy Kind of Love"). He also won an Oscar in 1999 for "You'll Be in My Heart," a song he wrote for Disney's animated film *Tarzan*. Gabriel has charted three Top 40 albums in the new millennium: *Up* (number 9 in 2002), *Scratch My Back* (number 26 in 2010, covers of songs by other artists, including David Bowie, Paul Simon, Neil Young, Radiohead, Bon Iver, and Regina Spektor), and *New Blood* (number 30 in 2011, orchestral recordings of selected past work), though no singles cracked the Hot 100. Collins himself charted two new Top 40 albums during this same period: *Testify* (number 30 in 2002) and *Going Back* (number 34 in 2010, a collection of Motown covers using three surviving Funk Brothers as instrumental support). Interestingly, in 2012, the year after Collins began suggesting that he might retire from music for health reasons (not hearing well in his left ear and a dislocated vertebra made drumming difficult), his album *Hits* (1998) re-entered the charts at number 6.

11.3.5: On the Classical Side

The confluence of rock and classical music need not always come from the rock side of the spectrum. Several composers with classical backgrounds have incorporated rock styles into major productions. Perhaps the most publicized of these works was *Mass* by Leonard Bernstein. Commissioned to write a work for the dedication of the John F. Kennedy Center for the Performing Arts in Washington, D.C., Bernstein created a theater piece loosely based on the Roman Catholic mass. In addition to orchestra and chorus, there is a boys' choir, a pipe organ, a rock organ, and rock and jazz ensembles. Interspersed throughout *Mass* are several songs in various rock styles. Other examples of classical composers exploring the world of rock, or vice versa, include Lalo Schifrin's *Rock Requiem*, the Electric Prunes' *Mass in F Minor*, and the surrealistic opera *Elephant Steps* with music by Stanley Silverman and text by Richard Foreman.

11.4: Nontheatrical Art Rock by Unaccompanied Rock Groups

OBJECTIVE: Identify some of the most important art rock groups

In the opening section of this chapter, six typical approaches to the confluence of rock and classical music were introduced. The sixth and most innovative approach is to create an extended work modeled on a classical form, using the musical language of rock. Rock operas and **musical theater** fall into this category; the distinction between an opera and a musical is that the former is set to music from beginning to end, while the latter includes spoken dialogue to advance the narrative. The difference between an opera and a rock opera (or between a musical and a rock musical) is simply the style of music utilized. Examples of rock operas include *Jesus Christ Superstar* and *Tommy*, while *Hair*, *Grease*, and *Rent* would be appropriately labeled rock musicals.

There is a subcategory of this sixth approach to combining rock and classical music that we have not discussed: the unaccompanied rock group creating an extended work related to a classical model, but not an overtly theatrical work. "Symphony for the Devil/Sympathy for the Devil," by Blood, Sweat &Tears falls into this category. Creating a work of this type is probably the most demanding assignment in the area of art rock. Accordingly, in considering such works, we will meet several of the most technically virtuosic groups in the history of rock.

11.4.1: Emerson, Lake & Palmer

More than anyone else, Keith Emerson has persistently and successfully pursued the concept of art rock. An incredibly talented keyboardist, Emerson (born in 1944) first became known with a group called The Nice. Originally a quartet, it soon evolved into a trio, featuring Emerson's multiple keyboards, contrasting with the more common rock instrumentation, including lead guitar. The Nice's second album, *Ars Longa, Vita Brevis* (1969), featured an extended work in four

movements and suggested future directions for The Nice and Emerson. On their 1969 album *Five Bridges Suite*, the five-movement title work is an excellent example of Emerson's versatility and technique as he moves fluently from rock to jazz to a Bach-like classical style. Accompanied by the Sinfonia of the London Orchestra, it is a good example of art rock, since it combines multiple approaches to combining rock and classical music (i.e., approaches 1, 4, 5, and 6 described early in this chapter). The recording contains a rock ensemble-with-orchestra adaptation of Jean Sibelius's "Intermezzo," from the *Karelia Suite*, as well as rock interpretations of the third movement of Tchaikovsky's Sixth Symphony and a unique combination of Dylan's "Country Pie" and fragments from Bach's Brandenburg Concerto No. 6. The last Nice album with Emerson, *Elegy* (1971), contained an extended rock version of Bernstein's "America" from *West Side Story*. For a dazzling display of Emerson's improvisations with The Nice, listen to "She Belongs to Me" (a Dylan song) as performed at the Fillmore East (*Live at the Fillmore East December 1969*).

Emerson, Lake & Palmer, 1973.
SOURCE: Pictorial Press Ltd/Alamy Stock Photo

At a performance at the Fillmore West, Emerson met guitarist-vocalist Greg Lake, who was there performing with his group King Crimson. The next year, Emerson and Lake recruited drummer Carl Palmer, creating Emerson, Lake & Palmer (ELP).

Musical Career of ELP

Among the very talented art rock groups, ELP is considered one of the very best, expanding the horizons of rock music through long-form compositions and demonstrating impeccable musicianship. This section will explore some of their most significant works.

Emerson, Lake & Palmer—ELP debuted in August 1970 at the Isle of Wight Festival; shortly after this performance, the band released its first two albums: *Emerson, Lake & Palmer* (number 18

in 1971) and *Tarkus* (number 9 in 1971). The band's debut album contained the single "Lucky Man" (number 48). "The Three Fates" from the first album is in three parts, the first being a solo on pipe organ, the second a piano solo, and the third a work for the entire trio. As with much of their work, it is almost impossible to classify stylistically, owing to the effective blend of classical, jazz, and rock elements. That, of course, is the ultimate goal of a blended style—to be so perfectly fused that the contributing elements are barely distinguishable. The remarkable keyboard work of Emerson, the clean drumming of Palmer, and the coordination between all three represented a new level of sophistication in rock music. Listen carefully to "The Barbarian" or "Take a Pebble" from that first album to hear how tightly coordinated the trio was.

Tarkus—*Tarkus* begins with a seven-part series of songs (the title track); especially interesting is "Eruption" (the first part of the suite). Further into the album is "Bitches Crystal," which is impressive for its variety of combined styles and technical virtuosity. "Are You Ready Eddy?" is an ELP-ized version of Jerry Lee Lewis–style 1950s rock.

Pictures at an Exhibition—ELP's third album, *Pictures at an Exhibition* (number 10 in 1972), was a landmark art rock album. Based on a work by Russian composer Modest Mussorgsky (another example of approach 4), the suite represents the composer's impressions as he strolls through an art exhibition. The "Promenade" theme recurs as he moves from painting to painting; the other segments of the work reflect the paintings he sees. ELP's album adapts a significant amount of the original work, including "Promenade," "The Gnome," "The Old Castle," "The Hut of Baba Yaga," and "The Great Gate of Kiev." There are also some added movements by ELP: "The Sage," "The Curse of Baba Yaga," and "Blues Variation." For the most part, Mussorgsky's themes, rhythms, harmonies, textures, and internal forms are preserved in the ELP version.

Triology—The next album, *Trilogy* (1972), rose to the number 5 position and features some landmark performances and compositions. In the midst of "The Endless Enigma" (parts 1 and 2) lies a most impressive fugue, fully developed in classical form and performed impressively by Emerson (assisted by Lake). There is another electronic rock adaptation of a classical work: the "Hoedown" from *Rodeo*, by twentieth-century American composer Aaron Copland. Two impressive art rock compositions on this album are "Trilogy" and "Abaddon's Bolero." In addition, this album contained ELP's only Top 40 single, "From the Beginning" (number 39).

Brain Salad Surgery—It is with *Brain Salad Surgery* (number 11 in 1973) that ELP really put it all together. As with the Beatles on *Sgt. Pepper*, ELP draws together all of its earlier ideas into one consummate album. There is the rock adaptation of a classical work, the challenging fourth movement of Argentine contemporary composer Alberto Ginastera's First Piano Concerto; there is the cute piece, "Benny the Bouncer"; there is the normal (for ELP) song "Still … You Turn Me On"; there is the spiritualistic "Jerusalem"; but the masterpiece of *Brain Salad Surgery* is *Karn Evil 9*, one of the most impressive achievements in the history of rock. This work will be discussed in more detail in the Musical Close-Up later in this chapter. Suffice it to say here that this three-movement work fulfills completely the goals of the sixth approach described near the beginning of this chapter: an extended work for a rock group, using a classical model but in the musical language of rock.

The American Tour—Touring America in 1974, ELP amazingly managed to recreate *Karn Evil 9* in live performances. They hauled 36 tons of equipment with them, including six Moog synthesizers, two organs, an electric piano, and a Steinway grand piano for Emerson. With Palmer's drum set, synthesizer, timpani, gongs, chimes, and so on, moving the band around for four months was quite a project.

Works, Volume 1—Following the 1975 American tour, the trio began developing individual interests, resulting in the double album *Works, Volume 1* (number 12 in 1977). *Works* contains Emerson's Piano Concerto no. 1, a three-movement work modeled on the classical piano concerto but using Emerson's highly personalized blend of classical, jazz, and rock idioms. The next five tracks belong to Greg Lake, whose songs are accompanied by orchestra and chorus. Carl Palmer is then featured on tracks that include references to classical works by Prokofiev and Bach, plus a remake of "Tank." The album ends with the trio's extended version of Copland's famous "Fanfare to the Common Man" and the original extended piece "Pirates."

Fall of ELP—*Works, Volume 1* was quickly followed by *Works, Volume 2* (number 37 in 1977). However, these successful albums were followed by the comparatively unimpressive *Love Beach* (number 55). ELP soon disbanded. Emerson and Lake began discussing a reunion in 1985, but Palmer was unavailable due to his contractual obligations with his current band, Asia, which had released two highly successful albums in the early 1980s: *Asia* (number 1 in 1982) and *Alpha* (number 6 in 1983), resulting in four Top 40 hits, including "Heat of the Moment" (number 4 in 1982). Cozy Powell stepped into the drumming role for *Emerson, Lake & Powell* (number 23 in 1986). As a result of the serendipity of finding a drummer with the same last initial, this iteration of the band is often referred to as "ELP2." The original ELP lineup reappeared in the mid-1990s, releasing a strong album in 1992, *Black Moon*, followed by a series of live albums in the 2000s.

11.4.2: Frank Zappa

You may have noticed that every band discussed thus far in this chapter has been British. Indeed, as stated earlier, art rock was primarily a British development. However, it was left to an American artist to provide what many feel is both the best (and the worst) in art rock. If that sounds contradictory, wait until you meet the leader of this band. He is a study in inconsistency and self-contradiction. The adjectives that describe Frank Zappa include creative, enigmatic, erratic, puerile, pseudointellectual, unique, sophomoric, genius, and (above all) iconoclastic. That last word, to paraphrase Dictionary.com, refers to attacking cherished beliefs, traditional institutions, etc., as being based on error or superstition (Dictionary.com 2018). Zappa goes well beyond that definition; he attacks or ridicules everything: political and religious groups, women, men, and even himself.

Life and Musical Career of Frank Zappa

Frank Zappa is one of the most unique artists in the history of rock and roll. If the Beatles and the Beach Boys pushed the boundaries of rock music, Zappa, quite simply, set dynamite to the entire venture. His musical influences included some of the most innovative art music composers of the twentieth century—influences that can be heard clearly in a significant portion of his work.

Early Life—Frank Zappa was born in Baltimore on December 21, 1940, and later settled in Lancaster, Pennsylvania. He studied music during his brief college career and played with various local bands. Zappa's early musical enthusiasms were for R&B and contemporary classical music, especially the work of twentieth-century composers Igor Stravinsky and Edgard Varèse, the latter of whom was an early experimenter in rhythmic complexity, the use of unpitched percussion, *atonality* (music not in a traditional key), and electronic music. Generally considered a pioneer who was slightly ahead of his time, Varèse became Zappa's musical idol.

Frank Zappa with the Mothers of Invention, c. 1967.

SOURCE: Pictorial Press Ltd/Alamy Stock Photo

Zappa moved to Los Angeles in 1964, where he joined with Ray Collins (vocals), Jim Black (drums), and Roy Estrada (bass) in a band called the Soul Giants. Zappa increasingly stepped into the role of leader and changed the group's name to the Mothers of Invention. Becoming an underground favorite in Los Angeles in 1965, their "freaky" music, looks, and behavior gained them considerable notoriety.

Freak Out!—They released their first album, *Freak Out!*, in mid-1966 on MGM/Verve Records. It was a double album and is often mentioned as the first real concept album, coming a full year before *Sgt. Pepper*. However, the concept is rather elusive, unless it is, as David Walley says, "a living testament to L.A. freakdom" (1972, 60).

Some mid-1960s listeners to *Freak Out!* must have assumed that the Mothers had to be stoned or otherwise inebriated to cre-

ate such weird music. However, Zappa was vehemently opposed to drug abuse and was himself a teetotaler. He recommended a spiritual high and advised his fans against fooling themselves with chemical and/or agricultural short-cuts.

The *Freak Out!* album was made by five Mothers: Zappa, Collins, Black, Estrada, and guitarist Elliot Ingber. After that, the personnel of the Mothers was constantly changing, but the force of Zappa's personality provided the consistency that was needed.

Uncle Meat—Of Zappa's numerous creative albums released during the late 1960s and early 1970s, two deserve special comment: *Uncle Meat* and *Fillmore East, June 1971*. *Uncle Meat* (number 43 in 1969) began as music for a movie that was never finished. By the late 1960s, the Mothers had expanded to 10 members who could play any combination of over two dozen instruments. In some ways, *Uncle Meat* brings together all of the elements of Zappa's prior work in the way that *Sgt. Pepper* did for the Beatles and *Brain Salad Surgery* did for Emerson, Lake & Palmer. Electronic effects are expanded, and there is spoken monologue, 1950s rock parody, contemporary classical music, jazz **licks**, and improvisation. Like most Zappa albums, *Uncle Meat* is meticulously assembled. Producer Tom Wilson called Zappa "a painstaking craftsman, and in some ways it's a pity that the art of recording is not developed to the extent where you can really hear completely all the things he's doing" (Walley 1972, 64). Referring to the care with which the multiple layers are assembled and with which the seemingly kaleidoscopic chaos is created, Zappa said, "These things are so carefully constructed that it breaks my heart when people don't dig into them and see all the levels that I put into them" (Walley 1972, 80). Among the better cuts on *Uncle Meat* are "Dog Breath, in the Year of the Plague" and "Dog Breath Variations," "The Uncle Meat Variations," "Prelude to King Kong," "Project X," and all the "King Kong" segments. Parts of *Uncle Meat* use up to 40 overdubbed tracks; electronic manipulations are used to modify normal sounds (e.g., on "Dog Breath," clarinets are sped up to sound like trumpets). Like much of Zappa's work, *Uncle Meat* (most of which was recorded in late 1967 and early 1968) is years, if not decades, ahead of its time. As has been stated earlier, however, many of these same ideas were being integrated into the classical art music of the mid-twentieth century.

Fillmore East—The live album, *Fillmore East, June 1971* (number 38), contains a mini-opera about an aspiring rock group whose first hit was moving up the charts. The story line deals with their experiences with some groupies and ends with a more or less authentic presentation of the imaginary band's hit single, "Happy Together" (actually, a number 1 hit for the Turtles in 1967).

Zappa's Image—A trend toward pubescent humor increasingly detracted from Zappa's artistic stature through the 1970s. Brock Helander (1982, 655) notes Zappa's "penchant for puerile themes" and his "tendency toward cheap vulgarity." Ken Tucker accurately observes that

> Zappa spent the decade of the 1970s consolidating his reputation as an ornery oddball whose talents were, depending on your point of view, either squandered or used to decidedly avant-garde ends. Much of the goodwill Zappa had accumulated with the public and critics in the 1960s for his hard-edged, adventurous music dissipated in the 1970s

as Zappa began to emphasize sophomoric humor. (Ward, Stokes, and Tucker 1986, 619)

Tucker further concluded that "Zappa's work came to seem schizophrenic" (Ward, Stokes, and Tucker 1986, 619).

Later Career—Surveying Zappa's post-1970 work, one is tempted to paraphrase an old nursery rhyme: "When he was good, he was very very good / And when he was bad, he was horrid." By 1976, Zappa had stopped referring to the ever-changing lineup of his backup musicians as the Mothers of Invention and simply recorded under his own name. For all practical purposes, Zappa's effective leadership within the music scene declined severely.

Writer Ken Tucker comments that "the title [of Zappa's 1982 album—*Shut Up 'n' Play Yer Guitar*] suggested what many of his once-and-future fans felt" (Ward, Stokes, and Tucker 1986, 619).

After releasing more than 80 albums, Frank Zappa died in 1993, a victim of cancer. During the final decade of his life, Zappa became an activist on the topics of individual liberty and censorship; a proposal that recordings should be "rated" (and labeled) based on their content served as his call to arms. He fought hard against this proposal by the Parents Music Resource Centre, an organization formed by four senators' wives and including Tipper Gore (Al Gore's wife), testifying before a Senate committee, along with John Denver and Dee Snider (Twisted Sister).

ANALYSIS OF FREAK OUT! *Freak Out!* is an amazingly creative album, especially for the mid-60s. While we have discussed elsewhere in the book the impressive innovations of the Beach Boys and the Beatles during this same pre-*Sgt. Pepper* period, the level of musical innovation represented in Zappa's work increases by an order of magnitude. Many diehard Zappa fans believe that the Mothers' debut album remains Zappa's finest. The first 11 tracks are relatively normal songs, although all are touched by Zappa's musical eccentricity and verbal iconoclasm. "Who Are the Brain Police" is miles away from anything being done in pop music at that time. Several parodies of 1950s soft rock ("Go Cry on Somebody Else's Shoulder" and "Wowie Zowie") reveal Zappa's perfect understanding of that style and his ability to recreate it with tongue-in-cheek humor. "Motherly Love" suggests Zappa's off-color side, which would increasingly manifest itself on subsequent albums.

Three Extended Pieces of the Album "Freak Out"

The last few tracks—three extended pieces—live up to the album's title.

"Trouble Every Day"—The first of the extended pieces ("Trouble Every Day") provides a serious commentary on the racial riots in Watts. At about the most basic that you will ever hear Zappa musically, this song exemplifies a blues-based feel and very simple three-chord structure. There are elements of the song (the use of harmonica and "talking blues" vocal) that is reminiscent of Bob Dylan, not a comparison one makes often regarding Zappa's music.

"Help I'm Rock"—"Help, I'm a Rock" provides an ideal first glimpse into Zappa's approach to art rock. Many contemporary classical composers have concentrated on timbre and improvisation as generative elements in their compositions rather than the more commonly used elements of melody and harmony. They have avoided what they might have considered antiquated concerns with keys, melodies, traditional chords, and metrically organized rhythms. Much of "Help, I'm a Rock" sounds disorganized and even chaotic—like a real freak-out. However, the work is actually structured intentionally in a manner that sounds unstructured. Unless the listener has heard a good bit of avant-garde classical music, "Help, I'm a Rock" sounds like a work by a group of deranged performers.

The song begins normally enough with guitar and drums vamping in triple meter. The first section includes nonsense language and various groans, squawks, and other vocal sounds, followed by a mini-explosion (at 2:02). The vamp returns, and the voices superimpose the repeating words "help, I'm a rock" and "help, I'm a cop," interrupted by Zappa's seemingly improvised monologue. More nonsense vocals, sheep-like bleating, and another monologue follow. The triple-meter vamp is interrupted by a second major section (at 4:00) that features some female heavy breathing and various vocal noises that at times sound like simulated birdcalls or other animal sounds.

"It Can't Happen Here"—The third section is one of Zappa's finest works: "It Can't Happen Here." This song-within-a-song may sound quite disorganized, but—despite what many perceive as disorganized, random chaos—it really does create a tightly structured form.

Arch Form

$$\begin{array}{ccc} & C & \\ B & & B \\ A & & A \end{array}$$

This unique form combines two common classical forms: the arch form and the rondo. The first five sections create a form that proceeds to a center point and then doubles back on itself, repeating the opening sections in reverse order (hence the term **arch form**), as shown in the above figure.

Then Zappa begins alternating the A section with new material, which is the principle behind the classical **rondo** form. There are many points of interest as the Mothers work with various vocal timbres. For example, note the improvisation on the word "Minnesota" (at 0:51). As one singer repeats "mi-mi-mi-mi-mi," and so on, he alters the timbre of his voice almost as if an electronic filter were being applied. Also, listen to the female voice in the "I remember" section (D). After the third phrase, she sings "bop-bop-bop" on widely scattered pitches (at 3:03); gradually, these are shortened to become mere clicks (listen carefully because this happens quickly).

Listening Guide: "It Can't Happen Here" (the Mothers of Invention)

0:00–0:32	Section A	Nonmetric, nontonal expansion of this lyric.
0:33–1:08	Section B	First part improvises vocally on the word "Kansas"; second part improvises vocally on the word "Minnesota."
1:09–1:53	Section C	Instrumental break. Piano and drums in a fragmented, nontonal, **pointillistic** style.
1:54–(2:15?)	Section B	Vocal improvisation on the city name "Washington, D.C." Section A quietly enters under the "AC/DC" improvisation. Gradually, section A takes over.
(2:16?)–2:47	Section A	Line begun in previous section gradually dominates.
2:48–3:04	Section D	Metric (duple meter); three phrases.
3:05–3:18	Section A	Slight variation on section A.
3:19–3:47	Section E	Suzy Creamcheese section (dialogue referencing a semifictional Zappa character).
3:48–3:55	Section A	Brief return of "It can't happen here" with echo and filtered voices.

"Help, I'm a Rock" provides considerable insight into Zappa's approach to art rock. Unlike Jon Lord, Rick Wakeman, and so many others, Zappa emulated the most up-to-date experiments in classical music. His interest in nonmetrical, atonal music aligned with the interests of many art music composers; his use of vocal improvisation and his concentration on timbre and texture, often without traditional melody and harmony, was thoroughly contemporary. As we mentioned earlier, when many rock musicians and listeners think of classical music, they think of Bach, Mozart, Beethoven, and Tchaikovsky, but those composers lived and worked in the eighteenth and nineteenth centuries. For art rock to be a truly contemporary creation, one must blend contemporary rock with contemporary classical sounds. Zappa's understanding of the compositional styles of Igor Stravinsky, Edgar Varèse, Karlheinz Stockhausen, and John Cage allowed him to approach this challenge more authentically than most others.

JOURNAL

The Benefit of Repeated Listening

Upon initial listening, music that falls outside one's "comfort zone" seems inaccessible or even weird and chaotic. The purpose of this assignment is to provide you with an exercise that can be applied to any such music by the listener interested in expanding her musical horizons. Listen one time to Frank Zappa's "Help, I'm a Rock," composing a paragraph *as you listen* that documents your reaction to the sounds you hear and the organizational structure of the piece. After you complete this initial task, re-read the previous section discussing this composition; then, listen to the piece again, carefully following the listening guide. Listen to the complete composition *at least* two more times, either with or without the listening guide. After having listened to the piece four times (or more), compose a second paragraph documenting your more informed reactions. Compare the two paragraphs you have composed. What differences, if any, emerge as a result of this repeated listening exercise?

 The response entered here will appear in the performance dashboard and can be viewed by your instructor.

Submit

11.5: Musical Close-Up on Karn Evil 9 by Emerson, Lake & Palmer

OBJECTIVE: Analyze Emerson, Lake & Palmer's artistic approach to *Karn Evil 9*

During the mid-1970s, *Karn Evil 9* was played in a shortened version on many progressive FM radio stations. As a result, many listeners became familiar with a relatively brief segment of this work, but unless one listens to the entire 30-minute, three-part composition, it is easy to miss both the ideological point (the narrative) and the impressive musical value or its innovation.

11.5.1: "First Impression" Part 1

Karn Evil 9 is in three movements, called "impressions." Thus, the macro form is like that of a classical concerto with the usual three movements: fast, slow, fast. The "First Impression" is in two parts. Let us begin by looking closely at Part 1 of "First Impression."

The lyrics of Part 1 set the scene quite effectively, intentionally incorporating certain key words and phrases to describe the world into which we are thrown:

cold and misty morning	age of power
seeds have withered	silent children shivered
jackals for gold	suffering in silence
betrayed	hurt
beat	terrible
survival	no compassion
sorrow	helpless
refugee	

In fact, *cold* and *sorrow* occur twice in this section. We certainly get the feeling that whatever (or whenever) this place

Listening Guide: *Karn Evil 9*, "First Impression," Part I (Emerson, Lake & Palmer)

0:00–0:24	Introduction	Brief introduction featuring keyboard; when drums and bass enter, they are tightly coordinated with the keyboard part.
0:25–0:49	Verse 1 (Section a)	Vocal enters four phrases.
0:50–0:57	Verse 1 (Section b) (Refrain)	Two three-note descending patterns announce the short refrain.
0:58–1:36	Interlude	Instrumental elaboration on material from Introduction.
1:37–2:01	Verse 2 (a)	Vocal returns. Slight change in accompaniment (compared to verse 1).
2:02–2:08	Verse 2 (b) (Refrain)	Refrain (again preceded by two three-note descending patterns).
2:09–2:18	Interlude	Similar to earlier interlude, but interrupted by the instrumental break.
2:19–2:43	Instrumental break	New material. Notice the very tight coordination among all three instrumentalists, with each reinforcing the rhythmic patterns of the others.
2:44–2:55	Interlude	The interrupted interlude resumes.
2:56–3:16	Verse 3 (a)	Vocal returns to yet another varied accompaniment.
3:17–3:24	Verse 3 (b) (Refrain)	Lyrics added to the three-note descending patterns, which occur three times instead of the usual two.
3:25–3:41	Codetta	Closing section has new lyrics and new accompaniment.

may be, it is rather bleak and dreary. Then, our hero promises us repeatedly that he will "be there"—that he will come "to heal [our] sorrow, to beg and borrow, fight tomorrow."

Musically, part 1 of "First Impression" consists of an introduction, three verses (interrupted by an instrumental break), and a **codetta**. A **coda** ("codetta" simply constituting a smaller version, typically, of shorter duration that closes an internal section of a piece) is a closing section of a major work, comparable to an introduction at the beginning. The introduction is brief, but notice how tightly the trio is coordinated. Listen carefully to Palmer's drums; you will find that he is changing his patterns with every measure, perfectly reinforcing the accents and rhythmic patterns of Emerson's keyboard lines. Then, listen to Lake's bass line, and you will find that he is doing the same. This is analogous to what goes on in a symphony orchestra. The percussion section and the cellos and basses do not simply play continuous patterns throughout; each measure and note is carefully set into the changing fabric of the sound of the entire ensemble.

11.5.2: "First Impression" Part 2

In Part 2, ELP compares their imaginary society to a carnival sideshow. At carnival sideshows we see unusual, freakish exhibits—things we do not see as a normal part of our lives. After a typical carnival barker welcomes us to "the show," he points out a row of bishops' heads in jars and a bomb inside a car. Possibly, the bishops symbolize organized religion; apparently, this imaginary society does not include organized religion in its normal, everyday life. Perhaps the bomb represents terrorism, humanity's spectacular cruelty to itself. Next, we are shown a real specialty: some tears (could these represent human emotion?). And so it goes, as we are shown laughter (human emotion and joy), a ragtime band (music), a stripper (human sexuality and sensuality), Jesus (faith), and grass (natural phenomena), as if these things no longer exist in the real world, but are set aside as museum exhibits. The world ELP is describing is totally devoid of the characteristics—good and

ELP's "Karn Evil 9" - 1st Impression (1973)

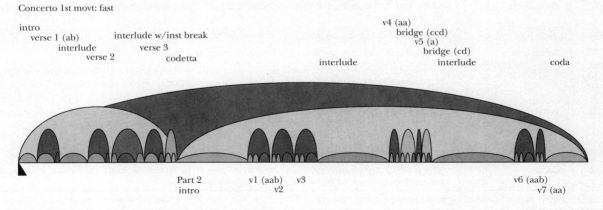

A visual representation of the sections of the "First Impression" of *Karn Evil 9* (Parts 1 and 2).

bad—that make humans human, and the carnival analogy helps to drive this message home.

11.5.3: "Second Impression"

"Second Impression" is entirely instrumental. It is largely **through-composed**—that is, it consists of a series of ever-changing musical sections carrying us forward. However, there are some repeated melodic and rhythmic motives that unite the various sections. In section A, listen for a descending two-note motive (which we will call "motive T") in the upper range of the piano.

Watch MOTIVE T

This simple, two-note motive plays an important role in providing a sense of structural organization within this long, complicated composition.

In section C, motive T becomes very important. We hear it first as ascending chords (inverted) on the piano:

Watch MOTIVE T (INVERTED)

This listening example is similar to the previous example, but notice that while the two-note sequence in the previous example descends (the second pitch is lower than the first), in this "inverted" example, the opposite occurs: the second pitch is *higher* than the first.

Throughout section C, we hear motive T, sometimes in its original form (descending) and sometimes inverted (ascending). The real clue to the meaning of section C, and indeed the entire "Second Impression," is suggested by a steady ticking sound that enters at about 4:10, as the piano plays a series of runs and more statements of motive T; the ticking assumes an association with the tick-tock of a clock. We are being transported through time (musically) to the society ELP described in "First Impression."

Listening Guide: *Karn Evil 9*, "First Impression," Part II (Emerson, Lake & Palmer)

3:42–4:51	Introduction (Part 1)	Lengthy introduction featuring synthesizer and organ; fast tempo in 7/4 meter.
4:52–5:21	Introduction (Part 2)	Based on a **pedal point** (a repeating note, usually in the bass, that continues to sound as the chords change above it).
5:22–5:54	Verse 1 (aab)	Vocal begins with "Step inside!" Two four-bar phrases (each with new lyrics) followed by a 4-bar refrain. Two-bar instrumental transition connects aa to the refrain (b). Drumroll provides transition to verse 2.
5:55–6:27	Verse 2 (aab)	First two phrases (aa) have new lyrics, followed by a transition and refrain. Transition to verse 3 is new (descending and ascending organ **glissandi**).
6:28–7:00	Verse 3 (aab)	Same internal form as first two verses, with new lyrics for aa. Followed by a transition and refrain. A series of descending drumrolls serves as a transition to next section (Interlude).
7:01–8:38	Interlude	Instrumental section featuring guitar. As this reaches its climax (at about 8:35), texture is reduced to a synthesizer pedal point similar to the one in the Introduction (to part 2), except that it is in a higher pitch range. Pedal point fades (to allow the listener to turn over the LP and listen to the second side; it was a different era!).
0:00–0:05	Interlude (continued)	Resumes pedal point from previous section (sets up accompaniment for verse 4).
0:06–0:21	Verse 4 (aa)	Abbreviated verse. First phrase ("Welcome back") accompanied by synthesizer pedal point. Organ added for second phrase. Usual transition and refrain are eliminated.
0:22–0:43	Bridge (ccd)	Similar form to the verses, but with new music and lyrics. Two 2-bar phrases (cc) followed by a new refrain (d) on "You've show."
0:44–0:51	Verse 5 (a)	Shortened to only one 4-bar phrase (a) with new lyrics.
0:52–1:06	Bridge (cd)	Bridge shortened to two phrases—first phrase of bridge and refrain.
1:07–3:02	Interlude	Instrumental interlude begins with an impressive improvisation featuring Emerson's organ virtuosity. Returns to a theme from the earlier interlude (guitar lead). Pedal point that ended the earlier interlude is replaced by a drum solo.
3:03–3:31	Verse 6 (aab)	Drum solo continues to become the accompaniment for the first phrase (a); new lyrics. Full accompaniment for second phrase (a; note old-fashioned piano sound on the words "Alexander's ragtime band"). Transition and refrain (b; "Roll up!"), as in earlier verses. Drumroll provides transition to verse 7.
3:32–3:46	Verse 7 (aa)	Abbreviated verse as in verse 4. New lyrics. Usual transition and refrain are eliminated.
3:47–4:46	Coda	Begins with a brief vocal. Short drum solo leads to a return of the fast 7/4 meter and material from the introduction (synthesizer lead). Ominous chords lead to the final cadence.

NOTE: The CD and the digital download versions of this recording both divide "First Impression," Part II, as it was presented on the original LP (due to the need to turn the record over). Therefore, the timing designations in this Listening Guide are based on the divided tracks. They begin as a continuation of "First Impression," Part I (at 3:42), and at the divide for the new track (Part II), timing is reset to 0:00.

Listening Guide: *Karn Evil 9*, "Second Impression" (Emerson, Lake & Palmer)

0:00–1:06	Section A	Features the piano. Motive T occurs several times in the upper range of the piano.
1:07–2:53	Section B	Repeating accompaniment figure (called an **ostinato**). Latin-influenced sound. At 2:29, lead shifts from synthesizer to acoustic piano; several piano flourishes end the section.
2:54–5:00	Section C	Pensive section with no rock beat. Frequent occurrences of motive T (ascending and descending). Steady clock ticks begin at 4:10.
5:01–5:43	Section D	Piano lead; expands a brief motive first heard at the beginning of section C. Glissando connects to next section.
5:44–7:07	Section E	Boogie-woogie bass (ostinato) with elaborate piano improvisation. Notice quick reference to motive T at the very end (6:58).

11.5.4: "Third Impression"

"Third Impression" thrusts us into the midst of ELP's imaginary society of the future. Our hero is there to do battle. After assuring us that he will act as our knight in shining armor, he bravely announces that no one in his "army" will yield to the enemy. But even as he speaks, we encounter the enemy (a computer) who warns our hero, in a ring-modulated vocal timbre, of impending danger and advises him to load a program (instead of a weapon) and suggests

the computer and our hero are really one and the same. Our hero is not intimidated. He says that no computer can stand in his way; only human blood can settle this ultimate battle. He calls on all the guardians of a "new clear [nuclear?] dawn" to join him as the maps of war are drawn. With that, our hero engages the computer in a musical battle.

As the musical representation of the furious battle ends, our hero returns to report on the results. He tells us that we can rejoice in a great victory and assures us that our young warriors have not died in vain. In fact, he says that there is no need to memorialize the dead with flowers on their graves because their names have all been stored permanently in a computer ("the tapes have recorded their names"). Our hero has actually lost but does not realize it. He, too, has become consumed by the inhuman technology of the computerized society. After all, we do not need flowers to remember our dead; the computer has their names all safely stored in its memory tapes. Our pathetic hero says proudly, "I am all there is," but the victorious computer tells him that he has been allowed to live. Our hero argues that the computer, after all, was created by humans to do good things. The computer simply replies that there was no choice; its creation was inevitable. In the closing seconds of the multi-movement composition, it asks, "I'm perfect! Are you?"

THE CLOSING SECTION *Karn Evil 9* is a major musical composition that is nearly 30 minutes long. Through both music and lyrics, it presents a philosophical and relevant confrontation between technology and humanity. To bring this elaborate work to a close, ELP created the most

Listening Guide: *Karn Evil 9*, "Third Impression" (Emerson, Lake & Palmer)

0:00–0:22	Introduction	March-like introduction – features "horn calls" played on synthesizer.
0:23–1:05	Verse 1 (ab)	Voice enters. First section (a) is eight bars plus a one-bar transition. Second section (b) is eight bars followed by a five-bar transition to verse 2.
1:06–1:40	Verse 2 (ab)	Internal form similar to verse 1, beginning with the eight-bar "a" section and a one-bar transition; "b" section is also eight bars, but is followed by a one-bar transition that sets up the accompaniment to the bridge.
1:41–2:32	Bridge (c)	New material. Our hero is confident about no man yielding. After a brief fanfare, the computer challenges him. The computer's words are electronically modified human speech.
2:33–2:55	Bridge (continued)	After his dialogue with the computer, our hero insists on no computer standing in his way (same melody that began the bridge). He ends with his declaration of war.
2:56–3:55	Instrumental break	Introduction to the battle sequence. Based on the melody of verse 1 (a) in the first section, transformed into a march.
3:56–4:26	Instrumental break (second section)	Introduces *pedal point* (a repetitive pitch) in a very rigid rhythmic pattern. Suggests the presence of the enemy (the computer).
4:27–5:50	Instrumental break (third section)	Lengthy improvisation featuring organ. Typical ELP rock style. Note the return of the repetitive rhythmic pattern near the end (5:31).
5:51–7:36	Instrumental break (fourth section)	Sudden drop in intensity. Drumrolls and swirling patterns in the low range of the organ. Gradual build in intensity. Note return of the computer's rhythmic pattern at 6:30. Increased dissonance and higher ranges as the climax is approached. Drums and organ chords provide the transition to the next section.
7:37–(8:32?)	Closing section (d)	Vocal returns. New material. Dialogue between our hero and the computer. Note that the computer has the last word (the repetitive rhythmic pattern returns at 8:25). Final chord fades as the coda begins.
(8:33?)–9:03	Coda	Repetitive pattern on sequencer gradually accelerates and moves more and more rapidly back-and-forth between the stereo speakers. The end is an abrupt cutoff.

appropriate coda imaginable. As the final synthesizer chord fades, a sequencer pattern begins. Of all instruments, the sequencer is the most automatic—and perhaps the least human. The 1970s-vintage step sequencer was an electronic instrument that, when programmed, triggered a sequence of pitches, rhythms, timbres, and volume levels on the synthesizer. Once programmed, the sequencer would cycle the pattern forever (or until someone pulled its plug). It really was a music machine. For the coda of *Karn Evil 9*, ELP starts the sequencer and then moves the resulting synthesizer sequence back and forth between the right and left stereo channels; as the sequence itself gets faster and faster, so does the left-to-right-to-left movement (or circular movement in the quadraphonic and surround sound versions). Finally, the sequence becomes almost a blur as it whips from speaker to speaker. Abruptly, it ends. Only silence remains.

11.5.5: Sixth Approach to Art Rock

Karn Evil 9 is an exceptionally fine example of the sixth approach to art rock. There is no string quartet and no orchestra; the musical language is the language of rock. Yet, in its concept, it is more like classical music. It is a serious work of large proportions, designed to develop a central thought through a series of internal movements and sections. Appropriate music is created to serve each section as the central idea unfolds. The music is technically demanding; the playing is superb. Every measure is tightly coordinated and fulfills its role in the total scheme of the composition. It qualifies on every count as a highly virtuosic artistic creation, realized through the language of rock, in other words: art rock.

BECOME AN ACTIVE LISTENER: FINDING CLASSICAL ELEMENTS IN ROCK

Now that you have had a chance to review the many combinations of rock and classical music presented in this chapter, it is time to return to your own collection of recordings, to your streaming service, or to the Internet to identify, independently, some of these elements in other musical examples.

Find examples of classical forms or sounds in the music that you enjoy, including,
1. The use of orchestral instruments

2. A song cycle or suite

3. An extended work following a classical form

4. A rock opera or series of songs that tells a story

Summary: Art Rock

While a number of impressive examples have been described in this chapter, the goals of the art rock movement remain largely unfulfilled. With few exceptions, the attempts to effectively blend classical music with rock were undermined by several factors:

1. *Many art rockers had a naïve and outdated notion of classical music.* Thus, their products were combinations of current rock and centuries-old classical style. Deep Purple, for example, played some true mainstream rock in their attempts at confluence, but the classical element was woefully outdated. On the other hand, Zappa's classical style was quite contemporary, but many would note that, as the classical elements ascend in his works, the rock elements recede; rarely, if ever, does he achieve a true balance.

2. *Some groups unnecessarily softened their rock style,* supposedly to blend more effectively with their outdated notion of the classical style. Some of the work by Rick Wakeman and the Moody Blues illustrates this pitfall.

3. *The transient nature of rock undermines the long-term developmental process* that is usually necessary to achieve a long-term musical goal. Even the greatest classical composers rarely created masterpieces on their first or second try. Jon Lord's *Gemini Suite* is better than his earlier concerto; Wakeman's *King Arthur* is an improvement, musically, over *Journey to the Centre of the Earth*. But rock styles change rapidly, and the creators/performers move on to the next thing, often leaving the previous style unfulfilled.

The art rock trend receded as the 1970s progressed, but it did not end. Musical experimentation by rock artists continued into the 80s and 90s in the guise of "prog rock," keeping the art rock ideal alive.

Take Note: Art Rock

• *How did art rock absorb classical music influences?*—Art rock of the late 1960s and early 1970s incorporated elements of classical music. This was achieved in many different ways, including quoting from the classical repertory or using a classical melody as the basis for a rock song, creating a series of rock songs to form a suite or song cycle, taking a full classical form (such as an opera) and using it as a model for a rock composition, incorporating classical instrumentation into a rock group, or creating a long-form rock composition deriving from the form of an extended classical compositions.

• *Why did some rock bands begin performing with orchestras in the early 1970s?*—Incorporating an orchestra into a rock band is one of the simplest ways to achieve a fusion of classical music and rock, as superficial as that alone might be. The Moody Blues took this approach in their album *Days of Future Passed*, in which the orchestra doesn't interact significantly with the group itself, but primarily performs instrumental interludes between the band's songs. A more sophisticated approach was taken by Deep Purple, thoughtfully integrating the orchestral instruments more equitably and experimenting with extended compositions modeled on classical forms, like *Gemini Suite*, composed by keyboardist Jon Lord. Procol Harum, along with other groups of the era, also melded classical orchestration with their music.

• *What was the impact of rock opera and other types of theatrical works?*—The gathering of rock songs into extended song cycles (sometimes referred to as concept albums) led some to compose full-scale rock operas, telling a story through a series of songs. One of the most successful and influential of these works was The Who's 1969 three-record set, *Tommy*. Although not originally created for the stage, it went on to be staged successfully in several versions. Staged rock musicals that followed included *Jesus Christ Superstar* (1971), composed by Andrew Lloyd Webber and lyricist Tim Rice, and *Grease* (1972), a very successful musical based on 1950s society with a rock and roll soundtrack. Keyboard virtuoso Rick Wakeman, who performed for a time with Yes, specialized in adapting science fiction and mythological stories to create long-form works, including *Journey to the Centre of the Earth* (1974), based on Jules Verne's nineteenth-century novel, and *The Myths and Legends of King Arthur and the Knights of the Round Table* (1975). Wakeman used synthesizers and traditional orchestral instruments as integral and equally important musical resources for these works, in contrast to the rather superficial use of the orchestra evident in the music of the Moody Blues. Genesis also experimented with long-form theatrical works, including *The Lamb Lies Down on Broadway* (1974). On tour, lead singer Peter Gabriel portrayed the main character, whose story is told through a series of songs.

• *What other types of art rock flourished during this period?*—Several groups took a highly sophisticated approach to creating extended works using the language and instrumentation of rock. Emerson, Lake & Palmer created extended works that revealed the influence of rock, jazz, and classical music. Frank Zappa created an eclectic musical hybrid that was influenced by everything from 1950s doo-wop to the electronic experimentations of twentieth century classical composer Edgard Varèse. Many of Zappa's albums featured extended compositions ("Help, I'm a Rock," for example) that revealed his knowledge of classical forms; "It Can't Happen Here," for example, is modeled on the rondo form.

SHARED WRITING

Contemporary Examples of Combining Classical Music and Rock

Select a recording by a rock artist, preferably by one of your favorite artists, that was released during the past decade in which elements of classical music have been integrated into the musical style. Which of the six approaches are represented in the music of this artist? Provide at least three specific songs with an explanation of how the approach(es) is/are integrated into the chosen tracks. Share your response with at least two other students as you review theirs. In your experience, is the art rock approach common in contemporary popular music? Based on your own reflection and exchanges with fellow students, would you say this is more or less common than during the late 1960s and early 1970s, the primary period covered in this chapter? Provide a rationale that might explain this change.

 A minimum number of characters is required to post and earn points. After posting, your response can be viewed by your class and instructor, and you can participate in the class discussion.

Post   0 characters | 140 minimum

Chapter 12
Mainstream Rock

Learning Objectives

12.1 Explain the trends that influenced the continued fragmentation of rock styles

12.2 Outline the varying trends of mainstream rock emerging in the 1970s

12.3 Identify the leading mainstream rock artists of the 1980s

12.4 Explain the continued success of rock performers beyond the 1980s

12.5 Analyze the implications associated with explicit lyrics in rock music

In the 1950s, rock and roll was born. Although many people were a part of this revolution, one man—Elvis Presley—figured the largest. In the 1960s, another revolution took place: the Beatles, who fused the fractured elements of pop music into one multifaceted style. Other styles grew out of this expanded definition of rock: folk rock, soul music, jazz rock, and art rock. Mainstream rock, which had nearly disappeared in the early part of the decade, was rejuvenated by the British bands of the mid-1960s and split into two related but separate styles: the harder, blues-based style of the Rolling Stones and their followers and the more refined, expansionist style of the Beatles and their followers. The counterculture of the United States pursued the harder mainstream style, creating psychedelic or acid rock. Just as the 1950s had given birth to rock and roll, the 1960s gave birth to a series of important sub-styles and witnessed a rebirth of mainstream rock, and again, just as Presley had dominated the 1950s, the Beatles became the giant symbol of the 1960s.

12.1: The Decade of Nondirection

OBJECTIVE: Explain the trends that influenced the continued fragmentation of rock styles

The 1970s did not begin well. The Beatles, musical and spiritual leaders of a generation, announced that they were disbanding. During a Vietnam War protest at Kent State University, National Guard troops fired into a group of protesters, killing four students. For all practical purposes, those shots ended the student protest movement of the 1960s. The counterculture was shocked even further by the deaths of Jimi Hendrix, Janis Joplin, and Jim Morrison—all between September 1970 and July 1971. Coming on the heels of the disillusioning violence at Altamont in December 1969, these events seemed to deflate the hope engendered previously by the "flower power" generation of the 1960s. The openness, love, and hope inherent in that idealistic youth movement were over.

Stunned and disheartened, a generation withdrew. In comparison to the highly creative decade and a half that preceded it, there would be no exciting new trends, no revolutionary styles, and no musical giants in the 1970s. Instead, this period would consist primarily of fragmentation, reaction, and continuation.

12.1.1: Fragmentation of the Rock Market

Evolving out of the variety of rock subgenres that appeared during the previous decade, rock music of the 1970s and beyond revealed an even higher level of eclecticism. In this chapter, we will explore the reasons for the resulting fragmentation and several of the important styles that appeared, including those in the British and American mainstream, southern rock, rock divas, and others. We will also discuss the manner in which lyrics changed over the two decades since rock and roll emerged in the mid-1950s.

Progression of the Market Fragmentation

There are several dominant and interdependent characteristics of the 1970s. The first, and perhaps primary, characteristic was the fragmentation of the market.

We saw a similar phenomenon in the early 1960s, but it disappeared with the arrival of the Beatles and others associated with the British Invasion. The fragmentation of the 1970s would not be similarly overcome. Its roots lay in the new mentality of the 1970s: "Me first!" The youth generation of the 1960s had addressed itself to society as a whole. It worried about war between nations, inequality between races, the relationship between humanity and the environment, and the inequity evident between men and women.

However, by the end of the decade, the focus turned toward self-realization and self-fulfillment. People wanted to "find themselves." Students of the 1970s were less concerned with world peace and racial equality and more concerned with acquiring the skill needed to get a job and make money. As a by-product of the new me-ism, there seemed to be a reaction against the heavy issues, the obscure texts, and the intricate complexities of 1960s rock. Instead of the experimentation of the Beatles and the sophistication of jazz rock and art rock, many went back to the basics and embraced the simpler styles of disco, country-oriented rock, and hard rock.

Society fragmented into hundreds of self-interest groups. The relative simplicity of the old demographics—male and female; youth and adult; black and white; lower, middle, and upper classes—fragmented into a complex array of clusters. As John Naisbitt (1982) wrote in *Megatrends,* we moved from being an either–or society to being a multiple options society. For example, by the end of the decade, instead of three television networks, cable systems offered the viewer over 40 choices, which may seem unimpressive when looking back from a time when cable offers hundreds of channels, but the options were increasing significantly. A similar explosion of choices occurred in food (from mustards to wine), magazines, books (a new "self-help" genre emerged), and many other aspects of life.

The music industry was no different. Radio discovered the concept of *formatting;* that is, programming certain styles of music for a specific audience, members of which typically purchased a predictable set of advertised products. Naisbitt (1982, 239) provides a partial list of these formats, as shown below.

album-oriented rock	disco	country rock
easy-listening pop	punk rock	progressive rock
big-band jazz	rhythm & blues	
progressive jazz	oldies but goodies	

To this list could be added Top 40, classical music, ethnic music, Christian programming, talk radio, and all news. For the first time, record stores carefully segregated their products into bins, following these (or similar) categories. The world waited for the next Presley or Beatles but slowly began to realize that that was no longer possible. No one person or group could possibly cut across all those radio formats, all those record bins, and all those demographic mini-groups.

12.1.2: Consolidation within the Record Industry

If fragmentation was a central characteristic of the "me decade," a second characteristic within the music world was the consolidation of power within the record industry. As Ken Tucker points out, "By the end of the 1970s, the rock market would be controlled by just six major companies: CBS, Warner Communications, Polygram, RCA, MCA, and Capitol-EMI" (Ward, Stokes, and Tucker 1986, 521). The huge music conglomerates were big business; within the industry, music was considered less as an art and more as a product, like a pencil sharpener or an electric toothbrush. The formula was simple: Identify a viable (monied) submarket through sophisticated market research, determine what that submarket was willing to buy, design a product that met those criteria, create the product, and then mass-produce and mass-market it. Thus, the 1970s music industry sold some hard rock, some soft rock, some neo–folk singers, some neo-country, some neo–jazz rock, some art rock, some disco, some punk, some heavy metal—each to a clearly defined segment of the market. This corporate approach, implemented using a business-oriented, profit-driven philosophy was solid: Do not get too experimental or innovative because it might not sell; stick to the proven product.

As a result, we will find that most of the musical categories to be considered in this chapter, and several others that follow in this course, are basically continuations of earlier initiatives. If there was one characteristic that cut across the 1970s music scene, it was the explosion of electronic technology. The synthesizer and its various electronic spin-offs permeated virtually every style. Sound reproduction at live concerts and in record studios reached incredible heights of sophistication. The rock historian of the future may look back at the bewildering kaleidoscope of styles in the 1970s and, finding little to tie it all together, simply call it the decade of electronic rock.

Diversity of Contemporary Rock Subgenres

At the time this book was published, there was a highly diverse array of rock subgenres in evidence, some continuations of styles discussed in this book and others that have emerged since or simply were not mentioned herein. As you think of the popular music surrounding you, would you consider the present more like the 1950s (a limited number of primary styles), like the transition to the 1960s (an expansion and diversification of rock subgenres), or like the 1970s (an explosion of diverse styles). In your journal entry, identify three to five current subgenres you listen to with some frequency. For each, provide the name of the subgenre and at least one specific recording as an example (provide artist name, song title, album upon which it was released, and year of release). Select the two subgenres you consider to be most different one from another, then use your musical vocabulary to provide a clear explanation of the sonic differences between the two styles.

▶ The response entered here will appear in the performance dashboard and can be viewed by your instructor.

Submit

12.2: Mainstream Trends of the 1970s

OBJECTIVE: Outline the varying trends of mainstream rock emerging in the 1970s

In other sections of this course, we have already explored some of the artists whose initial impact came in the 1960s but who continued into the 1970s—groups like the Rolling Stones; Chicago; Emerson, Lake & Palmer; The Who; and the Grateful Dead. Having already discussed their work beyond the 1960s, we will here confine our attention to artists whose principal impact first came in the 1970s and 1980s. The scene was so fragmented that, if one lists 100 bands, one is tempted to devise 75 categories. Although some fit nicely into defined categories, many developed individual styles that elude simple categorization. To bring some order to the bewildering array of artists, we will concentrate on mainstream styles in this chapter, survey various combination styles in another, and then devote two following chapters to a discussion of heavy metal and dance music. Several of these styles, in turn, fragment into additional sub-styles. Quite a few bands straddle two or even three categories, and a few seem to fit no category but their own. The reader should consider these categories merely as aids in structuring the total discussion and take care to avoid pigeonholing the artists. With that caveat, let us plunge squarely into the mainstream.

By 1967, the first British Invasion had run its course, with few groups beyond the Beatles and the Stones continuing to have a major impact on U.S. charts. During the last two years of the 1960s, however, a host of new British bands launched a second invasion. In earlier areas of this course, we have already met a number of these "second wave" bands—The Who; the Moody Blues; Procol Harum; Emerson, Lake & Palmer; Deep Purple; Genesis; and Yes—whose peak popularity came in the 1970s. As we have already noted, the rock mainstream entered the 1970s as a two-way split (Beatles vs. Stones influences); running parallel to this dual mainstream was the primarily British art rock trend (covered in detail in another part of this course). As the 1970s continued, these styles would fragment even further. Some of the bands that began as hard-rocking, blues-based mainstream bands (the Stones' side) veered off toward art rock; they became known as **progressive rock** bands. On the other hand, some bands increased the heaviness of their sound and evolved into **heavy metal** bands. Heavy metal developed into a major rock style—one that continued strongly through the 1980s and into the 1990s and beyond. Still others on the harder side of the mainstream took a turn toward **glitter rock** or *glam rock*—essentially a visual or theatrical (not musical) distinction. Finally, some rebelled against *everything* and developed the **punk rock** trend. The less strident Beatles' side of the mainstream also fragmented, although less dramatically. A number of these groups also drifted toward art rock, joining in the so-called progressive rock trend; others moved toward a more commercially popular sound (Top 40-oriented), and a few steered a course right down the center of mainstream rock.

12.2.1: The Harder Side of the British Mainstream

As we begin to explore the continuing fragmentation of rock in the 1970s, we will start with the mainstream. When we discuss mainstream rock of this era, the groups divide into a harder, blues-based sound and a softer, pop-influenced sound. There were highly impressive and innovative artists in each category during this period, as you will discover.

Important Performers from the Blues-Rock Tradition in the 1970s

Three British rockers whose careers began in the 1960s reached their greatest success as performers from the blues-rock tradition in the 1970s: guitarist Eric Clapton, keyboard player-vocalist Steve Winwood, and flamboyant rock vocalist Rod Stewart.

Eric Clapton—When we spoke of Eric Clapton in an earlier section of this course, he was a member of the Yardbirds, a British, blues-based band that stressed lengthy improvisational solos. Clapton's interest in blues and improvisation continued in his next group, Cream, formed in 1966, which enjoyed a brief but successful career lasting slightly over two years. Their second album, *Disraeli Gears* (late 1967), includes several examples of their improvisational solos. Like other such groups, the band would superimpose a series of long improvisational solos over a basic riff. "Sunshine of Your Love" (number 5, 1968) contains one of the most familiar (and often-imitated) riffs in rock. Cream's repertoire included original songs as well as authentic American blues material. The double album *Wheels of Fire* (number 1, 1968) offers several excellent examples of Cream's use of the 12-bar blues (note especially "Politician" and "Crossroads"). Internal tensions led to the dissolution of the band in late 1968.

Following the breakup of Cream, Clapton formed two short-lived bands: Blind Faith (1969) and Derek and the Dominoes (1970–1972). Tortured by a severe drug problem and an on-and-off love affair with Patti Harrison (George's wife)—whom he eventually married—Clapton retreated from the limelight for a while. He returned in 1974 with the number 1 album, *461 Ocean Boulevard,* issued under his own name. This album contained the number 1 hit "I Shot the Sheriff," a cover version of a reggae song composed by Bob Marley. Throughout the following three decades, Clapton continued to record as a solo artist; he continues to be considered one of rock's most influential guitarists and one to whom we shall return later in this chapter.

Stevie Winwood—One of England's finest rock keyboard players was Stevie Winwood (born in Birmingham, England, in 1948). Winwood formed the group Traffic in late 1967. For a fine example of Traffic's work, listen to *John Barleycorn Must Die* (number 5 in 1970). Especially impressive was the strong playing of Winwood and the always tasteful work of woodwind player Chris Wood. Following the release of *When the Eagle Flies* (1974), which featured more excellent keyboard work by Winwood, the group disbanded. Winwood experienced significant solo success in the mid-1980s with the triple-platinum *Back in the High Life,* which included two Top 10 singles: the Grammy-winning "Higher Love" (number 1; featuring Chaka Khan) and "The Finer Things" (number 8). In 1988 came a number 1 album, *Roll with It,* that included three hit singles: the title track (number 1), "Don't You Know What the Night Can Do?" (number 6) and "Holding On" (number 11). Winwood continued to release recordings into the new millennium, two of which pierced the Top 20: *Nine Lives* (number 12 in 2008) and *Live From Madison Square Garden* (number 14 in 2009).

Rod Stewart—Rod Stewart was born in London in 1945 to Scottish parents. In early 1967, he helped form the Jeff Beck Group with Beck and bassist-guitarist Ron Wood; in his two years with Beck, Stewart gained initial exposure to a wide audience in England and the United States. By 1970, a British mainstream band, Small Faces, reorganized as Faces and brought on Ron Wood and Rod Stewart. Stewart had already signed as a solo artist with Mercury Records, so he pursued a dual career as a soloist and as a member of Faces. However, Stewart's solo career gradually overshadowed the group's work, and Faces disappeared by the mid-1970s.

Stewart's second album, *Gasoline Alley* (1970), made the U.S. Top 30 and was the real beginning of his solo success. It was a hard-rocking album with clear blues roots. Stewart's hoarse, raspy voice was distinctive and seemed just right for the shouting tradition of blues-based mainstream rock. Stewart's follow-up album, *Every Picture Tells a Story* (1971), became a number 1 album and contained the hit single "Maggie May" (number 1, 1971). He developed a flamboyant and spectacular stage act, complete with flashy costumes and his distinctively wild, blond hairstyle.

Following *Never a Dull Moment* (number 2, 1972), Stewart's popularity seemed to decline for several years. However, in 1975, he re-emerged with the successful *Atlantic Crossing* album, making the U.S. Top 10. Although it is sometimes felt that Stewart's post-1975 work falls short of his earlier blues-based classics, he continued to be an important rock personality. More recently, Stewart released a series of significantly mellower recordings, including *Human* (2001) and a series of recordings of jazz standards and show tunes in a series titled *The Great American Songbook*, several of which placed in the Top 5. In 2009, he released *Soulbook*, an album containing covers of soul and Motown classics, and in 2012 he published an entertaining memoir entitled *Rod: The Autobiography*.

Listen to Rod Stewart singing a live version of "Maggie May."

Click or tap the video title to listen to "Maggie May":

https://www.youtube.com/ watch?v=ek4cUOlxwgQ[*]

JOURNAL

"Sunshine of Your Love" (A 12-Bar Blues Variant)

Cream's Classic "Sunshine of Your Love" consists of a recognizable riff played by the guitar and bass, which forms the basis for the song. The song also provides an excellent example of the manner in which the 12-bar blues form, prominent in the pre-rock and roll R&B examples covered in an earlier section of this course, provides a foundation for the song in a slightly altered form. Listen carefully to the song, and compose a response describing how the form of the piece follows (or does not follow) the traditional 12-bar blues form; in paragraph one, describe those elements that follow the common 12-bar blues form, and in paragraph two describe how this song varies from that traditional form. You will likely find it valuable to review some of those earlier R&B examples, so that you can ensure an accurate memory of the 12-bar form.

 The response entered here will appear in the performance dashboard and can be viewed by your instructor.

Submit

---

*By clicking this link, you will be redirected to a third-party site.

12.2.2: The Gentler Side of the British Mainstream

As we have mentioned, the harder side of the British mainstream of the 1970s fragmented into basic hard rock, heavy metal, glitter rock, and punk–new wave. Meanwhile, there was also the continuation of the somewhat less outrageous, less deafening, less shock-oriented side of the mainstream.

FLEETWOOD MAC   One of the most successful of these mainstream groups began on the harder, blues-based side and crossed over to the softer side in the mid-1970s. A quartet formed by three former members of John Mayall's Bluesbreakers—Peter Green, Mick Fleetwood, and John McVie—plus guitarist Jeremy Spencer debuted as Green's Fleetwood Mac at the British National Jazz and Blues Festival in August 1967.

Listen to Fleetwood making singing a live version of "Don't Stop."

Click or tap on the video title to listen to "Don't Stop":

https://www.youtube.com/ watch?v=I9gj2RiscrM[*]

ELTON JOHN   Another standout musician of the 1970s was Elton John. Although he was enormously successful, his level of celebrity did not rival that of Elvis Presley or the Beatles, since he did not evince the requisite high level of influence across all existing markets. Of course, in an era when the markets were fragmenting and expanding, the evolution of the market itself played a role in creating an environment in which this feat (i.e., a single artist or group dominating the entire popular music market) was simply no longer possible.

Elton John performing in 1975.
SOURCE: Daily Mail/Rex/Alamy Stock Photo

Musical Journey of Fleetwood Mac

The following section will provide highlights from the career of Fleetwood Mac, one of the most successful groups in the softer mainstream category.

Fleetwood Mac included songs by Elmore James, Howlin' Wolf, and Sonny Boy Williamson (plus several blues-based originals) on their first album, *Fleetwood Mac* (1968). For the balance of the 1960s, the band was popular in England but virtually unknown in the United States.

The transition from a strong blues base to a softer style began in the early 1970s as a result of various personnel changes (including the addition of McVie's wife, Christine, on keyboard and vocals). The first album with the new quintet was *Future Games* (1971). The old blues sound was now in the past, and the newer Fleetwood Mac emphasized ballads and more refined harmonies.

By 1974, the band had survived legal difficulties, more personnel changes, and they had moved to Los Angeles. There they recruited the duo of Stevie Nicks (vocals) and Lindsey Buckingham (guitar and vocals). The initial album featuring the new lineup (Fleetwood, two McVies, Nicks, and Buckingham) moved from the harder to the softer side of the rock mainstream.

Fleetwood Mac (1975)—with the same title as their debut album in 1968—was a commercial success, becoming their first number 1 album and producing three Top 20 hits: "Over My Head" (number 20), "Rhiannon (Will You Ever Win)" (number 11), and "Say You Love Me" (number 11). The follow-up album, *Rumours* (1977), was even more successful, holding the number 1 position for 31 weeks and turning multiplatinum with over 20 million copies sold; the album included four Top 10 singles, including the number 1 song "Dreams." With three songwriters contributing to the new repertoire (Nicks, Buckingham, and Christine McVie), there was no dearth of good material. The solid vocal harmonies, songwriting craftsmanship, and excellent musicianship of the entire band accounted for their high level of success. *Rumours* suggests the versatility of the band as they moved from the mainstream rock style of "Don't Stop" (number 3) and "Go Your Own Way" (number 10) to the soft-rock sound of "Dreams" (number 1). There is a liberal dose of folk rock style and even elements of country.

With time, relationships within the band became rather complex as the McVies divorced and Nicks and Buckingham separated; amazingly, perhaps, neither of these changes significantly damaged the group's professional work. The double album *Tusk* was released in 1979, providing further evidence for the versatility of the group toward a true eclecticism and yielding three Top 20 hits: "Tusk" (number 8), "Sara" (number 7), and "Think About Me" (number 20). However, as the 1980s began, the individual members of Fleetwood Mac increasingly pursued solo projects. The most successful was Stevie Nicks, who enjoyed seven Top 40 hits in the early 1980s and continued to release recordings into the 2000s (e.g., *In Your Dreams*, 2010). After self-releasing a four-song EP in 2013 (*Extended Play*), the classic lineup of the band reunited in 2014 for a world tour, including Christine McVie, who returned after a 16-year absence.

Musical Career of Elton John

The following section will provide highlights from the career of Elton John, another highly successful performer in this gentler mainstream category.

Elton John was born Reginald Dwight in Middlesex, England, in 1947. After joining the band Bluesology, John began a period of some six years knocking around the British music business. Finally, thanks to a massive PR effort by Uni Records, his single "Your Song" entered the U.S. Hot 100 and rose to the Top 10 in early 1971. The music for "Your Song" was written by John, but the lyrics were by Bernie Taupin. The team of John and Taupin wrote virtually all of John's music through 1976.

John's most significant recordings were released from late 1971 through early 1976, though he produced numerous hits through the end of the 1990s. During Elton's peak period, beginning with *Madman Across the Water,* he released 11 albums, 7 of which went to number 1 and the others all charted in the Top 10. Along with these impressive album sales, there were 19 Top 20 hits, including six number 1 songs. Of particular interest is the *Honky Chateau* album, which de-emphasized the huge string arrangements and featured more guitar-oriented rock. The hits "Honky Cat" (number 8) and "Rocket Man" (number 6) appeared on this album. Also notable was "Crocodile Rock" (number 1) from *Don't Shoot Me, I'm Only the Piano Player;* it is a clever piece of nostalgia based on the late 1950s soft-rock sound (compare it with Paul Anka's "Diana," for example). "Saturday Night's Alright for Fighting" (number 12) is a strong example of John's mainstream rock style; on songs such as this, he would jump up and down at the piano, recalling the antics of Little Richard and Jerry Lee Lewis. "Bennie and the Jets" (number 1) features some very fine piano work by John plus some strong falsetto singing. His version of "Lucy in the Sky with Diamonds" (number 1) was appropriately recorded with the assistance of Dr. Winston O'Boogie (a.k.a. John Lennon).

In 1974, Elton John signed an $8 million contract with MCA Records (the largest contract in rock history until Stevie Wonder topped it in 1975 with his $13 million Motown contract). In 1975, John starred in the movie version of *Tommy,* and in 1976, he recorded his final album of this early period in collaboration with Taupin. In 1978, he released *A Single Man,* yet another platinum album. Since then, Sir Elton John has continued to record, and his albums and singles continue to sell well. In 1997, he and Taupin reunited to remake "Candle in the Wind," a song originally written as a tribute to Marilyn Monroe. The new version was created for and performed at the funeral of Princess Diana in the UK.

John and Taupin continued their renewed collaboration on *Peachtree Road* (2004) and *The Captain and the Kid* (2006); in 2011, Elton released an album of covers, appropriately entitled *The Covers Record*, including songs by a diverse array of songwriters (e.g., Leadbelly, Cat Stevens, John Fogerty, Paul McCartney, and Nick Drake). John also had significant success composing movie soundtracks (*The Lion King*, *The Road to El Dorado*, and *All the King's Men*). Showing his compassion, Elton John assisted several other artists as they endured personal and professional crises. For example, he toured during the 1990s with fellow singer-songwriter Billy Joel (plagued by alcoholism), supported Eminem during his drug rehab, and rescued 1970s superstar Leon Russell from near obscurity with the release of their collaboration, *The Union* (2010). In 2016, Elton released his 33rd studio album, *Wonderful Crazy Night*, reminiscent of the sound of his 1970s recordings, though without the chart-topping commercial success.

PETER FRAMPTON Still, there was no one star that equaled the success of Elvis or the Beatles. However, for a brief moment, one musician was poised to become the decade-defining musician for the 1970s. Mention the name of Peter Frampton now, and you might only get a blank look, but for a period of slightly less than two years, from 1976 to 1977, Frampton was being mentioned in the same breath as Presley and the Beatles. Frampton was a singer-guitarist who had played with a group called the Herd in the late 1960s and with Humble Pie (a hard rock band) in the early 1970s. Pursuing a generally undistinguished solo career, Frampton suddenly burst on the scene with a tremendously successful live double album, *Frampton Comes Alive!* (1976), which zoomed to number 1 and stayed there for 10 weeks. The song "Do You Feel Like We Do" featured a *voice box,* a device that routes the electric guitar signal through a tube into the singer's mouth, thus allowing the mouth to shape the guitar timbre into "words."

Frampton became a superstar almost overnight. The follow-up album, *I'm in You* (1977), reached number 2, but it did not come close to the sales records established by *Alive!* Another blow to his career came when Frampton played the role of Billy Shears in the movie *Sgt. Pepper's Lonely Hearts Club Band,* which was badly received by both critics and the public. Frampton was involved in a severe automobile accident in 1978, and the success of his recordings during the 1980s and 1990s was not impressive. He regained at least some level of critical acclaim in the new millennium, winning a Best Pop Instrumental Grammy for *Footprints* (2006), but his days as a potential "next Elvis" had long passed.

12.2.3: Mainstream Rock in the States

For each British mainstream fragment—harder mainstream, softer mainstream, heavy metal, glitter rock, and punk/new wave—there was an American parallel. Generally speaking, the American mainstream rock groups tended to be less hard than their British counterparts.

American Mainstream Rock Groups

The following section will provide information about some of the American rock artists that dominated the era.

Creedence Clearwater Revival, 1970.

SOURCE: Pictorial Press Ltd/Alamy Stock Photo

Creedence Clearwater Revival—Our first example is a group from San Francisco called Creedence Clearwater Revival (CCR). CCR shared very little in common with their Bay Area colleagues of the late 1960s. Their good-old-boy, deep South sound was largely determined by their leader, guitarist-vocalist, and songwriter John Fogerty.

Formed originally as a high school group in 1959, the band changed their name to Creedence Clearwater Revival in late 1967 and released a remake of an old 1950s hit, "Suzie Q" (number 11; originally sung by Dale Hawkins in 1957). Their second album, *Bayou Country* (1969), by its very title, fostered the deep southern image. From the album came a monster hit, "Proud Mary" (number 2, 1969). *Willy and the Poor Boys,* possibly CCR's most representative album, illustrates the band's typical styles: The deep southern sound is obvious in "Down on the Corner," "Cotton Fields," and "The Midnight Special"; songs like "Feelin' Blue" and "Side o' the Road" are very bluesy. "Effigy" is about as San Francisco-ish as CCR ever got. The southern sound was sometimes closer to rockabilly ("Suzie Q") and, at other times, closer to the black blues sound. An interesting melding of styles may be heard in the Motown hit "I Heard It Through the Grapevine" (number 43), in which CCR preserves the original's basic melody and harmonies but adds a lengthy guitar improvisation.

CCR's popularity continued into the early 1970s. However, by 1971, Tom Fogerty had grown uncomfortable with his younger brother's dominance, so he left the band. In October 1971, the group disbanded. Following the breakup, John Fogerty released a series of six solo recordings between 1973 and 1998, including *Centerfield* (number 1, 1985) and *Blue Moon Swamp* (1997), which only reached number 37 but earned a Grammy for Best Rock Album. Fogerty continued to release recordings into the 2000s.

Doobie Brothers—Another San Francisco band that succeeded in 1970s mainstream rock was the Doobie Brothers. Formed in San Jose in 1969, the Doobies endured a bewildering series of personnel changes throughout their career. Normally using a lineup of two guitars, bass, and two drummers, the band's early recordings fit perfectly into the category of mainstream rock. Their second album, *Toulouse Street* (number 21, 1972), included the popular anthem "Listen to the Music" (number 11). The unique voice of Tom Johnston with strong vocal harmonies established the band's appeal. As with many U.S. bands, the Doobies were not as hard as their mainstream British counterparts. They combined good vocals, solid harmonies, and clean playing with sophisticated production. A representative sample of early 1970s Doobie Brothers may be heard on *The Captain and Me* (number 7), which included the major hits "Long Train Running" (number 8) and "China Grove" (number 15).

The sound of the band changed somewhat in 1975, when Tom Johnston fell ill; he continued intermittently with the band, but, in early 1977, he parted company with the Doobies (only to return in the late 1980s). With the loss of Johnston, a new Doobie sound emerged with the title song from the 1976 album, *Takin' It to the Streets* (number 8), strongly influenced by new keyboardist-vocalist and songwriter Michael McDonald, who had previously performed with Steely Dan. The harmonies became more sophisticated and even a bit jazz-oriented, as is evident in the title track from *Takin' It to the Streets*. However, personnel changes constantly plagued the band, and, by 1982, the Doobies had passed their peak of popularity.

Steve Miller—Although associated with the late 1960s San Francisco scene, Steve Miller achieved his greatest success in the 1970s. Raised in Dallas, Miller moved to Chicago after college, where he played with local bluesmen such as Muddy Waters. Miller formed his own band in San Francisco in 1966, but his big break did not occur until late 1973 with his ninth album, *The Joker;* the album hit number 2, and the title song rose to number 1. Miller's popularity ebbed and flowed through the 1970s, but, in 1982, he hit big again with *Abracadabra* (number 3). Miller's mainstream style showed his blues roots, sometimes colored by touches of country and even vestiges of the old San Francisco sound. Miller continued to tour and in 2010 released his first studio album in 17 years, *BINGO!* (number 37), containing covers of songs by Chicago blues and R&B artists.

Journey—One other San Francisco band began in the 1970s and endured to become a major act of the 1980s. Journey began in 1973 with two former members of Santana—keyboardist Gregg Rolie and guitarist Neal Schon—as its nucleus. Journey's first three albums were not big sellers. Lead singer Steve Perry was added in 1977 and was largely responsible for the success of their fourth album, *Infinity* (number 21).

In the early 1980s, Journey became firmly established as an important mainstream rock band. Their album *Frontiers* (number 2, 1983) yielded four hit singles: "Separate Ways (Worlds Apart)"(number 8), "Faithfully" (number 12), "After the Fall" (number 23), and "Send Her My Love" (number 23). It is an interesting album as the opening songs represent milder material, and the later songs on the album reflect a style that is closer to hard rock and heavy metal. Such stylistic diversity typified Journey. They could produce ballads like "Open Arms" (number 2) and "Faithfully" without sounding like a soft-rock group; they could also move to the other extreme and sound like a heavy metal band (but more artistic than many) in songs like "Edge of the Blade," also from *Frontiers*. In between was a hard mainstream rock style that featured Perry's strong, high voice (always perfectly controlled, even when he was shouting or screaming), Schon's superb guitar breaks, and solid musicianship by the rest of the band.

Sly and the Family Stone—It is no doubt becoming apparent how fragmented rock really was in the 1970s. Black music also fragmented, as various artists moved in different directions. One of the first stylistic directions evolved in San Francisco, as Sylvester Stewart combined soul music with psychedelic rock to create a style called *psychedelic soul*. Stewart was born in Dallas in 1944 but soon moved with his family to northern California. There, Sly, as he became known, organized the Stoners in 1966, and, by 1967, the band had evolved into the seven-member Sly and the Family Stone. Their fourth album, *Stand!* (number 13), became Sly's first truly successful album, yielding four hit singles, including the number 1 "Everyday People." Their performance at Woodstock (featured in the documentary film about the event) enhanced the group's popularity, especially with their sensational performance of "I Want to Take You Higher."

Sly's style combined many elements. At its foundation was a basically funky beat and bass line; horns added a jazzy element, reminiscent of the old Memphis and Stax-Volt soul sound; some of the guitar work and the band's relatively loose performance style were associated with the San Francisco psychedelic sound, as were some of their drug-oriented lyrics. Of particular interest was the vocal format. There were frequently two or three lead singers; the mixture of a female voice and two distinctly different male voices created a unique sound. Although almost any Sly song will reveal the group's style, one of the best examples is their early recording "Dance to the Music" (number 8, 1968).

The late 1971 album, *There's a Riot Goin' On*, reached number 1, but the end was near. *Fresh* (1973) was Sly's last Top 10 album, and "If You Want Me to Stay" was his last Top 20 hit (number 12). Subsequent albums through the late 1970s fared less well.

Listen to Creedence Clearwater Revival on YouTube.

Click or tap on the video title to listen to "Down on the Corner":

h t t p s : / / w w w . y o u t u b e . c o m / watch?v=vrMvblpZFq0

12.2.4: Southern Rock

Leaving San Francisco, we move back to the South, where rock and roll was born. Other than the soul recordings in Memphis and Muscle Shoals, rock had left its birthplace. Most rock of the 1960s had come from places like Detroit, Los Angeles, San Francisco, Philadelphia, New York City, Liverpool, and London. However, in the early 1970s, there was an effort to get back to the basics of southern rock and roll.

Key Bands of the Southern Rock Sound

The following section will provide information about those artists who combined rock and roll with elements of C&W and country to establish another popular subgenre: southern rock.

Allman Brothers—In 1969, Duane and Gregg Allman (born in Nashville in 1946 and 1947, respectively) formed a band that would initiate the southern rock trend. The band's real breakthrough came with the Allman Brothers Band's live album, *At Fillmore East* (number 13, 1971). The blues-based rock style was evident on songs like "In Memory of Elizabeth Reed" and the 23-minute rendition of "Whipping Post" (or listen to "Midnight Rider" from the earlier *Idlewild South* album). Sadly, Duane Allman died in a motorcycle accident in late October 1971. *Eat a Peach* (number 4, 1972), a double album, contained Duane's last performances. Slightly over one year later, the band's bassist, Berry Oakley, was killed in a motorcycle accident near the site of Duane's death.

Despite these tragedies, in 1973, the band managed to produce a new album, *Brothers and Sisters*; it became the Allman Brothers Band's only number 1 album. A good example of the southern blues rock is "Southbound," a traditional 12-bar blues that displayed a perfect blending of R&B and rock. (An earlier example of the Allman Brothers' 12-bar blues rock is "Statesboro Blues.") However, by 1976, the band had fragmented. After several years, Gregg Allman reassembled a band and continued to perform and record into the new millennium. Tragically, after being diagnosed with hepatitis C in 1999 and receiving a liver transplant shortly thereafter, Gregg Allman was destined to die of complications related to liver cancer in 2017. His final album, *Southern Blood* (2017) was released posthumously.

The Allman Brothers were key to the beginning of the southern rock sound. Their work in the period from 1970 to 1973 established the return of rock to its southern, R&B roots.

Lynyrd Skynyrd—Following in the footsteps of the Allman Brothers was Lynyrd Skynyrd, a band whose roots can be traced back to the mid-1960s in Jacksonville, Florida. The Allman Brothers Band had been a sextet with two drummers (like the Doobie Brothers) and a dual lead guitar format. Lynyrd Skynyrd added a third lead guitar, becoming a rock septet.

Lynyrd Skynyrd established a strong reputation as a live performance band, partially as a result of their tour with the Who in 1973. Their peak popularity dates from the Top 10 hit "Sweet Home Alabama" (number 8, 1974) through 1977, during which time three of their four albums made the Top 10. Taking the Allman Brothers' blues-based sound and adding a slightly harder rock sound, the band achieved a unique style. However, in 1977, the band's charter plane crashed, killing vocalist Ronnie Van Zant and two other band members and injuring others. Three days before the crash, *Street Survivors* had been released; it reached number 5 on the album chart, the highest chart position for any Skynyrd album. Due to the tragedy, the group disbanded for 10 years. They reformed in 1987 with Van Zant's younger brother Johnny as the lead singer and continued to perform and record into the new millennium.

12.2.5: The Midwest and the Rest

Continuing our survey of the American mainstream of the 1970s, we move from the South to the Midwest. We have explored some of the primary artists in the British mainstream and then moved on to the American continent to determine which artists were dominating the charts during this period. In both Britain and America, the mainstream had divided into two branches, one hard rock and the other rock with softer sounds. Some of the most interesting bands simply defied assignment to any existing category.

Other Rock Bands of the 1970s

The following section will identify some of the remaining mainstream groups that don't fit as neatly into the broader categories outlined elsewhere in this chapter.

Kansas—The group Kansas is sometimes considered to be a progressive or art rock band, based on the fact that the band prominently included violin and that the musical form of some of their compositions extended well beyond a simple verse-chorus structure. Indeed, there are moments when the classical training of several of Kansas' members can be discerned (e.g., "Lonely Wind" and "Journey from Mariabronn," especially with the latter song's meter changes and modal melodies). However, more often, the overall sound is that of a sophisticated form of mainstream rock.

The six members of Kansas were fine players and singers. Their rock sound was solid; their harmonies (vocal and instrumental) were well conceived and impeccably performed. From Topeka, Kansas, the band was formed in 1971. Kansas experienced their greatest success between 1976 and early 1978 with the albums *Leftoverture* (number 5, 1976), which contained the masterful "Carry On Wayward Son" (number 11, 1977), and *Point of Know Return* (number 4, 1977), which included the number 6 hit "Dust in the Wind." Success proved elusive afterward, and, in 1983, the group disbanded. They reformed briefly in 1986 and experienced fleeting success with *Power* (1987), containing the Top 20 single "All I Wanted." Later albums were less commercially successful; even when the original members of Kansas reconvened in 2000 (substituting Billy Greer on bass) to release *Somewhere to Elsewhere*, the audience did not materialize.

Styx—The problem of categorization continues when we encounter Styx, a band hailing from Chicago. Although some writers would place them in the progressive rock category as well, their biggest hit, "Babe" was a soft-rock ballad.

In early 1975, *Styx II* (number 20), which had been released back in 1973 and included the single "Lady" (number 6), finally entered the Top 20. The 1977 album, *The Grand Illusion* (number 6), became a smash hit and was the first of a series of five platinum albums. Along with the albums came a series of successful singles, including five Top 10 hits and the number 1 song "Babe" (1979). Styx's mainstream style could lean toward a harder sound at times and toward a softer sound at other times; there were even occasional touches of progressive rock. Taken overall, their style is a good representation of American mainstream rock of the late 1970s to early 1980s.

Foreigner—Tying the British and American mainstream together was Foreigner, formed by three New Yorkers and three Londoners. Established in 1976 by guitarist Mick Jones and Ian McDonald, they released their first album, *Foreigner* (number 4), in 1977. As with Journey and Styx, Foreigner was capable of moving from a hard rock mainstream norm toward heavy metal on one side or toward the softer side. Their 1981 album *4* was a monster hit, becoming Foreigner's only number 1 album. Two of their most successful singles, "Waiting for a Girl Like You" (number 2, 1984) and "I Want to Know What Love Is" (number 1, 1985), were among Foreigner's softer rock sounds.

12.3: Mainstream Rock in the 1980s

OBJECTIVE: Identify the leading mainstream rock artists of the 1980s

With all of the fragmentation, subcategories, cross-fertilizations, and individualized styles of the 1970s and 1980s, whatever happened to basic mainstream rock? Amidst all the hyphens and adjectives, was there any band that consisted of a gutsy singer, a drummer, some guitarists, a piano player, and maybe a saxophonist playing good old, dead-center rock and roll? The answer was yes, but it was a rather well-kept secret until the 1980s.

12.3.1: Bruce Springsteen

Bruce Springsteen achieved superstar status in the 1980s. Having paid his dues through years of work in the music industry, he was no overnight sensation.

Musical Career of Bruce Springsteen

The following section will provide highlights from the career of Bruce Springsteen, one of the most successful rockers of the 1980s and beyond.

Early Career—Springsteen was born in 1949 in Freehold, New Jersey. As a teenager, he worked in a series of bands in the New Jersey and New York City (Greenwich Village) area. In 1972, he caught the attention of John Hammond, the A&R (artists and repertoire) representative for Columbia Records. Hammond, whom we discussed previously in the sections of the course on Bob Dylan and Aretha Franklin, had a penchant for spotting unique, nontraditional vocalists like Dylan—those with a rough and raw basic sound.

Bruce Springsteen (right) with Clarence Clemons on stage in 1975.
SOURCE: John Ares/Alamy Stock Photo

Springsteen's first Columbia album, *Greetings from Asbury Park, New Jersey* (1973), was a slow seller. For his 1974 tour, Springsteen formed what was to become his excellent backup band, the E Street Band. Springsteen's breakthrough to mainstream success came with the release of *Born to Run* in 1975. Accompanied by a massive PR campaign (over $200,000 worth), the album broke the Top 5.

Born to Run—With *Born to Run,* Springsteen became known to a much wider public. Beginning with the title track, side two of this album, especially, revealed the multifaceted appeal of Springsteen's music. "Born to Run" was mainstream rock (true of most Springsteen music); note especially the instrumental break, featuring the tasteful performance of saxophonist Clarence Clemons. This is not art rock, jazz rock, folk rock, or any other kind of mixed rock; it is quintessential, mainstream rock and roll. Springsteen has a raw, unsophisticated vocal timbre, as did Dylan, Joplin, and Hendrix.

"Meeting Across the River," the penultimate track on the album, is an example of Springsteen in a softer mode. The trumpet obbligato played by Randy Brecker adds a nice touch to this haunting song. The final track, "Jungleland," may be the most interesting song on *Born to Run*, beginning quietly with piano and strings. Springsteen sets the scene: the street life of New York City or urban New Jersey after dark. In the second verse, the tension builds, and the textures gradually thicken. As Springsteen reaches the title line, "Jungleland," the full E Street Band enters, and the subsequent verse conforms to Springsteen's typical mainstream rock style. A strong instrumental break, once again, reveals the impressive musicianship of the band. After several verses, the rock beat slows to half speed for Clemons's mournful sax solo. As the beat resumes, Clemons continues to drive the song toward its conclusion, but there is yet another interruption as the energy dissipates; the beat stops, and the texture thins to acoustic piano. Springsteen re-enters in a softer style, reminiscent of the opening verses. For the final verse, the tempo quickens and slows, reflecting the meaning and mood of the text. The music throughout "Jungleland" is skillfully manipulated to fit the text—the ultimate goal of any music-and-text fusion.

Springsteen's Lyrics—The lyrics are references to the frustrations, confusions, dreams, and disappointments of the average working-class American. The themes of unemployment, social issues, the difficulties of Vietnam veterans, and the rage and frustration of being unable to beat the establishment pervade almost all of Springsteen's songs. In that way, his music is related to the heritage of the folk rock trend of the 1960s—one of the few remnants of that sentiment in the 1970s and 1980s.

Rising Charts—Spending much of his time touring, Springsteen returned to the studio in 1980. From these sessions came *The River* (1980), Springsteen's first number 1 album. This strong double album produced a number 5 single ("Hungry Heart") and launched Springsteen into his 1980s superstar status.

With this newfound success, Springsteen took a potentially dangerous step with his next album, *Nebraska* (1982). This brooding, introspective album was all acoustic and was recorded at his home on a four-track cassette recorder, and yet the album went to number 3 on the album chart.

But Springsteen's biggest commercial success came in 1984 with *Born in the U.S.A.* The title song became a popular anthem of the mid-1980s. The album reached number 1 and yielded two other singles, "Dancing in the Dark" (number 2) and "Cover Me" (number 7). "Born in the U.S.A." was perceived by many as a patriotic song. However, as with many Springsteen songs, there is an underlying conflict between the promise of the American dream and the stark disappointment of those who fail to attain it.

In 1986, Springsteen released a five-record boxed set called *Bruce Springsteen & the E Street Band Live: 1975–85*. It revealed a rock star who had maintained his own unique style, apparently ignoring the transient ebb and flow of rock-related sub-styles. Springsteen's final album of the 1980s was *Tunnel of Love*, which also reached number 1 and yielded two Top 10 hits ("Brilliant Disguise" and the title song).

Later Career—In late 1989, Springsteen split from his longtime associates, the E Street Band. Throughout the 1980s and 1990s and then into the new millennium, "The Boss" (a name often used by fans to refer to Springsteen) remained true not only to his own musical principles, but to the historic principles of mainstream rock and roll: to express popular sentiments in a hard-driving, uncomplicated, but musically proficient style. His recordings during the 1990s, though critically acclaimed, sold less well than his earlier work. A 1999 reunion tour with the E Street Band reinvigorated both the artist and his audience. Springsteen produced one of the most austere and poignant artistic responses to the tragedy of 9/11 in his album *The Rising* (number 1, 2002), initiating a resurgence of his own. Including *Rising*, Springsteen produced five Top 5 studio albums during the decade, including a collection of protest and folk songs by Pete Seeger (*We Shall Overcome*; number 3, 2006). Four of these albums reached the top of the album chart: *The Rising* (2002), *Devils & Dust* (2005), *Magic* (2007), and *Working on a Dream* (2009). Springsteen continued his success beyond that initial decade with *Promise* (number 16, 2010) and *Wrecking Ball* (number 1, 2012). In 2016, The Boss authored a very well-written and informative autobiography entitled *Born to Run*.

Listen to Bruce Springsteen on YouTube.

Click or tap on the video title to hear Springsteen's "Born to Run":

https://www.youtube.com/watch?v=IxuThNgl3YA[*]

12.3.2: U2

Springsteen, Michael Jackson, and Madonna (we will discuss these last two in another section of this course) proved to be the superstars of the early 1980s (and beyond). In the last half of the decade, two superstar rock groups emerged: U2 and Huey Lewis and the News.

U2, an Irish rock group, was formed in 1976 by drummer Larry Mullen, originally under the name the Hype. The quartet paid its dues for four years by opening for other bands and touring England and Ireland, obtaining a record contract in 1980 with Island Records.

12.3.3: Huey Lewis and the News

One of the more interesting entries on the gentler side of the 1980s mainstream was Huey Lewis and the News.

Lewis's first album, *Picture This* (1982), produced one Top 10 hit, but *Sports* hit number 1 in 1983 and yielded five Top 20 hits: "Heart and Soul" (number 8), "I Want a New Drug" (number 6), "The Heart of Rock and Roll" (number 6), "If This Is It" (number 6), and "Walking on a Thin Line" (number 18). They continued their success with "The Power of Love" (number 1, 1985) from the soundtrack for the movie *Back to the Future*.

Lewis followed *Sports* with another number 1 album, *Fore!*, which contained five Top 10 hits, including two that reached number 1 ("Stuck with You" and "Jacob's Ladder"). His last album of the decade was *Small World* (1988), a particularly creative album that included some brilliant work by the Tower of Power horn section (discussed in a later section of this course) and guest artists Stan Getz and Bruce Hornsby, but produced only two Top 40 hits: "Perfect World" (number 3) and "Small World" (number 25).

In some ways, Lewis's success is surprising. A levelheaded, intelligent, and content family man, he is a stark contrast to many flamboyant 1980s rock performers. He is almost a nostalgic throwback to the earlier days of rock and roll. In the words of Christopher Connelly, "Videos of [Huey Lewis and] the News have become a welcome oasis of normality in the broken-glass and leather-bikini world of MTV" (McDonough 1985, 161). Like Springsteen, he projected the image (apparently genuine) of being just a regular guy playing and singing some good old rock and roll.

[*]By clicking this link, you will be redirected to a third-party site.

Musical Career of U2

The following section will provide highlights from the career of U2, one of the most popular and long-lasting rock bands to emerge in the 1980s.

Two early albums (*Boy* and *October*) fared poorly; *War* (1983), *Under a Blood Red Sky* (1983; a live album), and *The Unforgettable Fire* (1984) began to reveal the band's potential, both musically and commercially. For example, both the title song and "A Sort of Homecoming" from *The Unforgettable Fire* are strong, well-performed mainstream rock songs. The haunting "4th of July" evokes a New Age feeling (more about New Age later). "Bad" has a repetitive, minimalistic accompaniment. However, lead singer Bono's vocal abilities are strained in songs like "Promenade" and "MLK."

Lead singer Bono (born Paul Hewson) is unusually candid about his own talents. In one interview, he said, "I can't really work out why anyone would buy a U2 record. When I listen to it, I just hear all the mistakes…. But I don't like the way I've sung on any of the records. I don't think I'm a good singer, but I think I'm getting to be a good singer" (Bronson 1988, 673). In the macho, egotistical world of the self-aggrandizing rock star of that era, such remarks are quite rare.

How could this rather undistinguished group become superstars of the late 1980s, extending their reign well into the new millennium? By 1987, U2 had been together for 11 years with no change of membership. The results were an undeniable tightness among band members and noticeably stronger performance skills for each individual. *The Joshua Tree* (1987) not only achieved the number 1 position (for nine weeks) but was awarded a Grammy as Album of the Year and included two number 1 singles ("With or Without You" and "I Still Haven't Found What I'm Looking For"). U2 had established themselves as an important rock band of the 1980s.

One big album does not equate to superstardom (remember Peter Frampton?). In 1988, U2 followed with *Rattle and Hum*, initiating a series of four consecutive number 1 albums (adding *Achtung Baby*, 1991; *Zooropa*, 1993; and *Pop*, 1997), yielding an impressive series of hit singles and several Grammy Awards. Comparing an early album such as *Under a Blood Red Sky* with *Rattle and Hum* provides a lesson in the remarkable improvement that time and perseverance can yield to a band that stays together and pays its dues over the years. There are tight, solid, and powerful performances of mainstream rock songs such as "Helter Skelter" and "Hawkmoon." There is a moving performance of "I Still Haven't Found What I'm Looking For," complete with a strong gospel feel. Even when Bono's voice is fully exposed, as on "Love

Rescue Me," the lead singer comes through with a strong, steady tone and reliable intonation. Like Springsteen, U2 often incorporates social, political, and even spiritual messages in their songs: "Pride (In the Name of Love)" and "MLK" are tributes to Martin Luther King, "Silver and Gold" is a song protesting apartheid, "God Part II"—dedicated to John Lennon—questions many forms of hypocrisy in society.

U2's success continued into the new millennium with *All That You Can't Leave Behind* (number 3, 2000), *How to Dismantle an Atomic Bomb* (number 1, 2004), and *No Line on the Horizon* (number 1, 2009). In what proved to be a significant miscalculation, U2 teamed with Apple to provide their album *Songs of Innocence* (2014) free on every new iPod; over 500 million iTunes users received the album, and, as it turns out, many did not want it, preferring to pick music for themselves! This marketing ploy resulted in over 80 million people listening to at least some of the album, though the blowback was significant. In addition to individual consumer complaints, critiques were equally harsh, referring to the move as "dystopian junk mail" (*Washington Post*) and the users' "lack of consent" (*New Yorker*).

The Edge and Bono of U2 on stage in 2005.
SOURCE: Pictorial Press Ltd/Alamy Stock Photo

As the first decade of the twenty-first century came to a close, Bono and the Edge teamed with renowned director Julie Taymor to create a superhero drama for the Broadway stage based on the tale of Spider-Man; at the time, it was the most expensive Broadway musical ever staged and gained more attention for its backstage intrigue and injuries to cast members than for the book or music created for the project. Though naysayers claimed that the musical would close soon after its opening, the production ran on Broadway for well over three years.

12.3.4: Female Stars

The 1980s found more women in mainstream rock than in any previous decade. One of the most remarkable comebacks in rock history was achieved by Tina Turner, whose early career with Ike Turner was discussed in an earlier section of this course. After disappearing from the charts for a full decade, Tina Turner reappeared in the mid-1980s as a "new" star. Her album *Private Dancer* moved to number 3 in 1984 and yielded three Top 10 hits, including the number 1 song "What's Love Got to Do with It." Turner capitalized on the new video trend, even as she turned 50 years old in 1988.

New female stars also appeared and were well-received by the rock audience. From the New York City punk–new wave scene came Blondie, a male quintet plus lead singer Debbie Harry. The band produced a series of hits from 1979 to 1981, beginning with "Heart of Glass" (number 1, 1979). Also coming from a punk background, Joan Jett and the Blackhearts hit the top spot in 1982 with "I Love Rock'n'Roll." Jett's cover version of "Crimson and Clover" (originally by Tommy James and the Shondells in 1969) also reached the Top 10. Pat Benatar, a classically trained singer, produced three consecutive Top 5 albums from 1980 to 1982. Her strong vocals placed her in the rock mainstream, where she produced a Top 10 hit in 1980, "Hit Me with Your Best Shot." The successes of Grace Slick (Jefferson Airplane) and Janis Joplin had opened the door to this possibility, which would continue.

JOURNAL

Lyrics & Music

Listen carefully to Bruce Springsteen's "Jungleland" (from *Born to Run*) while reading the lyrics, which you can locate easily online. After listening one time, read the lyrics through a couple of times as if poetry. Then listen again and pay close attention to the relationship between the music and text, identifying places where the music may reflect, emphasize, or add another layer of meaning to the text. In your response, identify two or three of the combinations you find most interesting, describing each relationship and its impact in the context of this song.

 The response entered here will appear in the performance dashboard and can be viewed by your instructor.

Submit

12.4: Mainstream Rock beyond the 1980s

OBJECTIVE: Explain the continued success of rock performers beyond the 1980s

In the history of rock and roll, several artists have retained a high degree of popularity across multiple decades. This is no small feat when one considers the number of new artists appearing each year and the high level of competition in the popular music market. Classic rock acts that maintained a significant musical presence at the beginning of the twenty-first century include the Rolling Stones, Aerosmith, and the Eagles (initially, this was primarily through the solo recordings of Don Henley, then following the band's reunion in 1994). As time marched on, some of these artists—including Eric Clapton, Sting, Elton John, and the Eagles—who were undoubtedly considered revolutionaries during the 1960s and 1970s, tended to become more mellow.

12.4.1: The Musical Maturation of Mainstream Rock

Other musicians balanced this musical shift by also producing a significant amount of material that retained the rebellious, energetic, and often loud aspects of rock and roll. As a result, artists like Bruce Springsteen, Rod Stewart, Paul McCartney, and Billy Joel managed to retain their maturing fans from earlier decades, while attracting a whole new audience of post-boomers.

As part of the process of musical maturation, several rock artists turned toward classical music as a creative outlet. In an earlier section of this course, we described Paul McCartney's *Give My Regards to Broad Street* (1984). In 1991, McCartney premiered his first classical composition, *Liverpool Oratorio*, receiving a lukewarm reception. In 2000, following the death of his wife after a battle with breast cancer, he released *A Garland for Linda* (number 7, classical), a collection of modern classical pieces, including one of his own titled "Nova." Elvis Costello's *The Juliet Letters* (1993) represents an ambitious collaboration between Costello and England's Brodsky String Quartet, resulting in a song cycle. In addition, Costello collaborated with Burt Bacharach on the soundtrack for *Grace of My Heart* (1996), resulting in a Grammy nomination for the song "God Give Me Strength." As mentioned previously, Elton John turned to composing film soundtracks for animated features, such as *The Lion King* (1994; including the Academy Award–winning Best Original Song "Can You Feel the Love Tonight"). In 2001, Billy Joel released *Fantasies & Delusions: Music for Solo Piano* (debuted at number 1, classical). Credited to "William Joel," performed by virtuoso Richard Joo, and recorded in Vienna at the famous Mozartsaal in the Vienna Konzerthaus, this recording reveals an earnest attempt by a veteran rock and roller to communicate with his audience via classical music, using only a solo piano.

This trend toward rock artists reaching for a place in so-called "serious" art music is likely to continue, although it should be noted that most of these artists maintain an outdated concept of classical music as described in the discussion of art rock in another section of this course.

12.4.2: Eric Clapton

We have already discussed Eric Clapton in this chapter, but, because he serves as a prime example of a mellowing rock legend and because his acoustic version of "Layla" (1992) allows a direct comparison with his performance on the original recording (a hit for Derek and the Dominoes in 1970), let us take a closer look at this revered guitarist.

Analysis of Clapton's *Unplugged* Performance

The following section provides a detailed comparison of Eric Clapton's *Unplugged* performance of "Layla" to the original recording by Derek & the Dominoes, on which the guitarist Duane Allman also played.

Layla Guitar Riff

In 1992, Clapton appeared on MTV's *Unplugged* series, performing acoustic versions of many of his songs, including "Layla." In the 1992 version, the high-energy rock feeling of the early recording is replaced by a relaxed, laid-back musical feel. What are the specific musical elements that make this later recording sound so different? The overall instrumentation changed, replacing the two screaming rock guitars of Clapton and Duane Allman with acoustic guitar and acoustic piano. Clapton's vocal style is much lighter on the *Unplugged* performance, resulting in a more mature, introspective sound. Most noticeable, however, is the complete absence of the prominent guitar riff that pervades the original version, as shown above.

Layla guitar riff (quadruple subdivision)

Why is such a memorable aspect of the original tune left out of the cover version? This question leads us to a discussion of the most changed musical aspect of Clapton's later recording: the rhythm. Most obvious is the significant change in tempo. The original recording was much faster, falling somewhere between 114 and 120 beats per minute, depending on which section one listens to. In contrast, the *Unplugged* version remains at a steady 93 beats per minute throughout. Listen carefully to both versions of "Layla," concentrating on how the beats are subdivided. If you focus your attention on the drummer's hi-hat cymbal in the original version or the tambourine part in the later recording, it is possible to hear an interesting difference between the two. In the verses of the original recording, the beat is divided in half (duple subdivision), while the beat in the choruses, where the word "Layla" enters, is divided into four (quadruple) subdivisions. In contrast, the MTV performance incorporates a triple subdivision of the beat, often with only the first and third notes of this subdivision being played. The resulting long-short, long-short rhythm is sometimes referred to as a shuffle beat and is associated with a more relaxed musical style, as shown above.

If we look closely at the rhythm of the guitar riff from the Derek and the Dominoes recording, we can determine why this musical signature of the original was not incorporated into the later version: Because of the beat subdivision, it could not have been used without destroying the underlying shuffle rhythm. The guitar riff requires that each beat be divided into fourths rather than thirds. Therefore, Clapton chose to use the melody and harmony of the original, while altering both the timbre and rhythm for this remake of his classic tune. The recording of his MTV session earned Clapton six Grammys, including Record of the Year, Song of the Year, and Best Pop Vocal Performance, Male, for "Tears in Heaven" (number 2, 1992), a song inspired by the tragic death of his four-year-old son.

Following a brief reunion with his fellow band members for Cream's induction into the Rock and Roll Hall of Fame, Clapton returned to his roots, releasing a collection of classic blues tunes entitled *From the Cradle* (number 1, 1994) that won a Grammy for Best Traditional Blues Album. Through the 1990s and into the new millennium, he alternated between recording original material and covering traditional blues tunes, including a duets album with longtime mentor and friend B. B. King (*Riding with the King*; number 3, 2000) and an homage to blues great Robert Johnson (*Me and Mr. Johnson*; number 6, 2004). Continuing to reveal his musical influences and concurrently reconfirm his own musical relevance, Clapton released a collection of old-time blues and originals (*Clapton*) that reached number 6 in 2010.

BECOME AN ACTIVE LISTENER: COMPARING VERSIONS OF A SONG

Now that you have had a chance to review the many fragmented subgenres presented in this chapter, it is time to return to your own collection of recordings, to your streaming service, or to the Internet to identify, independently, some of the differentiating elements in recordings with which you may be more familiar.

Compare two versions of the same song, either by the same artist or by two different artists, and identify, specifically, how the two recordings are different one from another:

1. Is the vocalist's singing style different?
2. Does the instrumentation change?
3. Is the tempo different?
4. Is the meter or beat subdivision altered?
5. What other differences do you notice? (return to the discussion of "Elements of Music" early in this course to remind yourself of the many ways musical sound can be differentiated)

12.5: Musical Close-Up on Rock Lyrics

OBJECTIVE: Analyze the implications associated with explicit lyrics in rock music

Technically speaking, lyrics are not a musical element. Nevertheless, throughout the history of music, words and music have been intimately related. After all, the most natural (and cheapest) instrument is the human voice. Music alone is a powerful, communicative tool, but its communication is nonverbal. The addition of words provides a more specific and understandable form of communication. A given piece of music may make us feel sad in a general way, but the words tell us what there is to be sad about (the loss of a love relationship, for example).

In spite of the importance of the guitar, drums, and various types of keyboards, rock has been, above all, vocal music. The overwhelming number of artists discussed in this book were singers; granted, most also played one or more instruments. In some cases, rock songs began with the music, the words being added to fit; but just as often, a song originated with a poem (lyrics) to which music was added. It works both ways.

Early rock lyrics were usually about boy-girl romantic situations or about good times. Sex was rarely involved, and when it was, the references were implicit or hidden in double entendre. Among the most popular 1950s rockers, Little Richard came the closest to suggestive lyrics (listen, for example, to "Good Golly Miss Molly" and "Long Tall Sally").

The 1960s brought about major changes in rock lyrics. Although the surfers were still concerned with romance and good times—add sun, surf, and cars to the list—and the dance craze focused (obviously) on dancing, the rising folk music trend brought social and political issues to rock lyrics. It was at this point that these songs ceased being merely a mirror of society and began to be an active agent of change in society. The lyrics of the folk rockers pointed the way to what they believed could be a better way of life—life without war, violence, racial prejudice, and environmental pollution.

By 1967, rock lyrics had made steady and impressive progress from the walk-talk, arms-charms rhyme schemes of the 1950s to the thought-provoking lyrics of Dylan, the Beatles, the Byrds, and others; but, around 1967 (including the Summer of Love), further changes began to take place. Prior to this particular year, the subject of drugs in song lyrics had been regarded as taboo. Occasional references to drugs were accomplished by means of the double entendre. Songs like "Eight Miles High" (the Byrds) and "Lucy in the Sky with Diamonds" (the Beatles) created controversy but were excused because of the possibility of an innocent alternative meaning. In 1967, however, songs like "White Rabbit" by the Jefferson Airplane and "A Day in the Life" by the Beatles began to appear, and rock took a significant step from the innocent and the occasionally suggestive double entendre to the blatant enunciation of taboo topics.

12.5.1: Drugs

Since the late 1960s, explicit references to drugs have become rather common in rock lyrics. Because the drug culture has an ever-changing jargon of its own, many rock song drug references are perfectly clear to the initiated but pass right by the nondrug-oriented listener. While Country Joe McDonald sang overt drug songs like "Acid Commercial," others resorted to drug jargon in songs like "Along Comes Mary" (the Association) and "Lady Jane" and "Jumpin' Jack Flash" (both by the Rolling Stones). The drug references functioned in a dual capacity: They reflected the drug-oriented segment of the rock community that produced the songs, but because of the wide distribution of the music, they also spread the pro-drug message to a broader spectrum of society that otherwise might not have been tempted by drug use. So, to the oft-asked question, "Did rock music merely reflect the growing use of drugs in the 1960s and 1970s, or was it an active agent in that trend?" the answer is "yes," it served both purposes.

12.5.2: Sex

What of the other major taboo, sex? Again, the music of the late 1960s edged ever closer to overt and explicit sexual references. In British rock, the Rolling Stones led the way toward more explicit references to sex; on this side of the Atlantic, the "credit" goes to Frank Zappa. The latter's *Fillmore East* (1971) album contained explicitly sexual lyrics, although couched in Zappa's typical dirty-joke context. More menacing was a song on the Stones *Goats Head Soup* (1973) album, originally titled "Starfucker." The song refers to the sexual adventures of a groupie who relentlessly pursues rock and movie stars. (Atlantic Records label head Ahmet Ertegun insisted on the change of title to "Star Star.")

Granted, there had always been underground groups that had produced sexually explicit songs, but Zappa and the Stones were superstars. Once the barriers were broken, the trend was unstoppable. The level of sexual explicitness remained more or less constant through the 1970s and intensified in the 1980s. Particularly noticeable were two new aspects in sexual rock lyrics: (1) the combination of sex and violence (often using the latter as a metaphor for the former) and (2) the fascination with so-called deviant sexual behavior.

Songwriters have used many different metaphors when referring to sex. They have described the innocence and spring-like beauty of sex with references to "the birds and the bees"; referring to the thrill and excitement of sex, they have written of "bells and fireworks" and even "thunder and lightning" (the title of a 1972, Top 20 hit for Chi Coltrane). In the 1980s, though, more violent metaphors became common. Songs by Mötley Crüe, Kiss, The Who, AC/DC, Judas Priest, Dokken, and Marvin Gaye describe the male sex organ as a gun, a knife, a sword, a steel rod, or a pipe; Kiss and AC/DC refer to the female sex organ as a cake to be cut or butter to be sliced; ejaculation is the act of shooting the gun; and semen consists of bullets. In some of the songs, the references could mean either sex or violence, but it is the virtually synonymous use of the two that makes one uncertain, which is intended, alarming many observers.

The second subtrend in sexual lyrics has been the inclusion of sex beyond the common "missionary position." Leading the way here was Prince, who sang of incest ("Sister"), masturbation ("Jack U Off"), group sex ("When You Were Mine"), and oral sex ("Head"). There are songs that combine sex and the occult and songs that describe sadomasochism. The uses of explicit language to describe straightforward sex are simply too numerous to mention, and, of course, there are songs that, using nonverbal utterances (sighs, moans, screams, etc.), are musical depictions of the sex act (e.g., Ray Charles, Donna Summer, and Prince). This represents a significant departure from the era of "I Want to Hold Your Hand."

12.5.3: Violent Rebellion

Drugs and sex were not the only themes to find increasingly explicit expression in rock lyrics of the 1970s and 1980s. Themes of rebellion took a variety of forms. Of course, rock and roll, even in its earliest forms, was inherently rebellious, but the lyrics of those early rock songs were rarely overt in their rebellion. In the 1960s, folk, folk rock, and other socially-oriented styles criticized existing society and offered "a better way"; these songs represented a more positive type of rebellion (in fact, a better word might be "reform").

Perhaps, in part, because of the disillusionment of the late 1960s youth movement, the rebellion of the 1970s and 1980s grew increasingly angry and negative. AC/DC's "School Daze" provides a stark contrast to Chuck Berry's "School Days." Whereas Berry suggested that at three o'clock, students lay down their educational burdens and swing down to a malt shop to dance, AC/DC screams at them to burn down the school. School itself is referred to as a "juvenile prison" and a "homework hellhouse." Negative views of education had been expressed earlier by Pink Floyd in the lyrics to "Another Brick in the Wall—Part II"

Songs by Kiss and Mötley Crüe expressed rebellion against school, parents, and other authority figures. Twisted Sister shouted angrily, that they weren't going to take it anymore and characterized adult (parental) society as being "condescending," "trite," "jaded," and "boring." Ozzy Osborne warned teachers and authority figures in general, about making them wish that they had never been born. Twisted Sister shouted at parents, daring them to try and make them do anything.

The angry sentiments of the metal bands were carried to even further extremes by some rappers (specifically gangsta rappers, as you will see in a later section of this course). For these rappers, the targets of their lyrics were less likely to be parents and education. Gangsta rappers aimed their hostility primarily at women, the police, and white society in general. These lyrics, too, were extremely explicit in their references to acts of violence and sex. Once again, such sentiments can be seen as reflections of normal teenage rebellion. However, there has always been much discussion about the possibility that the open defiance and angry hostility expressed in these songs may have the effect of intensifying normal (and even healthy) teenage rebellion, turning it into something more destructive.

12.5.4: Satanism

Another form of rebellion that can be found in rock lyrics of various periods is the trend toward the occult and, in its most extreme form, satanism. Although one can trace satanic references back to songs like "Sympathy for the Devil" and "Lucretia MacEvil," such references were rather innocuous and, in fact, painted a distinctly unflattering image of the devil. However, by the 1980s, some groups were not merely referring to the devil, but seemed to be advocating satanism. *Venom*'s album notes say as much: "We are possessed by all that is evil; the death of you, God, we demand. We spit at the virgin you worship, and sit at Lord Satan's right hand." Groups such as Mercyful Fate, Exciter, Slayer, Megadeth, Iron Maiden, AC/DC, and King Diamond expressed similar messages. Although some of the satanic groups simply used this rather extreme form of rebellion as a sales gimmick, others seemed to be genuinely devoted to their messages.

12.5.5: Suicide

There has always been a vigorous debate about the effect of rock music on violent behavior and, particularly, suicide. There had been a brief fascination with death in a few songs of the late 1950s and early 1960s (e.g., Mark Dinning's 1960 "Teen Angel" and the Shangri-Las' "Leader of the Pack" and Jan and Dean's "Dead Man's Curve," both from 1964). Suicide had been specifically referenced in Jody Reynold's morose song of 1958, "The Endless Sleep." However, by the 1980s, teen suicides had tripled within a 30-year period and had become the second leading cause of death among people under age 25. Compounding concern about this development, an alarming number of teens had committed suicide while listening to rock songs with lyrics that referred to killing oneself, including the oft-cited "Suicide Solution" by Ozzy Osbourne. Similar sentiments are expressed in songs by Pink Floyd, AC/DC, Black Sabbath, and Metallica. In most cases, the bands and their defenders offer alternative interpretations for the lyrics. Some people see these songs as reflective of a troubled teenage society, not a cause of suicide. Others fear that this kind of negative message may push depressed teenagers over the edge and cause them to commit suicide. As with other themes in rock and roll, like sex and violence, it is often impossible to tell which comes first—the music or the social trend.

12.5.6: Effect of Explicit Lyrics

The five themes described above—drugs, sex, violent rebellion, satanism, and suicide—have raised concerns about the effects of the more explicit rock lyrics on teenagers. Groups such as the National Parent Teacher Association

and the Parents Music Resource Center communicated such concerns to the recording industry and also attempted to alert parents and teenagers to the potential dangers. Citing Joe Stuessy, author/co-author of previous editions of this text, *Rolling Stone* magazine's 2010 list of "The 100 Moments That Rocked Our World" included a reference to these activities. With the concurrence of educators and psychiatrists armed with considerable research, they suggest that some (not all) rock lyrics may have gone so far that they have become potentially dangerous to the impressionable minds of teens and preteens, a topic that will be addressed again near the end of this course.

What is virtually unarguable is that rock lyrics changed dramatically over rock's first five decades. By the turn of the century, one could truthfully say that there was no topic that was taboo to the rock lyricist; the language of those lyrics had virtually no limitations on explicitness. The innocence of the 1950s and the idealism of the 1960s were, for the most part, gone. A song like Madonna's "Material Girl" with its proud statement of purely materialistic values might have been received with total revulsion 20 years earlier (1965); in 1985, it reached number 2 on the Hot 100. The acceptance of explicit lyrics into the mainstream is evident if one compares the Oscar-winning song of 1977 ("You Light Up My Life" by Debby Boone) to the Oscar winner just 18 years later ("It's Hard Out Here for a Pimp" by Three-6 Mafia).

Much of the concern over explicit lyrics has centered on heavy metal and rap bands, and, indeed, they seem especially prone to such antisocial lyrics, but it is noteworthy that not all heavy metal and rap bands produce such lyrics, and some other artists not associated with either of these musical genres have produced very explicit lyrics (e.g., Prince and Marvin Gaye). Furthermore, many songs never touch on any of these topics. We have dealt with these topics because some were relatively new to rock in the 1970s (e.g., satanism and suicide), and some were new in their level of explicitness (sex, drugs) and vehemence (rebellion).

U2 on Martin Luther King, Jr.

In contrast to the formerly taboo lyrical topics described in the previous section, lyrics for many rock songs tackle difficult and socially relevant issues. Examine the lyrics of U2's "Pride (In the Name of Love)" from *The Unforgettable Fire* (1984) and discuss the different meanings that can be attributed, including the intended tribute to Martin Luther King. After studying the lyrics in isolation, listen to the song and describe what the music adds to the text. Identify at least one other rock song that focuses on MLK. How does the approach to this second song, both lyrical and musical, differ from U2's "Pride"?

 The response entered here will appear in the performance dashboard and can be viewed by your instructor.

Submit

Summary: Mainstream Rock

The rock and roll revolution continued into the 1970s and 1980s, revealing an explosion of subgenres as the market fragmented significantly. Mainstream trends persisted and were evident in the music produced by both British and American artists. As described in this chapter, mainstream rock of these two decades could be divided into at least two camps: one with a harder edge and the other representing a gentler side. One important subgenre that emerged, influenced significantly by rock's C&W roots, was southern rock. Superstars like Bruce Springsteen and U2 appeared during this period and solidified their relevance over the ensuing decades. Following the lead of Grace Slick and Janis Joplin, female artists were among the most successful of the era. As the 1990s approached, some of the most successful artists seemed to initiate a period of maturation and mellowing in their musical output. As we continue with this course, you will see that the fragmentation initiated during this era continued and a number of these subgenres evolve and, in some cases, fuse to create even more possibilities for the future of rock and roll.

Take Note: Mainstream Rock

- *Why were the years between 1970 and 1980 known as the "me decade"?*—Unlike the 1960s, during which social movements such as the Civil Rights and the anti-Vietnam War movements brought people together, the decade of the 1970s was characterized by a focus on individual pursuits. Self-help movements arose to help individuals "find themselves." Rock music reflected this overall trend as it fragmented into a series of sub-styles, each listened to by a subset of the larger population of rock music listeners. However, mainstream rock continued to flourish as a major focus of the record industry.

- *How did mainstream rock evolve during the 1970s?*—The British Invasion of the 1960s continued to produce new popular rock performers into the 1970s. As in the previous decade, both harder rock styles (such as Eric Clapton and Rod Stewart) and softer styles (represented by Fleetwood Mac and Elton John) flourished on the charts. American acts that performed mainstream rock included the rock-revivalist group Creedence Clearwater Revival, the psychedelic soul of Sly and the Family Stone, and the southern rock of the Allman Brothers and Lynyrd Skynyrd.

- *Who were some of the leading artists and bands of the 1980s mainstream?*—Bruce Springsteen emerged as a major mainstream rock star in the 1980s, beginning with his 1984 release, *Born in the U.S.A.* From Ireland, U2 found success a few short years later with their album *The Joshua Tree.* Both Springsteen and U2 became major stars thanks to their performances in large stadiums, developing a devoted fan base through extensive touring. On the radio, Huey Lewis & The News were potent hit makers, performing a softer form of rock in the early through mid-1980s. Notable female stars of the era included a comeback by 1960s soul singer Tina Turner; the rise of new wave superstar Debbie Harry, the lead singer of Blondie; and hard rocker Joan Jett.

- *How have mainstream rock performers continued to be popular since the 1980s?*—Mainstream performers who have enjoyed careers over several decades have continued to find an audience, either by sticking with a tried-and-true formula (Rolling Stones), focusing on softer musical styles (Eric Clapton), or by expanding their reach by composing in classical styles (Billy Joel and Paul McCartney) or for film soundtracks and Broadway shows (Elton John).

SHARED WRITING

Emerging Rock Subgenres During the 1970s

Based on the content of the present chapter, identify three subgenres of rock that emerged during 1970s. Utilizing your growing musical vocabulary (especially the musical elements), provide a detailed description of the consistent characteristics within each of these styles. What are some of the most important traits that differentiate these subgenres one from another? What was the primary audience for each subgenre, and how was the music marketed to this potential audience? Read the responses of at least three of your classmates, then add a brief paragraph to your own response that explains how the subgenres identified by your peers either (a) fit into the same subgenre categories you chose or (b) require adding other subgenres to the three you identified.

 A minimum number of characters is required to post and earn points. After posting, your response can be viewed by your class and instructor, and you can participate in the class discussion.

Post

0 characters | 140 minimum

Chapter 13
The Continuing Fragmentation of Rock

Learning Objectives

13.1 Explain how art rock changed to progressive rock

13.2 Describe the evolution of jazz rock into fusion

13.3 Outline the evolution of the singer-songwriter movement

13.4 Identify influences on folk and reggae music after the 70s

13.5 Analyze the changes to country music in the 70s and 80s

13.6 Explain why jam bands became popular during the 1980s

13.7 Summarize the evolution of soft rock from the 70s to the 90s

13.8 Compare the musical elements of country and rock music

The fragmentation that became evident during the 1970s continued apace during the coming decades, resulting in a complicated, multifaceted series of branches emerging from the R&B, Pop, and C&W roots of the rock and roll tree. A number of subgenres that appeared during the previous decade continued to evolve (American and British mainstream rock and southern rock) and new styles developed (heavy metal and hip-hop/rap).

The Evolution of Rock as Fragmentation Continues

The following section will provide an overview of the evolution of some of the subgenres of rock that emerged as the fragmentation continued from the late 1960s into the 1970s.

Sub-Styles of the 60s Evolve—With the arrival of the Rolling Stones and the Beatles, rock's mainstream divided into harder and gentler sides, and then even these branches fragmented further. In the 1960s—due mostly to the Beatles but also influenced by the Beach Boys, Frank Zappa, and others—the musical language of rock became more sophisticated and creative. This decade also saw the emergence of folk rock, jazz rock, art rock, and soul music. We will see that in the 1970s and 1980s these combination styles continued to develop, although several of them acquired new names: jazz rock became fusion; folk rockers became singer-songwriters; art rock became progressive rock; and country rock was, in some cases, called progressive country. An exception seemed to be soft rock, which continued, unswerving, from its inception with Pat Boone and Elvis Presley straight into the new century.

Emergence of Heavy Metal/Rap—Two styles that were new in the 1970s and then developed dramatically in the 1980s were heavy metal and rap (a chapter is dedicated to each later in this course). Both of these new styles (each in its own way) were strongly antiestablishment, despite the strong societal desire for youth to tend to their own interests and pursue success within the establishment. While the 1970s were known as the "me decade," this characteristic was compounded in the 1980s—called by some the "Decade of Greed." Of course, in any decade, there are those—especially among the youth—who rebel against norms. For them, heavy metal and rap were the perfect expressions of anger and frustration with the establishment.

Music as a Reflection of Society—In the mid-1970s, the Watergate crisis resulted in a heightened distrust of the government, in general, and of the American political system, specifically. The sordid affair eventually resulted in President Nixon's resignation from office. For young people who were skeptical of the government and politics, the Watergate crisis alienated them even further. Their rebellion was musically embodied in heavy metal

From 1980 to 1988, the White House was occupied by President Ronald Reagan, a conservative Republican. His vice president, George H. W. Bush, succeeded him as president from 1988 to 1992. During the Reagan years, the economy expanded, and the era, at least in comparison to directly preceding decades, constituted a period of relative peace. Those who functioned within the system flourished. However, there were those who felt disenfranchised. This later group, especially, included many African Americans. The rise of rap music (or hip-hop) became an expression of their resentment.

As is almost always the case, during this period, society and music reflected each other. Those who were content to work within the system to enhance their own hopes and dreams tended to be rather nonrebellious. They appeared to be content as well with the continuation of musical styles that were simply extensions of the past (even if new names were assigned). For those who were disaffected by the Watergate crisis of the 1970s and those who did not benefit during the Reagan years, heavy metal and rap provided outlets for their frustration and discontent.

Let us continue our survey of the 1970s and beyond by looking at the various styles that emerged from the 1960s. Even though these styles were essentially continuations, we will see, as we did with the mainstream styles, that each style fragments into an array of distinct sounds performed by representative artists.

13.1: Art Rock Evolves into Progressive Rock

OBJECTIVE: Explain how art rock changed to progressive rock

The type of art rock represented by Jon Lord's *Concerto* and *Gemini Suite* and Rick Wakeman's *Journey to the Centre of the Earth* (number 3, 1974) and *The Myths and Legends of King Arthur and the Knights of the Round Table* (1975) receded after the mid-1970s, as did rock opera. The groups that continued to produce new music—such as Yes and Emerson, Lake & Palmer—relied on the musical language of rock to create longer, more complex works that they hoped could be taken as seriously as classical works. To distinguish them from the earlier rock with orchestra and rock opera advocates, the term **progressive rock** replaced art rock. The progressive rock groups of the 1970s were from England and the United States as well as from several other European countries. As with most 1970s genres, these groups represented a considerable range of styles.

13.1.1: Pink Floyd

Pink Floyd was formed in London in 1965 from the remnants of several previous groups. Though the band did not experience immediate commercial success, even their early albums received significant critical acclaim. The group's initial creative leader, Roger "Syd" Barrett, became increasingly affected by psychological problems reportedly intensified by drug abuse; as a result, he left the band in 1968.

Pink Floyd's breakthrough came in 1973 with *The Dark Side of the Moon*. Having become associated with the psychedelic rock trend, this album established Pink Floyd as progressive rock superstars. Created in collaboration with producer Alan Parsons, *Dark Side,* which took some nine months to produce, not only became a number 1 album but also became the longest-running chart album in history, remaining on the charts for over 14 years! This archetypal British progressive rock album deals with alienation, paranoia, and insanity. The heavy use of electronics was typical of Pink Floyd. Although the album was rather dark and brooding, there were rock songs like "Time" and "Money" (note the sextuple meter of the latter). The song "Us and Them" shows the influence of producer Parsons (compare to the later "Time" by the Alan Parsons Project). "Brain Damage," a song about insanity, foreshadows later trends in heavy metal lyrics. There are touches of jazz (note the sax work on "Us and Them"), soul (the female vocal on "The Great Gig in the Sky"), and pure electronic experimentation ("On the Run").

Pink Floyd's success continued through the mid- and late 1970s. The tour that promoted *The Wall* (number 1, 1979) involved an elaborate set, including a 30-foot high wall that toppled (of course) just before the end of the show. Utilizing extra singers and instrumentalists, video, elaborate lighting, and more giant plastic inflatables, the Wall tour was among the most elaborate in rock history. In spite of internal squabbles, lawsuits, and personnel changes, Pink Floyd produced two number 1 albums in the 1990s (*The Division Bell* in 1994 and *P.U.L.S.E.* in 1995). Cofounder Roger Waters has been the most active of the original members of Pink Floyd. From 2006 to 2008, he performed *Dark Side* more than 118 times around the globe, raking in over $60 million; then, beginning in 2010, he initiated a 30th anniversary tour of *The Wall* with even more elaborate staging than the original tour, as captured in the documentary *Roger Waters: The Wall* (2014). Waters' emotional reaction to the U.S. election of 2016 resulted in his release of *Is This the Life We Really Want?* (2017).

Watch "Money" by Pink Floyd.*

https://www.youtube.com/watch?v=-0kcet4aPpQ

13.1.2: King Crimson

King Crimson was one of the leading British progressive rock groups of the 1970s. The ever-changing personnel of this band included a number of prominent 1970s rock musicians: Greg Lake (ELP), Ian McDonald (Foreigner), Bill Bruford (Yes and Genesis), John Wetton (Asia and Uriah Heep), and Boz Burrell (Bad Company). The guiding force of King Crimson was Robert Fripp. Their first album, *In the Court of the Crimson King* (number 28, 1969), was critically acclaimed. The album contained five extended pieces and revealed the art rock (i.e., progressive) creativity of Fripp.

King Crimson established a wide following in England and Europe but a relatively small (if loyal) following in the United States. *Larks' Tongues in Aspic* (number 61, 1973) is a fascinating album, especially for its extended works, including the title song (parts 1 and 2), "Exiles," "Easy Money," and "The Talking Drum." Throughout, the band's sound changes often and dramatically. There are moments of genuine hard rock, experiments with minimalism, changing meters, sound effects, interesting violin and viola work, and electronics. It is thoughtful music, utilizing a wide spectrum of sound resources in a diverse variety of styles, and, thus, provides an interesting perspective regarding the state of British progressive rock in the mid-1970s.

In late 1974, Fripp disbanded King Crimson. He later joined with Brian Eno to create several albums exploring the minimalist concepts that would be developed later by new wave and new age groups. Fripp's fascination with electronics led to the development of "Frippertronics," a style that involved creating a tape delay system through the use of two tape recorders and guitar. Although many bands happily answered to the phrase *progressive rock* in the 1970s, few truly deserved that title more than King Crimson.

King Crimson sprang to life again in 1981 with a new sound and new personnel. A series of impeccably produced recordings followed, including *Discipline* (1981), *Beat* (1982), and *Three of a Perfect Pair* (1984), disbanding after the third album. Fripp later created a third incarnation of the band and released *Thrak* (1995). Various permutations of the performances continued into the new millennium, "fractualized" (Fripp's word) into four "ProjeKcts."

13.1.3: Jethro Tull

Jethro Tull released recordings that spanned a wide range of styles from mainstream (*Aqualung*) to progressive rock (*Thick as a Brick*, 1972, and *A Passion Play*, 1973). Ian Anderson (flute, sax, guitar, and vocals) moved the band's sound away from its blues-based starting point toward the new progressive rock sound. Tull found a more receptive audience in the United States than in their native England. By far, their most commercially successful album was their fourth release, *Aqualung* (number 7, 1971), which sold over three million copies and garnered significant FM airplay for "Cross-Eyed Mary" and "Locomotive Breath." *Thick as a Brick* (number 1, 1972), consisting of a single, album-long song, established the band in the ranks of progressive rock groups. Anderson's flute solos shifted between sounds of rock, jazz, and classical music. The next album, *Living in the Past,* yielded a popular single (the title song) that may have been the first hit single in quintuple meter since Dave Brubeck's "Take Five" of 1961. The concept album *A Passion Play* (number 1, 1973)—like *Thick as a Brick*, a single piece occupying the entire album—was critically scorned, but rose to number 1 regardless. Several albums from 1974 to 1977 sold well in the United States, but the band never did quite as well after that, although it released albums into the 2000s.

13.1.4: Other British Art Rockers

British leadership in art and progressive rock continued throughout the 1970s and included such bands as the Electric Light Orchestra (ELO), Soft Machine, Gentle Giant, and Henry Cow. Of these, the most popular by far was ELO. Soft Machine and Gentle Giant produced some very sophisticated progressive rock but failed to have major commercial impact. Henry Cow may have been one of the most innovative and creative of these bands. They remain largely unknown but, like all of these progressive groups, they can open up a new musical experience to the adventurous listener.

An offshoot of the progressive rock trend was the movement toward heavily electronic rock—later called synth-pop, technorock, or electropop—characterized by a strong reliance on high-tech synthesizers and related electronic keyboards. One of the most successful early ventures into this branch of art rock was made by Mike Oldfield. In 1972, he released the impressive solo album *Tubular Bells* (number 3). Oldfield played a wide variety of instruments on the album, which had over 40 tracks in the studio and countless overdubs. An excerpt from the 49-minute work was used as the theme for the movie *The Exorcist* (1973), which assured its commercial success despite—or, perhaps, because of—its off-kilter, changing meter feel.

---

*By clicking this link, you will be redirected to a third-party site.

13.1.5: Progressive Rock in Europe and North America

Several German groups enjoyed success in the field of heavily electrified progressive rock. Passport was perhaps the best of these; purely instrumental, the band relied primarily on Klaus Doldinger's saxophone and keyboards and combined elements of rock and jazz with a strong dose of tasteful electronic keyboards. Triumvirat, another German group, sounded remarkably like Emerson, Lake & Palmer. Kraftwerk surpassed Passport and Triumvirat commercially by achieving a Top 30 single, "Autobahn" in 1975; the album from which this title track was taken reached number 5.

Gradually, progressive rock spread from England and Germany to other European countries. One of the best was the band led by guitarist Terje Rypdal in Norway. Rypdal's band shifted smoothly between a progressive rock style and jazz-rock fusion. Rypdal's 1974 album *Whenever I Seem to Be Far Away* is a good example of his work. From Holland came Focus, another band that moved deftly between progressive rock and jazz-rock fusion. Focus was formed in 1969 by organist and flutist Thijs Van Leer, a graduate of the Amsterdam Conservatorium. Featuring the fine guitar work of Jan Akkerman, Focus was capable of a variety of styles, as illustrated on *Focus 3* (1973), a double album. "Love Remembered" is a hauntingly beautiful soft-rock song with jazz overtones, somewhat similar to parts of Pink Floyd's *Dark Side of the Moon* and much of the Alan Parsons Project's work. "Carnival Fugue" is a particularly interesting work that begins like a classical fugue but soon moves to a jazz-rock fusion style. *Hamburger Concerto* (1974) places the band firmly in the progressive rock category; the title work, a six-movement suite (not really a concerto in the classical sense), contains classical references and is a more or less successful attempt at "serious" rock.

RUSH By the mid-1970s, the influence of progressive rock was felt in North America, resulting in the emergence of Kansas (discussed later in this course), Styx, Todd Rundgren's Utopia, Rush, and many other musically adventurous groups. Among the most successful of these groups was Rush, a Canadian power trio. Rush's first three albums were not big sellers, and it was not until their fourth album, *2112* (1976), that sales began to improve. For the balance of the 1970s, Rush attracted a relatively small but loyal following.

In the 1970s, the band had flirted with a hard rock/heavy metal style, especially on *Fly by Night* and *Caress of Steel* (both 1975). Some of their heavier songs from this early period (e.g., "Finding My Way" [*Rush*] and "Anthem" [*Fly by Night*]) approach the sound of heavy metal bands of the period, but their continuing musical evolution suggests that they belong more appropriately to the category of progressive rock bands. During the 1980s, Rush seemed to lessen the heavy aspects of their sound and found a significantly bigger audience. If one compares *Rush* (number 105, 1974) with *Grace Under Pressure* (number 10, 1984), one finds not only a remarkably different image, but also a strikingly different musical style. Although vestiges of their earlier, heavy style remained, much changed. Lead singer Geddy Lee's voice dropped from his earlier adenoidal screaming to a somewhat more typical, male vocal range. The band also adds a heavy dose of synthesizers, some of which were played live by Geddy Lee using a foot pedal controller. Rush's more mature style adhered more closely to strong, mainstream hard rock. Rush's success continued into the 2000s, touring and releasing new material, including three Top 10 albums: *Vapor Trails* (number 6, 2002), *Snake and Arrows* (number 3, 2007), *Clockwork Angels* (number 2, 2012).

JOURNAL

Music in a Cinematic Context

Listen carefully to Mike Oldfield's "Tubular Bells, Part I." Though I hope you listen to the whole piece, given its length, make absolutely certain to listen to at least the first five minutes. Write three to five sentences describing your thoughts about and response to this interesting musical sound. Then, with your instructor's assistance, find two or three excerpts from the film *The Exorcist* (1973) that are accompanied by this music and watch those scenes. Compose a second paragraph about your reaction to the music in this cinematic context. How did the combination of musical sound with visual images alter your perception of or expectations for the music?

 The response entered here will appear in the performance dashboard and can be viewed by your instructor.

Submit

13.2: Jazz Rock Evolves into Fusion

OBJECTIVE: Describe the evolution from jazz rock to fusion

Groups like Blood, Sweat, and Tears; Chicago; and Chase were typical of jazz rock's first phase. These groups combined horn lines with basic rock instrumentation, as described earlier in this course. As the 1970s began, a new style of jazz rock was born; to distinguish this newer approach, it became known as *fusion*. The seminal album in this trend came in 1970 with *Bitches Brew,* a double album by jazz trumpeter Miles Davis. Among the musicians on this album were many of the key figures in the fusion trend of the mid- and late 1970s: John McLaughlin, Chick Corea, Wayne Shorter, Bennie Maupin, and Joe Zawinul. To Davis's rather austere style of modal jazz of the late 1950s (*Milestones* and *Kind of Blue*)—a style emulated by other pioneering artists in the early 1960s (e.g., John Coltrane's *My Favorite Things, Impressions*, and *A Love Supreme*)—were added electric guitar, electric bass, electronic keyboards, and modified rock beats and bass lines. In contrast to Blood, Sweat, and Tears' and Chicago's approach of adding jazz elements to their rock style, Davis performed the reverse, adding rock elements to his jazz style.

To the average listener, *Bitches Brew* presented a forbidding sound. The songs were long (usually a full side) and sounded like rather aimless, disjointed improvisations, containing few or no "tunes" and no simple jazz or rock beats. However, Davis had started some of the best musical minds in jazz and rock thinking about an alternate musical path into the future. Several would take his basic, uncompromising style and modify it to create a popular style of jazz-rock fusion for the 1970s. Davis planted the seed, and then stepped back as the idea began to take root.

13.2.1: John McLaughlin

One person influenced by Davis was John McLaughlin, generally regarded as one of the premier guitarists of the 1970s. In 1971, he assembled a band consisting of Czechoslovakian keyboardist Jan Hammer, drummer Billy Cobham, bassist Rick Laird, and violinist Jerry Goodman. The group, known as the Mahavishnu Orchestra, established itself as a popular, jazz-rock fusion group with *Birds of Fire* (number 15, 1973). McLaughlin took Miles Davis's basic concept of fusion and moved this ideal closer to the progressive rock style. Cobham's drum patterns, although complex and technically demanding, were still recognizable rock beats; similarly, Laird's bass patterns were derived from more familiar rock-style bass lines. As McLaughlin, Hammer, and Goodman played tunes and improvisations over these drum and bass foundations, the results sounded less foreign to the typical rock listener. At times, Mahavishnu moved closer to jazz, creating a true jazz-rock fusion; at other times, they moved closer to rock, giving the impression of a progressive rock band. The band's playing was virtuosic at times, as they moved through various meters and technically impressive solos. Mahavishnu's *Apocalypse* (1974), recorded with the London Symphony Orchestra, was an effective essay in art rock. After breaking up in 1975, an attempt to revive the band in 1984 (*Mahavishnu*) proved unsuccessful. McLaughlin has continued recording and performing throughout the 1990s and 2000s, releasing *To the One* (2010), inspired by John Coltrane's *A Love Supreme*.

13.2.2: Weather Report

Another alumnus of *Bitches Brew* was keyboardist Joe Zawinul, who joined with soprano saxophonist Wayne Shorter (also a Davis alumnus) to form Weather Report, one of the most influential of the 1970s fusion bands. Like Mahavishnu Orchestra, Weather Report modified the *Bitches Brew* concepts, making their sound more palatable for a larger audience, but unlike Mahavishnu, which moved toward progressive rock, Weather Report leaned

toward jazz. Although Weather Report could certainly play straight-ahead jazz and incorporate recognizable rock influences, they could also create an ethereal, delicate sound, characterized by tinkling bells and otherworldly electronics. Most often, their songs (which rarely included vocals) were structured around several melodic motives, one or more bass patterns, and an accompanying riff; from there the musicians improvised. Weather Report's albums ranked consistently high for a jazz-oriented group: *Mysterious Traveller* (number 46, 1974), *Tale Spinnin'* (number 31, 1975), *Black Market* (number 42, 1976), *Heavy Weather* (number 30, 1977), and *8:30* (number 47, 1979). The band continued as an influential jazz ensemble into the mid-1980s. (As you learned earlier in this course, *Chicago VII* (number 1, 1974) reflected the newer fusion style of the mid-1970s, influenced especially by the sound of early Weather Report recordings.)

13.2.3: Jazz Artists Turn to Fusion

Through the 1970s, a number of jazz artists moved toward the fusion style by adding electric bass, electronic keyboards, and rock-derived bass lines and rhythms. One of the most successful was Herbie Hancock. He had played piano with earlier Miles Davis groups and established himself in the 1960s as a formidable jazz pianist (his funky "Watermelon Man" was especially popular). His album *Head Hunters* (1974) revealed an appealing fusion style and rose to number 13, an unusually high ranking for a jazz-oriented record, and included his only single that nearly broke into the Top 40 ("Chameleon," number 42, 1974). In 1983, he released the single "Rockit" (number 71), which received significant play at dance clubs around the world. Hancock emphasized electronic keyboards, complete with filters, wah-wah pedals, and synthesizer modifications. The follow-up album, *Thrust (1974)*, also reached number 13; listen to "Actual Proof" from *this album* to get a good idea of Hancock's fusion style, revealing significant funk influence.

Jazz keyboardist Chick Corea (yet another *Bitches Brew* alumnus) also moved into the fusion sound, producing a series of moderately successful albums from 1976 to 1978: *Leprechaun* (number 42, 1976), *My Spanish Heart* (number 55, 1977), and *Mad Hatter* (number 61, 1978). One of the most popular jazz pianists of the 1960s was Ramsey Lewis. Lewis had actually enjoyed a number 5 single in 1965 (his funky "The In Crowd"). In the mid-1970s, he turned toward the new electronic jazz-rock fusion sound. As an example, listen to "Tambura," an especially good cut from his *Sun Goddess* album (1974), which reached number 12.

13.2.4: Santana

Through the 1970s and 1980s, others pursued the second-phase jazz-rock fusion trend, including Oregon, Spyro Gyra, and Julian Priester, but there were fusion groups whose roots were not to be found in Davis's *Bitches Brew*. Santana, for example, had begun in early 1967 as a blues-based band.

Carlos Santana on stage in 1969.

SOURCE: INTERFOTO/Alamy Stock Photo

13.2.5: Earth, Wind & Fire

From a musical perspective, one of the finest bands of the 1970s was Earth, Wind & Fire, formed in 1970 by Maurice White, who had worked as a session drummer at Motown and Chess Records before touring with jazz pianist Ramsey Lewis for three years. Earth, Wind & Fire was a large band, consisting of Maurice White and his brothers Verdine (bass) and Fred (percussion), plus six other musicians.

> **Watch "Shin.ing Star" by Earth, Wind & Fire***
>
> **h t t p s : / / w w w . y o u t u b e . c o m / watch?v=Zu9a29UR2dU**

*By clicking this link, you will be redirected to a third-party site.

Musical Career of Santana

The following section will provide highlights from the career of Santana, one of the most successful groups in the jazz-rock fusion trend.

Born in Mexico, Carlos Santana moved to San Francisco and later began working with Michael Bloomfield (Electric Flag) and Al Kooper (Blood, Sweat & Tears). He formed his own band to combine Latin and African rhythms with rock instrumentation. Appearing at Woodstock in 1969 as a virtually unknown band, Santana electrified the crowd with their "Latin rock." Santana's debut album yielded a Top 10 hit in 1969: "Evil Ways."

In the early 1970s, Santana became one of the most popular bands not only in the United States but also, because of their international tours, in the world. With their album *Caravanserai* (number 8, 1972), there was a decided turn toward jazz-rock fusion. Although the album sold well, the new sound undoubtedly disconcerted many Santana fans. Certainly, there was still the technically proficient guitar work of Carlos Santana and the solid keyboard work of Gregg Rolie, but the old Latin rock sound was less evident.

With *Amigos* (number 10, 1976), Santana returned to a Latin-oriented style. By that time, Carlos Santana was the only remaining original member of the band. Subsequent albums through the mid-1980s sold well, although of equal interest have been Carlos's recordings outside of his own band with artists such as John McLaughlin, Alice Coltrane, Herbie Hancock, Wayne Shorter, and Willie Nelson, among others.

Santana's popularity waned in the later 1980s, but he returned with a vengeance as a pop artist in 1999 with the album *Supernatural,* which reached number 1 and sold over 15 million copies (21 million worldwide). The single "Smooth," a Latin-beat pop song, spent 12 weeks at the number 1 position, and the album received nine Grammy Awards. Since then, Santana has continued to release studio recordings, several of which reached the Top 10 (e.g., *Shaman* 2002; *All That I Am*, 2005; and *Guitar Heaven*, 2010), the last consisting of covers of classic guitar-oriented songs previously recorded by other bands, including Led Zeppelin, Cream, the Beatles, AC/DC, the Doors, Deep Purple, Jimi Hendrix, and others. In 2014, reuniting most of his band from the 1969 Woodstock performance, Carlos released *Santana IV.*

Musical Style and Career of Earth, Wind & Fire

The following interactive will provide highlights from the career of Earth, Wind & Fire, another of the most successful groups in the jazz-rock fusion trend.

The early *Last Days and Time* (1972) was a musically impressive album. Of particular interest on this album is

"Power," a 7-minute cut that begins and ends with a kalimba, an African "thumb piano," an instrument in which a series of tuned metal tongues are fixed to a resonating board, or box. A strong rhythmic vamp is established, over which Ronald Laws improvises a soprano sax solo; after a guitar solo, the rhythm breaks for a multilayered section for flutes. The insistent beat returns for a brief keyboard solo that fades back into the kalimba as the song ends.

The band's first number 1 album was *That's the Way of the World* (1975). "Shining Star" became the band's only number 1 single. In the 1970s, Earth, Wind & Fire placed a series of eight consecutive albums in the Top 10.

Listening to any of Earth, Wind & Fire's mid-1970s albums gives a good impression of the band's style.

Gratitude (number 1, 1975), *Spirit* (number 2, 1976), and *All 'n All* (number 3, 1977) reveal a talented band that both sings and plays with equally high levels of musicality. Vocals are smooth and well-harmonized. In contrast with Maurice White's lyrical baritone voice, there is frequent use of falsetto (usually by vocalist Philip Bailey). Rhythms are rock-based but are often more complex than common mainstream rock patterns; the

tight coordination among drums, bass, rhythm guitar, and keyboards is not unlike the best of the fusion groups. Earth, Wind & Fire's horns are used in a variety of ways, from the short, punctuating style of the 1960s Stax/Volt horns to a genuine jazz-rock fusion.

"Magic Mind" from *All 'n All* shows their mature style of the mid-1970s. There is the solid, insistent accompaniment pattern played by drums, bass, and rhythm guitar; there are solid vocal harmonies, including falsetto; particularly impressive are horn sections, such as the one near the end of the song that is rhythmically quite complex as a result of its multilayered construction. Earth, Wind & Fire set a high standard for horn-dominated, jazz-influenced music of the 1970s.

Maurice White stopped touring with the band in 1994 and revealed (just prior to the band's induction into the Rock and Roll Hall of Fame in 2000) that he had been diagnosed with Parkinson's disease. Despite the challenges, he continued to be actively involved in the music industry as a producer, songwriter, and vocalist until his death in 2016.

13.2.6: Tower of Power

Somewhat similar, stylistically, to Earth, Wind & Fire was a San Francisco band called Tower of Power. Impacted by constant personnel changes, Tower of Power did not achieve the level of commercial success experienced by Earth, Wind & Fire but certainly produced a high caliber of music. Originating in San Francisco's East Bay Area, Tower of Power became an alternative to the psychedelic sound of the Haight-Ashbury society (discussed earlier in this course). Formed in 1967 by Emilio Castillo, the band did not achieve major success until the talented vocalist Lenny Williams joined in 1973. Tower of Power's next three albums featured Williams, and all three made the Top 30: *Tower of Power* (number 15, 1973), *Back to Oakland* (number 26, 1974), and *Urban Renewal* (number 22, 1975).

The soulful sound came primarily from the lead singer's style but was reinforced by the funky rhythmic foundation and the Stax/Volt-derived horn lines. The horn section consisted of three saxes (and other woodwinds) and two brass (sometimes two trumpets, sometimes trumpet and trombone). One of Tower of Power's finest albums was *Back to Oakland* (1974). The opening and closing theme of this album, "Oakland Stroke," shows the rhythmically syncopated style of the band, as complex rhythmic patterns are distributed throughout the ensemble. The sublime blend of Williams's voice and the Tower of Power horns is best illustrated on "Just When We Start Makin' It" (also note Chester Thompson's

fine organ solo on this track). The rhythmically complex accompaniment patterns in "Can't You See (You Doin' Me Wrong)" create a jittery sound beneath Williams's smooth vocal line. The Motown-derived emphasis on baritone sax is evident in "Squib Cakes," a particularly strong example of jazz-rock fusion that features excellent solos.

Watch "What is Hip" by Tower of Power*

https://www.youtube.com/ watch?v=o1KCoX_dDBE

13.2.7: Other Fusion Artists

A wide variety of jazz-oriented artists and groups that were also influenced heavily by rock and other forms of popular music emerged during the 70s as these two distinct musical styles converged into the subgenre known as fusion. In the following section, we will explore some other artists who fit into this category.

Other Jazz-Oriented Fusionists

The following section will provide highlights from the careers of other successful fusion groups.

Jeff Beck—We have mentioned Jeff Beck before—as a member of the Yardbirds in the mid-1960s (he replaced Eric Clapton). After leaving the Yardbirds, Beck formed his own group in 1967. His first two albums, *Truth (1968)* and *Beck-Ola (1969)*, featured Rod Stewart as lead vocalist and both reached number 15 on the album chart. In 1975, Beck issued *Blow by Blow*, his highest-charting album (number 4). Featuring Beck's quartet (guitar, keyboards, bass, and drums), *Blow by Blow*, produced by George

---

*By clicking this link, you will be redirected to a third-party side.

Martin (the "fifth Beatle," as discussed earlier in this course), was a thoroughly impressive album. Several follow-up albums continued the fusion sound, with Jan Hammer supplying excellent keyboard work. Beck remained one of rock's most creative guitarists. He continued to record and perform into the 2000s, including reunions with both Rod Stewart and Eric Clapton and making an impressive return to the charts with *Emotion and Commotion* (number 11, 2010).

Chuck Mangione—Coming from still a different direction was Chuck Mangione. Classically trained at the Eastman School of Music, Mangione formed an excellent jazz quartet, featuring his own work on flugelhorn. Accompanied by the Rochester Philharmonic Orchestra, Mangione produced a live album, *Friends and Love* (1971). Combining classical concepts with jazz and softer-rock elements, Mangione's style evolved into a kind of art-jazz-rock-pop style. Always tasteful and accessible, Mangione brought a comfortable jazz sound to a wide audience. His most successful album, *Feels So Good* (number 2, 1977), produced a Top 5 hit (the title song).

Steely Dan—On the outer edges of jazz-rock fusion is Steely Dan. Leaning toward the rock side of the fusion style, this band reveals subtle jazz influences combined with the gentler side of the rock mainstream. Two key musicians served as the brain trust for Steely Dan: bassist/guitarist Walter Becker and keyboardist Donald Fagen. They formed Steely Dan in 1972 as a quintet. Their third album, *Pretzel Logic* (1974), reached the Top 10 and contained the Top 5 hit, "Rikki Don't Lose That Number" (number 4).

Steely Dan was something of an enigma; they had a unique sound that, even though often characterized as jazz-rock fusion, was unlike other fusion bands. With an ever-changing membership of impressive studio musicians, a sophisticated and enigmatic style, and an unalterable aversion to touring (until the new millennium), it is amazing that they achieved such commercial success. *Katy Lied* (number 13, 1975) revealed more obvious jazz influences (e.g., listen to "Doctor Wu," with solos by jazz saxophonist Phil Woods). This initial period of Steely Dan concluded with the release of *Aja* (number 3, 1977) and *Gaucho* (number 9, 1980), which were not only big sellers but yielded five Top 40 hits. In the early 1980s, Becker and Fagen went their separate ways, with Fagen gaining considerable respect for his solo album *The Nightfly* in 1982 and others that followed.

After over 10 years, in 1993, Becker and Fagen reunited for a national tour, despite their prior resistance to live performance. Although they continued to record separately, they joined again as Steely Dan to release *Two Against Nature* in 2000 (number 6), winning three Grammy Awards, including Album of the Year. In 2003, they released *Everything Must Go*, their second consecutive post-reunion Top 10 album, though neither produced any Top 40 hits.

JOURNAL

The Fusion of Jazz and Rock Elements

Listen to "Birdland" by Weather Report and "Shining Star" by Earth, Wind & Fire. As you have learned throughout this course, to become familiar with a recording, it is important to listen multiple times, which I hope you will do with each of these songs as you complete this assignment. For each track, identify the musical characteristics that emerge from jazz and those that identify it as rock. On a continuum between jazz and rock, where would you place each of these recordings? How would you describe the balance between jazz and rock elements in each of these recordings? Which of the two do you like best and why?

 The response entered here will appear in the performance dashboard and can be viewed by your instructor.

Submit

13.3: The Singer-Songwriters of the 1970s

OBJECTIVE: Outline the evolution of the singer-songwriter movement

The first explosion of folk rock had dissipated by 1968; however, from the prototypes established by Dylan, Baez, the Byrds, Simon and Garfunkel, Buffalo Springfield, and others (discussed in an earlier section of this course), came a number of major new acts of the 1970s. Some strayed from the folk rock vein toward a country-oriented style; still others moved closer to a pop-oriented or softer sound. One or two even flirted with jazz. These 1970s latter-day folk rock performers are called **singer-songwriters**.

According to Janet Maslin, "the term singer/songwriter ... was always more of a catchall than a legitimate musical genre" (Miller 1980, 339). Indeed, the term implies nothing at all about style but merely tells us that a person composes and performs songs. Moreover, it seems to distinguish a group of performers for what they *were not* instead of for what they *were*. It usually referred to a musician who (obviously) composed and sang her or his own songs in a post-Dylan folk or folk-rock style and who was not oriented toward mainstream rock, art rock, jazz rock, soul, or disco. Even with that broad definition, one can think of a few exceptions.

As we saw when we traced Dylan, Baez, and Simon and Garfunkel into the 1970s, several changes took place as the style evolved. First, the lyrics changed from a focus on the world's problems (war, racial equality, the brotherhood of humankind, etc.) to a focus on the self. Second, in many cases (not all), the folk-rock trend toward electronic rock increased dramatically. The 1970s singer-songwriter happily utilized the latest advancements in studio technology, electronic keyboards, and synthesizers.

13.3.1: Joni Mitchell

We will begin our survey of 1970s singer-songwriters with one of the most creative and talented of them all: Joni Mitchell. Born in 1943 in Alberta, Canada, Joni Mitchell (née Roberta Joan Anderson) was raised in Saskatoon, Saskatchewan. After the breakup of her marriage to folk singer Chuck Mitchell, she moved to New York City where she became a part of the folk-music scene. Signed to Reprise Records, her first four albums (1968–1971) sold progressively well and revealed a developing talent for more refined musicianship and inventive melodies. Her lyrics focused on themes of romantic love.

Switching to Asylum Records, Mitchell hit her commercial peak with *Court and Spark*, which rose to number 2 in 1974 and yielded a major hit with "Help Me" (number 1). "Help Me" exemplifies Mitchell's songwriting ability at its best. The melodic line is wide ranging and inventive; rhythmic interest comes not only from the occasional metrical changes, but from the rhythmic inflections of the melody that often conflict with the established meter; the harmonic material is quite sophisticated and reveals a relation to jazz. Mitchell's clear, pitch-perfect voice is evident in this and other songs on *Court and Spark*. Of particular note is the decidedly jazzy song "Twisted." Mitchell's performance perfectly depicts the mental distortion that is the song's subject—including the overdubbed duet on the schizophrenic final lines.

Subsequent albums found Mitchell drifting further toward a jazz-influenced style. The double album *Don Juan's Reckless Daughter* (number 25, 1977) firmly broke with her pop-folk past; using jazz musicians from Weather Report, she included the side-long "Paprika Plains," accompanied by a full symphony orchestra. The 1979 album *Mingus* (number 17) moved even farther in the direction of jazz. In preparation for some 18 months, the album began as a collaboration with jazz great Charles Mingus but became a memorial when Mingus died in early 1979. Two of the album's songs are Mitchell's, but four are Mingus's music and Mitchell's words. Fusion greats Wayne Shorter, Herbie Hancock, and Jaco Pastorius are among the musicians on this remarkable album. Mitchell has continued to record in her own unique style through the 1990s and early 2000s, returning to the Top 20 with *Shine* (2007).

13.3.2: Carole King

The other leading female singer-songwriter of the 1970s (other than Baez, of course) was Carole King. A member of the famous Brill Building group of songwriters, King (with and without her husband, Gerry Goffin) had written a staggering number of hit songs for other artists since the early 1960s, including the Shirelles; the Drifters; Bobby Vee; the Everly Brothers; Steve Lawrence and Eydie Gorme; Little Eva; Herman's Hermits; the Animals; Blood, Sweat & Tears; the Monkees; Aretha Franklin; and the Byrds. By the late 1960s, she had dissolved the songwriting team and divorced Goffin.

King's second solo album, *Tapestry* (1971), became a monster hit. It reached number 1 and held that position for 15 weeks; it eventually stayed on the charts for 304 weeks and was the biggest-selling pop album in history up until that time. "It's Too Late," backed with "I Feel the Earth Move," became number 1 hits. Other strong songs on this album were "You've Got a Friend," "Smackwater Jack," and "(You Make Me Feel Like) A Natural Woman." Subsequent albums sold well but lacked the impact of *Tapestry. Wrap Around Joy* (number 1, 1974) was a particularly strong album and even hinted at a slight bend toward jazz, although not as pronounced as Joni Mitchell's releases. The hit single "Jazzman" (number 2, 1974) featured a sax solo by the L.A. Express's Tom Scott. However, other than a couple of live albums released in the new millennium (*Living Room Tour* and *Live at the Troubadour*), King's albums after 1977 sold less well.

King's style emphasized simple piano accompaniments and a pop or soft rock musical style. If her basic style was affected by any other style at all, it might have been a light touch of funk-soul-gospel (e.g., "We Are All in This Together," from *Wrap Around Joy*). As mentioned in an earlier section of this course, a Broadway musical (*Beautiful: The Carole King Musical*), based on her music, debuted in 2014.

Watch Carole King singing "I Feel the Earth Move"*

https://www.youtube.com/watch?v=6913KnbMpHM

13.3.3: James Taylor

James Taylor, born in Boston in 1948, was raised in an affluent and musical family. His early attempts at a recording career were not successful, so he moved to London where he impressed Paul McCartney and Peter Asher, signing with Apple Records in 1968. His first album, *James Taylor,* did not fare well, although it contained several songs that revealed significant promise (e.g., "Something in the Way She Moves" and "Carolina in My Mind"). Asher managed to negotiate a new contract for Taylor with Warner Brothers and produced his next album, *Sweet Baby James* (number 3, 1970), which was a great success and yielded the major hit "Fire and Rain" (number 3). Taylor sang in a soft folk-rock style with perhaps just a touch of country influence. A morose look at

---

*By clicking this link, you will be redirected to a third-party side.

the depression of lost love, "Fire and Rain" exemplifies the inward turn and self-orientation of the singer-songwriter trend of the 1970s. Taylor's follow-up album, *Mud Slide Slim and the Blue Horizon* (number 2, 1971) contained Carole King's "You've Got a Friend." Even this relatively positive and outgoing song sounded sad and introspective in Taylor's version.

In 1972, Taylor married singer Carly Simon. *One-Man Dog* (number 4, 1972), which was recorded at his home in Martha's Vineyard, contained the attractive (but sad sounding) "Don't Let Me Be Lonely Tonight" (number 14), with excellent sax work by Michael Brecker. *Gorilla* (number 6, 1975), a refreshing album, actually had a brighter, more upbeat sound, as exemplified by "Mexico" (number 49) and the Holland-Dozier-Holland song "How Sweet It Is" (number 5).

In the late 1970s, Taylor recorded with other artists, including Simon and Garfunkel and his wife Carly Simon. Taylor became one of the style setters among the softer, post-Dylan singer-songwriters. Unlike some of the others, he never turned toward the heavily electronic sound or to jazz or the mainstream side of rock. Taylor has continued to record and perform. His album *Hourglass* (number 9, 1997) won a Grammy for Best Pop Album. During the first decade of the twenty-first century, he placed four studio albums in the Top 20 (*October Road, James Taylor at Christmas, One Man Band*, and *Covers*). In the spring of 2011, Taylor received a Medal of Honor from President Obama and performed at Carnegie Hall as part of the Perspectives series, a privilege previously reserved almost exclusively for classical musicians. In 2015, he released *Before this World*, his 17th studio album and first with all-new material since 2002. The album debuted at the top of the chart, the first number 1 album of his career.

13.3.4: Jim Croce

Jim Croce's songs were usually as upbeat and positive as Taylor's were morose and depressing. Ironically, Croce's own story became one of the saddest of the 1970s. Croce was born and raised in Philadelphia. Signed to Capitol Records, he and his wife, Ingrid, released a duet album in 1969 that did not sell well. However, with the help of some friends, Croce was signed as a solo artist to ABC Records. With good production and strong backup musicians, Croce's *You Don't Mess Around with Jim* moved to number 1. The title song made the Top 10 and "Operator" made the Top 20, firmly establishing Croce as a bona fide, commercially successful member of the 1970s singer-songwriter trend.

Croce's vocal timbre was unique; among all of the singer-songwriters of the time, Croce's voice was one that was easily and instantly recognizable. Croce's songs were well-constructed musically, had appealing melodies, and often had a lilting rhythm that reflected his upbeat attitude. There were the character songs (e.g., "You Don't Mess Around with Jim," "Rapid Roy," and "Bad, Bad Leroy Brown") and the plaintively beautiful songs ("Photographs and Memories" and "Time in a Bottle"). Either way, Croce made the listener feel good.

Croce had recorded his third ABC album, *I Got a Name*, in the summer of 1973, but before the album could be released, he was killed in a plane crash near Natchitoches, Louisiana. He was 30 years old. Released posthumously, *I Got a Name* became a number 2 album and yielded three Top 40 hits: "I Got a Name" (number 10), "I'll Have to Say I Love You in a Song" (number 9), and "Workin' at the Car Wash Blues" (number 32). "Time in a Bottle" was also released (from the first ABC album), and reached the top of the chart in late 1973.

13.3.5: Cat Stevens

The folk and folk-rock trends of the 1960s and the singer-songwriter trend of the 1970s were primarily American phenomena. An important exception was Cat Stevens (born Steven Georgiou in London, 1948). Several early albums and singles did well enough in England but made little impact in the United States. However, *Tea for the Tillerman* (1971) caught on and moved to number 8 on the American Hot 100; the single "Wild World" rose to number 11. The song "Father and Son" is a particularly touching song that is somewhat reminiscent of Bob Dylan.

Stevens accompanied himself on acoustic guitar; like Croce, he was unique and instantly recognizable, not only for his vocal timbre but for his enunciation. Most of his songs were rather gentle; even the more rhythmically oriented songs (e.g., "Wild World," "Moon Shadow," and "Peace Train") were gentle when compared to mainstream rock.

Stevens released a series of popular albums from 1971 to 1977 that yielded a string of hits, including "Morning Has Broken" (number 6, 1972) and "Oh Very Young" (number 10, 1974). By 1978, Stevens had turned to the Muslim religion and adopted a new name (Yusef Islam), and he then dropped out of the music industry for almost three decades. The former musician found himself in the news again in September 2004 when, due to the appearance of his name on a national security watch list, the plane upon which he was flying from London to the United States was diverted to Maine and grounded. Islam (Stevens) was questioned and detained prior to being returned to Britain. In the early 2000s, Yusef Islam released a series of spoken word and children's song albums on his own label; then, in 2006, he released *An Other Cup*, which, though returning to a more folk-pop sound, contained lyrics with a clearly religious message. *Roadsinger* (2009) charted just shy of the Top 40.

13.3.6: Billy Joel

One of the few 1970s singer-songwriters to persevere into the 1980s and beyond with continuing commercial success was Billy Joel. Born on Long Island in 1949, Joel was a classically trained pianist. From 1964 to 1976, Joel knocked around the music business. His primary early success came with *Piano Man* (1974), an album that made the Top 30 and yielded the number 25 hit of the same name. From 1977 to 1980, Joel released three Top 5—and, stylistically, very different—albums (*The Stranger, 52nd Street,* and *Glass Houses*), yielding three major hit singles, including his first number 1 song, "It's Still Rock and Roll to Me." These successes propelled Joel headlong into the 1980s where he found continued success. By the end of 1984, Joel had achieved 22 Top 40 hits, including the number 1 "Tell Her About It" and the number 3 "Uptown Girl," both from *An Innocent Man* (number 4, 1983).

Joel does not fit the post-folk rock, singer-songwriter trend in the way that Taylor, Croce, Stevens, Mitchell, and others do. He moved closer to mainstream rock (if, typically, the softer side) and toward more elaborate production. His refusal to become typed into any one style has led to some criticism (recall similar problems with Elvis Presley, Bob Dylan, Aretha Franklin, and others). For example, *An Innocent Man* (1982) features a shouting R&B-derived mainstream song ("Easy Money"), a doo-wop-oriented song ("The Longest Time"), and a ballad-style song (the title song). On this same album, there is also the 1950s-style, soft rock of "This Night" (complete with melodic references to the second movement of Beethoven's Piano Sonata in C Minor, Op. 13 ["Pathétique"]); there is good-time rock and roll in "Tell Her About It," the Four Seasons–like "Uptown Girl," and the Sam Cooke-ish "Careless Talk." There are reminiscences of Jerry Lee Lewis and Little Richard in "Christie Lee" and touches of jazz in the harmonica work of Toots Thielemans on "Leave a Tender Moment Alone." Joel's solid musical background is evident in the flawless craftsmanship evident in his songs and his impressively energetic performance technique.

Joel's success continued into the 1990s with *River of Dreams* (number 1, 1993). The album's title song reached number 3 on the Hot 100. He also completed several very successful international tours with Elton John (1994 and 1999). Like a number of maturing rock artists, Joel decided to expand his mellowing musical horizons by composing music in a classical vein; in his case, this came into existence through *Fantasies & Delusions: Music for Solo Piano*, credited to "William Joel" and performed by concert pianist Richard Joo. The album reached only number 83 on the Billboard 200, but hit number 1 on the classical album chart. In 2005, Columbia released a boxed set (*My Lives*) that was a compilation of demos, B-sides, alternate versions, and a few Top 40 hits. In 2007, Joel released the first song with lyrics he had composed in almost 14 years: "All My Life," which failed to chart.

13.3.7: Crosby, Stills, Nash & Young

The term *singer-songwriter* usually refers to a soloist; however, one group—Crosby, Stills, Nash & Young—fits stylistically into the singer-songwriter trend. As Brock Helander (1982, 116) notes, "More an aggregation of three (and four) individuals than a group, Crosby, Stills, Nash (and Young) created a characteristic sound that the three original members have attempted to maintain, somewhat equivocally, into the late-Seventies."

We have met David Crosby (the Byrds), Stephen Stills (Buffalo Springfield), Graham Nash (the Hollies), and Neil Young (Buffalo Springfield) in earlier sections of this course.

Crosby, Stills & Nash

SOURCE: INTERFOTO/Alamy Stock Photo

Musical Career of Crosby, Stills, Nash & Young (CSNY)

The following section will provide highlights from the career of CSNY, one of the most successful groups in the singer-songwriter subgenre.

As the first wave of folk rock dissipated in 1968, Crosby, Stills, and Nash formed their new group after an informal jam session in Los Angeles. Releasing their first album for Atlantic (*Crosby, Stills & Nash*), the group emphasized excellent vocal harmonies and socio-political commentary. All three played guitar, with Stills dubbing in keyboard and bass parts (drum parts were supplied by Dallas Taylor). Neil Young joined the group in 1969 in time to perform with them at Woodstock. The addition of Young enabled the group to execute rather complex four-part harmonies. There was a firm reliance on acoustic guitar, with only light use of electric guitars and keyboards.

The title song of the quartet's first album, *Deja Vu* (number 1, 1970), provides a good sample of the Crosby, Stills, Nash & Young (CSNY) musical style. Tight vocal harmonies change in relatively fast rhythm in its opening moments. After a short vocal solo section, the vocal harmonies re-enter, reflecting some jazz influence. Some Beach Boy–like vocal polyphony follows; changing to falsetto, the group sings the hook line, "We have all been here before." With its frequent sectional changes, "Deja Vu" is a very effective song. ("Carry On" illustrates similarly complex and beautifully performed vocal harmonies.)

There can be little doubt that CSNY was one of the most sophisticated vocal groups of the early 1970s. Their musical style was the natural extension of the work of the Byrds and Buffalo Springfield from the late 1960s. There were even the occasional country-oriented sounds developed by the earlier groups (e.g., "Teach Your Children").

A live album, *4 Way Street,* was released in 1971 and also went to number 1, but by that time, the group had gone their separate ways. Each recorded solo albums, often with the assistance of at least one of the other former CSNY members. The quartet reunited for a tour in the summer of 1974, propelling their greatest hits album released that year to number 1 (rare for a hits album). From the mid-1970s onward, the group was on-again, off-again, often uniting around political events (e.g., the antinuclear MUSE—Musicians United for Safe Energy—demonstration in 1979 and the Survival Sunday concert in 1980). The band has reunited occasionally for tours and recordings since then, and members of the group have remained active as solo artists. Neil Young has been particularly prolific in the new millennium, placing six of the numerous albums released during the early 2000s in the Top 20. He has continued to communicate socio-political messages through music, as is evident in *Greendale* (number 22, 2003), a rock opera; *Living With War* (number 15, 2006); and *Waging Heavy Peace* (2012). As the political turmoil increased in the United States during the Bush, Obama, and Trump presidencies, Young's voice was needed, a request he was ready to fulfill. Four albums released during the second decade of the new millennium all reached the Top 30: *Le Noise* (number 14, 2010), *Treasure* (number 29, 2011), *Americana* (number 4, 2012), and *Psychedelic Pill* (number 8, 2012).

JOURNAL

Billy Joel as a Musical Chameleon

Listen to the following four songs by Billy Joel: "Piano Man," "Zanzibar," "It's Still Rock and Roll to Me," and "The Longest Time." Do these sound like recordings by the same artist? Take a moment to describe the musical elements that make each song unique in comparison to the others. After you have considered the differences, enumerate at least three elements that are consistent among the four recordings. Then, identify at least one artist of the new millennium whose music is very familiar to you and whose recordings provide a variety of musical styles. Considering three or four songs, each from a different album, describe the music of this artist in a manner similar to that used to illuminate differences and similarities in the music of Billy Joel. Do you believe that the stylistic variability in the Joel examples listed above or that of your chosen artist is greater? Why?

▶ The response entered here will appear in the performance dashboard and can be viewed by your instructor.

Submit

13.4: Folk Influences in the 80s and 90s

OBJECTIVE: Identify the influences on folk and reggae music after the 70s

A popular style of Jamaican music, calypso, enjoyed brief popularity in the late 1950s and played a role in the early days of the folk music revival. In the 1970s, reggae, a new Jamaican musical style, gained great popularity in both the United States and England. Reggae originated in Jamaica in the mid-1960s and was closely tied to the Rastafarian religion, which revered the late emperor of Ethiopia, Haile Selassie (common name: Ras Tafari). Speaking for the deprived and dispossessed classes of Jamaica, reggae music spoke of the dream of an eventual return to the African homeland. The music has a dry, staccato (detached) beat and guitar accompaniment; moderate tempos prevail; and the beat is relatively gentle, often emphasizing syncopated rhythms. The Jamaican dialect colors the lyrics, which often express the political beliefs of the Rastafarians.

13.4.1: Reggae and Bob Marley

Reggae was closely associated with singer-songwriter Bob Marley, whose recording career began in the early 1960s, but whose first real success came with "Simmer Down" in 1964. Over the next few years, Marley and his Wailing Wailers recorded some 30 songs and became the hottest group in Jamaica. In the early 1970s, the Wailers became known throughout the Caribbean, but it was not until 1972 that they signed with Island Records and began to build an international reputation. Marley's *Natty Dread* (1975) brought the Wailers to the U.S. charts. However, it was not until 1976 that Marley made a major impact with *Rastaman Vibration* (number 8). "War" (from *Rastaman Vibration*) was based on a speech by Emperor Selassie; "Roots, Rock, Reggae" became a minor hit (number 51, 1976).

Bob Marley

SOURCE: Pictorial Press Ltd/Alamy Stock Photo

By the late 1970s, reggae's popularity had begun to fade. *Exodus* (number 20, 1977) was Marley's last Top 40 studio album; subsequent albums sold moderately. Bob Marley died of cancer in 1981 at the age of 36; he was given an official funeral by the people of Jamaica, who had awarded him the nation's Order of Merit one month before his death.

The reggae style was particularly influential in Britain. The Rolling Stones and quite a few of the British punk groups showed its influence. In addition, artists as varied as Paul Simon, Led Zeppelin, Stevie Wonder, the Police, the Clash, and Eric Clapton (Marley's "I Shot the Sheriff") all reflected the reggae influence in particular songs.

Since the beginning of recorded history, folk music (sometimes referred to as *roots music*) has provided a common musical experience for members of a given social group. The music of Woody Guthrie and Pete Seeger provided a foundation for much music of the 1960s (the Kingston Trio; Bob Dylan; and Peter, Paul, and Mary) and on into the 1990s (Tracy Chapman and Jewel). During the 1990s and at the beginning of the twenty-first century, there were signs of revitalized interest in these familiar musical influences. The surprise popularity of the soundtrack for the film *O Brother Where Art Thou?* (number 1, 2001) resulted in a stay of well over a year on the album chart. The first track on the album is a recording of "Po Lazarus," an authentic **worksong** performed by James Carter and other prisoners working in a chain gang at the Mississippi State Penitentiary. The song was captured in a 1959 field recording by folk music historian Alan Lomax. This recording, including music by a variety of artists, juxtaposed authentic recordings of roots music from long ago, new recordings by roots artists, and new renditions of period songs by contemporary artists. What appeared to be a roots revival as a result of this soundtrack and follow-up releases lasted only a couple of years, but other folk styles continued to exert their influence on popular music.

13.4.2: Bob Dylan

In a manner similar to the way in which Santana's commercial revival confirmed the importance of Latin music, the reappearance of Bob Dylan during the 1990s heralded a revitalized interest in folk-influenced music. A new generation of listeners became aware of Dylan's legacy by listening to the music of the Wallflowers, a band formed in 1990 by Dylan's son, Jakob. Bob Dylan's *Time Out of Mind* (number 10, 1997) placed higher on the charts than any album he released since his first recording as a born-again Christian, *Slow Train Coming* (1979). The album earned the songwriter three Grammy Awards, including Album of the Year, Best Contemporary Folk Album, and Best Male Rock Vocal Performance for "Cold Irons Bound." Garth Brooks recorded a cover version of "To Make You Feel My Love," another track from *Time Out of Mind*, resulting in a number 1

hit on the country chart. In 2000, Dylan composed "Things Have Changed" for the *Wonder Boys* soundtrack; the song not only won a Grammy, but it also earned Dylan's first Oscar for Best Original Song. As described earlier in this course, his reign continued successfully into the new millennium. Dylan's autobiography, *Chronicles, Volume One,* in 2004 and the Martin Scorsese documentary *No Direction Home* (2005) provide very interesting information, from varying perspectives, about the career of this pioneering artist.

13.4.3: Tracy Chapman

Other folk-influenced performers and singer-songwriters have continued to carry on the folk music tradition within the popular music industry that began in earnest with the Kingston Trio in the late 1950s. The release of Tracy Chapman's self-titled debut in 1988 and the surprising commercial success of several tracks ("Fast Car" reached number 6) suggested that—at a time when radio airwaves were pumping out the music of George Michael, Van Halen, Bon Jovi, and the soundtrack from *Dirty Dancing*—the record-buying public was also interested in music that was reflective and introspective. Chapman's follow-up album, *Crossroads* (1989), reached number 9 and *New Beginning* (number 4, released 1995) contained "Give Me One Reason" (number 3).

13.4.4: Jewel

During the mid-1990s, Jewel Kilcher, daughter of the members of a folk duo from the 1970s, seemed poised to become one of the most successful female solo artists in the history of rock music. Her recording debut, *Pieces of You* (1996), garnered little attention until over a year following its release. "Who Will Save Your Soul" and "You Were Meant for Me" were minor hits, eventually pushing the album to number 4 on the *Billboard* chart, selling over 12 million copies. The third single, "Foolish Games," was included in the soundtrack for the film *Batman and Robin* (1997). Jewel's participation in Lillith Fair, an all-female concert tour organized by Canadian singer-songwriter Sarah McLachlan, placed her in a prominent position during a period when the number of female artists on the album charts surpassed the number of men for the first time. Other performers who participated in this important music festival over the years included Shawn Colvin, Sheryl Crow, the Dixie Chicks, Indigo Girls, Queen Latifah, Monica, and Liz Phair. Jewel's follow-up recording, *Spirit* (1998), debuted at number 3. Although the first single, "Hands," reached number 6, follow-up singles failed to reach the Top 50. She continued to record folk-influenced music, placing five albums in the Top 10 between 2001 and 2010, but only one single in the Top 20 ("Intuition," 2003).

REVIEW FOLK INFLUENCES OF THE 80s AND 90s

The following fill-in-the-blank questions will review your knowledge of folk musicians of the 80s and 90s.

13.5: The Evolution of Country Rock

OBJECTIVE: Analyze the changes to country music in the 70s and 80s

C&W was one of the progenitors of rock and roll, and rockabilly emerged as one of the three basic trends of early rock, but, by the early 1960s, rockabilly had almost completely died away. For much of the 1960s, the C&W influence in rock was virtually nonexistent. Only near the end of the millennium did there appear to be some tentative interest in rekindling the old partnership between C&W and rock.

13.5.1: Country in the 70s

As the 1970s began, another surge of interest came from a rather surprising source: San Francisco. The Grateful Dead took a definite turn toward country rock with their two albums released in 1970: *Workingman's Dead* (number 27) and *American Beauty* (number 30). Jerry Garcia was actively involved with a new San Francisco country rock band of the early 1970s known as New Riders of the Purple Sage. The New Riders' albums sold moderately from 1971 to 1974 but tapered off dramatically after that.

Somewhat in the same vein were the Flying Burrito Brothers, with a band membership that included Chris Hillman and Gram Parsons. This post-Byrds country rock band existed from 1969 to 1975 and released some half dozen barely successful albums, none entering the Top 100. Somewhat more commercially successful was Pure Prairie League, a Cincinnati band whose albums in the mid-1970s were considered important contributions to the country rock style. *Bustin' Out* (1975), *Two Lane Highway* (1975), and *If the Shoe Fits* (1976) all entered the Top 40.

Yet another country rock band of the 1970s was Bob Dylan's backup group, the Band. Their first recognition (aside from the Dylan connection) came in 1968 with *Music from Big Pink* (number 30). Several albums between 1969 and 1976 sold quite well (three of these studio albums made the Top 10), and they were among the groups responsible for the re-emergence of interest in country-influenced rock.

Country Rock Bands

The following section will provide highlights from the careers of several of the country rock pioneers that emerged during this period: the Eagles, The Charlie Daniels Band, The Marshall Tucker Band, and Linda Rondstadt.

The Eagles—The most successful of the country rock bands was the Eagles, formed in 1971 in Los Angeles. *Eagles* (number 22, 1972) yielded a Top 10 hit, "Witchy Woman." Their third album, *On the Border* (1974), reached the Top 20 and contained the band's first number 1 song, "Best of My Love." The band's peak years were 1975 and 1976, as four consecutive albums reached number 1 (*One of These Nights*, *Greatest Hits 1971-1975*, *Hotel California*, and *The Long Run*), yielding three more number 1 singles ("One of These Nights," "New Kid in Town," and "Hotel California").

As with most of the country rock bands, the Eagles moved between mainstream rock, a post–folk rock style, and country rock. Their first number 1 album, *One of These Nights* (1975), illustrates this versatility. Songs such as "After the Thrill Is Gone," "Hollywood Waltz," and "Lyin' Eyes" (number 2) are perfect examples of 1970s country rock. The lead and backup vocals, the beat, and the instrumental accompaniment all contribute to the country-oriented sound. However, a song such as "Journey of the Sorcerer" moves toward progressive rock; the timbre of the mandolin may recall bluegrass music, but there is no stylistic incorporation of bluegrass. Several songs on the album show little or no derivation from country music (e.g., "Visions," "One of These Nights," and "Too Many Hands"); such songs are nearer the gentler side of mainstream rock.

Subsequent albums, beginning with *Hotel California* (1976–1977) and the addition of rock guitarist Joe Walsh, revealed a drift away from the country rock sound so evident in the Eagles' first four albums. By 1981, founder Glenn Frey (guitar, keyboards, and vocals) called it quits, and so did the Eagles. They reunited in 1994 for a very successful tour, and they released a number 1 album; based on the band's stock response to anyone asking about the possibility of a reunion during the 1980s and early 90s, the album was appropriately named *Hell Freezes Over*. The band was inducted into the Rock and Roll Hall of Fame in 1998. In early 2001, the Eagles' *Their Greatest Hits, 1971–1975* surpassed Michael Jackson's *Thriller*

(1983) as the greatest-selling album up to that time (29 million); it is worth mentioning that the rush in sales since Jackson's death have placed the sales of his album beyond 33 million. In addition to a consistent flow of greatest hits collections, the band hit the top of the charts again in 2007 with *Long Road Out of Eden*. Having sold over 100 million albums in total, the Eagles have proven to be one of the most significant forces in the history of rock music.

The Charlie Daniels and Marshall Tucker Bands—It seems only natural that some of the southern rock bands of the 1970s would turn toward C&W as an influence. Whereas bands like Lynyrd Skynyrd and the Allman Brothers leaned toward R&B influences, other southern bands, like The Charlie Daniels Band and The Marshall Tucker Band, were primarily influenced by C&W and rock.

Charlie Daniels, who was from North Carolina, played on several Dylan albums, including *Nashville Skyline* (1969), early in his career. In the early 1970s, Daniels formed his own band and first hit the charts with "Uneasy Rider" (number 9), a satire of "The Ballad of Easy Rider" from the hit film *Easy Rider*. Daniels's band was a genuine 50/50 blend of country and rock. Their first gold album, *Fire on the Mountain* (number 38, 1975), featured several strong country rock songs, such as "Long Haired Country Boy" (number 56) and "The South's Gonna Do It Again" (number 29), a 12-bar blues often called *southern rock boogie* or *southern boogie and blues*. Southern country rock lyrics often dealt with broken romances (a C&W tradition), alcohol, and gambling; the vocalists' enunciation emphasized southern roots. At times, the music moved toward a purer rock style, as in "No Place to Go."

The Charlie Daniels Band played at sites as varied as the Grand Ole Opry in Nashville and President Carter's inauguration. They found their biggest success with the *Million Mile Reflections* album (number 5, 1979) with its hit single "The Devil Went Down to Georgia" (number 3).

Similar in concept to The Charlie Daniels Band, The Marshall Tucker Band began in 1970 as the Toy Factory (named after guitarist Toy Caldwell), changing their name by 1972. There is no person named Marshall Tucker in the band; the name supposedly refers to a local piano teacher in their hometown of Spartanburg, South Carolina. Their first three albums were reasonably successful, but in 1975, *Searchin' for a Rainbow* made the Top 20. Performing as many as 300 concerts per year, Marshall Tucker found themselves increasingly popular as a live performance and album band, but without major impact on the singles charts. In fact, their only Top 40 singles were 1975's "Fire on the Mountain" (number 38) and 1977's "Heard It in a Love Song" (number 14). The former is a good example of Marshall Tucker's country rock sound, with its steel guitar introduction, gentle rock beat, and country-oriented vocal. The style is basically country with a light rock influence; note woodwind player Jerry Eubanks's flute line near the middle of the song, adding an interesting timbre that made Tucker's sound unique among country rock bands. Another good example is "Virginia" (also on *Searchin' for a Rainbow*), which uses a rock-derived guitar and bass riff to tie the song together. Of special interest is Eubanks's brief but lovely soprano sax solo.

Linda Ronstadt—Possibly because of the early precedents set by the Byrds and Buffalo Springfield, most country rock of the 1970s involved groups, rather than solo performers. A significant exception to this rule was solo artist Linda Ronstadt.

Her career started off slowly. However, her 1974 album *Heart Like a Wheel* yielded her first number 1 song ("You're No Good") and "When Will I Be Loved" (number 2). Ronstadt's next six studio albums were all Top 5 sellers, and in that span (1975–1980), she placed over a dozen songs in the Top 40, making her the leading female solo vocalist on the rock scene at the time.

Ronstadt had folk-oriented beginnings, but she became known as a country rock singer. Certainly, albums such as *Linda Ronstadt* and *Don't Cry Now* reinforced that image (e.g., listen to "Silver Threads and Golden Needles" from *Don't Cry Now*). Throughout the 1970s, she continued to perform in a country-influenced style. *Heart Like a Wheel* contained the country-oriented "When Will I Be Loved" and even a version of Paul Anka's "It Doesn't Matter Anymore" (Ronstadt's version of this song was much more "countrified" than Buddy Holly's original Pop-style version). On *Prisoner in Disguise* (1975), even Smokey Robinson's "Tracks of My Tears" comes out country, as does Neil Young's "Love Is a Rose." Still, she produced a number 5 hit in 1975 with Holland-Dozier-Holland's "Heat Wave," in a decidedly noncountry style. In the 1980s, Ronstadt had incredible success with several albums that featured old songs from the 1930s and 1940s in lush arrangements backed by bandleader Nelson Riddle. She had even dabbled with the new wave trend by singing several Elvis Costello songs on 1980's *Mad Love* and with mariachi music in 1987's, *Canciones de Mi Padre*. In the same year as *Canciones*, Rondstadt's romantic ballad duet with James Ingram, "Somewhere Out There" from the animated movie *American Tale* topped the Hot 100. Returning to her country roots during the transition to the new millennium, she placed two albums in the Top 10 on the country chart.

Willie Nelson and Waylon Jennings—Around the edges of country rock were two other types of performer: country pop singers and progressive country (sometimes unflatteringly referenced as "redneck rock") singers. Interest in country rock naturally led to pure country music. The central figure of this trend was Willie Nelson. Nelson had moved to Nashville in 1961, where he had some success as a composer of country and pop songs

Willie Nelson at his Fourth of July picnic in Austin, Texas, in 1974.
SOURCE: CSU Archives/Everett Collection Inc/Alamy Stock Photo

for other artists, and, as a performer, he placed a few hits on the country charts. But Nelson felt that the Nashville country music establishment was too restrictive, and, late in 1969, he moved back to Texas. Several years later, he initiated his now-famous Fourth of July "picnics"—huge outdoor affairs that drew not only country music fans, but young rock fans. Nelson dropped the traditional country singer image; instead, he wore faded jeans and T-shirts, grew his hair long and braided it, sported an earring, and wore a bandanna around his head. By the norms of the traditional country music world, Nelson had become a rebel—an "outlaw." In their eyes, he was a redneck hippie.

In 1975, Nelson released *Red Headed Stranger* (number 28); "Blue Eyes Cryin' in the Rain" moved to number 21 on the Hot 100, opening the door for more crossover recordings by other progressive country singers: Tompall Glaser, Waylon Jennings, Kris Kristofferson, Jessi Colter (Jennings's wife), and Jerry Jeff Walker. RCA's progressive country sampler, *The Outlaws* (1977), brought the music of Nelson and some of the others to a wider audience (it became a platinum album—the first in country

music). Willie went on to have several more Top 40 hits in the early 1980s. His *Stardust* album (number 30, 1978) featured his versions of old pop favorites from the 1930s and 1940s (something of a precedent for Ronstadt's similar recordings). In 2017, just prior to his 84th birthday, Nelson released *God's Problem Child*, including a single entitled "Still Not Dead," a joke referencing a series of spurious news reports throughout his life; both the album and the single failed to chart.

Waylon Jennings's association with rock was only slightly stronger. Born in Texas, Jennings had played bass with Buddy Holly on his fateful last tour. Jennings had several country hits during the 1960s, but with the release of *The Outlaws,* he became a national figure. His *Ol' Waylon* album (1977) hit the Top 20 and yielded a Top 30 hit, "Luckenbach, Texas (Back to the Basics of Love)." He also recorded the theme song for the television show *The Dukes of Hazzard* (number 21, 1980) and sang with Willie Nelson on the major country hit "Mama Don't Let Your Babies Grow Up to Be Cowboys" (number 42, 1978). Jennings died in 2002 from diabetes-related conditions.

JOURNAL

Elements of C&W in Country Rock

Locate a recording of Charlie Daniels's "The Devil Went Down to Georgia." Listen to the recording at least three times as you identify a minimum of three musical elements that associate this sound with C&W music, as described earlier in this course. Now that you have identified the country elements, identify at least three characteristics that clearly identify this song as rock and roll. Do you think this song is more closely aligned with C&W or rock and roll? Provide an explanation for your response.

The response entered here will appear in the performance dashboard and can be viewed by your instructor.

Submit

13.5.2: Progressive Country

The progressive country movement was more a social phenomenon than a musical one. Nelson's music was firmly rooted in the country tradition. Rock elements were subdued or totally absent. What appealed was his rebel image.

In 1980, the film *Urban Cowboy* (starring John Travolta, but including musical appearances by some 14 country and country rock acts) made the country movement cool. Suddenly, people across the nation were wearing boots and broad-brimmed Stetson hats. However, the center of the progressive country movement stayed firmly in Austin, Texas, where the Armadillo World Headquarters became to this trend what the Fillmore had been to San Francisco. Huge country ballrooms, such as Gilley's in Houston and Billy Bob's in Fort Worth, capitalized on the urban-cowboy trend.

In the 1980s, crossover artists like Dolly Parton, Kenny Rogers, Eddie Rabbitt, Alabama, and the Oak Ridge Boys created a revived interest in country music within the general rock audience. As a result, sales of recordings by more mainstream country singers increased appreciably during the 1980s. George Strait, Reba McEntire, and Ricky Skaggs are credited with spawning a neo-traditionalist movement (Haislop, Lathrop, and Sumrall 1995). The success of crossover artists proved that there was still an audience for traditional country sounds. Many songs that hit number 1 on the country chart, like Strait's "Ocean Front Property" (1987) and Skaggs's "Lovin' Only Me" (1989), revealed an undeniable rock influence in their use of electric guitars and drums and in their general production quality. Multi-instrumentalist Skaggs even played an instrument called the *mandocaster,* a five-string instrumental cross between the mandolin and the Telecaster electric guitar. However, the basic songs were always identifiable as country music, incorporating the characteristic electric guitar twang, the pedal steel, and country-influenced vocal stylings.

In the mid-1980s, continuing the neo-traditionalist movement begun by George Strait and Ricky Skaggs, new artists (e.g., Randy Travis and Dwight Yoakam) enjoyed great national popularity. Songs like "On the Other Hand" and "Forever and Ever, Amen" brought Randy Travis to the top of the country chart in 1986 and 1987, respectively. During a period when country albums were considered highly successful if they sold a half million copies, sales of Travis's recordings were reaching into the multimillions, evidence that country music was, by the late 1980s, appealing to a wider audience.

Undoubtedly, some members of the rock audience had been turned off by the alternative music scene and the explicit violence of many rap recordings. As a result, they began searching for other musical styles with which they could be comfortable. Members of this group were among those who began to listen to country music and, liking what they heard, propelled the new generation of country artists toward an explosion of popularity in the 1990s. The year 1989 saw the release of a series of debut albums destined to bring country music to an extraordinary new height of popularity. Some of those emerging artists were Clint Black, Garth Brooks, Alan Jackson, Travis Tritt, and Mary Chapin Carpenter.

GLEN CAMPBELL AND KENNY ROGERS From the softer side of country came singers like Glen Campbell and Kenny Rogers. Campbell's gentle country-pop style first reached national attention in 1967 with a number 5 album, *Gentle on My Mind,* and a Top 30 hit, "By the Time I Get to Phoenix." After hitting what seemed to be a high spot in 1968 and 1969 with songs like "Wichita Lineman" (number 3) and "Galveston" (number 4), Campbell's popularity began to fade, but with the rising interest in country music in the late 1970s, Campbell enjoyed a significant comeback: "Rhinestone Cowboy" (number 1, 1975) and "Southern Nights" (number 1, 1977). Around 2011, Campbell was diagnosed with Alzheimer's but continued touring until 2014, passing away in 2017.

Kenny Rogers was born in Houston in 1941. Joining with several members of the New Christy Minstrels, he formed Kenny Rogers and the First Edition. They produced their two biggest hits in the late 1960s: "Just Dropped In (To See What Condition My Condition Was In)" (number 5, 1968) and "Ruby, Don't Take Your Love to Town" (number 6, 1969). In the mid-1970s, Kenny disbanded the First Edition and pursued a solo career. Emphasizing the country side, he had his first solo hits in 1977 with "Lucille" (number 5; no relation to Little Richard's song). Beginning with "She Believes in Me" (number 5, 1978) from *The Gambler,* Rogers initiated a long series of Top 20 hits that carried him into the 1980s as one of the most successful country-pop artists in the music industry. Both Campbell and Rogers stayed with the softer ballad style, and, in spite of his graying beard, Rogers did not follow the Nelson-Jennings outlaw image of progressive country.

GARTH BROOKS Although Garth Brooks eventually proved to be the most prominent country music artist of the early 1990s, it was Clint Black who initially led the pack of young country singers. After a short period of time, however, it became apparent that Brooks provided the definitive example of country crossover for the decade. Combining elements of rock and country into a series of incredibly successful recordings and a high-energy stage show, Brooks became the top-selling solo artist in history

(George-Warren and Romanowski 2001), selling over 100 million albums. His songwriting ability and charismatic appeal enabled him to transcend the boundaries of the C&W market without alienating his strong base of traditional country music fans.

Born in Oklahoma, Troyal Garth Brooks was turned down by several record labels during his initial trip to Nashville. Persistence paid off when he was seen by a Capitol Records executive performing "If Tomorrow Never Comes." His self-titled debut album hit number 2 on the country chart in 1989. It was with the arrival of his second release, *No Fences* (number 3 on the Hot 200, 1990), that Brooks stepped into the spotlight as the leader of the new generation of crossover country artists. Rock influences are obvious in the drumbeat and rock guitar riffs in his song "The Thunder Rolls." Notice the use of the 12-bar blues form in the verses for "Two of a Kind, Workin' on a Full House." The youthful energy of songs like "Friends in Low Places" or "Two of a Kind" is balanced by the more sentimental "Victim of the Game" and "Unanswered Prayers." Brooks seemed to be equally comfortable with both styles. *Ropin' the Wind* (number 1, 1991) was the first album in history to debut at the number 1 position on both the pop and country album charts. On the country album chart, *Ropin' the Wind* replaced Brooks's own previous album, *No Fences,* which was completing its 41-week reign at the top. This initiated an impressive series of albums that debuted at the top of both the country and pop charts: *Ropin' the Wind* (1991), *The Chase* (1992), and *In Pieces* (1993). "Against the Grain," the opening song on *Ropin' the Wind,* incorporates distorted rock guitar timbres and a driving backbeat, placing Brooks's musical style well within the boundaries of rock and roll. Listen to "Kickin' and Screamin'" and "The Night Will Only Know" from *In Pieces* or "The Old Stuff" and "The Fever" from *Fresh Horses* (number 2, 1995). Such songs are more accurately described as country-influenced rock than rock-influenced country. The verses of "Kickin' and Screamin'" are based on an altered version of the 12-bar blues form that provided the foundation for so many R&B and mainstream rock tunes during the 1950s and 1960s.

In 1999, Brooks made the bold decision to record an album as "Chris Gaines," a fictional Australian rock star he created. The album was promoted as a greatest hits collection and included a wide variety of musical styles, from new wave to R&B. Shunned by his country fans and ridiculed by critics, the album still managed to reach number 2 on the Hot 100 and sold over two million copies.

Garth Brooks provides an interesting exception to the image-conscious aesthetic that often drives the popular music industry. His slightly pudgy frame and receding hairline were reminiscent of the characteristics that predestined Bill Haley to be eclipsed by Elvis Presley as rock and roll emerged in the early 1950s. However, Brooks's consistently creative musical output, energetic stage show, and endearing personality overcame such cosmetic issues. Brooks's high-tech, high-energy stage show—revealing the obvious influence of theatrical rock bands like Bruce Springsteen, Queen, and Kiss—attracted both country and rock fans to his live performances, consistently selling out 60,000-seat auditoriums. However, after personal problems and fading record sales, Brooks moved out of the limelight by the middle of the first decade of the new millennium.

SHANIA TWAIN   The career of Shania Twain provides a quintessential rags-to-riches story. Shania Twain (born Eileen Twain) was raised in a working-class family in Ontario. Her parents, despite their economic condition, managed to send her to Toronto for voice lessons. She had the good fortune to be noticed by Mary Bailey, a well-known Canadian country singer, when Twain appeared on a national variety show. Bailey had the connections that eventually landed Shania in Nashville (Dickerson 1998). In 1991, with Bailey's assistance, Twain recorded a demo that earned her a contract with Mercury Records. In honor of the Ojibwe heritage of her stepfather, the singer changed her name to "Shania," meaning "I'm on my way."

Shania Twain on stage, 2004.

SOURCE: Sven Hoogerhuis/United Archives GmbH/Alamy Stock Photo

Her self-titled debut album (1993) did not perform well, but it afforded an opportunity for her to be heard by John "Mutt" Lange, former producer of rock bands, including Foreigner, AC/DC, and Def Leppard. The duo collaborated on her next album, *The Woman in Me* (number 5, 1995), which evidenced a fresh approach to country music, including upbeat energy, powerful rock guitars, and top-notch production standards. The album, containing only songs penned by Twain, eventually generated seven country hit singles, including "Any Man of Mine" and "(If You're Not in It for Love) I'm Outta Here." In 1997, Twain and Lange, then married, succeeded once again with *Come On Over* (number 2), containing an incredible nine country hits and becoming the best-selling album in country music history. In 1998, she received Grammy Awards for Best Female Country Vocal Performance and Best Country Song for "You're Still the One" (number 2), a song cowritten by Twain and Lange. In 2002, Twain reached the top of the charts with *Up!*, a two-disc release, each disc containing the same 19 songs, one version for the country market and one for the pop market. The songs included a cover of Abba's "C'est la vie" and a Latin pop song, "Juanita." After a trying period, both physically (she was diagnosed with dysphonia, a vocal cord disorder) and personally (her divorce from Lange in 2010), she came out swinging in 2017 with the release of *Now*, which debuted at number 1.

THE DIXIE CHICKS   Taking their name from a classic country rock song by Little Feat, "Dixie Chicken," the Dixie Chicks released their debut album in 1990 (*Thank Heavens for Dale Evans*). At that time, the group from Lubbock, Texas, consisted of sisters Martie and Emily Erwin, Laura Lynch, and Robyn Lynn Macy. Two more local albums followed before the group re-formed as a trio with new lead vocalist Natalie Maines replacing Lynch. The new trio would prove to be one of the most successful country rock acts of the 1990s, with Martie on fiddle and mandolin and Emily on guitar, dobro, and banjo.

With the release of *Wide Open Spaces* (number 1 country album, 1998), the Dixie Chicks attained superstardom. "There's Your Trouble" and "You Were Mine" both entered the Top 40 and, along with the title cut, and all three went to number 1 on the country singles chart. The album eventually sold over 12 million copies. The release of *Fly* (number 1, 1999) and the Top 40 singles "Cowboy Take Me Away" and "Without You," both of which topped the country singles chart, confirmed the group's superstar status. This level of success continued with the release of *Home* (number 1, 2002), containing two Top 10 singles: "Long Time Gone" and "Landslide," a song originally recorded by

Fleetwood Mac's Stevie Nicks. The Chicks became embroiled in a political controversy over a statement Maines made in March 2003 about being "ashamed" that President Bush was from their home state of Texas. A significant backlash occurred from the group's fan base, as some radio stations refused to play their music and some fans joined the protest by destroying their personal copies of the group's CDs. Maines eventually apologized for the remark. The Dixie Chicks' next album, *Top of the World,* a two-CD live concert set, was released at the end of 2003 but it did not soar to platinum status, as had the previous two releases. Deciding to confront the issue directly, the Dixie Chicks released a documentary entitled *Shut Up and Sing* (2006) during the same year as the successful and critically acclaimed *Taking the Long Way,* which returned the band to the top of the *Billboard* album chart and contained a song that addressed the controversy directly ("Not Ready to Make Nice," number 4).

OTHER COUNTRY ARTISTS   The careers of other country stars rivaled that of Garth Brooks. Clint Black, Travis Tritt, Mary Chapin Carpenter, Emmylou Harris, Alan Jackson, Hank Williams Jr., and a host of others all played an important role in keeping country music in the spotlight. The progressive country music of the Kentucky Headhunters, k. d. lang, and Lyle Lovett encouraged a generation of rock enthusiasts to broaden its musical horizons to include C&W. The crossover success of Billy Ray Cyrus's "Achy Breaky Heart" (number 4, 1992; number 1, country) succeeded in confirming the position of country music within the mainstream during the early 1990s, though, more recently, Cyrus is known primarily as the father of singer Miley Cyrus.

As country artists rose to their highest levels of popularity since the emergence of rock and roll, country music dance halls flourished. Providing music for such social gathering places presented a certain difficulty with the eclectic mix making up the new country audience. One attempt to meet this challenge, Brooks and Dunn's "Boot Scootin' Boogie" (1992), provided a curious blend of musical styles. The club-mix version of the song takes the fundamental country sound and dance hall lyrics, adding an unmistakable rock backbeat and synthesizer bass line, not unlike those found in recordings by Madonna or other pop-dance artists. Even the musical form exhibits close ties to rock and roll. Each verse is sung over a 12-bar blues, in which the final phrase is extended by two measures.

As the 1990s progressed, the fusion of country, folk, and rock achieved an overwhelming level of popularity. However, by the end of the decade, the number of country rock crossovers had declined noticeably.

13.6: The Jam Band Phenomenon

OBJECTIVE: Explain why jam bands became popular during the 1980s

Following in the footsteps of the Grateful Dead (and their post-Garcia incarnations as the Other Ones, the Dead, and Further) and amassing a similarly devoted fan base, a number of **jam bands** began to hit the scene during the 1980s and 1990s. These groups integrated the sounds of country, folk, bluegrass, rock, jazz, and even punk into an eclectic and highly energized musical performance. Like the Dead before them, studio recordings took a backseat to their live performances, and improvisation formed a significant part of their live performances. Such groups included Phish, the String Cheese Incident, and Widespread Panic. Many jam band fans, a nomadic bunch reminiscent of Deadheads, migrated with the bands from city to city on their concert tours and, like the Deadheads before them, openly traded bootleg tapes of concert performances—with the band's permission.

13.6.1: Phish

The most successful of the jam bands of this period was Phish, formed in 1983 at the University of Vermont by guitarists Trey Anastasio and Jeff Holdsworth, and drummer Jon Fishman. The term *jam* suggests a freedom in the style of performance, as opposed to the highly rehearsed sound of most commercial recordings, allowing for extended sections of improvisation, focusing on expressive communication from a performer to the other players and audience. This music's energetic style is one of the primary reasons that both musicians and audiences find jam bands so enjoyable to listen to. In their sometimes lengthy instrumental improvisations, band members draw from numerous musical traditions, including country, rock, and jazz.

In 1988, Phish recorded their debut, *Junta,* and sold cassette copies at their performances. The average track length on this album was almost 9 minutes long, with the longest ("Union Federal") occupying a full 25½ minutes. By the time of their second album, *Lawn Boy* (1990), the group had built a significant following and was one of the first bands to utilize the Internet as a means of information dissemination, maintaining contact with their fans and selling merchandise (including recordings). Beginning in 1993, the band's consistently acclaimed live performances began to translate into placement on the album chart, although Phish has never had a Top 40 hit single. This is perhaps not surprising given the influence of the Dead, who, as you'll recall, had only one Top 40 hit ("A Touch of Grey," number 9) in their astonishing multi-decade career. Phish continued to release recordings into the new millennium and played their "farewell" concert in 2004. Anastasio spent several years cultivating a moderately successful solo career before reuniting with his band mates in 2009 for a summer tour and the release of their 14th studio album (*Joy,* number 13), followed by *Fuego* (2014). During the summer of 2015, Anastasio joined the Dead for their historic reunion concerts at Soldier Field in Chicago, filling in for the late Jerry Garcia and celebrating the 50th anniversary of the band's first show as the Warlocks and the 20th anniversary of Garcia's last performance with the Dead (also at Soldier Field).

Following the success of Phish, other jam bands began to appear, including Widespread Panic, Disco Biscuits, ekoostic hookah, and Rebecca's Statue. An outgrowth of the jam band phenomenon, *jam-grass,* also emphasized improvisation but was primarily influenced by mountain music and bluegrass (e.g., Cornmeal's *In the Kitchen,* 2001).

13.6.2: The Dave Matthews Band

Although not typically included under the jam band rubric, the music of the Dave Matthews Band certainly matches the eclectic mix of musical styles evident in these performance-oriented groups, and the band built a similar fan base (also allowing bootleg recordings of their performances). Formed in 1991 in Charlottesville, Virginia, the band's rise to prominence resulted from a combination of superbly crafted studio recordings (*Remember Two Things,* 1993, and *Under the Table and Dreaming,* number 11, 1994), their appearance on the 1993 and 1994 H.O.R.D.E. tours (Horizons of Rock Developing Elsewhere), and performing as an opening act for Phish and Blues Traveler. On *Crash* (number 2, 1996), Matthews and his band exemplified an extremely high caliber of

musicianship. Whereas Phish might entertain their audience with an on-stage performance on a vacuum cleaner, Matthews's musical style included elements of world music, following the example of artists like Paul Simon, Peter Gabriel, and Sting.

In the late 1990s, the band returned to their live performance aesthetic, releasing several well-received live albums. As a new decade approached, their studio albums proved even more popular, resulting in three number 1 albums (*Before These Crowded Streets,* 1998; *Busted Stuff,* 2002; and *Stand Up,* 2005), Matthews's first solo album, *Some Devil* (number 2, 2003), and another series of live recordings.

Although almost any of Matthews's recordings would effectively illustrate their integration of musical styles, a particularly good example is provided by the opening tracks of *Crowded Streets.* The brief opening track, "Pantala Naga Pampa" (with its Indian title meaning "there's a python in my pants"), reveals Latin and Caribbean musical influence and segues directly into "Rapunzel" with its verses incorporating staccato and syncopated rhythms. The Middle Eastern influence of "The Last Stop" and its unveiled socio-political message provide stark contrast to the opening tracks. With "Don't Drink the Water," we return to a more traditional Matthews Band sound.

REVIEW THE JAM BAND PHENOMENON

The following fill-in-the-blank questions will review your knowledge of jam bands.

Statements
1. Rock groups that are highly eclectic in the styles they play—often integrating country, folk, bluegrass, rock, jazz, even punk, and other influences—and for which instrumental improvisation plays a significant part in their performances are known as _____.
2. Trey Anastasio, who performed with the Grateful Dead in their historic 2015 reunion concerts, initially performed with _____, one of the most successful jam bands of the 1980s and 1990s.
3. The jam band that fits least comfortably into this section, but integrates sounds of world music into its performances is _____.

Feedback: 1. Jam bands 2. Phish 3. The Dave Matthews Band

13.7: Soft Rock

OBJECTIVE: Summarize the evolution of soft rock from the 70s to the 90s

Just as in the 1950s and 1960s, soft rock was immensely popular in the 1970s, and, just as the other styles of the 1970s fragmented into subcategories, so too did soft rock.

Generally speaking, as hard rock grew harder (especially with heavy metal and punk rock), soft rock grew softer. Some of the artists discussed in this section sit squarely on the imaginary dividing line between soft rock and pure pop, moving back and forth across the line, depending on which album and which song one is considering. Recall that we consider a song to be soft rock if one or more of rock's basic musical elements is present—for example, a rock-like bass line or a rock-derived rhythmic pattern—no matter how gentle. If there is an absence of such elements, the song is considered pure pop music.

13.7.1: The Carpenters

The hottest soft-rock act of the early 1970s was the Carpenters. Brother and sister Richard and Karen Carpenter, from New Haven, Connecticut, were talented musicians. Richard sang and played keyboards; Karen sang and played drums. Their second album, *Close to You* (number 2, 1970), produced their first number 1 hit, the title track by Hal David and Burt Bacharach, and "We've Only Just Begun" (number 2). Both songs lie squarely on the soft rock–pop borderline. For example, the bridge of "We've Only Just Begun" has a stronger beat, complete with backbeat brass accents on the second beat and a steady eighth-note tambourine—enough to establish a soft-rock sound—but the other sections of the song withdraw these elements and, thus, lie more in the pop realm. "Close to You" was primarily a pop song, although there was a very light triple division of the beat (listen for the cymbals) in its bridge section. There are a few other very light touches of rock influence: syncopations; a steady quadruple beat, with all four beats about evenly stressed; and a few rock-style piano voicings. The Carpenters' lush, jazz-like vocal harmonies (listen to "Love to Surrender") are the result of multitracking, a technique with which Richard had been experimenting for several years.

The Carpenters

Their next album, *The Carpenters* (number 2, 1971), yielded three Top 5 songs: "For All We Know" (number 3), "Rainy Days and Mondays" (number 2), and "Superstar" (number 2). Again, in "Superstar," the formula included a bridge section with a more pronounced beat; in the other sections, the bass played a dotted quarter and eighth-note pattern, under a light but steady duple division of the beat. Many of the Carpenters' songs conform to this pattern: a pop sound with subtle rock elements, moving to a harder style (relatively speaking, of course) in the bridge sections. Karen Carpenter's excellent voice was capable of a variety of subtle changes; she was one of the finest pop-rock singers of the 1970s.

The Carpenters' popularity was consistent through 1975. Beginning in 1976, album sales began to slump. In 1983, Karen died of cardiac arrest at the age of 32, resulting from her long struggle with anorexia nervosa.

13.7.2: Barry Manilow

In the late 1970s, the biggest name in soft rock was Barry Manilow. After taking courses at City College of New York, the New York College of Music, and even Juilliard, Manilow found work in the music business, composing and performing commercial jingles. In 1974, he released a ballad called "Mandy"; the song climbed to number 1 by early 1975. His next album, *Tryin' to Get the Feeling* (1975), rose to number 5, with "I Write the Songs" reaching number 1. These two songs provide insight into Manilow's style. A fine singer in the soft, pop-rock style, Manilow often begins songs very quietly, with little accompaniment. Gradually, the texture thickens, as full orchestra and backup voices are added. Near the end, there is often a modulation up one-half step (you may recall a similar practice on many recordings by the Supremes, as discussed earlier in this course). Finally, full production resources are used to build a big finish. Notice especially the drum part; from the outset, there is typically a subtle backbeat on the second and fourth beats, but as the song nears its big finish, the backbeat becomes quite exaggerated, usually with considerable reverberation added in the mix.

Manilow did not compose "I Write the Songs." In fact, the song (composed by Bruce Johnston) had been recorded earlier by the Captain and Tennille and by David Cassidy. The lyrics refer to neither the singer nor even the song's composer, but to music as a concept. "I Write the Songs" is an eloquent acknowledgment of music's role in human society. Another effective ode to music's power is "Beautiful Music" (music by Manilow, lyrics by Marty Panzer). Midway through the song, Manilow moves as close to the gentler side of mainstream rock as he ever does. Listen to "A Nice Boy Like Me" to hear Manilow at his "rockiest." For the balance of the 1970s, Manilow was the premier figure in soft rock. By 1990, he had enjoyed over two dozen Top 40 hits, including 11 in the Top 10. Manilow has continued to record and perform into the new millennium, but has not had a Top 40 hit since the early 1980s ("Read 'em and Weep," 1983). He has channeled his music-making into the areas of swing, Pop standards, Broadway show tunes, and covers. In the early 2000s, he released a series of albums (all of which made the Top 20) containing selected songs from various decades (50s, 60s, 70s, and 80s) and a set of greatest love songs. In 2011, Manilow released a studio album entitled *15 Minutes: Fame … Can You Take It?*, which reached number 7 on the charts.

13.7.3: Neil Diamond

Neil Diamond has been a successful singer-songwriter for over 40 years. He wrote hits for other musicians; beginning with "Cherry, Cherry" (number 6, 1966), Diamond, the performer, had his own series of Top 20 hits. "Sweet Caroline" (number 4, 1969) initiated his greatest period of popularity (at least until his comeback in the early 1980s). He achieved six Top 10 hits between 1969 and 1974, including the number 1 hits "Cracklin' Rosie" and "Song Sung Blue." Diamond's strong voice, usually accompanied by full orchestra and vocal backup with very professional production, created a popular, soft-rock style. On occasion, a rock-derived beat and a rock bass line provided the necessary hint of rock to justify the label "soft rock" (e.g., on "Sweet Caroline" and "Longfellow Serenade").

Diamond's film debut in *The Jazz Singer* (1980) renewed his popularity. The soundtrack album reached number 3 and produced three Top 10 hits. "America" qualifies as soft rock; the album's other songs are in a pop style (although the bridge section of "Love on the Rocks" may cross the line into soft rock). Diamond's popularity continued into the new millennium with the release of several studio albums, including *Three Chord Opera* (number 15, 2001), *12 Songs* (number 4, 2005), *Home Before Dark* (his first number 1 album, released in 2008), and *Dreams* (number 8, 2010).

13.7.4: Olivia Newton-John

Moving from a harder to a softer style is fairly common. As you learned elsewhere in this course, Bobby Darin, Buddy Holly, Fats Domino, and even Elvis Presley followed this path. But moving the other way is both rare and difficult; nevertheless, Olivia Newton-John made this shift.

In addition to the soft-rock releases of the Carpenters, Barry Manilow, Neil Diamond, and Olivia Newton-John, there were many other soft-rock artists producing

Life and Career of Olivia Newton-John

The following section will provide highlights from the career of Olivia Newton-John, one of the most successful artists in the soft-rock subgenre during the 1970s.

Born in England, Newton-John launched her career with television and local pub appearances. Her version of Dylan's "If Not for You" hit the U.S. Hot 100 in 1971. In 1973, she cut "Let Me Be There"; in early 1974, it peaked at number 6 and earned Newton-John a Grammy for Best Female Country Vocal. Somehow this woman born in England and raised in Australia became identified as a country music singer!

She followed with two Top 5 hits in 1974, including her first number 1 song, "I Honestly Love You." Her success with soft, country-style ballads led to her being named 1974's Female Vocalist of the Year by the Country Music Association (CMA). Many country fans and artists were enraged; some of the artists pulled out of the CMA and formed the Association of Country Entertainers. Olivia followed in 1975 with two more Top 5 songs, including the number 1 "Have You Ever Been Mellow."

The year 1978 brought the beginning of a major change in her career. Appearing in the 1950s nostalgia film *Grease* (opposite John Travolta), Olivia portrayed Sandy Dumbrowski ("Sandra Dee"), a demure, ponytailed innocent who, at the end of the plot, is transformed into a leather-jacketed, sexy female in tight, leather pants. The soundtrack album reached number 1 and included three hit singles. The number 1 "You're the One That I Want" (written for the film adaptation of the musical) was a genuine rock song, lying between soft rock and the gentler side of the mainstream.

It seemed as though Sandy's transformation in *Grease* was replicated by Olivia's career. The new Newton-John released *Totally Hot* with its hit single, "A Little More Love" (number 3, 1978). Appearing in the 1980 film *Xanadu*, for which music was composed by Electric Light Orchestra, she had two hit singles from its soundtrack album: "Magic" (number 1) and "Xanadu" (number 8).

The image change became complete with the controversial song "Physical" (number 1, 1981). Was it about the physical fitness craze or just plain sex? Whichever it was (if not both), the song was a hit. Musically, most of Olivia's post-*Grease* songs were rock; the softer elements include the elaborate production and Olivia's soft-pop voice (and her image). Certainly she was closer to the mainstream than the Carpenters, Manilow, and Diamond.

exemplary music during the 1970s. In the next section, we will briefly identify several of these artists and provide information about their hits and individual performance styles.

Table 13.1 Other Important Soft-Rock Acts of the 1970s

Table 13.1 summarizes several more important soft-rock acts of the 1970s.

Name	Typical Hits	Comments
John Denver	"Take Me Home Country Roads" (number 2, 1971); "Rocky Mountain High" (number 9, 1973); "Sunshine on My Shoulder" (number 1, 1974)	Folk background; peak popularity from 1971 to 1976; folk roots flavored by light touches of C&W and soft rock
Osmonds (also Donny Osmond and Donny and Marie)	"One Bad Apple" (number 1, 1971); "Go Away Little Girl" (Donny Osmond, number 1, 1971)	Usually a quintet, they placed 10 songs in the Top 40 from 1971 to 1975; as a soloist, Donny had 12 Top 40 hits in the same period; later in the 1970s, Donny and Marie became a duet, hosting a successful national television show; by the end of 1978, the total Osmond family had created 33 Top 40 hits
Roberta Flack	"The First Time Ever I Saw Your Face" (number 1, 1972); "Killing Me Softly with His Song" (number 1, 1973); "Feel Like Makin' Love" (number 1, 1974)	Soul background; early experience in church music; style has elements of soul with influences of jazz and soft rock; many successful duet releases with Donny Hathaway
America	"A Horse with No Name" (number 1, 1972); "Ventura Highway" (number 8, 1972); "Tin Man" (number 4, 1974)	Trio known for solid vocal harmonies and enigmatic lyrics; George Martin produced many of their gentle rock hits
Seals and Crofts	"Summer Breeze" (number 6, 1972); "Diamond Girl" (number 6, 1973); "Get Closer" (number 6, 1976)	Duo from Texas; members of the Champs ("Tequila") in the late 1950s; soft-rock style with lyrics sometimes reflecting their Baha'i faith (e.g., "Hummingbird" and "East of Ginger Trees"); occasional touches of country influence

REVIEW SOFT ROCK

The following fill-in-the-blank questions will test your knowledge of soft rock.

Statements

1. _____, one of the hottest soft-rock acts of the 1970s, consisted of the brother-sister duo of Richard and Karen Carpenter.

2. _____ was the 1970s soft-rock artist who starred in the remake of The Jazz Singer in 1980.

3. _____ is an example of an artist who transitioned from soft rock into the dance music subgenre.

4. The artist responsible for the number 2 hit single "Take Me Home Country Roads" was _____.

Feedback: 1. The Carpenters 2. Neil Diamond 3. Olivia Newton-John 4. John Denver

Beginning with the Pop sound that, along with C&W and R&B, led to the emergence of rock and roll in the mid-1950s, softer sounds have been a consistent part of the popular music experience. With rare exceptions, even albums by the heaviest rock bands typically contain one or two ballads to balance the high level of energy and frenetic pace of the other tracks. As the 1980s began, a number of the most popular artists of the decade fit into the soft-rock category.

13.7.5: Lionel Richie

One of the most successful acts on the softer side of rock during the 1980s was Lionel Richie. Lead singer of the Commodores throughout the 1970s, Richie began moving away from the group in 1981. He wrote and recorded the theme for the movie *Endless Love* and saw it move to number 1. His first solo album, *Lionel Richie* (number 3,

1982), yielded three Top 5 singles, including the number 1 hit "Truly."

Richie's first number 1 album, *Can't Slow Down* (late 1983), produced an amazing five Top 10 singles, including two number 1 songs: "All Night Long (All Night)" and "Hello." Although Richie's biggest successes have been in the soft rock ballad style, he sometimes moves to a moderate or fast tempo—always with a funky dance beat (sometimes close to disco). The Jamaican influence in "All Night Long" was an interesting stylistic touch (note, for example, Richie's affected Jamaican enunciation and the nonsense syllable section—supposedly an old Jamaican chant).

Richie continued writing songs, performing, recording, and producing for himself and others into the late1980s. In 1985, he was co-composer (with Michael Jackson) for "We Are the World," a song (and video) produced by Quincy Jones to raise money for famine victims in Africa. The recording included a star-studded list of performers: Harry Belafonte, Ray Charles, Bob Dylan, Waylon Jennings, Billy Joel, Willie Nelson, Steve Perry (Journey), Smokey Robinson, Kenny Rogers, Diana Ross, Paul Simon, Bruce Springsteen, Tina Turner, Stevie Wonder, and many others.

Richie's 1986 album, *Dancing on the Ceiling*, became his second consecutive number 1 album. Although it proved to be his last of the decade, Motown pulled a string of Top 20 singles from the album, including "Say You, Say Me" (number 1), "Dancing on the Ceiling" (number 2), "Love Will Conquer All" (number 9), "Ballerina Girl" (number 7), and "Se La" (number 20). Richie's streak of hits came to an abrupt halt in the late 1980s, and he took a break after two decades in the music business. He continued to perform throughout the 1990s and 2000s, but never again enjoyed the level of success he experienced during his early solo years. In 2012, Richie released *Tuskegee*, an album containing 13 of his past songs, performed in a country-influenced style in collaboration with some of the biggest country stars of the time, including Willie Nelson, Kenny Rogers, Shania Twain, Tim McGraw, Rascal Flatts, Kenny Chesney, and Jimmy Buffett. The album topped the chart, but failed to produce any Top 40 hits; in fact, the highest-charting single was his remake of "Endless Love," a duet with Shania Twain, which reached only number 116.

13.7.6: Pop Divas of the 1980s and 1990s

Several female singers found tremendous success in the field of 1980s soft rock, though the style of these artists revealed significant versatility, often including a strong dance beat. Whitney Houston had her first hit single in 1985 ("You Give Good Love") and then reeled off ten Top 10 hits before the end of the decade, including a remarkable seven consecutive number 1 hits, breaking the previous record of six in a row established by the Beatles and the Bee Gees. Her first two albums, *Whitney Houston* (1985) and *Whitney* (1987), both hit number 1. After a long battle with drug addiction, in February 2012, Houston was found drowned in a bathtub with cocaine-use paraphernalia nearby.

Paula Abdul's success came near the end of the decade with three consecutive number 1 hits in 1988 and 1989 ("Straight Up," "Forever Your Girl," and "Cold Hearted"). Her first album, *Forever Your Girl*, hit number 1 in 1989 and held that spot for 10 weeks; it was followed by a second number 1 album, *Spellbound* (1991). In 2002, she reignited her popularity as a cohost, along with Simon Cowell, of *American Idol*.

A new group of solo female artists emerged in the 1990s, representing a wide array of musical styles. According to Dickerson (1998, 17), "1996 was a landmark year. It was the year female solo artists out-charted their male counterparts on the Top 20 chart for the first time in history." Of the artists scoring Top 20 hits that year, 61 percent were female, and, the following year, the percentage fell only slightly, to 60 percent. We now turn to one of those artists, whose vocal skill brought new range, quite literally, to the world of rock.

13.7.7: Mariah Carey

A vocalist of incredible technical ability, Mariah Carey experienced a rise to stardom and commercial success rivaled by only a handful of her predecessors. Exhibiting a five-octave vocal range, her recordings reveal both a sultry ballad singer and virtuoso vocal technician. In addition to her impressive vocal technique, Carey was actively involved in writing and producing her recordings.

Mariah Carey on stage, 2009.
SOURCE: Lee/Everett Collection

Carey's vocal style reveals heavy R&B and gospel influences. Listen, for example, to "Vision of Love" (number 1) from her debut album. Carey's vocal delivery in this song is heavily blues-inflected, especially in its use of blue notes throughout. Her melismatic style of singing is similar to that of Aretha Franklin's gospel recordings (see the discussion of soul music and the related Musical Close-Up in an earlier section of this course). The difference between Mariah and her predecessors is in her incredible vocal range and willingness to use it completely, as exhibited in the final chorus of this song. As Carey sings a variation of the melody on one track of the recording, she harmonizes with herself on a second track, incorporating her extreme high pitch range (up to three octaves above middle C). The song concludes with an extended melisma (at one point, with no instrumental accompaniment), incorporating obvious blues and gospel influences.

Carey's Career Success

The following section will provide highlights from the career of Mariah Carey.

Carey's self-titled, debut album reached number 1 in 1990 and contained four number 1 hit singles ("Vision of Love," "Love Takes Time," "Someday," and "I Don't Wanna Cry"); her second album, *Emotions* (1991), reached number 4 with a second series of hit singles. With this album, Carey made history, becoming the first artist whose initial five singles all went to number 1.

In fact, eight of her first ten singles would eventually reach the top of the chart.

In 1992, her *Unplugged* recording produced a number 1 cover of "I'll Be There," a number 1 hit for the Jackson Five in 1970. After marrying Tommy Mottola, an executive at Columbia Records who was almost twice her age, Carey continued her commercial success with *Music Box* (number 1, 1993), resulting in three more Top 10 hits: "Dream Lover" (number 1), "Hero" (number 1), and "Without You" (number 3).

In 1994, following a number 2 duet with Luther Vandross ("Endless Love"), she released *Daydream* (number 1), containing the number 1 hits "Fantasy" and "One Sweet Day." The latter song featured 1990s vocal group Boyz II Men and held the number 1 position for 16 weeks. "One Sweet Day" is listed by Joel Whitburn (2010, p. 864) as the number 1 hit in *Billboard* Hot 100 history between the years of 1955 and 2009. With the release of this recording, Carey became the first female in the history of rock music to have three albums with sales of over eight million copies each.

In 1997, Mariah released *Butterfly* (number 1, 1997), revealing evidence of hip-hop influence, as clearly demonstrated in the song "Honey," a collaborative effort with rap artists Ma$e and the Lox. "My All," a second number 1 hit from the same album, followed in 1998. A greatest hits collection followed, and then *Rainbow* (number 2, 2000), containing the number 1 hit "Heartbreaker," providing an appropriate end to the decade in which Mariah dominated the charts and became its best-selling female artist (Whitburn, 2010). Her interest in fusing the upbeat musical style of her recordings with elements of hip-hop continued with vocal appearances by a variety of rap artists, including Jay-Z and Snoop Dogg.

In 2001, Carey signed an $80 million, multi-record deal with Virgin Records (the largest ever to date), announcing that her first release would be a soundtrack to a film (*Glitter*), in which she would play the starring role. At the time, there seemed to be little risk involved in such a plan, but as is often the case in the music industry, even the best-laid plans sometimes go astray. Mariah was not the only artist to flounder during this year of falling record sales. According to *Rolling Stone* magazine (Goodman 2002, 21), it was "the kind of year the music business would just as soon forget ... the most dramatic year of decline since the disco boom went bust in the late Seventies." As a result of the dismal commercial performance of the film (although the soundtrack album reached number 7 in 2001) and declining record sales, Carey and Virgin parted ways, with the record company paying off $28 million of the contracted amount.

Carey's personal life also made headlines as her behavior became increasingly unpredictable. After releasing the album *Charmbracelet* (number 3, 2002), Carey initiated a big comeback in 2005 with two consecutive number 1 albums (*The Emancipation of Mimi* and *E=MC²*), the latter containing two Top 20 hits: "Touch My Body" (number 1) and "Bye Bye" (number 19), and a return to her dance-pop sound. As the second decade of the new millennium was about to commence, in 2009, Carey re-released *Merry Christmas* (originally released in 1994) and, then in 2010, released *Merry Christmas II You* (number 4). From May 2015 through July 2017, she had a concert residency at Caesars Palace in Las Vegas entitled "#1 to Infinity."

13.7.8: Other Soft-Rock Sounds

Soft rock continued into the 1980s with groups like Air Supply and the Alan Parsons Project. The Australian band Air Supply combined lush instrumental backgrounds, highly professional production work, and strong vocals. The Alan Parsons Project, though fitting comfortably into the soft-rock subgenre, often veered toward progressive rock.

A rather interesting phenomenon in the world of late 1980s soft rock was the popularity of some young teen groups. The most successful of these was the quintet New Kids on the Block. The New Kids were between the ages of 11 and 15 when the group was formed in 1984 by producer Maurice Starr. Several years earlier, Starr had gathered some 13- to 15-year-olds from Boston into a reasonably successful group called New Edition, and the group placed six hits in the Top 40 between 1984 and 1988. On the basis of that success, Starr had high hopes for the New Kids. He was not disappointed; their 1989 album *Hangin' Tough* rose to number 1 and yielded five Top 10 hits, including two at number 1 ("I'll Be Loving You" and the title song). The New Kids became the hottest soft-rock group of the late 1980s, especially with younger rock fans. Their style alternated between soft ballads (4 out of 10 cuts on *Hangin' Tough*) and a techno-dance style much like Madonna's. Starr played or programmed all of the instruments on the album.

As the decade turned, the New Kids released another number 1 album, *Step by Step* (1990), which yielded several more single hits, including the number 1 title song. The group disbanded after 1994's *Face the Music* (number 37), but reunited 14 years later to release *The Block* (number 2, 2008) and tour; the album resulted in only one Top 40 hit. New Kids on the Block collaborated with Backstreet Boys to release *NKOTBSB* (number 7) and initiated a joint tour. The New Kids, New Edition, and other packaged acts of the late 1980s were harbingers of the so-called boy bands (and girl bands) of the 1990s (covered in a later section of this course).

13.7.9: New Age Music

Before we move past soft rock, we must note the advent of the softest style of music to hit the popular market since the mid-1950s: New Age music. The musical origins of New Age music seem to be within that branch of new wave music that tended toward minimalist classical music. Precedents can be found in some music by Brian Eno and Robert Fripp. There is certainly a relationship with the technorock groups of the 1970s (e.g., Passport and Kraftwerk) as well as classical electrominimalists such as Philip Glass and Steve Reich.

A good example of electronic New Age music is Tangerine Dream. This prolific German group, headed by Edgar Froese and Chris Franks, emphasizes electronic keyboards. The music is usually rather quiet and serene, bathing the listener in waves of shimmering electronic sounds and repetitive, overlapping patterns (a hallmark of the minimalists). For a sample, listen to *Tangram* (1980). Tangerine Dream, in the tradition of art rockers, usually opts for side-long works that gradually unfold in a stream-of-consciousness idiom; the group has remained incredibly prolific well into the new millennium. Another group that has been dubbed "New Age" is Mannheim Steamroller. Similar in general concept to Tangerine Dream, Steamroller produced a series of albums named *Fresh Aire I, II, III,* and so on; then, in the 1990s and 2000s, they focused primarily on holiday music and style-focused releases (Renaissance, Romantic, etc.).

Not all New Age music is heavily electronic. Its gentle, soothing sound also can be accomplished with acoustic instruments or combinations of electronic and acoustic instruments. Leading this field in the late 1980s was the Windham Hill Record Company, a California label that grossed over $25 million in 1985 and grew steadily thereafter. By 1986, Windham Hill accounted for 15 to 20 percent of the billings for its distributor, A&M Records. Quiet, almost Muzak-like, Windham Hill records (and others similar in concept) surround the listener with a soft, soothing sound environment. Several of the more well-known names in this style are pianist George Winston and guitarist Will Ackerman (cofounder of Windham Hill). Although there is some derivation from rock, New Age is essentially

JOURNAL

Pop Divas

Listen to Whitney Houston's "How Will I Know," Paula Abdul's "Straight Up," and Mariah Carey's "Vision of Love." After an initial listen, which of these vocalists do you like best? What is it about the vocal timbre, expressive performance, or musical accompaniment of your selection that results in this preference? In your explanation, be as specific as you can, relying on the musical vocabulary you have developed in this course.

 The response entered here will appear in the performance dashboard and can be viewed by your instructor.

Submit

anti-rock. Where rock has historically been stimulative music, most New Age music seems to offer the antidote for the loud, screaming tension; the driving beat; and the shock mentality of much rock and roll, but it may be more than a reaction against rock. It may also have been a reaction against the stressful tensions and fast-paced tempo of life in the 1980s.

13.8: Musical Close-Up on Rock Elements in the New Country Sound

OBJECTIVE: Compare the musical elements of country and rock music

Country music re-emerged as one of the most commercially successful musical styles during the late 1980s and early 1990s. However, the C&W that played such an important role in the careers of many early rock stars (e.g., Bill Haley, Elvis Presley, and Jerry Lee Lewis) bears only a faint resemblance to the country music that gained popularity toward the end of the twentieth century.

As we have discussed earlier in this course, the audience for country music of the early 1950s was well defined, and the style of the music was fairly consistent, centering on simple, singable melodies and lyrics. Most songs were based on diatonic harmonies (frequently no more than three or four chords) and basic, straightforward rhythms. Singers often incorporated an affected nasality in their vocal production, or other techniques like yodeling, falsetto, or allowing the voice to crack with emotion. C&W performers of the 1940s and 1950s played acoustic instruments almost exclusively (e.g., acoustic guitars, string bass, etc.). The pedal steel (slide guitar) and fiddle rounded out the traditional C&W ensemble. Recall that most of the early C&W groups did not use a drummer. As a result, the bass player not only supplied the music's harmonic foundation, but was also responsible for providing the rhythmic drive. Often, the bassist would slap the neck of the instrument percussively, while playing the notes of a simple bass line. These bass lines normally consisted of the first and fifth notes of the musical scale for each chord of the harmony.

Watch A SIMPLE BASS LINE
This example represents a very basic C&W bass line. As the chord changes, the bass player alternates between the root and fifth scale degree of each chord.

13.8.1: Three Primary Chords

Eddy Arnold's "Bouquet of Roses" (number 1 country, 1948) exemplifies the simple melody, three-chord harmony, and uncomplicated rhythm associated with C&W. The presence of the pedal steel and fiddle place this song squarely in the category of country music. The absence of drums is made less noticeable by the acoustic guitar player's emphasis on beats two and four; that is, the backbeat: chunk-a-CHUNK chunk-a-CHUNK. The bass line for this song is a good example of the typical C&W bass line previously illustrated. Arnold's eventual crossover into the Pop market is evident even in the vocal style of his early recordings, which incorporate a lead vocal style more closely related to the Pop crooners than the nasal style of his fellow C&W artists and a highly trained group of backup singers.

Kitty Wells's "There's Poison in Your Heart" (1955) and Hank Williams's "Your Cheatin' Heart" (1953) provide additional support for these same basic C&W musical characteristics. The acoustic instrumentation is identical to Arnold's "Bouquet of Roses." Vocal techniques are typical of those heard in recordings by other C&W artists. Wells's emphasis on consonants (e.g., "r" in the word "heart"), rather than sustaining pitches on vowel sounds, gives her vocal style a less refined, untrained character. Williams's emotive vocal cracks have similar effect, giving the music a comfortable feeling, lacking any semblance of pretense. The manner in which the fiddle and piano take turns carrying on a back-and-forth musical dialogue with the vocalist is a technique often incorporated in C&W.

The love-oriented lyrics for these three songs are typical of C&W. "Bouquet of Roses" speaks of a young romantic bringing a gift to his beloved, while both "There's Poison in Your Heart" and "Your Cheatin' Heart" provide examples of the heartache experienced by a jilted lover. The series of harmonic videos that follow is provided to confirm the simplicity of the harmonies used in each of these songs. Notice the predominance of three primary chords (I, IV, and V) and the infrequent use of chromatic harmonies (marked with an asterisk).

TRANSFORMATION OF COUNTRY MUSIC: CLINT BLACK Country music of the 1990s retained several of the musical characteristics associated with C&W, but there were a number of significant differences. The following discussion will focus primarily on the music of Clint Black and Travis Tritt, but any of the artists we have mentioned could serve just as well.

To provide a clear example of this new country sound, you will find a Listening Guide for "Put Yourself in My Shoes." As you listen to the song, follow along with the Listening Guide, which provides a narrative to help you focus on some of the most important aspects of the musical sound, identifying specific country and rock influences.

Examples of Three-Chord Harmony

The listening examples in the following section represent some of the basic, three-chord harmonies found in C&W. The three chords typical consist of the **tonic chord** (a triad built on the primary note of the key; i.e., a "C"' in the key of C), the *dominant chord* (built on the fifth degree of the scale), and the *subdominant chord* (built on the fourth degree of the scale).

"Bouquet of Roses"—original key: ♭ major

"Bouquet of Roses"

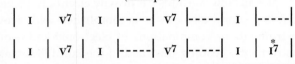

"Bouquet of Roses"—original key: D major
(Example B)

| I | V⁷ | I |-----| V⁷ |-----| I |-----|
| I | V⁷ | I |-----| V⁷ |-----| I | I⁷* |

"There's Poison in Your Heart"—original key: G major

"There's Poison in Your Heart"

"There's Poison in Your Heart"—original key: G major
(Example C)

| I |-----| IV | I | I |-----| V⁷ |-----|
| I |-----| IV | I | I |-----| V⁷ | I |

"Your Cheatin' Heart"—original key: C major

"Your Cheatin' Heart"

"Your Cheatin' Heart"—original key: C major
(Example D)

I	-----	IV	-----	V	-----	I	-----
I	-----	IV	-----	V	-----	I	I⁷*
IV	-----	I	-----	II⁷*	-----	V	-----
I	-----	IV	-----	V	-----	I	-----

Musical Style of Clint Black

The transformation of country in the 1990s involved a merging of C&W and rock elements. As you listen to the following examples, pay careful attention to both rock and country influences on the sound.

Black's debut album *Killin' Time* (number 31, 1989) was accurately classified as a country album, evidenced by the traditional instrumentation (acoustic guitars, fiddle, steel guitar, and harmonica) and the singer's vocal style. The title song opens with what can be described as a blues-influenced rock guitar riff, though the bass line, fiddle parts, and vocal style are pure country. "Better Man" provides an interesting juxtaposition of country and rock styles. The introduction and choruses incorporate a strong rock-influenced backbeat, while, during the verses, the drummer's style lightens substantially beneath stylistic inflections typically used by country performers. Although rock elements were certainly evident, this debut album was well within the boundaries of country music of the time.

However, the title song from his second release, *Put Yourself in My Shoes* (number 18, 1990), stretches the definition of country almost to the breaking point. The yodeling vocal line assists in retaining at least a modicum of country sensibility. However, the blues-influenced harmonica introduction and fiddle fills interspersed throughout the song suggest an evolution of musical style. Perhaps the most obvious deviation is in the increased complexity and chromaticism of the harmony, as outlined in the above video. Click or tap the play button in the Revel course to watch the video of "Put Yourself in My Shoes."

Notice the high degree of chromaticism in this piece (identified by the asterisks) in comparison to the C&W songs outlined earlier in this section. Such chromaticism was often utilized in pop tunes and soft rock. "Put Yourself in My Shoes" presents a hybrid song form, consisting of both country and rock characteristics.

"Put Yourself in My Shoes"

"Put Yourself in My Shoes"—original key: A major
(Example E)

Intro: | IV $\sharp$IV*dim | I VI*⁷ | $\flat$VI*⁷ V⁷ | I |

Verse: | I | II*⁷ | IV | I | I | II*⁷ | IV | I |

| IV | III*⁷ | vi⁷ | II*⁷ | I | II*⁷ | $\flat$VI*⁷ V⁷ | I |

Chorus: | IV*⁷ | I | IV*⁷ | I | IV*⁷ | I | II*⁷ | V⁷ $\flat$V*⁷ IV*⁷ |

| IV*⁷ | I | IV*⁷ | I | IV $\sharp$IV dim | I VI*⁷ | $\flat$VI*⁷ V⁷ | I |

The vocal style and instrumentation hardly deviate from what was typically heard on C&W recordings. Especially noticeable is the prominent role retained by the pedal steel. However, the chromatic harmonies; the blues riffs played by the harmonica, fiddle, and lead guitar; the heavy drumbeat heard in the chorus; and the shouting vocal style in the chorus reveal undeniable rock influences.

Click or tap the play button in the Revel course to watch the video for "Put Yourself in My Shoes" (bass line).

"Put Yourself in My Shoes" bass line

Several of Black's later recordings bear little resemblance to C&W, country rock's predecessor. Listen carefully, for example, to "Wherever You Go" from *One Emotion* (1994). The electric guitar performance techniques used throughout are taken directly from mainstream rock and use a performance technique called *barre chords* (sometimes called "*bar chords*"). The performer plays only the root, the fifth scale degree, and doubles these two pitches in higher octaves on the remaining strings, resulting in the chord shown in the figure on the following page. Click or tap the play button in the Revel course to watch a video of the F barre chord.

F barre chord

This chord contains the first and fifth scale degrees (an open fifth), but the third degree of the chord is absent (the dampened string marked with an "x" in the graphic). As a result, the tonality is ambiguous, neither major nor minor, accommodating equally well either a major third (A in the chord above), minor third (A♭ in the chord above), or a pitch somewhere in between the two (a *blue note*). In addition, this fingering pattern can be moved to any position on the guitar neck to form a chord, requiring only a minimal amount of technical expertise to play any chord of the chromatic scale. Barre chord technique has been used to great advantage throughout the history of rock. The opening measures of Deep Purple's "Smoke on the Water," for example, provide a clear musical demonstration of this bar chord technique. With that in mind, listen closely to Black's "Wherever You Go," and notice the distinct contrast between this style of country music and early C&W.

Watch "Clint Black singing "Put Yourself in My Shoes."*

https://www.youtube.com/watch?v=sWar8oK6jUw

TRAVIS TRITT With Travis Tritt, the transformation of country into a subgenre of rock music was complete. "Put Some Drive in Your Country" from Tritt's debut album is a case in point. Notice, for example, the distorted rock guitar timbre and the musical texture, consisting of multiple rhythmic guitar lines subtly intertwined underneath a

Listening Guide: "Put Yourself in My Shoes" (Clint Black)

0:00–0:09	Introduction (4 measures)	Begins with a blues-influenced "harp" (harmonica) melody over a mellow acoustic guitar and light drumbeat. Unlike a typical country song, the level of chromaticism in the chord progression is extremely high, as four of the seven chords in the introduction are outside of the key (see the chord chart presented previously). This rivals the level of chromaticism evident in some examples of the Beatles music discussed earlier in this course.
0:10–0:18	Verse 1 (aaba')(16 measures total) a = 4 measures	As the vocal enters, the nasal quality of the voice and the yodeling technique anchor this section clearly in the country style, though the chromatic harmonies continue to suggest an evolution of musical style. Pedal steel guitar takes over the blues-inflected "response" to the "call" of the vocal lines.
0:19–0:27	a = 4 measures	Repeat of the preceding melodic phrase with different lyrics.
0:28–0:36	b = 4 measures	The chord progression changes although the overall instrumentation and style remain consistent.
0:37–0:45	a' = 4 measures	A variation of the opening phrase, incorporating a highly chromatic chord progression; the addition of an apostrophe to the microstructure label (a') represents this slight alteration.
0:46–1:03	Chorus (bb') (16 measures total) b = 8 measures	With the lyric referring to putting oneself in my shoes, a dramatic change takes place in the musical sound, revealing significant rock influence: heavier drumbeat, periodic integration of a growling vocal style, and a rock-style "walking bass line" (see accompanying music notation). Also, a blues-influenced lead guitar, trading off with a fiddle, adds an additional rock component. In the final measure of this section, the syncopated rhythms and the anticipation (i.e., early arrival) of the D major chord leading to the first measure of the next section represent a slight increase in rhythmic complexity.
1:04–1:22	b' = 8 measures	A variation of the preceding phrase, ending with a highly chromatic chord progression, interestingly similar to the progression at the end of the verse.
1:23–1:31	Interlude (4 measures)	Reappearance of the instrumental passage used for the introduction.
1:32–2:08	Verse 2 (aaba') (16 measures)	In this verse, the fiddle provides "answers," replacing the role of the pedal steel in the first verse. The last vocal phrase in this verse incorporates a growling vocal style at times similar to that in the chorus.
2:09–2:42	Chorus (bb') (16 measures)	As before. Lead guitar licks show evidence of direct rock influences.
2:43–2:59	Extension of chorus	The high falsetto tone of the lead vocal in this extension of the chorus is a clear throwback to the vocal sound of Jerry Lee Lewis and mainstream rock of the 1950s.
3:00–3:15	Coda	The song concludes with the same instrumental passage used for the introduction and interlude.

*By clicking this link, you will be redirected to a third-party side.

sustained electric slide guitar. The resulting sound is reminiscent of 1970s southern rock. In addition, Tritt's shouting-style vocal delivery and the strong, consistent drumbeat, including a heavy backbeat, further emphasize the rock-country fusion. In the chorus of this song, Tritt's lyrics even state his case explicitly: He mentions a childhood promise he made to himself, to combine southern rock and country.

Rock influences are a consistent feature of Travis Tritt's recordings. Even his ballads exhibit characteristics clearly derived from rock. Listen to "Anymore" (from *It's All About to Change*, 1991). Notice that the soft acoustic guitar accompaniment and vocal melody line heard at the beginning gradually build to a powerful rock ballad, adding a solid drumbeat, distorted rock guitars, and culminating in a rock-style electric guitar solo. Gone is the pedal steel break typical of country ballads. The way that this song builds is reminiscent of Led Zeppelin's classic "Stairway to Heaven." "Bible Belt" is a straight-ahead rock song with little country influence; also noteworthy in this song are the rock bass line, driving drumbeat, and shouting vocal style, with its bluesy inflection. The instrumental solos also reveal significant rock influence. The pedal steel characteristic of country music is replaced by an electric slide guitar in the style of Duane Allman, followed by a honky-tonk piano solo in the style of Jerry Lee Lewis. The driving, blues-oriented rock style of "Leave My Girl Alone" and "Blue Collar Man" (both from *T-r-o-u-b-l-e*, 1992) have more in common with the music of Eric Clapton and Led Zeppelin than with George Strait or Ricky Skaggs. The guitar timbre and performance style incorporated in these songs are derived completely from rock and roll. Notice also that the harmonic structure of "Leave My Girl Alone" is that of the 12-bar blues. "Blue Collar Man," cowritten by Tritt and Lynyrd Skynyrd guitarist Gary Rossington, is a 16-bar blues that simply repeats the first four measures of a basic 12-bar blues progression. Recall from earlier in this course the similar extension incorporated by the Rolling Stones in "19th Nervous Breakdown."

SHANIA TWAIN Shania Twain's landmark recording *Come On Over* (1997)—the title itself a double entendre reference to the musical crossover—contains further evidence that rock music's influence on the new generation of country artists was not short term. The opening synthesized horn riff, followed by a Madonna-esque spoken cue ("Let's go, girls …") and distorted rock guitar tracks, sets the tone for the album. "Love Gets Me Every Time" initiates a recurrent alternation between, in addition to the integration of, rock and country elements. Listen to the brief, one-measure rock guitar tremolo, followed by three measures of a rock riff, then one measure of country fiddle. The verse structure combines the rock guitar riff with the fiddle part,

adding a pedal steel and vocal inflections (not to mention lyric choice; e.g., "gol darn") to shift toward the country side of the stylistic continuum. "From This Moment On" has more in common with the rock ballads of Journey and the R&B crossovers of Celine Dion and Luther Vandross than with its country ancestor, right down to the rock guitar solo accompanied by a repeated 16th-note synthesizer pattern. The title track provides an interesting integration of the accordion-dominated zydeco music of New Orleans and Jamaican reggae, along with the by then typical fusion of country and rock elements.

Like Tritt's "Put Some Drive in Your Country," Shania Twain includes her own anthem explicitly touting the musical integration of rock and country: "Rock This Country." Opening with straight-ahead rock guitar and a powerful quadruple meter rock drum foundation, the stylistic alternation is evident in the recurring chorus section, presenting a musical dialogue between the rock guitar and fiddle, trading off every two measures. An element of consistency is maintained by the continuing rock drumbeat, emphasizing the backbeat. With this recording, there was certainly no doubt that Twain had, in fact, "come over" to rock and roll.

13.8.2: Comparing C&W and Country

In summary, there are both commonalities and significant differences between the C&W and country music of the 1990s.

Commonalities and Differences between the C&W and Country Music of the 1990s

The section below enumerates several of the similarities and differences between traditional C&W and rock-influenced country of the 1990s.

As in C&W, the melody and lyrics (frequently love oriented) retain their position of primary importance. The nasal quality, falsetto, and emotive cracks in the voice are often incorporated into more recent country, though yodeling has been used less frequently. However, later country music often juxtaposes a shouting style of vocals reminiscent of R&B and mainstream rock with traditional country vocal techniques.

Many of the more traditional-sounding country songs use instrumentation quite similar to that of C&W, though drums are almost always present in these later recordings. The pedal steel and fiddle provide a strong link with the country past. However, many of the rock-influenced country songs dispense with the pedal steel in favor of an electric slide guitar. Wearing a metal or glass cylinder on one finger of the left hand (for a right-handed performer), the guitar player slides the cylinder up and down the neck in lieu of pressing the strings into the fingerboard, creating a *glissando* (sliding pitch) effect.

This style of playing was pioneered by early blues guitarist Robert Johnson, mastered by Duane Allman and Dicky Betts of the Allman Brothers Band, and adopted by many other southern rock bands of the 1970s. Contrast the sound of the traditional pedal steel in Garth Brooks's "Two of a Kind, Workin' on a Full House" to the use of the rock-influenced slide guitar in "Thunder Rolls."

The rhythm section in later country music took on a much more prominent role. The drums often propelled the music forward, powerfully emphasizing the backbeat and, at times, introducing tightly synchronized, syncopated rhythms with the bass player. With the drummer providing a consistently solid beat, the bass player was no longer tied to the simple two-beat bass lines found in most C&W of the 1940s and 1950s. In their search for new musical ideas, many bass players gained musical inspiration from rock bass lines. The simple harmonies of C&W were emulated in many recent country songs. Frequently, however, the chord changes incorporated creative alterations and higher levels of chromaticism than those of traditional C&W.

Finally, it is worth noting that the general production quality of country music recordings increased significantly in the transitional period from the late 1980s into the 1990s, rivaling the studio sound quality of major rock artists.

It seems that the role of musical influence has almost come full circle. As rock music emerged in the early 1950s, C&W exerted considerable influence on many of the artists as well as on the music itself. At various stages (rockabilly, southern rock, etc.), country revived its influence on this younger musical sibling. During the final decade of the twentieth century, however, rock music exerted considerable musical influence on country music. Many musical characteristics of rock became an integral part of the new style of country.

BECOME AN ACTIVE LISTENER: IDENTIFYING CROSSOVER EXAMPLES

It is time to put your ears to the test again. For each of the items in the following section, find a musical recording that meets the stated combination of musical styles.

Find examples of music that crosses these genres/styles. Explain how the different styles are incorporated in your examples:
1. Country and another musical style
2. Rock and another musical style
3. Rap and another musical style

Review your responses below. Click or tap "Print" to print your response.

Summary: The Continuing Fragmentation of Rock

The fragmentation of the rock market that began in the 1970s continued in the 1980s and 1990s. Art rock evolved into progressive rock; jazz rock evolved into fusion; the singer-songwriters emerged anew; Jamaican reggae and reggae-influenced rock became popular; folk/roots music remained of interest; country rock garners a higher level of attention, evolving into progressive country; bands influenced by the Grateful Dead initiated the jam band phenomenon; soft rock retained its popularity; and a new generation of powerful, talented female performers dominated the charts. We also took time to reconsider how rock elements are found in country rock and progressive country of the period, in contrast to the C&W and southern rock trends discussed elsewhere in this course. Moving forward, this course will look closely and in more detail at a few of the most important musical developments that proved particularly significant during the 1980s, 1990s, and beyond: heavy metal, dance music, hip-hop, and alternative music.

Take Note:

The Continuing Fragmentation of Rock

- *Why did the fragmentation of rock continue during the 1970s and beyond?*—The continuing fragmentation of

American society, in general, during this period was reflected in the multitude of rock subgenres. Watergate in the mid-1970s further disillusioned young people from entering politics, while the Reagan era of the 1980s brought a new era of conservatism to America. Rock reflected these trends with music that built on the styles of the late 1960s but did not venture much beyond these established genres.

- *What is progressive rock, and how did it evolve out of art rock?*—Progressive rock evolved out of the art rock experiments of the late 1960s and early 1970s. Progressive rock groups like Pink Floyd, King Crimson, and Jethro Tull used the musical language of rock to create longer, more complex works using classical models. In extended works like those found on Pink Floyd's *Dark Side of the Moon*, King Crimson's *Larks' Tongues in Aspic*, and Jethro Tull's *Thick as a Brick*, these groups created ambitious compositions that should be considered just as "serious" as any classical work.

- *How did jazz rock evolve into fusion?*—The jazz-rock movement was primarily led by rock artists who added jazz instrumentation and elements of jazz improvisation into their music. Fusion groups were primarily led by jazz musicians who were incorporating rock instrumentation and rhythms into their music. Among leaders in the fusion movement were Miles Davis, John McLaughlin and the Mahavishnu Orchestra, Weather Report (led by jazz musicians Joe Zawinul and Wayne Shorter), Chick Corea, and Herbie Hancock. Carlos Santana experimented with fusion in his early 1970s work. On the more soul- and funk-influenced end of fusion were the groups Earth, Wind & Fire and Tower of Power.

- *How did the singer-songwriter movement evolve during the 1970s and 1980s?*—Growing out of the folk rock movement of the 1960s and heavily influenced by the music of Bob Dylan, a group of performers arose who composed songs in a folk rock style with lyrics often focusing on personal issues. Key performers in this subgenre included Joni Mitchell, Carole King, and James Taylor. Singer-songwriters weren't limited to folk rock; Billy Joel was highly successful with his artful blend of pop-rock styles in the 1980s, and Crosby, Stills & and Nash also enjoyed success melding rock with folk-inspired harmonies.

- *How did reggae music make an impact in the late 1970s?*—Although Jamaican music in the form of calypso had briefly enjoyed popularity in the late 1950s, the reggae music of the late 1970s was the first time that a Jamaican style enjoyed worldwide popularity. Thanks primarily to the artistry of Bob Marley and the Wailers, reggae songs enjoyed chart success and the music's upbeat rhythms were emulated by established rock groups like the Rolling Stones, Led Zeppelin, the Clash, and the Police.

- *What was the role of folk music during the 1980s and 1990s?*—Bob Dylan returned to prominence as a major artist in the late 1990s with his album *Time Out of Mind*. His melding of traditional folk themes with retro-rock accompaniments continued through the early twenty-first century on albums like *Love and Theft* and *Modern Times*. Meanwhile, a new generation of singer-songwriters arose to take on Dylan's mantle, including Tracy Chapman (who focused on social issues as well as personal ones) and the singer-songwriter Jewel (who later crossed over to become a country artist).

- *How did country rock and progressive country come to the fore beginning in the 1970s?*—In the early 1970s, rock artists like the Grateful Dead, the Flying Burrito Brothers, and the Band recorded a series of albums revealing the heavy influence of country music, bringing country rock back into fashion. They were followed by the hugely successful group, the Eagles, whose initial hits were squarely in the country rock style. Out of the South came the Charlie Daniels and Marshall Tucker bands, combining their interest in country with a hard-rocking style. Singer Linda Ronstadt also began her career in country music, and while she had many pop hits, she also continued to cover country songs throughout her career. And "outlaw" country artists like Waylon Jennings and Willie Nelson helped bring rock influences into country music itself, particularly in the mid-1970s with hit singles and concept albums, like Nelson's *Red Headed Stranger*. Their work highly influenced the progressive country movement, as did the success of the film *Urban Cowboy*. While some country artists focused on blending the music with mainstream pop (like Kenny Rogers), others returned to more traditional country, while continuing to incorporate rock influences. Among the most successful of these performers were Garth Brooks, Shania Twain, and the Dixie Chicks, all of whom dominated the country charts in the 1990s through the early 2000s.

- *Why did jam bands become popular during the 1980s?*—Influenced primarily by the Grateful Dead, a number of groups emerged in the 1980s and 1990s that focused on live performances relying heavily on extended improvisations. Phish was one of the most popular bands in this style, building a fan base that was as loyal as the original Deadheads. Growing out of this movement was the popular group The Dave Matthews Band, which showed a similar eclectic mix of styles but does not completely fit the jam band mold.

- *What performers arose in the soft-rock category during the 1970s?*—As with many styles of the 1970s, soft rock broke into numerous subgenres during this period; although, in general, soft-rock performers moved increasingly toward pure pop music. Groups like the Carpenters and solo artists like Barry Manilow, Neil Diamond, and Olivia Newton-John focused on the pop-oriented elements of their music to achieve great commercial success.

- *How did soft rock continue to evolve during the 1980s and 1990s?*—R&B stars of the 1970s and later participated in the soft-rock movement. Singers Lionel Richie, Whitney Houston, Paula Abdul, and Mariah Carey all achieved chart success by recording material with a light soul feeling. Richie's specialty was soulful ballads, like "Truly" and "Say You Say Me." Similarly, Houston achieved multi-platinum success with her cover of Dolly Parton's "I Will Always Love You," a pop ballad. Mariah Carey began her career recording gospel-flavored songs like "Vision of Love," achieving massive success in the mid-1990s along with funkier songs like "Emotions," "Dreamlover," and "Fantasy."

Other soft-rock sounds of this period included "boy bands" like New Kids on the Block, whose vocal harmonies and songs about teenage love were geared toward the youngest rock fans. At the other end of the spectrum was New Age music, a gentle, soothing style that was geared for older listeners who preferred a lighter, more relaxed musical style.

SHARED WRITING

Identifying Subgrenres Within Rock

Compare Garth Brooks's "Thunder Rolls" (*No Fences*, 1990) with Bon Jovi's "Wanted Dead or Alive" (*Slippery When Wet*, 1986). After reading this chapter, which label would you apply to each of these songs: country, progressive country, mainstream rock, or some other? Support your answer using at least three clear rationales for each song (you can reference both the music and the lyrics in your response). Once you have completed your own independent answer, share this response with at least two fellow students as you read their responses. After reading the rationales provided by peers, is there any aspect of your initial answer that you would revise? Do so.

 A minimum number of characters is required to post and earn points. After posting, your response can be viewed by your class and instructor, and you can participate in the class discussion.

Post

0 characters | 140 minimum

Chapter 14
(Heavy) Metal

Learning Objectives

14.1 Summarize the characteristics of the emerging British heavy metal rock style

14.2 Outline the significant developments in early American heavy metal

14.3 Explain how heavy metal evolved in the 1980s

14.4 Describe the influence of heavy metal on alternative rock

Writing about heavy metal is like aiming at a moving target. **Heavy metal** (as a musical style) has certain quantifiable musical characteristics, just as jazz rock, R&B, disco, and other styles do. Yet, to too many heavy metal fans (and some writers), *heavy metal* is a more subjective, relative term—one that is subject to change if a heavier form of metal comes along. The transition from the descriptor "heavy metal" (which was liked by none of the bands so-labeled) to simply "metal" is represented by the use of parentheses in the title of this chapter.

Different Aspects of Heavy Metal

The following section will provide information about the musical style and audience associated with heavy metal. It also begins to address the content of lyrics for metal songs.

Style—Broadly considered, heavy metal has been a rather static style—not dramatically changed from the mid-1970s into the 2000s. What have changed over the years are the lyrics and the extra-musical factors (e.g., image and theatrics). Beginning with Alice Cooper's shocking theatrics through to metal's original antihero mentality, each band must be louder, more rebellious, and more shocking than its predecessors. With each step of this progression, the most recent groups become heavy metal (if the term is used qualitatively), and the "old timers" slip into an often derided "softer" category. Paradoxically, the changes are rarely in the music itself.

Audience—For most of the 1970s and 1980s, heavy metal was the hardest of the rock styles. It appealed primarily to those whose self-image was that of the angry, macho, anti-establishment rebel. The general profile of the heavy metal fan was that of a 13- to 18-year-old Hispanic or Caucasian male, often from less affluent and more turbulent family circumstances. (Of course, there are also a vast number of exceptions to the general profile.) It is often assumed, correctly or not, that heavy metal consumers were disillusioned and angry and that the music helped them act out their frustration with society.

Lyrics—Certainly the lyrics were a big part of this angry rebellion. Violence, suicide, and the occult are not uncommon themes in heavy metal songs, but the expression or representation of anger was not limited only to the lyrics. Musical elements, such as extreme volume; distorted timbre; screaming vocals; insistent, repetitive riffs; and screeching, lightning-speed guitar solos—all seem to reinforce the disaffected youth who has decided that he is "not gonna take it anymore" (in the words of hair metal band Twisted Sister).

In this chapter, we will trace the evolution of heavy metal from its late 1960s roots into the 1970s, first from the British groups and then from the American groups. We will then discuss three heavy metal bands from the 1980s that typify the style in that decade. Finally, we will see how heavy metal moved through the 1990s and combined with another antiestablishment style—rap—to create yet another blended style.

14.1: British Heavy Metal Evolves

OBJECTIVE: Summarize the characteristics of the emerging British heavy metal rock style

From the British, blues-based bands evolved a harder mainstream rock style. A developmental line can be drawn from groups such as the Rolling Stones, the Yardbirds, and The Who to mainstream groups such as Cream, Blind Faith, Traffic, and Faces. This hard rock mainstream continued through the 1970s and into the 1980s, but branching off from this mainstream was a style that was eventually called heavy metal.

Musically, heavy metal began as an exaggeration of hard rock. If hard rock was loud, heavy metal was louder; if hard rock was simple and repetitive, heavy metal was more so; if hard rock singers shouted, heavy metal singers screamed. One of the prototypes of British heavy metal was Deep Purple (discussed previously in this course). When keyboardist Jon Lord and his colleagues were not creating works like the *Concerto for Group and Orchestra* and the *Gemini Suite,* the band was developing a harder style of mainstream rock that was an early harbinger of heavy metal.

14.1.1: Led Zeppelin

The premier British heavy metal band of the 1970s was Led Zeppelin. In 1968, after the Yardbirds disbanded, guitarist Jimmy Page recruited Robert Plant (lead vocals and harmonica), John Bonham (drums), and John Paul Jones (bass and keyboards) to form Led Zeppelin.

Led Zeppelin: Jimmy Page, John Bonham, John Paul Jones, and Robert Plant, 1976.

SOURCE: Pictorial Press Ltd/Alamy Stock Photo

After initially spurning digital music sales by online sellers, in 2014, the remaining members of Led Zeppelin

Musical Journey of Led Zeppelin

The following section will provide highlights from the career of Led Zeppelin, a band whose music represented many styles, including heavy metal.

Signed almost immediately by Atlantic Records, the band released their first album, *Led Zeppelin,* in 1969; it proved to be their least popular album, reaching "only" number 10 on the U.S. Hot 200 album chart. Of their next eight albums, six were number 1 and two were number 2. Although Zeppelin would eventually place half a dozen singles in the U.S. Top 40, they never released a single in Great Britain.

Following several tours of the United States, Zeppelin released *Led Zeppelin II* (1969), their first number 1 album. A shortened version of "Whole Lotta Love" became a hit (number 4), and the band was firmly established. "Whole Lotta Love" (the album track, not the single version) gives a good idea of the heavy metal sound in its early years. There is an insistent 16th-note (quadruple) subdivision of each beat; a strong, low-range guitar riff repeats under each verse; and the vocal is high pitched, bordering on the full shouting style. There is guitar distortion, and, if played properly, it is loud, … very loud. A long break in the middle of the song (not included in the single version) is reminiscent of San Francisco acid rock, psychedelic-style electronic experimentation (much feedback and distortion over a continuous beat). A brief guitar solo leads to the return of the basic riff and vocal; a free-tempo, shouted vocal solo breaks the pattern briefly, but the vocal and riff return and lead to the final fade-out. "Whole Lotta Love" is hard rock—only harder. Another interesting song

on this album is "What Is and What Should Never Be," a song that alternates between sections of heavy metal and "softer" sections. "The Lemon Song," a 12-bar blues, illustrates the continuing thread from old R&B through the blues-based British bands to early heavy metal.

Led Zeppelin III and *IV* continued Zeppelin's popularity. Ironically, their most famous song, "Stairway to Heaven" (from *IV*), was never released as a single. It is a classic of early 1970s hard rock–heavy metal. As the Listening Guide shows, the song begins quietly with 12-string guitar and recorders (flute-like, woodwind instruments). It gradually builds to a climax in the seventh (final) verse. The coda is most effective: a simple **a cappella** vocal phrase that reiterates the hook line.

Zeppelin's preeminence continued through *Houses of the Holy* (1973), *Physical Graffiti* (1975), and *Presence* (1976), all number 1 albums. Page's fascination with the occult was well known. Some of Zeppelin's surrealistic lyrics led to interpretations ranging from Celtic mythology to druidic symbolism to pure satanism. There have been allegations of backward satanic messages in some songs (e.g., "Stairway to Heaven").

Zeppelin's problems began in 1975, when a series of personal tragedies struck Robert Plant. Zeppelin's 1979 concert, their first live appearance in England since the mid-1970s, was panned by critics. The final blow was the death of drummer John Bonham in September 1980. However, the remaining three band members reunited several times in the 1980s, and Jimmy Page and Robert Plant collaborated on *No Quarter* (1994) and *Walking into Clarksdale* (1998). In 1997, a collection of Zeppelin's live BBC session performances reached number 12 and was certified platinum. In

1999, the recording industry announced that Zeppelin was only the third act in history to achieve four or more diamond-certified albums (10 million copies sold). In the new millennium, Robert Plant maintained the most commercially successful solo career, releasing several Top 40 albums, including a collaboration with Alison Krauss (*Raising Sand*, number 2, 2007) and *Band of Joy* (number 5, 2010), named after Plant's first band with John Bonham. Forming a band called the Sensational Space Shifters, Plant's new group released *Carry Fire* (2017), which blended Eastern, American, and Celtic roots music.

began to release "deluxe editions" of their recordings, beginning with their first three albums. As a result, their music sales spiked again, introducing a whole new generation to the sounds of one of rock's pioneering heavy metal bands.

14.1.2: Black Sabbath and Ozzy Osbourne

Going deeper into the British heavy metal sound and the black magic image was Black Sabbath, a quartet from Birmingham, England. Formed in 1969, they released their first album, *Black Sabbath*, in 1970, which was a moderate success (number 23). Lead singer John "Ozzy" Osbourne's voice was distinctive: high pitched, screaming, and mostly on pitch. The lyrics centered on mystical references to the soul, fantasies, and insanity. There were the distorted, repetitive guitar riffs and steady duple subdivisions of the beat that were to characterize heavy metal. The vocal style and the musical ambiance seemed to project attitudes of anger, defiance, and aggression; where most earlier rock styles had been good time, "rockin' and partyin'" music, this music seemed to be clenching its fists. Although Black Sabbath had no Top 40 hits during these early years, their albums sold well through the 1970s. Osbourne left the group in 1978 to become a major heavy metal solo act of the 1980s. He was replaced for three albums (1980–1983) by Ronnie James Dio. Ian Gillan, former lead singer for Deep Purple, joined the lineup for one album (*Born Again*, 1983).

All four original members of Black Sabbath came together for a live recording in 1997, which was released the following year (*Reunion*, number 11). Then, in 2013, the original members came together to record their first studio album since 1978, *13*, which debuted at number 1. During these later periods, the band did, in fact, garner several Top 40 hits: "Turn Up the Night" (1981, number 24), "Psycho Man" (1998, number 3), "Selling My Soul" (1999, number 17), "Devil Cried" (2007, number 37), "God is Dead?" (2013, number 7), and "End of the Beginning" (2013, number 38).

Black Sabbath, c. 1973; (L to R) Tony Iommi, Ozzy Osbourne, Geezer Butler, and Bill Ward.

SOURCE: Pictorial Press Ltd/Alamy Stock Photo

Listening Guide: "Stairway to Heaven" (Led Zeppelin)

0:00–0:52	Introduction (16 bars)	Four 4-bar phrases (aabb). First phrase played by solo 12-string guitar; recorders enter at second phrase.
0:53–1:45	Verse 1 (16 bars)	Same internal form as introduction (aabb). Vocal enters in first phrase; recorders added for second phrase.
1:46–2:13	Verse 2 (8 bars)	Shortened to two phrases (aa). First phrase includes vocal; second phrase is instrumental (recorders and guitar).
2:14–3:05	Verse 3 (16 bars + 2 bars)	Four 4-bar phrases (ccaa) plus 2-bar instrumental transition. Electric guitars added. First two phrases (cc) are new material second two phrases (aa) are taken from earlier verses (with slight variation in underlying harmonies).
3:06–3:55	Verse 4 (16 bars + 2 bars)	Similar to verse 3 (with new lyrics).
3:56–4:43	Verse 5 (16 bars + 2 bars)	Similar to verses 3 and 4 (with new lyrics). Significant change in timbre by adding strong drumbeat beginning at the third phrase.
4:44–5:33	Verse 6 (16 bars + 2 bars)	Similar to verse 5 (with slight melodic changes and new lyrics).
5:34–5:54	Transition	Fast strums on electric guitar set up the guitar solo (next section).
5:55–6:43	Instrumental break (20 bars)	Guitar lead over 2-bar riff.
6:44–7:44	Verse 7 (26 bars)	New vocal over the instrumental break's 2-bar riff. Features screaming vocal, distorted power chords, and driving drumbeat. Climax of the song in full heavy metal style. Vocal is out for last 6 bars; accompaniment slows to a stop in bar 26.
7:45–8:02	Coda	A capella vocal solo leads to final statement of the hook line (including the song title); refers back to the b section of verse 1.

As a solo artist, Osbourne fared well commercially after his split from Black Sabbath. The antihero concept pioneered by the Rolling Stones (discussed earlier in this course) reached new levels with Osbourne; a glance at the cover of *Bark at the Moon* (1983) suggests how far rock had "progressed" from the days of Presley or the Beach Boys. The song "Rock 'n' Roll Rebel" is a teenage anthem, but not in the same way as Dylan's "The Times They Are a-Changin'." Ozzy challenges parents to try and make him confirm whereas Dylan asked them to "please get out of the new one [road]/If you can't lend your hand."

The early British heavy metal of 1970 does not sound significantly different from that of 1987. Ken Tucker explains this:

> Heavy metal … is the primary music of teenage rebellion and, almost by definition, something a listener outgrows. As such, it is also an ideal commercial proposition, for it bypasses such sticky items as an artist's changing ambitions or inevitably uneven output. In the world of heavy metal, a new set of teens is ever entering the marketplace, and with them arrives the latest set of outrageous stars, whose popularity lasts just about as long as its generation of teens. (Ward, Stokes, and Tucker 1986, 486)

Of course there were some exceptions to this state of affairs, as illuminated by the preceding discussions of Led Zeppelin and Black Sabbath.

JOURNAL

Comparison of Led Zeppelin and Black Sabbath

Listen to two or three of the songs discussed in the previous section that were recorded by Led Zeppelin and Black Sabbath; for the purpose of this assignment, I recommend sticking to their music produced in the 1970s. Which band do you like best? What are the specific musical elements that you find more interesting and/or appealing in the music of the chosen group? What is it, specifically, that you don't like as much about the band that was not selected? Identify at least two or three groups who appear to have been influenced by the heavy metal sound of one or both of these bands.

 The response entered here will appear in the performance dashboard and can be viewed by your instructor.

Submit

14.2: American Heavy Metal

OBJECTIVE: Outline the significant developments in early American heavy metal

As in England, some American mainstream bands of the late 1960s turned the power up a bit higher and drifted steadily into heavy metal. In 1968, for example, Steppenwolf had a number 2 hit with "Born to Be Wild"; contained in the song's lyrics was the phrase "heavy metal thunder," which some believe is the source for the name of the musical genre. Also called *"power rock,"* American heavy metal seems to have developed simultaneously in California and Michigan with groups like Iron Butterfly, Steppenwolf, MC5, Grand Funk Railroad, and Alice Cooper.

American Heavy Metal Groups

The following section will provide information about several popular and influential American heavy metals bands.

Iron Butterfly—Iron Butterfly, formed in 1966 by keyboardist Doug Ingle, moved from San Diego to Los Angeles where they became the house band at the Whisky a Go-Go. The band is remembered primarily for its 17-minute "In-A-Gadda-Da-Vida," released on the band's second album by the same name in 1968; the title track occupied the entire B-side of the album. A powerful work, it features a series of solos organized around repetitive bass riffs, in line with the concept of the long instrumental improvisations being developed simultaneously by some of the San Francisco groups and British blues-based bands.

Steppenwolf—Steppenwolf, formed in Toronto by German-born John Kay, moved to Los Angeles and signed a contract with Dunhill Records. By today's standards, Steppenwolf barely qualifies as heavy metal; they seem to be more of a mainstream hard rock band. They tended to be more sociopolitically oriented and less prone to ultra-loud repetitive chords and riffs than the purer heavy metal bands. By 1972, Steppenwolf's popularity had waned, and they disbanded. Kay reorganized the band in 1974, but they failed to regain their earlier appeal.

MC5—MC5 was an early heavy metal band from Detroit. Their initial album, *Kick Out the Jams* (1969), was a live album and contained some profanity that caused repercussions with some record stores and eventually with their label, Elektra Records. Moving to Atlantic, MC5 released one more album before disbanding.

Grand Funk Railroad—Far more commercially successful was Grand Funk Railroad, a power trio formed in the mid-1960s in Flint, Michigan. Able to play a strong mainstream rock style while transitioning to a heavy metal style when desired, Grand Funk released a series of eight Top 10 albums from 1970 to 1974. In the meantime, they produced nine Top 40 singles, including two number 1 hits: "We're an American Band" (1973) and "The Loco-Motion" (1974), both reaching number 1 on the Hot 100. (For several years, from 1973 to 1975, the band dropped "Railroad" from their name.)

As we have noted, 1970s American hard rock groups were usually not as hard as their British counterparts; similarly, the early American heavy metal groups were not as consistently heavy as the British heavy metal groups. Often, they would venture into a heavy metal style (e.g., Grand Funk's "Sin's a Good Man's Brother" on *Close to Home*), only to retreat to a more mainstream style for the majority of their repertoire.

14.2.1: Alice Cooper

As mentioned previously, as each new heavy metal band managed to "out-heavy" its predecessors, each of those predecessors slowly receded to a comparatively "softer" category. With Alice Cooper, a new brand of heavy metal was initiated, one that added the element of shock, as though heavy metal were an active attempt to be as repulsive, disgusting, and perverse as possible. (Cooper's foray into this realm predates Ozzy Osbourne's solo career and the punk trend of the later 1970s.) Here, it is worth noting that several of the artists covered in this chapter ventured into the heavy metal sound, though the majority of their repertoire fits comfortably into the category of mainstream rock. Cooper is among those; like Grand Funk Railroad, however, there are songs that can be identified as meeting the musical

criteria for heavy metal ("You Drive Me Nervous" from *Killer*, 1971).

Alice Cooper, 1980.

SOURCE: Moviestore collection Ltd/Alamy Stock Photo

Alice Cooper is the name of the band as well as the stage name of its lead singer, Vincent Furnier. (Cooper took his stage name from the story of a sixteenth-century

Musical Career of Alice Cooper

The following section will provide highlights from the career of Alice Cooper, an artist who was a pioneer in the dramatically theatrical presentation of music.

Born in Detroit in 1948, Alice Cooper eventually settled in Phoenix. While playing for a memorial birthday party for Lenny Bruce, Cooper was heard by Frank Zappa, who signed the band to a contract with his new label, Straight Records. Their first two albums, *Pretties For You* (1969) and *Easy Action* (1970), were commercially unsuccessful.

Creating a highly theatrical stage act that consisted of tidbits of violence, the occult, sadomasochism, and animal abuse, Cooper began to achieve local notoriety. In 1969, while performing at a local Detroit ballroom, Cooper ended the evening's entertainment by throwing several live chickens out into the crowd; the crowd responded by ripping the chickens to shreds. The resulting publicity apparently convinced Cooper that if his music was getting him nowhere, perhaps shock could do it for him.

Cooper's first Warner Brothers album, *Love It to Death* (1971), made the Top 40 and yielded the number 21 hit, "Eighteen." This song, a typical teen frustration song, was not particularly heavy, but it did feature Cooper's shouting vocal style. *School's Out* (1972) really launched Cooper to national status as America's premier shock rock–heavy metal band. The album reached num-

ber 2, and the title song climbed to number 7. "School's Out" remains a good representation of early 1970s American heavy metal: repetitive guitar riffs, power chords, distorted guitar solo, shouted lyrics, and a driving beat (especially near the end). It is a forerunner of later heavy metal songs, such as "School Daze" by AC/DC and similar works by Metallica and others.

The peak year for Alice Cooper was 1973. *Billion Dollar Babies* became Cooper's first and only number 1 album, yielding three Top 40 singles. On the highly publicized album tour, Cooper sang the title song while abusing a toy doll—beating, kicking, stabbing, and throwing it, simulating intercourse with it, and decapitating it.

The major tour that promoted *Welcome to My Nightmare* (1975, number 5) was a full theatrical production, with Cooper in facial makeup, portraying a series of scenes from his "nightmare." Subsequent albums were not as popular, and Cooper labored through the late 1970s and early 1980s with only moderate success. During a comeback tour in 1987, he pulled out all of his old tricks: representations of child abuse, abuse of women, sadomasochism, insanity, necrophilia, and murder by strangulation and impalement.

As Brock Helander notes (1982, 103), "Alice Cooper was one of the first rock groups consciously to dupe the unwitting media into promulgating a totally negative image for commercial gain." Cooper was capable of good mainstream rock and roll (e.g., "Under My Wheels"); his "Be My Lover" uncannily resembles the sound of Jagger and the Stones. His attempts at ballads ("Desperado" and "Only Women Bleed") suggest that his shouting vocal style must be preferred over his attempts to really sing. In all likelihood, Cooper will be remembered more for initiating the shock rock phenomenon than for any musical innovation, though,

in a cameo appearance for the film *Wayne's World* (1992), he was the recipient of some significant fan worship. In 2017, he returned with his 27th album (*Paranormal*), featuring musicians from U2, ZZ Top, and his own original band.

woman who was burned at the stake for witchcraft; he had dreamed that he was her reincarnation.)

14.2.2: Kiss

With theatrics and makeup, Kiss (and Cooper, for that matter) drew a connection between heavy metal and the glitter rock trend that was more prominent in England. (American versions of glitter rock, however, were more macho in image and avoided the androgynous image of Bowie, for example.) Kiss's musical style was pure heavy metal—the heaviest of the American groups up to that time.

Kiss; (L to R) Gene Simmons, Paul Stanley, Peter Criss, and Ace Frehley.

SOURCE: Pictorial Press Ltd/Alamy Stock Photo

JOURNAL

Theatricality as a Part of Heavy Metal Performance

American heavy metal groups, in particular, seem to have considered a highly theatrical performance style important to their success. Locate a live performance of Kiss's "Strutter" and Alice Cooper's "Ballad of Dwight Fry" using your favorite Internet video archive (e.g., YouTube). Watch the performances carefully, and then write a paragraph describing how you think the theatrical performance adds to or detracts from the musical presentation. Identify two or three contemporary rock artists who integrate significant theatricality into their live performance. How do these artists' stage acts compare to the Kiss and Alice Cooper performances you just watched?

▶ The response entered here will appear in the performance dashboard and can be viewed by your instructor.

 Submit

Musical Career of Kiss

The following section will provide highlights from the career of Kiss, one of the most commercially successful early American metal bands.

Musical Style—Kiss was formed in 1972 by bassist Gene Simmons, and the band established their reputation through their shock rock–heavy metal live performances. In fact, through 1984, only four of their 16 albums reached the Top 10; they have had only two Top 10 hit singles (both ballads!): "Beth" (1976, number 7) and "Forever" (1990, number 8). However, as Brock Helander says (1982, 312), "Kiss … endeared themselves to legions of prepubescent fans … with gimmicks such as mock blood vomiting, fire breathing, explosions and fireworks, dry ice fogs, and rocket-firing guitars in performance." As with Cooper, the success of Kiss resided as much in the image and theatrics as in the music.

Rising Charts—Sales began to slip in the early 1980s; thus, as a possible shot in the arm, the band unmasked for their 1983 album *Lick It Up (number 24)*. They enjoyed something of a comeback in the mid-1980s. *Lick It Up* went gold within the year; the follow-up album, *Animalize* (1984, number 19), went platinum. Kiss's message for the mid-1980s was explicitly sexual (e.g., "Fits Like a Glove" from *Lick It Up* and "Hot Blood" from *Animalize*).

Later Career—The original band members reunited for a performance on MTV in 1996, which inspired a tour (the highest grossing concert tour of the year) and the release of *Psycho-Circus* (1998, number 3). In 2003, *Kiss Symphony* found the band performing with orchestral accompaniment (like Metallica had done in 1999). *Kissology Volume One (1974–1977)* was released in 2006 as the first of a series of DVD sets that includes concert footage, interviews, and never-before-seen clips. In 2009, the band attained their highest chart position ever with the release of *Sonic Boom* (number 2), their first studio album in 11 years.

14.3: Heavy Metal Continues into the 1980s

OBJECTIVE: Explain how heavy metal evolved in the 1980s

In the 1980s, heavy metal had a major impact. There was a long list of successful heavy metal bands—far more than we can discuss here. We will, therefore, focus on three bands in more detail and then survey some of the others.

14.3.1: Van Halen

If one metal band from the 1980s came close to superstar status, it would be Van Halen.

Three members of Van Halen on stage in 1984; (L to R) Michael Anthony, David Lee Roth, and Eddie Van Halen.

SOURCE: Pictorial Press Ltd/Alamy Stock Photo

Eddie and Alex Van Halen were born in Holland, and their family immigrated to the United States in 1968. Trained in classical music, they soon turned to rock and roll. After establishing their reputation with hard rock and heavy metal bands in Southern California, they signed a recording contract with Warner Brothers records, with Eddie playing guitar, brother Alex on drums, Michael Anthony on bass, and David Lee Roth as lead singer.

Many readers are no doubt crying, "But Van Halen isn't heavy metal!" Remember our moving target concept? Even though rock historians, such as Joel Whitburn, Ken Tucker, and Charles T. Brown, all describe Van Halen as a heavy metal band, today's heavy metal fan is likely to dismiss the group as having "gone commercial" or "softened up" because current heavy metal is so much heavier than it used to be. As is often said, "That's rock and roll."

14.3.2: Guns N' Roses

One of the most successful rock bands of the late 1980s, Guns N' Roses was a quintet based in Los Angeles. Their big breakthrough came in 1988 with the album *Appetite for Destruction*. It rose to the number 1 position and stayed there for five weeks. The album produced three Top 10 singles, including the number 1 "Sweet Child o' Mine." The success of the next album, *GN'R Lies*, was somewhat surprising because it was a reissue of their 1986 EP *Live Like a Suicide*, adding four new tracks. Yet even this eight-song album sold sufficiently to achieve a number 2 ranking.

Overall, Guns N' Roses presents an interesting and varied profile. They have been typed as heavy metal, but only some of their music actually falls into that category. They certainly are heavily derivative (not necessarily a put-down because all musical styles derive from one or more prior styles, including rock and roll itself). For example, a quick tour through *Lies* suggests images of singer-songwriters, Zappa, Led Zeppelin, and Chuck Berry. Guns N' Roses drew considerable criticism, not only because of some lyrics but also because of the bad-boy behavior of Axl Rose. To the more common charges of being vulgar and sexist were added the charge of racism. The band's antics (e.g., late and canceled concerts, fistfights, etc.) were reminiscent of the old Rolling Stones bad-boy image, discussed previously in this course.

Through the 1980s, Guns N' Roses performed as a quintet. In addition to Rose, there was Duff McKagan (bass), Steven Adler (drums), and guitarists Izzy Stradlin

Musical Career of Van Halen

The following section will provide highlights from the career of Van Halen, an extremely successful early American metal band with strong mainstream appeal.

From the release of their initial album, the band's level of success established an impressive trajectory: *Van Halen* (1978, number 19), *Van Halen II* (1979, number 6), *Women and Children First* (1980, number 6), *Fair Warning* (1981, number 5), and *Diver Down* (1982, number 3), leading to the band's commercial and musical triumph, which arrived in late 1983 to early 1984 with *1984 (MCMLXXXIV)*, an album that rose to number 2 and yielded a monster hit, "Jump" (number 1) and two other Top 20 singles ("I'll Wait" and "Panama"). "Jump" was based on a catchy series of syncopated chords on synthesizer over a pounding, steady eighth-note bass. A harmonically interesting guitar solo and a vir-

tuosic synthesizer solo made "Jump" one of the most popular and musically valid songs to come out of heavy metal in the 1980s.

It was generally agreed that Eddie Van Halen had become one of the premier guitarists in rock (not just heavy metal); but it was Roth, with his sexy, bad-boy image, who provided the charisma for the group. However, by 1985, tensions between lead singer David Lee Roth and the Van Halens had reached the breaking point, and Roth announced that he was leaving the band. However, the replacement of Roth with singer Sammy Hagar did not deter Van Halen. Their next four studio albums (*5150*, 1986; *OU812*, 1988; *For Unlawful Carnal Knowledge*, 1991; *Balance*, 1995) all reached number 1. However, after the replacement of Sammy Hagar by Gary Cherone (former lead vocalist for Extreme) in 1996, Van Halen's fortunes ebbed. Although *Van Halen III* (1998) reached number 4 and certified gold, it was the first Van Halen album not to attain at least double-platinum.

Different Styles Represented by Guns N' Roses on the Album "Lies"

The following section will provide highlights from the career of Guns N' Roses, another American metal band with strong mainstream appeal.

Lies is a good album to study because it represents the sound of Guns N' Roses before and after their rise to stardom. There is a surprising variety of styles represented between the 1986 and 1988 material. The first two songs (both from 1986) are typical heavy metal, complete with a screaming vocal; fast, pounding rhythm; steady, duple subdivision of the beat; distorted, power guitar accompaniment; and defiant lyrics. With the album's third song, "Move to the City," Guns N' Roses moves back to a hard rock mainstream style.

The difference between late 1980s hard rock and heavy metal can be a rather fine distinction, but in "Move to the City," notice that lead singer Axl Rose lowers his voice range from the high scream of the first two songs. Also, notice that the beat is no longer a steady duple subdivision (straight eighth notes), but a more swinging long-short pattern. This difference is also evident on the last of the 1986 songs, "Mama Kin." Here the guitar accompaniment is almost Chuck Berry–like at times.

With the 1988 cuts, there is even more variety. The album's Top 5 hit, "Patience," begins with acoustic guitars and whistling. When the vocal begins, one is reminded of the opening verses of Led Zeppelin's "Stairway to Heaven," but, unlike "Stairway," "Patience" does not build to a powerful climax. Instead, it continues to develop in a style quite close to a typical singer-songwriter recording of the 1970s (except perhaps for Rose's more forceful vocal delivery at the end).

"Used to Love Her" is the sort of song that can easily create controversy because of the lyrics (e.g., "Used to love her, but I had to kill her"). In some cases, the musical style of such songs makes the lyric seem frighteningly serious, but in this Guns N' Roses song, one gets the feeling that the band is just kidding. There is a gentle rockabilly tone that makes the song seem lighthearted.

"You're Crazy" continues with a rather gentle rocking beat. Here, Rose varies from a heavy metal scream to a Frank Zappa–like vocal style (even the lyrics may remind one of Zappa). *Lies'* last cut, "One in a Million," also bears some kinship to the older singer-songwriter style but is beefed up by a much harder accompaniment. Again, the lyrics are controversial; not only does Axl refer to "police and niggers," but he complains that "immigrants and faggots" are spreading diseases and speaking unintelligible languages. Remember, theatricality and an aggressively bad-boy image had become part of the heavy metal aesthetic.

(Jeffrey Isbell) and Slash (Saul Hudson). In the 1990s, there were fierce squabbles and personnel changes. Although Guns N' Roses (with Axl Rose) continued into the new century—*Chinese Democracy*, the band's first studio album in 15 years reached number 3 in 2008—the commercial success of the band and the solo projects of its various members provided only a pale reflection of their popularity in the late 1980s and early 1990s.

14.3.3: Metallica

Many hardcore heavy metal fans view Metallica as the archetypal representative of the heavy metal style of the mid-1980s through the 1990s. The California-based band was formed by Lars Ulrich (drums) and James Hatfield (guitar and vocals) in 1981. Guitarist Kirk Hammett joined the band in 1982 and Jason Newsted (bass) in 1986, following the tragic death of Clifford Lee Burton in a tour bus accident. The group released three albums between 1984 and 1987 with some success; however, they did not crack the Top 10 until 1988's ... *And Justice for All*. Rather unexpectedly, the album produced a Top 40 single ("One"). Hardcore heavy metal bands did not place many singles on the charts in the 1980s, because the typical heavy metal song was not considered appropriate for Top 40 airplay. Normally, for any heavy metal band to have success with a single, the song would need to be toned down several notches. Such is the case with "One," which is about as close to a ballad as Metallica comes. Even though the song is performed by a heavy metal band, it has few characteristics of the style. Nonetheless, the album as a whole is a good representation of Metallica's style. Musically, there are the requisite pounding, distorted, low guitar riffs; insistent heavy beat (and constant duple subdivision of the beat); growling vocals; and lightning-fast guitar solos. A few of the song titles suggest the rather gloomy tone of the album: "Blackened," "Harvester of Sorrow," "The Frayed Ends of Sanity," "To Live Is to Die," and "Dyer's Eve." Their lyrics reinforce this mood with frequent use of words such as the following:

Words Excerpted from "Blackened" by Metallica		
obscurity	*callous*	*mutilation*
death	*opposition*	*darkest*
dead	*agitation*	*expiration*
deadly	*decay/decadence*	*cancelation*
evolution's end	*frigid*	*smoldering*
blistering	*contradictions*	*darkening*
terminate/termination	*chill*	*hypocrisy*
kill(s)	*violation*	

This list of words was compiled from only one song ("Blackened"). Actually, it is one of the more positive songs on the album, concerning itself with threats to the environment. The tone of the lyrics (reinforced by the angry, driving music) pounds away at the impending doom of the planet and of humanity. Most of the album's songs are about the miserable ways of society and how these overpower the helpless victim, presumably Metallica's teen-aged listeners.

Whether Metallica's music is helpful or harmful to their angry, rebellious listeners is a serious question. In their defense, Metallica notes (in "Eye of the Beholder") that "energy derives from both the plus and the negative." If you listen to only one song on … *And Justice for All,* try "Dyer's Eve." It represents all of the characteristics of Metallica's style of heavy metal.

Metallica's popularity continued into the 1990s and beyond. All but one of their next five studio albums reached the top of the chart: *Metallica* (1991), *Load* (1996), *Reload* (1997), *Garage, Inc.* (number 2, 1998), and *St. Anger* (2003), Their success in the new millennium continued with *Death Magnetic* (number 1, 2008), *Lulu* (2011), *Beyond Magnetic* (2011), and *Hardwired … to Self-Destruct* (2016). *S&M* (1999, number 2) is a live collaboration with the San Francisco Symphony. They released a biographical film (on DVD) called *Some Kind of Monster* in 2005, documenting the band's experiment with group therapy.

14.3.4: Other Heavy Metal Bands

Besides Van Halen, Guns N' Roses, and Metallica, there were many other successful heavy metal bands in the 1980s and 1990s, including Mötley Crüe, Twisted Sister, W.A.S.P., Quiet Riot, Queensrÿche, Ratt, Staind, and Slipknot (with their outrageous S&M-style wardrobe). England was home to several bands that were considered leaders in heavy metal: Iron Maiden, Judas Priest, Whitesnake, and Def Leppard. In addition, metal bands came from numerous other countries, for example, AC/DC, from Australia; Krokus, from Switzerland; and the Scorpions, from Germany.

Over the past few decades, a few real guitar virtuosos have emerged, including Eddie Van Halen, Randy Rhodes, Jimmy Page, and Steve Vai. Vai is an especially talented guitarist and a creative musician. His early experiences were with Frank Zappa, an influence that is evident in much of his later work. For example, listen to the highly creative (and humorously eccentric) *Flexable,* recorded in 1983 and released in 1988.

Perhaps the most impressive guitarist to come from the heavy metal style is Swedish guitarist Yngwie Malmsteen. Representing an opposite extreme from the focus on hard-driving simplicity described at the outset of this chapter, Malmsteen sought to combine aspects of classical music (its longer forms and technical virtuosity) into the world of heavy metal. According to Robert Walser, Malmsteen "adapted classical music with more thoroughness and intensity than any previous guitarist, and he expanded the melodic and harmonic language of metal while setting even higher standards of virtuosic precision" (2007, p. 239). A former lead guitarist with Alcatrazz, Malmsteen formed his own band called Rising Force. The band's 1988 album, *Odyssey,* managed to reach the number 40 position. Subsequent releases sold to a relatively small, in-the-know audience but did not enjoy the mass popularity necessary to reach high chart positions.

With the success of heavy metal in the 1980s, many hard rock bands moved toward that heavier aesthetic in some of their songs, and the line between hard rock and heavy metal became very fuzzy, especially by the late 1980s. Often, a given band could be categorized either way. As is often the case, precise, rigid definitions and categorizations can be elusive when dealing with music.

14.3.5: Metal Fragments

By the mid-1980s, **hardcore** began to give way to a heavy metal-based spinoff referred to as **thrash metal**. Blending elements of 1970s heavy metal bands like Black Sabbath with the speed and intensity of hardcore, the post-punk rock audience (known as *"headbangers"*) was given a rawer alternative to mainstream heavy metal. Credit for the first full-fledged thrash metal recording goes to Metallica.

Derivative Styles of Heavy Metal
The following section will describe a number of derivative styles of heavy metal that evolved during the late 1980s and 1990s.

Thrash Metal—Metallica's original guitarist, Dave Mustaine, created an even harder-driving version of thrash metal, forming Megadeth on his departure from his Metallica bandmates in 1985. Elements of the thrash metal sound can be found in the 1970s recordings of Motörhead, Iron Maiden, Diamond Head, and AC/DC. Because most of these bands originated in England, this movement has sometimes been referred to as the new wave of British heavy metal.

Speed Metal—**Speed metal,** as this derivative style is sometimes called, was incorporated by many recording artists of the period, including rapper Ice-T's Body Count. "Skin o' My Teeth," "Architecture of Aggression," and "High Speed Dirt" on Megadeth's *Countdown to Extinction* (1992) all serve as excellent examples of speed metal. Notice how the high-volume electric guitars played by Mustaine and Marty Friedman dominate the musical texture, typically subdividing the beat into four equal parts (quadruple subdivision), doubling the rhythmic density of the duple subdivisions commonly found in early heavy metal. This insistent rhythm provides an accompanimental foundation that refuses to recede into the background, demanding the listener's constant attention as Mustaine's sinister vocals are heard above the energetic din. The driving rhythm of the guitars is solidly matched by Nick Menza's powerful drumming and completed on the low end by David Ellefson's electric bass.

Death Metal—Another derivative style, **death metal**, combined the tempo, loudness, and heavy metal distortion of speed metal with graphic images of death and destruction. This sub-style was exemplified in the music of Carcass, Cadaver, Napalm Death, and Slayer.

14.3.6: Nü Metal (Rap Metal)

As we shall discuss later in this course, spoken rhymes are not the sole property of hip-hop and rap performers, most of whom were black. One subgenre of rap was primarily performed by white rappers: the **nü metal** phenomenon, combining heavy metal and rap. A harbinger of this approach can be found in the music of Ice-T's project *Body Count* (1992) with its speed metal accompaniment providing a foundation for the rapper's spoken social commentary. For a specific example, listen to "There Goes the Neighborhood," although almost any musical track on this album will suffice.

Nü metal dripped with the angst that formed an inherent element of grunge but dispensed with subtlety. Whereas songwriters like Kurt Cobain of Nirvana often looked inside themselves for solutions to the world's problems and exhibited a high degree of tolerance, the lyrics for this hard-driving music were often loaded with misogyny, homophobia, and aggression. The aggression was often aimed at women, often represented as sex objects. By contrast, other groups, like Body Count, used the genre as an effective platform for political and social commentary.

Nü Metal Bands

The following section will provide highlights from the careers of several nü metal acts that appeared during the 1990s.

Rage Against the Machine—Also using music as a platform for social commentary was Rage Against the Machine. The group was formed in 1991 by Zack de la Rocha and Tom Morello, both children of social activists. The two connected with Brad Wilk (drums) and Tim Commerford (bass), producing a set of demo recordings that earned them a deal with Epic Records. The band refused to sign, however, until they were guaranteed complete creative control over their output, an astonishingly bold demand for

new artists. After their debut album earned them a spot on the Lollapalooza tour, their next two albums—*Evil Empire* (1996) and *Battle of Los Angeles* (1999)—debuted at number 1. The band's fourth album, *Renegades* (2000), was a set of cover songs, reaching "only" the number 14 position. In 2002, following de la Rocha's departure, the instrumentalists of Rage merged with Soundgarden lead vocalist Chris Cornell to form Audioslave. The new band released an eponymous CD (number 7) that, on its best tracks, combined the driving rhythms and urgency typical of Rage Against the Machine with the melodicism and vocal power of Cornell's former band. Their following releases, *Out of Exile* (number 1, 2005) and *Revelations* (number 2, 2006), continued the band's success. Furthering his socio-political activism, Tom Morello, guitarist for Rage and Audioslave, released a series of folk rock albums under the name The Nightwatchman, an alter ego who played a significant role in the Occupy Wall Street movement in 2012. In collaboration with David Crosby, Graham Nash, Jackson Browne, Patti Smith, Willie Nelson, Yoko Ono, and other artists, Morello participated in the release of *Occupy This Album*, a 99-track compilation.

Korn—Following the lead of Rage Against the Machine, Korn opened the door of mainstream music to nü metal. Although their initial, self-titled album received relatively little attention, the band's incessant touring and growing fan base helped its follow-up, *Life Is Peachy* (1996), debut at number 3 on the album chart. With the release of *Follow the Leader* and *Issues* (both debuting at number 1 in 1998 and 1999, respectively), nü metal proved a powerful force that continued well into the new millennium.

Limp Bizkit—Korn's influence also helped Limp Bizkit to attain superstardom. Joined in 1995 by turntable manipulator DJ Lethal (formerly with House of Pain), Limp Bizkit began its rise to prominence. The band was formed by rapper Fred Durst, who was, at the time, a tattoo artist in Jacksonville, Florida. When members of Korn visited his shop for tattoos, he took advantage of the situation and gave them his band's demo tape. Limp Bizkit's initial release, *Three Dollar Bill, Y'all$* (number 22, 1997), contained a rap metal cover of "Faith," a song written and originally recorded by George Michael (number 1, 1987). Their second release, *Significant Other* (1999), reached the top of the album chart, eventually selling over seven million copies. The band's performance at Woodstock 1999 was cited by some as the event initiating the "mayhem and hooliganism that ultimately brought the three-day festival down in flames" (George-Warren and Romanowski 2001, 567). *Chocolate Starfish and the Hot Dog Flavored Water* (debuting at number 1, 2000) was the fastest-selling rock recording of the year. In 2001, *Results May Vary* reached number 3 and attained platinum status, but the band's earlier level of success was not to be repeated.

After rap metal proved to be a popular genre with the record-buying public, other artists followed. Some of the more successful of these include Kid Rock, Staind, System of a Down, and Linkin Park.

14.4: Musical Close-Up on Meter in Heavy Metal and Related Subgenres

OBJECTIVE: Describe the influence of heavy metal on alternative rock

As you will recall from our discussion at the beginning of this chapter, the musical style of heavy metal is generally simple and repetitive. There are, however, many exceptions to this rule. As metal developed into the 1990s, interesting metrical structures became more commonplace.

Let us briefly review some music by early heavy metal pioneers, Black Sabbath and Alice Cooper. With few exceptions, the songs recorded by these bands are in quadruple meter and almost always use a duple subdivision of the beat.

Metrical Structures Used by Early Heavy Metal Pioneers

The following section will provide highlights from the careers of two bands that adopted the heavy metal sound (Alice Cooper) and were heavily influential on the direction of heavy metal music (Black Sabbath).

Alice Cooper—Both of the Top 40 singles from Alice Cooper's trio of breakthrough albums, *Love It to Death* (1971), *Killer* (1971), and *School's Out* (1972), exemplify the

simplicity of the metrical structure typical of this style. Listen to "I'm Eighteen" (number 21, 1971) and "School's Out" (number 7, 1972) to confirm the consistent meter throughout the song. Note also that these songs provide examples of the two basic types of subdivision, with the former illustrating duple subdivision and the latter illustrating triple subdivision. As further evidence, consider the complete set of tracks on *Killer*, focusing specifically on meter. "Under My Wheels," "Be My Lover," "You Drive Me Nervous," "Yeah, Yeah, Yeah," and the title track are all easily recognizable as quadruple meter with duple subdivision. Even the more theatrical tracks ("Desperado" and "Dead Babies") incorporate metrically consistent rhythms throughout their duration, although variety is provided through the use of musical texture and instrumentation. The single song on *Killer* in which the rhythmic structure does not remain consistent is "Halo of Flies," which uses quadruple meter throughout but changes from duple to triple subdivision about five minutes into the song (at the entrance of strings, leading to a bass ostinato that emphasizes the new subdivision).

Black Sabbath—Black Sabbath has exerted an influence on almost every heavy metal band (and most alternative bands). The driving rhythms and metrical regularity of their recordings, especially the early works with Ozzy Osbourne as vocalist, laid the foundation for this style of rock. Listen to "Paranoid," "Iron Man," "Hand of Doom," "Electric Funeral," "Sweet Leaf," "Lord of This World," or "Supernaut." Any of these could serve as a prototypical example of heavy metal (even the ballads) with their use of quadruple meter and duple subdivision.

In the rather rare instances in which Black Sabbath songs are in triple meter (e.g., "Solitude"), again, the meter is consistent throughout. However, exceptions to this rule exist. For example, the brief introduction to "War Pigs" incorporates triple meter with triple subdivision but leads into a series of verses and choruses clearly exemplifying quadruple meter with duple subdivision.

14.4.1: Alternative Trends

As heavy metal music merged with elements of newer alternative trends (addressed later in this course) in the early 1990s, some groups began freely manipulating the solid metrical foundation on which the style had been built. Some of the most interesting of these experiments can be found on recordings by Soundgarden and Tool. These metrical manipulations come primarily in two varieties: uncommon meters (those other than duple, triple, or quadruple) and complex metrical structures resulting from frequently changing metrical groupings.

Types of Metrical Manipulation

The following section will provide a discussion regarding the use of meter in heavy metal. Given the essential nature of the driving rhythm to this style of rock, it is interesting to observe the complexity evident in some of these tracks.

Uncommon Meters—One means of infusing a sense of metrical interest into a song is to base the rhythmic structure on meters—in essence, the number of beats grouped into one measure—that are not divisible by two or three (e.g., 5, 7, 11, etc.). As has been pointed out previously, duple, triple, and, especially, quadruple meter are by far the most common meters in all rock styles, including mainstream rock and heavy metal. Less common meters include those grouping five or seven beats, though these can be heard in the music of numerous art rock, "prog" rock, and even metal recordings.

Examples of Uncommon Meters—Some interesting examples of the use of uncommon meters include Soundgarden's "My Wave" (five beats per measure; clearly established with the entrance of the drums), Tool's "Ticks & Leeches" (seven beats per measure when vocals enter), and "Lateralus" (five beats per measure when vocals enter).

Complex Meters—Another metrical manipulation is to change the symmetrical subdivisions of a common meter into an asymmetrical pattern. For example, instead of the usual eight subdivisions in quadruple meter (2 + 2 + 2 + 2), the subdivisions could be arranged into a 3 + 3 + 2 pattern. You can hear this pattern in the verses of Tool's "Intolerance," as it becomes clear with the vocal entrance. In such cases, the meter is more accurately described as 3/8 + 3/8 + 2/8, rather than the more traditional 4/4. Such metrical patterns are sometimes referred to as **complex** or **asymmetrical meters**. The pattern of 3 + 3 + 2 found in "Intolerance" is one of the most commonly used complex patterns incorporated in the music of Tool. You can find another clearly audible occurrence of this pattern in "Disposition," another track on *Lateralus*. We have seen the practice of changing meters before (remember examples by the Beatles, the Byrds, Chicago, and others), and it has been a common element of art music since the early twentieth century.

Examples of Changing Meters—Tool's "Schism" provides an excellent, but relatively simple, example of this technique. Following a brief acoustic guitar introduction, the meter combines a group of five eighth notes and a group of seven eighth notes, each preceded by a quick ascending arpeggio. Listen carefully to this section until you can hear the pattern. Then, notice that as the vocals sustain the word "communication" (approximately one minute and 20 seconds into the piece), the metrical pattern shifts ever so slightly. At this point, the meter alternates a group of six eighth notes with the same group of seven eighth notes as before. The original meter returns when the vocalist sings "I know the pieces fit. ..."

Soundgarden's "Mailman" provides another example of changing meters. Listen to the introduction and first verse of this song, and notice that there is a consistent sequence of the following metrical groupings: 8 subdivisions + 8 subdivisions + 7 subdivisions + 6 subdivisions, representing meters of 4/4, 4/4, 7/8, and 3/4. Yet another example of changing meter can be heard in Marilyn Manson's "Get Your Gunn" (from *Portrait of an American Family*, 1994). This song alternates between sextuple groupings (4 + 2) in the verses and octuple groupings (4 + 4) in the chorus.

It can be enlightening to explore some of the more progressive forms of heavy metal and their various musical progeny. The creative manipulation of rhythmic structure is often an important reason why some songs sound fresh and interesting, while others seem mundane and boring, especially with repeated listening over time.

BECOME AN ACTIVE LISTENER: ELEMENTS OF (HEAVY) METAL

Now that you have had a chance to review the emergence and evolution of heavy metal presented in this chapter, it is time to return to your own collection of recordings, to your streaming service, or to the Internet to identify, independently, some of the differentiating elements in recordings with which you may be more familiar.

Find examples of these heavy metal style elements in the music that you enjoy:
1. Repetitive riffs
2. Screaming vocals
3. Aggressive lyrics
4. Distortion

Summary: (Heavy) Metal

In this chapter, we have reviewed some of the most influential rock artists in the metal subgenre, acknowledging the fact that many of the early heavy metal recordings no longer sound as "heavy" due to the continuing evolution of this style, which has become significantly harder since the 1970s. Aggression and violence are common themes in the lyrics of this music, and the high-energy music with driving rhythms, fast tempos, and duple (or, more intensely, quadruple) subdivisions of the beat echo this aggression musically.

We explored the evolution of heavy metal in both the U.K. and the United States, pointing out the addition of significant theatrical components in the American version. We reviewed the careers of two primary British heavy metal groups (Led Zeppelin and Black Sabbath) and two American artists (Alice Cooper and Kiss), and then described the evolution into the 1980s as represented by Van Halen, Guns N' Roses, and Metallica.

By the 1980s, metal was experiencing a fragmentation that had become common in rock since the 1970s, branching into thrash metal, speed metal, and death metal. Nü metal then merged the intensity of the metal style with rapped lyrics and was used as a means of delivering socio-political commentary by bands like Rage Against the Machine and Body Count. As a means of acknowledging the significant variety evident even in this subgenre of rock and roll, in the Musical Close-Up we then explored a number of specific tracks recorded by metal artists, revealing the complexity of metrical structures that can be found in the music of Soundgarden, Tool, and others.

From this highly intense form of rock, we will next turn our attention to less "heavy" form of rock that became dominant in the 1980s: dance music.

Take Note: (Heavy) Metal

- *What is heavy metal?*—Heavy metal is the hardest of hard rock forms. Its original appeal was primarily to those whose self-image was that of the angry, macho, antiestablishment rebel, or—in general—13- to 18-year-old males. Heavy metal lyrics often focus on violence, suicide, and rebellion, and its sound typically includes high loudness levels, distortion, screamed vocals, and repetitive riffs. Originating in the late 1960s, the style evolved in the hands of British and American bands over the following decades, particularly in terms of its presentation,

although its basic elements have remained relatively unchanged.

- *How did British heavy metal evolve in the 1970s?*—Arising out of the hard rock bands of the 1960s and early 1970s, British heavy metal was louder and more aggressive than its forebears. Key among British heavy metal pioneers was Led Zeppelin, whose "Stairway to Heaven" became a heavy metal anthem, though never a Top 40 single. Black Sabbath, with original lead singer Ozzy Osbourne, emphasized anger and aggression over the "good time" party atmosphere of previous rock groups.
- *What were the significant developments in American heavy metal in the 1970s?*—In America, late 1960s hard rock also evolved into heavy metal with groups such as Iron Butterfly, MC5, Steppenwolf, and Grand Funk Railroad. Pioneers included Alice Cooper, whose stage shows and music were designed to shock his audience, establishing a subgenre of "shock rock." The highly theatrical band Kiss combined comic book makeup with heavy metal style and themes.
- *How has heavy metal evolved in the 1980s?*—Heavy metal entered the rock mainstream in the 1980s, with groups enjoying great success both on the charts and on the road. Among the most successful bands was Guns N' Roses, led by the forceful vocals of Axl Rose and the high-energy guitar work of Slash. Van Halen achieved great success with Eddie Van Halen's virtuosic guitar work showing more subtlety and variety than the typical screaming lead guitar work favored by metal musicians. Metallica became the premier heavy metal band of the late 1980s and early 1990s, enjoying a hit single in 1989 with the song "One," initiating a number of Top 40 hits through the 1990s. By the mid-1980s, metal evolved into a variety of sub-styles, including hardcore, thrash metal, speed metal, and death metal. Perhaps one of the most interesting hybrids was the nü metal style of the 1990s that wed rap-style lyrics with metal musical accompaniment.

SHARED WRITING

Spinal Tap as Satire of Metal Culture

This is Spinal Tap, a 1984 film directed by Rob Reiner in collaboration with writers Christopher Guest, Michael McKean, and Harry Shearer (all four of whom also star in the movie), constitutes what is known as a "mockumentary," chronicling the fictional hardships of a British heavy metal band. While I would strongly recommend watching the entire film, almost any 15-minute excerpt would suffice for this assignment. Identify which specific heavy metal bands are being targeted by the humor of this movie. Discuss some of the stereotypes of 1970s and 1980s rockers that are portrayed in the movie. Share your response with your peers and review the responses of at least two others, integrating any new and relevant information into your own response.

 A minimum number of characters is required to post and earn points. After posting, your response can be viewed by your class and instructor, and you can participate in the class discussion.

Post

0 characters | 140 minimum

Chapter 15
Dance Music

After discussing the significant fragmentation of the market that occurred in rock and roll during the 1970s and has largely continued since, in this chapter we are going to explore some of the styles of dance music that emerged during this same period. Though dancing had often been an important aspect of rock music, whether up-tempo "rocking" or slow dancing to a ballad, in the late 1970s dancing returned with a vengeance. After illuminating some important developments, we will review some of the most important artists and subgenres of dance music as the evolution of rock continues into the 1980s and 1990s.

15.1: The Selling of Rock in the 1980s and 1990s

OBJECTIVE: Explain the factors that changed rock music in the 1980s and 1990s

In September 2009, prior to the beginning of a rock history course, the author of your present course asked some 415 students enrolled to name the five most important current rock music acts. The result was a list of 470 different bands with only 12 receiving more than 20 votes; the top four, all with 40 votes or more, were Red Hot Chili Peppers (70), Blink-182 (49), Green Day (44), and Linkin Park (40). This admittedly unscientific survey suggests that the fragmentation of the 1970s had continued unabated ... at least among students in my rock class.

During the 1980s, there were several new developments that transformed the music industry. The first and most important of these was the music video. The recording industry and the radio industry have been partners in the promotion of rock music since the mid-1950s, but, generally, television was not a major factor in the development of rock. To be sure, Presley, Lewis, the Beatles, the Stones, and others appeared on TV shows hosted by Ed Sullivan or Steve Allen, as well as other variety shows. Music-oriented shows like *American Bandstand, Hullabaloo, Malibu U.,* and *Shindig* promoted various bands, but the primary purveyor of rock and roll was radio airwaves.

With the advent of cable television in the late 1970s, there was an opportunity for a wide spectrum of specialized television formats, like all-news stations, all-weather stations, Christian-oriented stations, and all-movie stations. Why not an all-rock music station? Warner's Nickelodeon channel had experimented with a show called *Popclips*, featuring a *veejay* (video jockey) running music videos—video presentations of pop and rock songs performed by the original artists. The idea of visual presentations of rock songs was not new (you will recall the Beatles' promotional film for "All You Need Is Love" discussed earlier in this course and other examples from that earlier period), but with the increasing popularity of video technology, the idea of transferring the Top 40 radio format to television was innovative, if perhaps inevitable.

15.1.1: Music Television (MTV)

On August 1, 1981, an all-rock television channel debuted. Music Television (MTV) was allotted $20 million in start-up costs. Just as record companies had long provided promotional discs to radio stations for airplay, so they now provided their rock videos to MTV at no cost. The promotional value to the record company and to the artists was tremendous. Using personable veejays, MTV copied the successful radio format of "chatter and play," augmented by interviews, news about touring bands, and a variety of contests.

Artists and companies scrambled to create imaginative and technically innovative videos to accompany new releases of music. That the video often had little to do with the lyrics seemed to be of little concern. Video added a new weapon to the arsenal of the record companies in their continuing battle to promote artists and records. After the emergence of MTV, if the video itself had enough appeal, it alone could propel a song to popularity. Some bands owed their success largely to the video format (e.g., Duran Duran).

Naturally, the MTV idea spread. Soon, WTBS in Atlanta, another cable station, produced *Night Tracks*—six hours of videos on weekend nights; the USA Network launched *Night Flight* in 1990; and even NBC ran their *Friday Night Videos*. In the early 1980s, rock videos—and MTV specifically—were the hottest new thing in rock. Other music-only cable stations—for example, Country Music Television, the Nashville Network, Black Entertainment Television, the Box (pay-per-view), and VH-1, the sister channel launched by MTV in 1985 to appeal to an older audience—have challenged MTV's music video monopoly. Even the major networks, vying for the teen market, programmed music video offerings into weekend, late-night time slots. Music video channels have changed, chameleon-like, since their inception to reflect the most recent musical trends, giving each new musical direction and its associated artists an opportunity to be seen by a national audience. Some succeeded in taking advantage of this opportunity (Ice Cube, Nirvana, and Mariah Carey), while other "one-hit wonders" faded away almost as fast as they appeared.

CRITICISM OF MTV MTV had its detractors, though. One complaint was that the network emphasized white rock almost completely to the exclusion of black artists. This was undoubtedly the result of marketing studies that indicated that cable owners tended to be mostly middle- to upper-class urban whites. However, when Michael Jackson became a superstar, appealing to almost every demographic, MTV yielded to the pressures of the marketplace and belatedly ran not only Jackson's videos but videos by other black artists as well. In fact, by the mid-1990s, as rap merged into the musical mainstream (a topic covered later in this course), black artists rose to a position of prominence on MTV.

Another criticism of MTV (and music videos in general) had to do with the frequent emphasis on sex and violence. A study by Barry L. Sherman and Joseph R. Dominick (1986), titled "Violence and Sex in Music Videos: TV and Rock and Roll," was published in the *Journal of Communication*. Their study noted that about 56.6 percent of the rock videos contained examples of violent acts; they also reported that about 75.9 percent included representations of sexual activities. This raises the question of whether the industry's new emphasis on music videos was actually affecting the content of rock music—after all, the television and movie industries discovered many years ago that sex and violence sell.

Yet another problem was that the *image* of rock artists had become as important—sometimes more important—than their music. During the late 1980s, for example, the Hot 100 was often dominated by pretty faces and well-shaped bodies, rather than innovative musical talents. Compare the sound of Paula Abdul and Janet Jackson (examples of the former) to recordings by Aretha Franklin and Luther Vandross (examples of the latter). The culmination of this "image over substance" tendency was fully realized late in 1989 with revelations concerning Milli Vanilli. The band's album *Girl You Know It's True* won the Grammy Award for Best New Artist. As it turned out, the song was not sung by the "singers," Rob Pilatus (an out-of-work dancer and model) and Fabrice Morvan (a gymnast) but by Charles Shaw, a U.S. Army veteran. A producer in Munich, Frank Farian, had paid Pilatus and Morvan $4,000 each, plus royalties, to lip-synch to Shaw's vocals (Romanowski and George-Warren 1995). Once this deception came to light, an embarrassed Grammy committee rescinded the band's award. Lawsuits were filed against Arista Records and various concert promoters, resulting in a settlement that granted purchasers of the recording a rebate of up to $3. Over 80,000 claims were filed in response.

LIP-SYNCHING The use of lip-synching and so-called ghost artists is not new and is certainly not unique to Milli Vanilli. Recall that Ringo Starr was replaced by a studio drummer on early Beatles recordings (e.g., "Love Me Do" and "P.S. I Love You"). Members of the Monkees sang but did not play any instruments on their early recordings, leaving this task to various studio musicians. The Monkees eventually learned to play instruments well enough to perform their songs in live concerts. Later acts, such as Technotronics and C+C Music Factory, hired models to lip-synch to vocals supplied by less attractive singers (DeCurtis and Henke 1992). The line between such enhancement and outright fraud became decidedly blurred during the 1990s.

Complicating matters, artists performing on tour were forced to compete with their finely crafted music videos that were rapidly becoming, it seemed, a new musical form. Because of the physical impossibility of simultaneously performing the complex choreography, exaggerated theatrics, and vocal parts, many of these artists resorted to lip-synching at least portions of their live performances to meet the expectations of their video-viewing audience. Spontaneity, one of the cornerstones of early rock and roll, was thus cast aside in an effort to please an audience expecting a perfectly executed, visceral, multimedia experience.

NON-MUSIC PROGRAMMING   During the mid-1980s, MTV began to introduce non-music programming (game shows, adult-oriented cartoons, *MTV News,* and political coverage), a trend that increased dramatically over the following decade such that, by the arrival of the new millennium, it was sometimes difficult to find music playing on MTV. Despite this ongoing change, MTV continued to play an important role in the dissemination of music and exerted a significant influence on the direction of the evolution of popular music. *Yo! MTV Raps,* from the late 1980s, played an influential role in the popularization of rap music. Beginning in the early 1990s, MTV also sponsored a series of *Unplugged* concerts in which various rock artists performed, in most cases, entirely on acoustic instruments. Unplugged acts included rock and roll mainstays like Eric Clapton, Paul McCartney, Sting, Bruce Springsteen, Rod Stewart, Bob Dylan, the Eagles, and Aerosmith as well as more recent, up-and-coming artists (at the time), such as Mariah Carey, Nirvana, Hootie and the Blowfish, Alice in Chains, Babyface, Alanis Morissette, Jay-Z, Shakira, and Staind. These performances allowed the audience to hear alternate versions of familiar songs, focusing on the craftsmanship evidenced by the artists' songwriting talents.

TALENT SHOWS   In the 1990s and into the 2000s, network television hosted a number of shows documenting the creation of musical groups, awarding recording contracts and concert tours to the winners. Some of these programs were picked up by VH-1 and MTV. The winning performers were often quite successful initially, although long-term commercial success proved elusive to most. The hit television show *American Idol* also capitalized on the trend, although with solo singers instead of bands, making a season-long series out of searching the nation for talented young acts, a process in which the audience played an active role by voting for their favorite performers.

On March 24, 2000, *Making the Band* premiered on ABC. The band created in the process, O-Town, released an album that was certified platinum in 2001, which included the hit single "Liquid Dreams" (number 10). The WB Network responded with *Popstars,* which documented the creation of a five-member girl group, Eden's Crush; their debut album titled, not surprisingly, *Popstars* contained the hit single "Get Over Yourself" (number 8). In 2011, *Rolling Stone* entered the fray, hosting a *Choose the Cover* competition that provided the winning band (Sheepdog) the enviable opportunity to appear on the magazine's cover, a highly prestigious placement, indeed.

In 2000, VH-1 became an active participant in this movement, introducing *Bands on the Run,* a more typical "battle of the bands"-style competition. For this show, each group was given a band van and the opportunity to tour 11 American cities, promoting and playing 13 shows over an eight-week period. Members of Flickerstick, a Dallas rock quintet and winners of the competition, found themselves the subject of a bidding war among several major labels, eventually signing with Epic. In 2001, the band released *Welcoming Home the Astronauts,* containing one hit single, "Beautiful" (number 27), which remained on the Hot 100 for only eight weeks. Epic dropped the group from its roster a year later.

In some ways, this process of putting talented individuals together was nothing new. Examples date back to the girl groups of the 1960s and the formation of the Monkees for television. What was new, however, was the undeniable truth that there was serious money to be made out of the process of artist selection and image transformation, and through developing every aspect of the act into a public spectacle.

15.1.2: Evolving Media Formats

As technology developed at lightning speed during the last half of the twentieth century, recordings were released in a variety of formats. With each development, the sound quality (usually) improved significantly, and, in some cases, consumers purchased recordings they already owned in the new format so they could benefit from the sonic improvement and/or play the music on a new sound system that required the newer media format.

Media Formats for the Distribution of Rock Recordings

The following section will provide details regarding the manner in which the media upon which rock recordings were released (vinyl LPs, cassette tapes, CDs, etc.) changed between the 1960s and the present.

Whereas the 7-inch single was the primary medium of rock and roll in the 1950s, the 12-inch LP became the dominant medium in the 1960s. Throughout the 1970s, cassette tapes gained in popularity. At first, cassettes were quite unsatisfactory; sound quality was inferior, and there were frequent mechanical problems. However, the end of the 1970s brought solutions for these technical problems, as recently developed noise reduction technologies were introduced. In 1984, cassette sales surpassed album sales for the first time in history (Ward, Stokes, and Tucker 1986). By the late 1990s, however, cassette tapes were no longer a viable format for music distribution.

The decline in cassette sales was related to the growing popularity of compact discs (CDs). These small discs could not only hold more music than any other previous recorded format, but produced a superior sound compared to the cassette tapes. By 1991, the industry was shipping over 333 million CDs (up more than 16 percent over the previous year). Although this was still less than the number of cassettes shipped, the trend was clear. Industry representatives were understandably quite pleased with this development; CDs and tapes cost the same to manufacture, but the retail price for a CD normally ran between $13 and $17, whereas cassettes retailed for about $9 to $10, providing a significant boost to profits. CD sales continued a rising trend until the year 2000, when other factors initiated a decline that could signal the eventual death knell for this format as well. Concerning **LP**s, by the early 1990s, they had practically disappeared from the scene. The decline of the LP was dramatic: from 295 million units shipped in 1981 to just under 5 million in 1991—a decline of over 98 percent in just a decade. Meanwhile, the shipments of CDs rose from about 800,000 in 1983 to 333 million in 1991. In recent years, there has been a revival of interest in the (supposedly), analog sound of vinyl records. In 2016, Nielsen's year-end report quantified vinyl LP sales of 13 million units (11 percent of the physical album sales); this occurred during a time when the modest 3 percent increase in profits was primarily driven by a 76 percent increase in on-demand audio streaming services, off-setting declines in sales of physical copies of recordings (Nielsen 2017).

Another audio format, digital audio tape (DAT) in a mini-cassette format, never took hold in the consumer market, although many studios adopted the new format for a relatively brief period of time preceding the introduction of the computer-based digital recording studio. In the four years from 1985 to 1988, recorded music sales rose from $4.4 billion to $6.2 billion, a trend that reversed dramatically in the early 2000s, as music sales dropped from $13 billion in 1999 to $6.9 billion in 2010.

Other developments in the 1980s included the small portable cassette players (often with built-in AM and FM bands). The Sony Walkman™ and similar products became omnipresent. Now, the music fanatic could hook the player onto a belt, slap on lightweight headphones, and have music almost anywhere, at any time. Larger boom boxes (sometimes referred to using the questionable label "ghetto blasters") were less favored because of their bulky size and weight. However, they had the advantage of having speakers and could be enjoyed by several listeners, whereas the Walkman required headphones and could be listened to by only a single person. By the 1990s, the Discman™, the CD equivalent of the Walkman, had become equally popular. By 2007, both the Walkman and Discman devices were essentially replaced by the digital audio player, a small, portable device that stores and plays thousands of songs in a digital format (most commonly MP3 or AAC files), as well as movies and even books. In more recent years, this music playback function has been integrated into most "smart" mobile phones, so a separate device is not required for this purpose.

15.1.3: Rock Music Soundtracks

Continuing a trend that began in the mid-1950s, the movie soundtrack has allowed both record companies and the motion picture industry to advertise their products via a highly profitable, mutually beneficial distribution system. The bicycle-riding montage to the accompaniment of "Raindrops Keep Fallin' on My Head" (number 1, 1969) inserted into *Butch Cassidy and the Sundance Kid* is one of the first examples of a segment of film that was included solely for the purpose of marketing a song. Since then, hit singles have figured prominently in the filmmaking process. Between 1956 and 1958, soundtrack albums for *The King & I, Around the World in 80 Days, South Pacific,* and *Gigi* all reached the top of the Pop chart. From 1962 to 1963, Leonard Bernstein and Stephen Sondheim's soundtrack from *West Side Story* held the number 1 position for 54 weeks, setting a record that still stands.

In most of these cases, the music on the recordings was taken from scenes in the film when the entire cast broke out in song. This *diegetic music*—or source music—was assumed to be audible to all characters on the screen (Gorbman 1987). At other times, however, music is used for the purpose of setting a mood to highlight the drama of the action taking place. This *nondiegetic music*—or background music—is presumed not to be audible to the characters in the narrative, but serves to enhance the psychological drama for the audience. Throughout film history, this latter role has been fulfilled, typically, by hiring a composer to create an appropriate musical score. Since the 1970s, however, it has become commonplace to incorporate pre-existing hit singles into the soundtrack

(*American Graffiti*, 1973; *The Big Chill*, 1983; *Dirty Dancing*, 1987), matching the musical style and lyrics of this nondiegetic music to the cinematic narrative. It also is possible that music from the soundtrack will be heard by characters in the drama, as it emanates from a car radio, blares from the open doors of a nightclub, or plays softly from a bedside radio. Such music can serve to authenticate the era in which a film is set, to enhance the psychological drama of a scene, or, as in the movies *La Bamba* (1987) and *Great Balls of Fire* (1989), to tell the story of an important musical figure. Members of the audience who like the music are likely to purchase the soundtrack recording, and individuals who hear a soundtrack recording packed with hit singles may be influenced to attend the film—a win-win situation for both the record and film companies.

JOURNAL

Changing Formats for Music Recordings

With the enhanced pace of technological developments during the twentieth century, there was a series of changes to the manner in which music was sold—from LPs to eight-track tapes to cassette tapes to CDs to DATs, and, most recently, to digital downloads. Take a moment to document, if you have had the personal experience, a recording that you yourself chose to purchase in multiple formats so that the listening experience was improved. Then, take time to contact older parents or relatives, asking them about their experiences; which of these individuals holds the distinction of purchasing a single recording in the largest number of formats? For both the recording representing your own experience and that of the other individual who purchased the greatest number of formats, provide the name of artist, album title, list of formats purchased, and reasons for re-purchasing music that was already in one's music collection. Take a moment to reflect on how this change in formats might have had a positive impact on the recording industry's profits.

 The response entered here will appear in the performance dashboard and can be viewed by your instructor.

Submit

15.2: The Return of Dance Music

OBJECTIVE: Summarize the factors that led to dance music making a comeback during the 1970s

In the early days of rock, every song was assumed to be intended for dancing; whether "Blueberry Hill" or "Great Balls of Fire," people were supposed to dance to rock and roll. This assumption reached a peak in the early 1960s with the dance craze (represented most dramatically by Chubby Checker's "The Twist"). However, as the 1960s progressed, there were styles that were meant for listening, not dancing. Certainly, this was true of the folk music trend. As the music of the Beatles became more experimental, especially with

changing meters, dancing became almost impossible. Most of the music of the jazz rock–fusion and art rock–progressive rock styles of the late 1960s and 1970s were intended primarily for listening rather than for dancing. This is not to say that dancing went away.

15.2.1: Motown's Competition

Motown provided a steady diet of music that emphasized dancing, and there was certainly plenty of other music to dance to in both the 1960s and 1970s. However, after the dance craze faded in the mid-1960s, it was not until the mid-1970s that a style specifically for the purpose of dancing developed again: disco. To trace the evolution of disco, we need to turn our attention toward Philadelphia.

15.2.2: The Philadelphia Sound

Motown's level of success and position in the music industry receded in the 1970s. Stevie Wonder and Diana Ross remained the company's greatest strengths, but, as so many others left (e.g., Gladys Knight, the Jackson Five, the Four Tops, and the Miracles), Motown found it difficult to compete in an industry that had fragmented and now varied from psychedelic soul to heavy metal to glitter rock. In the early 1970s, a new black-owned company appeared that gave Motown considerable competition. Producer-songwriters Kenneth Gamble and Leon Huff formed Philadelphia International Records and, for a while at least, appeared to have created another Motown. Gamble, Huff, and partner-to-be Thom Bell were experts at providing lush orchestrations for their black vocal groups. In 1972, they produced a major hit with "Back Stabbers," by a quintet from Canton, Ohio, known as the O'Jays, followed by their number 1 hit, "Love Train" (1973).

The success of the so-called Philadelphia Sound was at least partially due to the consistently strong backing of a group of studio musicians known as MFSB (Mother, Father, Sister, Brother). In addition to providing the recognizable backing for most of Philadelphia International's vocal acts, MFSB had a major hit of their own with "TSOP (The Sound of Philadelphia)"; it moved to number 1 in 1974 and became the theme song for the popular black-oriented, music-and-dance television show *Soul Train*.

By 1975, Philadelphia International (PI) was grossing over $25 million per year and was second only to Motown among black-owned record companies. However, the young company soon encountered rough waters. Gamble and Huff were indicted on payola charges (Huff was eventually cleared, and Gamble was assessed a $2,500 fine). Gamble's personal problems, combined with desertions by key staff members and some artists, greatly reduced PI's dreams of Motown-like success. However, the style of Gamble and Huff's music is often cited as a precursor of one of the 1970s most popular trends: disco.

15.3: Disco

OBJECTIVE: Identify the leading performers of disco

The term *disco* is a shortened form of the word *discotheque*, a type of dance hall that had begun in France in the early 1960s. Cabaret owners found it far more economical to hire one disc jockey to spin records than to hire a live band; also, a variety of musical styles could be played authentically, some example of which was bound to please almost every customer's tastes.

15.3.1: Donna Summer

The year 1976 saw the first impact of one of disco's premier artists, Donna Summer. Born LaDonna Gaines, her first hit, "Love to Love You Baby," reached number 2 in early 1976, featuring Summer's breathy vocal enriched by her sexualized moaning and groaning. Originally a 4-minute song, "Love to Love You Baby" was increased to a version lasting nearly 17 minutes for disco play. Too long for the standard 7-inch single, it was released to the record stores on a 12-inch disc like the ones used by discotheque disc jockeys. The 12-inch single soon became a common medium for commercial disco releases.

With "Last Dance" (number 3, 1978), Summer proved herself to be a solid American pop singer capable of more than breathy double entendres. A slow, ballad-like section builds up to the disco beat. Once this style was established, Summer recorded a series of soft rock songs that were based on the familiar disco beat. One of her best, "MacArthur Park," became her first number 1 song; between 1976 and 1980, she released 10 Top 10 songs, including four that reached number 1: "McArthur Park" (1978), "Hot Stuff" (1979), "Bad Girls" (1979), and "No More Tears (Enough is Enough)" (1979).

The Evolution of Disco

The following section will explain how disco emerged in the 1970s and include some of the 1960s styles that led to disco's dominance of the dance scene.

During the 1960s, the discotheque concept was imported into the United States, at first in the form of "underground" clubs. Soon, discotheques catering to all segments of society were flourishing around the country. With the coming of the San Francisco–style concert halls and their live bands, discos faded out somewhat in the late 1960s and very early 1970s. Soon, however, they re-emerged, featuring music that was specifically designed for dancing—a style that became known, naturally enough, as disco.

Deejays (DJs) in 1970s discos were armed with two turntables so that they could segue smoothly from record to record without stopping the beat, which was almost always accompanied by pulsing colored lights and flashing strobe lights. During this LP-dominated era, disco recordings were formatted onto 12-inch vinyl discs, with one song per side. In the early 1970s, discos played pop and rock music, but they increasingly leaned toward the sound of Philadelphia International and similar styles. The music of the O'Jays, the Spinners, the Stylistics, the Temptations, Stevie Wonder, and Marvin Gaye was the typical fare of early 1970s discotheques.

By early 1974, several artists released records specifically designed for the new disco scene. The Hues Corporation's "Rock the Boat" and George McCrae's "Rock Your Baby" both reached number 1 in 1974. "Rock Your Baby" was written and produced by two engineers at TK Studios in Hialeah, Florida: Harry Wayne Casey and Richard Finch.

Soon forming their own nine-member band, Casey and Finch released more disco songs under the name KC and the Sunshine Band. They scored four number 1 hits from 1975 to 1977: "Get Down Tonight" (1975), "That's the Way (I Like It)" (1975), "(Shake, Shake, Shake) Shake Your Booty" (1976), and "I'm Your Boogie Man" (1977). KC's music featured a simple but insistent rhythm track that varied little from the first measure to the last. The vocal line typically consisted of short unison phrases, more in the nature of repeating patterns than a true melody, which might evolve musically over time in the traditional sense. Lyrics were simple and repetitive to the point of absurdity (e.g., "Wrap Your Arms Around Me," another song by KC and the Sunshine Band, repeats the title 29 times in its 3 minutes and 47 seconds—or once every 7 seconds). Horn lines were also typically simple and repetitive riffs and were used to punctuate the vocal line. All was subservient to the rhythm, a solid and persistent four beats per bar, most often with *quadruple beat subdivision* (each beat divided into four equal parts).

In 1975, disco exploded onto the national scene. Led by Studio 54 in New York City, discotheques opened everywhere—either glitzy new constructions or rejuvenated old clubs, barns, or ballrooms. Some reports estimate that there were 10,000 discos in North America at the height of the disco craze, with some 200 to 300 in New York City alone.

One of the biggest disco hits of 1975 was "The Hustle" by Van McCoy. With its gentle sound, infectious beat, flute lead, and attractive string countermelody, "The Hustle" was a cut above the average disco song. Hitting number 1 in the summer of 1975, the song spawned variants, such as the California hustle, the Latin hustle, the American hustle, the New York hustle, and the tango hustle (with shades of the twist). After the success of KC, Shirley and Company, the Hues Corporation, George McCrae, and others—even pop artists (pianist Peter Nero), jazz flutist Herbie Mann, trumpeter Doc Severinsen, and pop orchestra leader Percy Faith—made disco recordings.

Donna Summer, 1978.

SOURCE: Pictorial Press Ltd/Alamy Stock Photo

15.3.2: Saturday Night Fever and the Bee Gees

In 1977, disco became an international rage. Perhaps the most influential factor was the extremely popular film *Saturday Night Fever,* starring John Travolta. The film is about a young, working-class New York man who becomes a prizewinning disco dancer. The soundtrack album, which includes songs by KC and the Sunshine Band, MFSB, and Yvonne Elliman, sold over 25 million copies between 1977 and 1980, becoming the biggest-selling soundtrack album of all time to that date; overall, it has now sold over 40 million copies. In addition, there was a disco setting by Walter Murphy of the first movement of Beethoven's Symphony No. 5. This number 1 song, "A Fifth of Beethoven," seemed to show that virtually any previously composed music could be "discofied" simply by borrowing the melody and harmony and setting it to a disco beat and bass line.

Bee Gees; (L to R) Robin, Barry, and Maurice Gibb, 1979.

SOURCE: CSU Archives/Everett Collection Historical/Alamy Stock Photo

There is no doubt that the big winners from *Saturday Night Fever* were the Bee Gees, the three singing brothers: Barry, Maurice, and Robin Gibb.

Musical Journey of the Bee Gees

The following section will provide highlights from the career of the Bee Gees, one of the most successful groups during the disco era.

The Gibbs were anything but newcomers to the scene in 1977. The Gibb brothers began singing together as children in Manchester, England, and then moved with their family to Australia, where they became teen pop sensations. First hitting the U.S. charts in 1967 with "New York Mining Disaster 1941," they produced a series of Top 20 hits through 1969. The trio almost dissolved at the turn of the decade, but soon reunited to produce the number 3 song "Lonely Days" and their first number 1 song, "How Can You Mend a Broken Heart?," featuring Barry Gibb's signature wavering falsetto vocal.

The years 1973 and 1974 were difficult ones for the Bee Gees; they had no hit singles for the first time since 1967, and their albums fared poorly. Just as it appeared that they would fade, as so many others had before them, the new disco style offered salvation. Their 1975 album *Main Course* hit the Top 20 and contained the number 1 song "Jive Talkin'."

It was *Saturday Night Fever,* though, that turned the Bee Gees into a household name. Much of the film's music was written by the brothers; they sang six songs on the double album, three of which became number 1 songs in 1977 to 1978: "How Deep Is Your Love?," "Stayin' Alive," and "Night Fever." They followed with three more number 1 songs in 1978 to 1979 ("Too Much Heaven," "Tragedy," and "Love You Inside Out") and produced two more number 1 albums (*Spirits Having Flown* and *Bee Gees Greatest*). However, as the disco mania faded in the early 1980s, so did the Bee Gees, who had become typed as a disco act. In the 1990s, the group enjoyed a renaissance, primarily in the U.K. and Germany.

Among the other groups that found success in the late 1970s disco surge were Kool and the Gang, the Village People, Tavares, and Chic. By 1980, disco had been adopted by jet-set, upper-class society and, thus, became the target of intense ridicule by the rock community. After all, there had been disco songs by Ethel Merman, the Boston Pops Orchestra, and Barbra Streisand; there was even a Mickey Mouse disco album. It seemed as though everyone had a disco song or album—even Elton John ("Don't Go Breaking My Heart," 1976, with Kiki Dee), Rod Stewart ("Do You Think I'm Sexy," 1978), and the Rolling Stones ("I Miss You," 1978). Although one could still go to affluent metropolitan clubs and hear a steady diet of 1980s-style, synthesizer-oriented disco (called *technodance*), the basic style died an unmourned death around 1980. In the rock establishment, disco became an even more reviled and derided style than soft rock. Nevertheless, in the period from 1975 to 1980, it was an extremely potent force in the music industry.

Watch "Jive Talkin'" by the Bee Gees

Click or tap the video title to listen to "Jive Talkin'."

https://www.youtube.com/watch?v=-6F8B8KJyKg*

JOURNAL

A Fifth of Beethoven

Listen to a recording of the first movement of Beethoven's Fifth Symphony performed by a symphony; you can find many available online. Then, locate a recording of "A Fifth of Beethoven" from the *Saturday Night Fever* soundtrack. Write a paragraph to describe your general reaction to this disco setting for a well-known Western art music masterpiece. What do you like about the disco setting of this composition? What do you not like? What piece of art music (or song in another, non-dance style) would you like to hear set to a disco beat?

 The response entered here will appear in the performance dashboard and can be viewed by your instructor.

Submit

15.4: Motown Keeps Dancing

OBJECTIVE: Explain the influence of Motown music on dance music

Motown emerged as a potent force in popular music during the early 1960s, one of the few black-owned record companies at the time. With artists like the Supremes, the

Temptations, and Stevie Wonder, to name just a few, Barry Gordy and his artists established a hit factory in Detroit. The disco era provided a new breath of life to Motown, as it rolled into the 1980s.

15.4.1: Michael Jackson

Occasionally we hear of "bubble babies": babies who must stay in an enclosed, sterile environment to grow. Michael Jackson's "bubble" was show biz—the stage. Growing up in his insulated world of theaters, studios, microphones, and lights, Michael never learned "the streets" that so many other black performers knew. The Apollo Theater and the Motown and Epic studios—these were his elementary, middle, and high schools. In an industry of ultra-worldly people, Michael is a study in almost incredible naïveté. Jackson's stage image was just the opposite: He appeared to be the singing, dancing, jiving extrovert who was the ultimate example of black funk.

Michael Joe Jackson was born in Gary, Indiana, in 1958. The musical Jackson family was headed by Joe Jackson who saw to it that his six sons and three daughters knew music. The three oldest boys—Jackie, Tito, and Jermaine—formed a high school group that soon expanded with the addition of younger brothers Marlon and Michael. After several auditions, the group finally impressed Berry Gordy who later recalled that he liked their tight vocals and polished performance style.

THE JACKSON FIVE The Jackson Five's first three albums reached the Top 5 and yielded four consecutive number 1 hits ("I Want You Back," "ABC," "Love You Save," and "I'll Be There") and one number 2 hit ("Mama's Pearl"), all in slightly over a year (1970). The next nine Motown albums (through 1976) were not quite as spectacular but nevertheless yielded 11 more Top 40 hits. The undeniable musicianship of Michael Jackson dominates these recordings. His prepubescent voice was unmistakable (and not easily duplicated by would-be copycat groups).

In 1976, all but Jermaine switched to the Columbia-affiliated Epic Records. The loss of the Jackson Five did not delight Gordy. Motown sued Columbia for $20 million, but eventually settled for $600,000 and rights to the group's name. Thus, the group became The Jacksons and added younger brother Randy and sisters LaToya and Maureen. Their four studio albums for Epic in the period from 1976 to 1980 sold unevenly.

JACKSON'S SOLO CAREER Michael Jackson's solo career was fabulously successful, flamboyant, and controversial. His first important solo album came in 1979. *Off the Wall*, produced by Quincy Jones, sold over 8 million copies and resulted in four Top 10 songs, including two number 1

hits ("Don't Stop 'Til You Get Enough" and "Rock With You"). The album revealed Michael's versatility as he moved from fast, dance-oriented songs to softer ballads. As big an album as *Off the Wall* was (it eventually peaked at number 3), Michael continued to work within The Jacksons. Their album, *Triumph* (1980), was reasonably successful, rising to number 10 by the end of the year.

Even as The Jacksons' promotional tour for *Triumph* ended, Michael and Quincy Jones began planning the follow-up album to *Off the Wall*. The resulting *Thriller* album was released in 1982. The first hit single from the album was "The Girl Is Mine" (number 2), which featured Jackson and Paul McCartney.

As 1983 began, a second song from *Thriller*, "Billie Jean," began moving up the charts, reaching number 1 by early March. Michael created the basic rhythm on a drum machine; it was enhanced ("punched up") by a live drummer. The persistent bass line was added next, creating the interesting chug-chug sound of the song. Michael is reported to have recorded the lead vocal track in one take. The lyrics were heavier than had been typical of previous Jackson songs; they concerned paternity charges resulting from an illicit love affair. The infectious beat, the menacing tone of the vocal and instrumental lines, and the effective video combined to make "Billie Jean" a huge success.

Following "Billie Jean" up the charts was "Beat It," Michael's updating of the gang dance/rumble scenes from Leonard Bernstein's *West Side Story*. The bass and guitar riff from "Beat It" became instantly recognizable; the hard, macho vocal (macho for high-voiced Michael, at least) was appealing, as was the neo–*West Side Story* video. Adding to the unusually hard edge was a guitar solo by rocker Eddie Van Halen. By the time "Beat It" ended its three-week stay at number 1, it was becoming clear that *Thriller* was going to be a big album.

On May 16, 1983, NBC aired a two-hour salute to Motown's 25th anniversary. The show consisted primarily of old film clips, monologues, and updated performances by Motown's early favorites. Although much of this nostalgia-oriented show looked backward, one exciting moment was utterly up-to-date and provided a glimpse into the future. After The Jacksons had run through some earlier hits, Michael took the stage as a solo act (sequined white glove and all). After a few remarks, he launched into "Billie Jean." Gracefully moving through his dance steps, heavily oriented to the break-dancing style, complete with his smooth, backward "moonwalk," Michael clearly established himself in the nation's consciousness as a solo act, distinct from the old Jackson Five/Jacksons. His appeal cut across demographic lines, reaching the young, their parents, male and female, black and white. He was truly a superstar.

By the end of 1983, three more *Thriller* singles had made the Top 10: "Wanna Be Startin' Somethin'" (number 5), "Human Nature" (number 7), and "PYT (Pretty Young Thing)" (number 10). Early in 1984, the title song made its appearance on the Hot 100, eventually rising to number 4. The song's video was trendsetting ... a mini-film directed by feature film director John Landis. With elaborate staging, sophisticated visual effects, state-of-the-art theatrical makeup, a mini-plot, and lots of Jackson-style dance choreography, the "Thriller" video established an entirely new level of production quality for music videos. The song itself had all of the hooks: a uniquely recognizable bass riff, a catchy beat (with strong backbeat), a forceful vocal, superior production, and even the eerie voice of horror film star Vincent Price in a closing "rap." In more ways than one, it was a monster. The list of *Thriller*'s staggering accomplishments recalls similar lists for Presley and the Beatles: it has sold over 100 million copies worldwide (so far), the first album to surpass U.S. sales of 30 million, held the number 1 position for 37 weeks (second only to the soundtrack album from *West Side Story*), and yielded seven Top 10 hits, including two at number 1. *The Making of Michael Jackson's "Thriller,"* an hour-long video, sold over 350,000 copies within six months of its release.

MICHAELMANIA   Michael returned to the studio to work with his family on their next album, 1984's *Victory*, followed by a much-heralded tour. However, the concerts fell short of expectations. Ticket prices were high, and people wanted Michael—not The Jacksons. "Michaelmania" had run at fever pitch from late 1982 to 1984, but with no releases in 1985 or 1986, Michael's detractors—of whom there were many—happily pronounced him to be another certified fad. Proving them wrong, Michael's new album, *Bad*, was released in 1987 and became another monster hit. It debuted at the number 1 position and stayed there for six weeks. Granted, these numbers pale in comparison to those of *Thriller*, but so do those of almost every other album in history.

Michael Jackson on stage in 1988.

SOURCE: Trinity Mirror/Mirrorpix/Alamy Stock Photo

Bad is a strong album, producing seven hit singles (including five number 1 hits—the most ever drawn from one album). Again, produced by Quincy Jones, *Bad* shows Michael's continued strength in the style of "Beat It" and "Billy Jean." Indeed, most of the songs on *Bad* follow the general style of those earlier hits. An interesting exception is "I Just Can't Stop Loving You," a soft rock ballad sung with female vocalist Siedah Garrett. It is a beautifully written song with a well-shaped melody and beautifully blended harmonies. Jackson's and Garrett's voices are so well matched that one must pay very close attention to know who is singing at any given moment. It is also interesting to note a general similarity between the first two melodic phrases of this song and the opening phrases of "Home," the final song of the musical *The Wiz*. In the movie version of this musical, this powerful song was performed by none other than Michael's idol, Diana Ross.

MICHAEL'S PERSONAL LIFE   The rumors of the end of Michael Jackson's career proved to be greatly exaggerated. In 1991, he signed a $1 billion multimedia contract with Sony. Although Michael's recordings fared moderately well at best through the 1990s, he remained a pop icon. He was married several times (including for two years to Lisa Marie Presley, Elvis' daughter), endured several costly court battles, and established an admirable reputation as a philanthropist. Unfortunately, beginning in the 1990s and continuing into the new century, Michael was repeatedly accused of inappropriate behavior with children—a charge he vehemently denied. The negative impact of these allegations, however, was significant and the effects of a related trial in 2005 were devastating, both personally and professionally. Despite the outcome of the trial—Jackson was acquitted on all charges—he left the country to live in Bahrain. Little was heard from him until a 2009 announcement about an ambitious 50-concert tour during the summer of 2010. Less than one month before the tour was set to begin, tragedy struck. On June 25, 2009, Michael Jackson died of cardiac arrest caused by an overdose of the anesthetic Propofol; the dose was administered by his physician who was charged with involuntary manslaughter. Although his recordings continue to sell impressively, the commercial success of his later albums falls far short of his recordings made during the 1970s and 1980s. There is no doubt, however, that Michael Jackson was a megastar who exerted incredible influence on the direction of dance-oriented rock music.

15.4.2: The Commodores

Motown's other big success of the 1970s was the Commodores. The six members of this group met as students at Alabama's Tuskegee Institute; in 1971, they signed with Motown. Originally designed in the Motown tradition of the Temptations, Four Tops, and others, the Commodores capitalized on the disco trend and made their impact as one of the more lasting of the disco groups. Their peak years were 1976 to 1981, during which time they enjoyed five Top 10 albums and nine Top 10 singles, including the number 1 hits "Three Times a Lady" (1978) and "Still" (1979). By 1982, lead singer Lionel Richie had departed to pursue his successful solo career. The Commodores eventually regrouped but experienced a significantly lower level of success with *Commodores 13* (number 103, 1983), *Nightshift* (number 12, 1985), and *United* (number 101, 1986).

Dance Choreography in the "Thriller" Video

Take time to watch the extended video of "Thriller" (approximately 14 minutes), which is available on YouTube (identified as the "official video" via VEVO). After watching the complete mini-film carefully, return to the segment beginning 8 minutes and 25 seconds into the film, when the group of ghouls begins to dance. How would you describe this choreography to someone who had never seen the video? What do you think about this style of dancing? Do you like it? Why or why not? What dance moves do you consider most interesting and why? Identify at least one contemporary pop or dance music artist whose stage show reveals influence of Michael Jackson's dance style. Search the Internet for videos of this chosen artist and identify at least three specific examples of this influence in the choreography of the video you locate.

 The response entered here will appear in the performance dashboard and can be viewed by your instructor.

Submit

Watch "Thriller" by Michael Jackson

Click or tap the video title to listen to "Thriller."

https://www.youtube.com/watch?v=sOnqjkJTMaAF4280

15.5: Other Music for Dancing

OBJECTIVE: Describe other successful stars who popularized dance music styles beginning in the 1980s

After reviewing the evolving methods of music distribution during the 80s and 90s, discussing the importance of MTV and similar music video channels, describing the role of motion picture soundtracks in marketing popular music (including the Bee Gee's *Saturday Night Fever*), describing dominate record companies (i.e., the return of Motown and its competition with the Philadelphia Sound), and exploring the careers of two seminal artists (Donna Summer and Michael Jackson), we now turn our attention to other trends that emerged during this period. The following sections will introduce you to other artists recording dance music, including a new and exciting pool of female artists, a number of boy bands and girl groups, rave dance music, and the Latin invasion of the U.S. popular music scene.

New Stars of the 1980s

The following section will provide highlights from the careers of two of the new female stars of the 1980s: Cyndi Lauper and Janet Jackson.

Cyndi Lauper—Among the new stars in the 1980s was a flamboyant new female singer named Cyndi Lauper. Affecting a punk–new wave look, she hit hard with her debut album *She's So Unusual* (number 4, early 1984). In fact, Lauper's first album was the only debut album in history to yield four Top 5 singles. In spite of her punkish image, Lauper's music remained in the gentler side of the rock mainstream. Her voice has an unusually high-pitched (at times almost squeaky) timbre, reminiscent of some earlier female stars (e.g., Teresa Brewer). As mentioned in an earlier section of this course, Lauper has remained active in the new millennium, composing music for the Tony Award-winning Broadway musical *Kinky Boots* (2013) and releasing a series of albums, including *At Last* (number 38, 2003), *Bring Ya to the Brink* (number 41, 2008), and *Memphis Blues* (number 26, 2010), the last a set of classic blues covers. Following up the theme of cover tunes, she released *Detour* (2016), a set of classic country covers. This may seem to be a surprising move, but she did front Blue Angel, a rockabilly-influenced band, prior to her solo career. Unfortunately, *Detour* did not make the Billboard 200 and, so far at least, there have been no Hot 100 hits in the 2000s.

Janet Jackson—Janet Jackson was the youngest of the nine Jackson children and made her singing debut at the age of seven in Las Vegas with her famous brothers. Her first hit single came at the age of 20 ("What Have You Done for Me Lately"). She followed with numerous hit singles, including eight number 1 hits by the beginning of the new millennium. During that same period, Janet recorded five number 1 albums. With the release of *Damita Jo* (number 2, 2004), *20 Y.O.* (number 2, 2006), *Discipline* (number 1, 2008), and her greatest hits compilation *Number Ones* (number 22, 2009), Jackson proved that her career was not yet over. As if to confirm that fact undeniably, in 2015, she released her seventh number 1 album, *Unbreakable*. This accomplishment placed her in an elite group of rock artists (also including Bruce Springsteen and Barbra Streisand) who have released number 1 albums in each decade since the 1980s.

15.5.1: Madonna

The most successful female star of the mid- to late-1980s was Madonna (born Madonna Louise Veronica Ciccone in Detroit in 1958). Having attained a limited reputation as a disco vocalist, she released her first album, *Madonna,* in 1983. The album made the Top 10 and included two Top 10 singles ("Borderline" and "Lucky Star"). These two hits, along with several other Madonna singles ("Everybody" and "Into the Groove"), were style setters for 1980s dance music—a synthesized update of 1970s disco. (Techno, a largely synth-based dance music style, will be discussed later in this chapter.) Madonna's early dance hits have a gentle disco beat provided by a drum machine rhythmic pattern and synth bass lines. Bubbling synthesizers and simulated brass/wind interjections (and sometimes live backup vocals) provide timbral variety.

Madonna

SOURCE: Trinity Mirror/Mirrorpix/Alamy Stock Photo

Without question, Madonna's life as a superstar began in late 1984 with the release of *Like a Virgin* (her first number 1 album and single). "Virgin" is a well-crafted song, sung convincingly. The technodance style is also evident in Madonna's next hit, "Material Girl." It was not until the release of "Crazy for You" that the real vocal potential of Madonna became apparent. Even the song's writers, John Bettis and Jon Lind, admitted they questioned the choice of Madonna for their ballad. Bettis says his response was, "Excuse me? This is for Madonna? Really? Can she sing a song like this?" (Bronson 1988, 606). The song hit number 1 in May 1985.

Once Madonna broke out of the dance music stereotype, her career was off and running. Her broader talents were explored in films such as *Desperately Seeking Susan, Shanghai Surprise, Who's That Girl?, Bloodhounds of Broadway,* and *Dick Tracy.* Her next number 1 song, "Live to Tell," reinforced her newfound reputation as a talented singer outside of the dance music style.

True Blue (1986) was Madonna's second consecutive number 1 album. It yielded three number 1 singles, including "Live to Tell," "Open Your Heart," and the controversial "Papa Don't Preach." "Papa" is an interesting combination of dance music and lyrics about a girl delivering a difficult message about a pregnancy out of wedlock to her father.

Madonna's next musical bombshell was the number 1 album *Like a Prayer* (1989). Again, Madonna incited controversy (more due to the video—which featured Catholic images, including the crucifixion and a gospel choir—than to the song). Although the song, as always, is dance-able, Madonna and her backup singers drive to a relatively soulful climax. That soulful vocal style is also evident in "Express Yourself," another major hit from *Like a Prayer.*

Watch "Like a Virgin" by Madonna

Click or tap the video title to listen to "Like a Virgin."

https://www.youtube.com/watch?v=s__rX_WL100*

MADONNA'S IMAGE   In 1990, Madonna entered the new decade with *I'm Breathless,* an album of songs from, or inspired by, the movie *Dick Tracy.* Hits like "Justify My Love" and "Rescue Me" continue the technodance style under a mostly spoken lyric. Her appeal was primarily with young teen (and preteen) audiences, among whom she spawned many 12- and 13-year-old look-alikes. In the 1990s, she established a reputation as an actress, most notably for her title role in the movie *Evita.* In 1992, Madonna signed a seven-year, $60 million deal with Time Warner guaranteeing release of all albums, films, and books under her own production company. Since the turn of the century, her albums have met with varied success. *Music* (number 1, 2000) sold very well, but *American Life* (2003) was the lowest-selling album of her career. Her next studio album, *Confessions on a Dance Floor* (number 1, 2005), was very successful and led to a tour in 2006 that grossed over $260 million (one of the top grossing tours ever by a female artist). Followed by three more Top 10 albums (*Hard Candy,* 2008; *Celebration,* 2009; and *Sticky and Sweet Tour,* 2010), it was clear that Madonna was still going strong. She capped off this success by hitting

number 1 again both with her album *MDNA* (2012) and an album released by the cast of the TV show *Glee* entitled *Glee: The Music, The Power of Madonna* (2010).

No discussion of Madonna would be complete without a few remarks about her image. Modeling herself rather obviously after Marilyn Monroe, she unabashedly projected the female-as-sex-object stereotype. Her sexuality was tough—she lifted weights and was wiry and muscular, rather than fragile. Sometimes raunchy and brazen, she seemed to relish every minute in the spotlight. Her revealing costumes, sexually suggestive videos, and self-advertised lifestyle left little doubt that she intended to be the female sex icon of the 1980s (and 1990s). Her flamboyant persona was enhanced even more by her brief but eventful marriage to actor Sean Penn (1985–1989).

BUILDING ON MADONNA'S SUCCESS   Several female artists built upon the extraordinary success and entrepreneurship of Madonna in the realm of Top 40 dance music. On the pop end of the dance music spectrum were Christina Aguilera, Jessica Simpson, and Britney Spears. These artists often spoke openly of their Christian faith and espoused the virtue of virginity, a dramatic departure from the Madonna-esque "bad girl" image of the previous decade. Interestingly, as they espoused such values, these same performers often dressed in extremely revealing and sexually explicit clothing, presenting quite a contradiction between the verbal and visual messages communicated to their listening audiences. However contradictory, the combination of "sweet girl" and "sex kitten" proved very effective commercially.

Leading this pack after the first decade of the new millennium were Lady Gaga and Ke$ha. In comparison to Madonna's best work, however, the recordings of these artists fall flat or become excessively repetitive after the first two or three tracks, although their live performances are extravagantly produced and constitute musical events with extremely high entertainment value. For example, Lady Gaga sold an astounding 15.3 million digital tracks in 2009.

Although not fitting into the typical dance music genre, coming from the country-pop side of the spectrum, Taylor Swift was another female artist who achieved major success. Swift's *Fearless* was 2009's best-selling album, and her third album (*Speak Now,* 2010) went platinum during its first week of release, an almost-unheard-of accomplishment in the post-Napster era and the second-best week ever for a female artist (second only to Britney Spears's *Oops … I Did It Again,* 2000). According to an article entitled "Women Rule the Charts in 2010" in *Rolling Stone* magazine (March 4, 2010, p. 15), when Ke$ha hit number 1 in January 2010, only two artists in the Top 10 were male (and one was a Chipmunk!). Women also constituted five of the ten best-selling artists on *Billboard*'s Hot 200 and six of the Top 10 digital singles chart.

*By clicking this link, you will be redirected to a third-party site.

15.5.2: Prince

One of the more enigmatic acts of the 1980s was Prince. Born Prince Rogers Nelson, Prince combined a number of fragments into his persona: shocking lyrics and stage antics, lots of soul-funk, a touch of glitter (Little Richard style), occasional rap, some folk-like socio-political commentary, and even some hints of Michael Jackson. The one overt factor overriding all of these diverse internal elements was sex. Prince sold sex in all of its forms. His album *Dirty Mind* contained songs dealing with incest, oral sex, and group sex. Such subjects were nothing new to Prince, whose earlier albums contained songs like "Soft and Wet" and "I Wanna Be Your Lover."

Controversy (1981) contained a rather surprising rap: the full text of the Lord's Prayer. Other attention-grabbers were "Sexuality" and "Do Me Baby," the title of which speaks for itself—and that was only the first half of the album. The second half offered "Private Joy," "Ronnie, Talk to Russia" (a quick little ditty urging arms control), "Annie Christian," and "Jack U Off" (likewise, no explanation required). *Controversy* (as an album and as a technique) worked. Prince's next album, *Prince **1999*** (1982), reached the Top 10, and the single "Little Red Corvette" broke through all radio markets to reach number 6.

In 1984, Prince sailed to the top of the charts with the movie *Purple Rain*, a combination of fantasy and autobiography; the soundtrack album moved to number 1—selling over 13 million copies in its first year—and yielded four Top 10 songs, including two at number 1 ("When Doves Cry" and "Let's Go Crazy"). With the singles undoubtedly promoting album sales among a wide audience, many first-time Prince fans were probably surprised to hear a song like "Darling Nikki" with its reference to masturbation. Prince accepted the 1984 Oscar for the score to *Purple Rain* and murmured his thanks to God.

Prince's popularity continued throughout the decade with five more albums, including two that reached number 1: *Around the World in a Day* (1985) and *Batman* (1989). He also placed 16 songs in the Top 20, including four number 1 hits (the two from *Purple Rain* mentioned above, plus "Kiss," and "Batdance"). In 1993, Prince announced that, henceforth, he would be known as the Artist Formerly Known as Prince (AFKAP), later shortened to "the Artist." One year later, Warner Brothers dropped its distribution deal with Prince. Self-promotion and online distribution proved less effective and, as a result, singles and album sales for this artist were not impressive during the mid-1990s. However, with the release of *Musicology* (number 3, 2004), Prince became one of the top touring acts of the year, signaling a resurgence of interest in this talented, prolific, yet enigmatic performer, a trend that was successfully continued with the release of *3121* (number 1, 2006) and *LotusFlow3r* (number 2, 2009), a three-disc release, with each disc representing a distinctly different musical style.

Despite Prince's attempts (especially early in his career) to clearly differentiate himself from Michael Jackson, his tragic and untimely death ties him forever to that other seminal artist. In an era when opioid overdoses were having a devastating societal impact in the United States, both of these talented artists succumbed to the temptation of abusing the painkiller fentanyl. On April 21, 2016, at the age of 57, Prince was found unresponsive in the elevator of his Paisley Park Studio property; first responders were unable to revive him, and he died a short time later. Prince left behind an extensive catalog of unreleased recordings that are likely to provide his estate with significant income, and "new" music to delight his fans, for years to come.

Watch "Purple Rain" by Prince.

Click or tap the video title to listen to "Purple Rain."

https://www.youtube.com/watch?v=TvnYmWpD_T8*

Watch "Let's Go Crazy" by Prince.

Click or tap the video title to listen to "Let's Go Crazy."

https://www.youtube.com/watch?v=aXJhDltzYVQ*

JOURNAL

Religious Symbols in Madonna's "Like a Prayer" Video

Madonna's video of "Like a Prayer" provides an interesting commentary, both musically and visually, about the Catholic faith. Throughout the video, numerous religious symbols can be seen, and they take on new meaning in this musical context. Watch the video carefully (preferably three or more times), then record your reaction to these symbols as they appear in the video. How would you characterize the use of these powerful symbols in this video? How do you react to their presence? What is the message you think Madonna (and her collaborators) are attempting to communicate to viewers?

 The response entered here will appear in the performance dashboard and can be viewed by your instructor.

Submit

---

*By clicking this link, you will be redirected to a third-party site.

15.6: Dancing Through the 1990s and Beyond

OBJECTIVE: Explain how dance music has evolved since the 1990s

Many artists who appeared during the 1980s continued their success into the 1990s and beyond, including Madonna, Michael Jackson, Janet Jackson, and Whitney Houston. In addition, the 1990s revealed a number of artists who rivaled, and sometimes surpassed, the potential of these earlier stars. The rubric "dance music" is admittedly quite broad and encompasses a wide array of musical styles, but dancing continues to appeal to youth culture, and it remains an important function of music within contemporary society. In the following sections, our attention will focus on three categories of dance music, each of which contains a number of subcategories: pop dance music, rave, and Latin dance music. Pop dance music was driven by the marketing and promotional machines of the major record companies. The beginnings of rave dance music can be found in techno forms dating back to the work of Kraftwerk during the 1970s. Finally, the Latin invasion included a rising number of Latin American artists who attained remarkable commercial success in the United States for a brief period. No longer part of the world music genre, this style of dance music found its way into the mainstream of American musical culture. (A fourth dance style, rap dance, will be discussed in a later section of this course.)

15.6.1: Pop Dance Music

The pop music machine kept right on rolling into the new millennium, although generally declining record sales indicated that the public was beginning to tire of such packaged acts. The use of the term *pop* may be slightly misleading in this context because dance music of almost every description revealed significant R&B influences. Recall that during the 1940s and 1950s, many white artists and major labels recorded covers of R&B songs by African American artists, which were quite different (toned down and polished up) when compared to the original versions. During the 1990s, however, some white artists were quite accomplished at copying the style and delivery of authentic R&B, including the soulful interpolations, melismatic phrasings, and wide array of timbral variations for expressive purposes that were described in the earlier section of this course exploring soul music performance techniques.

15.6.2: *NSYNC

Following in the footsteps of successful boy bands of the 1980s (New Edition, New Kids on the Block, Menudo, and the Backstreet Boys), *NSYNC became a sensation. The members of *NSYNC—Chris Kirkpatrick, Joey Fatone, Lance Bass, Justin Timberlake, and JC Chavez—all came to the group with previous entertainment experience, varying from touring with a national children's choir to being regulars on the Disney Channel's *The New Mickey Mouse Club*. By 1995, *NSYNC was being handled by the same forces that had propelled the Backstreet Boys to international success: Lou Pearlman and Johnny Wright. The band appeared at the same European concert venues where the Backstreet Boys had recently performed and were signed to RCA. The band's eponymous debut album received little attention until after their taped concert performance was aired on the Disney Channel. Shortly after the show, the album reached number 2 and yielded one Top 20 single, "I Want You Back." Their seasonal album, *Home for Christmas*, reached number 7 and contained the Top 10 single "(God Must Have Spent) A Little More Time on You." A cover version of this same song by the group Alabama (featuring *NSYNC) reached number 29 that same year.

In 1999, the group left RCA for Jive Records, a move about which the rival Backstreet Boys (Jive recording artists themselves) were not at all happy. With *NSYNC's following release, *No Strings Attached* (number 1, 2000), there was no longer any doubt about which boy band reigned supreme. The almost inconceivable sales record set the previous year by the Backstreet Boys' *Millennium*, which sold 1.1 million copies during its first week, was more than doubled by the new *NSYNC recording that sold an astonishing 2.4 million copies in its first week. The album contained three Top 5 singles: "Bye Bye Bye," "This I Promise You," and "It's Gonna Be Me." Even the release of the Backstreet Boys' *Black & Blue* could not put a damper on the commercial success of *NSYNC's release, which sold consistently well into 2001. Although the rival Backstreet Boys' album sold 1.6 million copies during its first week—surpassing the sales of their record-breaking *Millennium*—when compared to *NSYNC, their performance was second best. *NSYNC's success continued unabated with the release of *Celebrity* (number 1, 2001). The success of Justin Timberlake's solo albums, *Justified* (number 2, 2002) and *FutureSex/LoveSounds* (number 1, 2006), tolled the death knell for the rest of *NSYNC's band members. Timberlake and his former Mickey Mouse Club costar Christina Aguilera were among *Billboard*'s Top 5 Artists of 2003, and both artists continued their success with more recent releases.

15.6.3: The Spice Girls

At the same time the boy bands were gaining popularity, a new batch of girl groups was on the horizon. Foremost among them was the Spice Girls, another manufactured group consisting of four female vocalists from Britain. Producers Bob and Chris Hebert ran an ad in *Stage* magazine that read simply, "Wanted: Streetwise, outgoing, ambitious, and dedicated girls to play in a band." Four out of the five members were hired through this ad, although the band soon broke free of their original management. In 1995, they signed with Virgin Records. Each member of the group was given a nickname by the contributors to *Top of the Pops,* a British teen magazine, based on her personality, looks, or interests: Geri Halliwell became "Ginger Spice," Victoria Adams became "Posh Spice," Melanie "Mel B" Brown became "Scary Spice," Melanie "Mel C" Chisholm became "Sporty Spice," and Emma Lee Bunton became "Baby Spice." Their first single, "Wannabe," debuted at number 1 in the U.K., the first debut single by an all-female group to enter at the top of the British chart, and became a number 1 hit in the United States in 1997. *Spice,* the group's debut album, reached number 1 in the U.K. and was the first debut album ever to enter the American album chart at number 1. The album contained three Top 10 hits: "Wannabe" (number 1), "Say You'll Be There" (number 3), and "2 Become 1" (number 4).

The group's second album, *Spiceworld* (1997), was released simultaneously with the opening of their movie of the same name, featuring the single "Spice Up Your Life." Ginger Spice left the band in 1998 to pursue a solo career, although her debut recording, *Schizophonic,* was not as successful as her work with her Spice sisters. The Spice Girls, now a quartet, released *Forever* in 2000. Compared to their previous success, this recording was considered a commercial failure, and the group members disbursed to pursue solo projects. The Spice Girls reunited in 2007 for a successful tour, selling out arena performances in the U.K., Europe, and the United States.

15.6.4: Destiny's Child and Beyoncé

Comparisons between Destiny's Child and the Supremes are inevitable, with lead vocalist Beyoncé Knowles being compared to Diana Ross (and enjoying the same level of individual attention). The four original members of the group were Knowles, Kelly Rowland, LeToya Luckett, and LaTavia Roberson. The original band (named Da Dolls) struggled for success, losing on the TV talent contest *Star Search* and having a recording contract canceled by Elektra after failing to produce an album. After Beyoncé's father took over their management, the group, now known as Destiny's Child, achieved their first success in 1997 with the hit single "No, No, No" (number 3). However, it was not until *The Writing's on the Wall* (number 6, 1999) that they broke through with four Top 40 hits, including two number 1 singles: "Bills, Bills, Bills" and "Say My Name." Unfortunately, this success bred problems within the group. On turning 18 years of age in 1999, Roberson and Luckett informed Knowles's father that they were terminating their contract with him and seeking independent management. By early the next year, the pair was no longer part of Destiny's Child, a fact they claimed to have learned by seeing

the video for "Say My Name," which included their replacements, Tenetria "Michelle" Williams and Farah Franklin. After less than half a year, Franklin was let go for reportedly missing performances. Destiny's Child—now a trio—recorded the song "Independent Women, Part 1" (number 1, 2000), which was included on the soundtrack for *Charlie's Angels.* Nominated for five Grammys, the group won two awards for "Say My Name." In 2001, Destiny's Child continued its winning streak with *Survivor* (number 1), containing two Top 10 singles: "Survivor" and "Bootylicious."

Beyoncé went on to establish a highly successful solo music career, as well as an impressive series of movie roles. After costarring as the romantic lead opposite Mike Myers in *Austin Powers in Goldmember* (2002) and Steve Martin in a remake of *The Pink Panther* (2006), she landed a role in the film adaptation of *Dreamgirls,* for which she earned two Golden Globe awards. In 2003, shortly after completing *Austin Powers,* she released her first album, *Dangerously in Love* (number 1), including guest appearances by Missy Elliott, Sean Paul, and Jay-Z. Her follow-up studio release, *B'Day* (2006), also reached the top of the chart, and her third studio album, *I Am … Sasha Fierce* (2008), debuted at number 1 and contained three Top 5 hits: "If I Were a Boy," "Single Ladies (Put a Ring On It)," and "Halo." The music video for "Single Ladies" won Video of the Year awards at both the BET Awards and the MTV Video Music Awards.

Beyoncé has also pushed the boundaries regarding the traditional method of music distribution. At the end of 2013, without fanfare, she stealthily released a self-titled album which shot to number 1 on the charts. Rather than following the traditional method of gaining record company support and promotion, she relied on the power of social media, simply using Instagram to push a message ("Surprise!") to her eight million-plus followers. For $15.99, consumers received 32 tracks, a total package including both audio recordings and videos. Following the success of this approach, within days after Prince's death, she dropped another surprise album (*Lemonade,* 2016).

15.6.5: A Sales Phenomenon

Beginning in 2009, a popular musical drama television series, *Glee* (briefly mentioned previously in our discussion of Madonna), resulted in a very successful series of soundtrack albums, extended play albums, compilation albums, and digital releases. Although sales have been spectacular (rivaling those of Elvis Presley and the Beatles), the music from *Glee* is limited exclusively to cover versions and is produced not by an artist or group in the historical sense, but by a cast of singers/actors. In that sense, *Glee* releases are not substantively different from soundtrack albums featuring the cast of musicals such as *Oklahoma* or *Hair* (except that those presented entirely new music rather than covers).

15.6.6: Rave Dance Music

During the 1980s and 1990s, dance music was a primary form of entertainment, and artists recording this music constituted many of the most commercially successful performers of the period.

Forms of Rave Dance Music

The following section will provide details about several types of rave dance music that emerged during the 1980s and 1990s: techno, house, and other important subgenres.

Techno—With the emergence of *techno*—dominated by the synthesizer, MIDI sequencers, digital sampling, and **loop-based composition**—technology played an integral role in the creation of the music and its performance. Emerging directly from the disco era, techno blended the incessant beat of disco with the high energy and devil-may-care attitude of punk. Incorporating segments of previously recorded music, drumbeats, television chatter, and other "found sounds," the music was intentionally repetitive and noisy, providing a background for dancing and all-night partying. The style emerged in Detroit, led by DJ Derrick May, and passed to the U.K., where associated underground psychedelic dance parties (raves) were wildly popular during the 1980s.

House—Contemporaneous with the emergence of techno was another genre of dance music known as **house**, reputedly named after the Warehouse Club in Chicago. It is possible to consider house music as the "style out of which most dance music since the mid-1980s has developed" (Fulford-Jones 2000, 758). In contrast to disco, to which it is also connected, house music was not a song-based form. Instead, many early house recordings consisted of a repetitive drum machine rhythm track in quadruple meter, an insistent bass drum pounding on every beat, and hi-hat cymbals emphasizing the offbeats. Bass lines and string parts (reminiscent of those typical of the disco era) were often performed live on synthesizers.

Subgenres—Techno and house music spawned numerous subgenres that were sometimes difficult to distinguish one from another, including **trip hop** (Massive Attack, Tricky, and Portishead), **dub** (Lee "Scratch" Perry), **electronica** (Aphex Twin), and **trance** (Jam & Spoon and Sven Väth). Trance is an extremely repetitive style that suited its utilitarian purpose as music to stimulate movement at rave parties. In 1996, DJ Shadow's trip hop album *Endtroducing* was among the first popular music recordings to be released that was constructed entirely out of **samples** (pre-existing recorded music).

Many rave/trip hop DJs maintained relative anonymity, working in dimly lit locations surrounded by cables interconnecting sound systems, turntables, and, often, a computer. As the rave dance music genre became more popular in the early 1990s, however, major labels began to take an interest in signing these DJs to recording contracts. Included in the first batch of signed DJs were 808 State, the Orb, Messiah, and Moby. Notable among such DJs for shedding his anonymity, Moby began to incorporate a variety of styles into his albums. In addition to the predictable high-speed, repetitive tracks, *Everything Is Wrong* (1995) integrated elements of heavy metal ("All That I Need") and blues-influenced punk ("What Love"). With *Play* (2000), Moby's audience expanded significantly, and two Grammy nominations provided evidence of growing critical acclaim. On this recording, Moby explored older styles of music, including traditional blues and gospel. Moby continued to release a series of recordings, each of which entered the Top 5 on the Top Electronic Albums chart, while performing less well on the general *Billboard 200*: *18* (2002), *Hotel* (2005), and *Go: The Very Best of Moby* (2006). He garnered only a single Top 40 hit: "South Side" (featuring Gwen Stefani of No Doubt), but has continued to release recordings, including *Last Night* (number 27, 2008), *Wait for Me* (Number 22, 2009) and *Destroyed* (number 69, 2011).

With the blinding pace at which computer technology is advancing from year to year, one can expect to see continuing development of these technology-related dance genres. Contemporary DJs continue to synchronize the beats of their dance music but often use laptop computers (or smaller portable devices) instead of turntables. Other electronica groups from the late 1990s and early 2000s include Prodigy, Chemical Brothers, Daft Punk, Chicks on Speed, Basement Jaxx, Stereo MCs, and Deadmau5. With a significant number of record labels devoted to the genre—for example, Tigerbeat6 (Oakland), Schematic (Miami), and Carpark (New York)—America led the way in the production of electronic dance music at the turn of the century (Reynolds 2001).

JOURNAL

A Focused Listening Task: *NSYNC's "Pop"

Listen to "Pop" from *NSYNC's *Celebrity*. Immediately after listening, restart the song, ready to pause the recording when you hear something you find surprising or interesting. On this second pass through the tune, stop the playback when you reach one of those spots of interest and, in your response, describe what is happening musically at that moment and your reaction to it. Proceed this way until you reach the end of the song, providing a running commentary for the entire track.

  The response entered here will appear in the performance dashboard and can be viewed by your instructor.

Submit

15.7: The Latin Invasion

OBJECTIVE: Describe the influence of Latin music on the pop dance music style

The 1990s brought a new round of Latin artists to the popular music scene. The level of success experienced by many of these performers suggested that Latin music no longer deserved to be considered part of that large (and dubiously named) category "world music." Rather, the Latin influence had worked its way, at least temporarily, into the fabric of the American mainstream. Successful Latin artists of the late 1980s and 1990s included Ricky Martin, Selena, Jennifer Lopez, Christina Aguilera, Enrique Iglesias, and Marc Anthony. Their dance-oriented music was often based on Latin rhythms like the cumbia and **salsa**. There was often a focus on sensuality, and this was a music in which the male singers were allowed, if not expected, to be emotionally vulnerable. If there were any doubt about the musical infusion of Latin culture, the success of Carlos Santana's *Supernatural* in 1999 provided final confirmation.

Setting the world stage for this Latin invasion was an accomplishment that required a potent superstar—someone to swarm the beach of the American popular music scene. Previous attempts had proven moderately successful but did not provide a foundation for a stylistic influx. Recall that Richie Valens recorded "La Bamba" (number 22, 1959) as the B-side for his hit single "Donna" (number 2, 1958), and Julio Iglesias experienced a mild degree of success recording duets with well-established American performers: "To All the Girls I've Loved Before" with Willie Nelson (number 5, 1984) and "All of You" with Diana Ross (number 19, 1984). During the 1980s, when it came to Latin performers, the role of superstar was effectively filled by Gloria Estefan and her band, the Miami Sound Machine.

15.7.1: Gloria Estefan

Beginning as lead vocalist for the Miami Sound Machine, a Latin American-flavored popular music group, Gloria Estefan's vocal and songwriting talents were highly marketable. Her father, bodyguard to the Cuban president, fled to Miami with his family in 1959 when Gloria was only two years old. The family left Cuba two years prior to the revolution placing Fidel Castro in the position of prime minister. In 1975, Gloria Fajardo (Estefan's maiden name) and her cousin auditioned for the Miami Latin Boys, a local wedding band led by keyboardist Emilio Estefan, Jr. Renamed the Miami Sound Machine and performing a mixture of dance and salsa music, the group proved to be one of the most popular in Miami. Three years later, Gloria married Emilio, becoming Gloria Estefan.

Gloria Estefan
SOURCE: Pictorial Press Ltd/Alamy Stock Photo

Musical Career of Gloria Estefan

The following section will provide highlights from the career of Gloria Estefan (including her role as lead vocalist for the Miami Sound Machine), one of the most successful artists in the Latin-influenced rock category.

The first recordings of the band were in Spanish, recorded on CBS's Hispanic subsidiary. Initially popular in the Latino market, Miami Sound Machine eventually gained widespread popularity as they began recording songs in English. After scoring a popular dance hit in the European market with "Dr. Beat" in 1984, they released their first English-only album, *Primitive Love*, which included three Top 10 hits: "Conga," "Bad Boy," and the ballad "Words Get in the Way." On their next album, *Let It Loose* (1987), Estefan's principal role in the group was explicitly confirmed, as the album was credited to Gloria Estefan and the Miami Sound Machine. Five Top 40 hits resulted from the release of this album, including her first number 1 single, "Anything for You."

Following the promotional tour for *Let It Loose*, Estefan began her career as a solo artist, releasing *Cuts Both Ways* in 1989. The two Top 10 singles resulting from her solo debut, "Don't Wanna Lose You" and "Here We Are," were both ballads, although the high-energy dance tune "Get on Your Feet" reached number 11. In the spring of 1990, Estefan sustained a serious injury when her tour bus was hit by a truck on an icy stretch of highway in Pennsylvania. Her follow-up album, *Into the Light* (1991), contained a song about the accident entitled "Coming out of the Dark" (number 1). *Hold Me, Thrill Me, Kiss Me* (number 9, 1994) contained the hit singles "Everlasting Love" (number 27) and "Turn the Beat Around" (number 13). The latter song was featured in *The Specialist*, a film starring Sylvester Stallone.

Maintaining a close connection to her cultural heritage, Estefan frequently recorded Spanish-language versions of her songs. *Cuts Both Ways* contains two such examples: "Si Voy a Perderte (Don't Wanna Lose You)" and "Oye Mi Canto (Hear My Voice)."

She also released an all-Spanish solo album titled *Mi Tierra* (1993), featuring performances by an impressive list of Cuban musicians, including Tito Puente, Luis Enrique, and Arturo Sandoval.

Gloria Estefan opened the door for a wide variety of Latin artists, including Mellow Man Ace ("Mentirosa" in 1990), Kid Frost ("La Raza" in 1990), Maná (*Dónde Jugarón los Niños?*), and many others. Confirmation of Latin music's successful invasion of the American Hot 100 came with the Bayside Boys mix of "Macarena" by Los Del Rios, maintaining the number 1 position in 1996 for 14 weeks.

The official year of the Latin invasion can be identified as 1999. Although various forces were building prior to that time, the arrival of commercially successful recordings by Ricky Martin (*Ricky Martin*, number 1), Jennifer Lopez (*On the 6*, number 8), Enrique Iglesias (*Enrique*, number 33), Marc Anthony (*Marc Anthony*, number 8), and Christina Aguilera (*Christina Aguilera*, number 1) confirmed the significance of this new subgenre of dance-oriented rock.

Watch "Conga" by Miami Sound Machine.

Click or tap the video title to listen to "Conga."

https://www.youtube.com/watch?v=54ItEmCnP80*

15.7.2: Selena

In 1989, Selena Quintanilla became the first artist signed to EMI's recently created Latin label, establishing her as an important harbinger of things to come. Selena's early success came as lead singer for her group, Selena y Los Dinos, including her older siblings Abraham (bass) and Suzette (drums). *Ven Conmigo*, the band's first recording, reached number 1 on *Billboard*'s regional Mexican chart in 1991 (Rosen 1996). Selena was not fluent in the Spanish language, but she became a superstar in the genre of **Tejano music**. After transitioning to solo-act status, Selena released *Entre a Mi Mundo* (1992) and *Live*, (1993) which both reached the top of *Billboard*'s Mexican chart. In 1993, her live album earned the singer her first Grammy for Best Latin American Performance. Her next album, *Amor Prohibido* (1994), illustrated a wide variety of musical influences, including Tejano, R&B, and hip-hop. The album went platinum, and the title track won Selena her second Grammy.

Just as crossover success seemed inevitable, tragedy struck. Concurrent with pursuing her musical career, Selena had opened two clothing boutiques. The singer's father had discovered paperwork proving that the manager of her shop in San Antonio, Yolanda Saldivar (founder and former president of Selena's fan club), was embezzling funds from the business. On March 31, 1995, Selena went to a motel in Corpus Christi to discuss these charges with Saldivar. The conversation turned into an argument, and as she turned to depart, the singer was shot in the back. Selena staggered into the lobby and named Saldivar as the shooter. Selena died later that afternoon, just before her 24th birthday. In the singer's honor, then-governor George W. Bush named April 16, the singer's birthday, "Selena Day." *Dreaming of You* (1995) was released posthumously and entered the *Billboard* chart at number 1, the first Tejano record ever to reach the top of the chart.

15.7.3: Ricky Martin

Ricky Martin (born Enrique Martin Morales) began singing and acting at the age of six. In 1984, at the age of 12, Martin joined the Puerto Rican boy band Menudo. Five years later, the singer was forced to leave the group (Menudo members agreed that no one in the band's rotating lineup could be over 16 years of age). Martin's initial major success in America came in 1994, not as a singer, but as an actor in the popular soap opera *General Hospital*, followed by a brief period appearing in the Broadway version of *Les Misérables*. While earning a living primarily as an actor, the singer also released four Spanish-language albums, culminating with *Vuelve* (1998; number 1 on the Latin chart). The single "La Copa de la Vida (The Cup of Life)" was used as the anthem for the 1998 World Cup competition. The song topped the singles chart in over 30 countries (but not in the United States), selling more than 11 million copies worldwide. As a result of this international success, "La Copa" became the biggest-selling single in the history of Columbia Records (George-Warren and Romanowski 2001).

Martin performed at the 1999 Grammy Awards, when he was awarded a Grammy for Best Latin Pop Performance. *Ricky Martin* (number 1, 1999) was the singer's first recording in English and contained the number 1 megahit "Livin' La Vida Loca," which became one of the best-selling singles since the beginning of *Billboard*'s Hot 100. In 2000, Martin released a follow-up album, *Sound Loaded* (number 4), resulting in only one hit single, "She Bangs" (number 12). He continued to release albums that consistently topped the Latin Albums chart but performed less impressively on the *Billboard 200*: *La Historia* (2001), *Almas del Silencio* (2003), *Life* (2005), and *Ricky Martin: MTV Unplugged* (2006). In 2011, Martin released

---

*By clicking this link, you will be redirected to a third-party site.

Musica + Alma + Sexo (number 3), made up mostly of material in Spanish; the album was released shortly after his autobiography in which he confirmed his sexual orientation as gay.

The popularity of Latin-influenced music rose substantially during the 1990s and constituted an "invasion" by 1999. According to the Recording Industry Association of America (RIAA), during a period of slumping shipments within the music industry at large, sales of Latin music CDs rose 9 percent during 2001 (RIAA 2002). In 2002, the RIAA reported a decline of 8 percent in the sales of Latin music, citing the issue of **music piracy** as a primary factor in this slump. Music sales for the genre have varied dramatically during the intervening years: sometimes on the rise, sometimes on the decline.

Watch "Livin' La Vida Loca" by Ricky Martin.

Click or tap the video title to listen to "Livin' La Vida Loca."

https://www.youtube.com/watch?v=p47fEXGabaY*

JOURNAL

Gloria Estefan's Dual Language Recordings

On *Cuts Both Ways* (1989), Gloria Estefan includes a pair of songs that are presented in both English and Spanish: "Don't Wanna Lose You"/"Si Voy a Perderte" and "Hear My Voice"/"Oye Mi Canto." Choose one of these songs and listen carefully to both versions of the song. Do you notice any differences in the performances, either vocally or instrumentally, between the English and Spanish versions of the recordings? First, take a moment to reflect upon and then write your thoughts about these differences and your general reactions to the English and Spanish language performances.

▶ | The response entered here will appear in the performance dashboard and can be viewed by your instructor.

Submit

15.8: Musical Close-Up on The Anatomy of Disco

OBJECTIVE: Analyze the musical elements of disco

It is, indeed, stating the obvious to say that the primary musical element in disco is the rhythm. In fact, the rhythmic element is almost the only common ingredient that ties

together the multitude of disco songs from the 1975 to 1980 period. Tonal elements—-melody and harmony—vary widely. The proof of this is that everything from Beethoven's Fifth Symphony to country songs to jazz tunes was adapted to the disco style simply by setting the respective tunes and harmonies over a disco beat. Texture varied also, from a solo voice to three- and four-voice vocal harmonies. A tour through the work of Donna Summer reveals an interesting variety of textures, even within one song, such as in "No More Tears (Enough Is Enough)." Forms also varied widely, from short, simple songs to longer, more complex forms.

If there is a secondary factor (behind rhythm), it is timbre. Most disco songs involve singer(s), drums, electric bass, rhythm guitar, strings, and sometimes brass. In fact, string lines consistently accompany the vast majority of disco songs, but these are not the lush string harmonies associated with Pop or soft rock. Instead, the disco string line is usually fast moving, providing a busy countermelody behind the vocal melody. Sometimes, strings punctuate the texture in much the way that brass and winds do in some other styles.

The overriding factor in disco, though, is the rhythm. Because of the format of most discotheques, a wide variety of tempos was considered inappropriate. Using two turntables, the disc jockey simply juxtaposed the end of one song with the beginning of the next, providing a continuous flow of dance music. Wide variances in tempo would have destroyed that flow. Therefore, disco songs lie within a relatively narrow range of tempos. In order to maintain the exciting, upbeat ambiance of the clubs, faster tempos were preferred.

15.8.1: The Disco Beat

Dancing is, of course, a physical activity, and disco music seems to connect in some visceral way with our physical systems. It is difficult to listen to disco music and not feel the urge to move with the beat. The typical disco tempo is a multiple (double) of the characteristic human pulse rate (about 60 beats per minute). As a result, some theories suggest that the most appealing disco tunes reinforce our body's "natural rhythm" by conforming to a tempo of about 120 beats per minute. For example, most of Donna Summer's disco songs range from 120 to 130 beats per minute (most often from about 124 to 130). Assuming that the pulse rate is likely to quicken somewhat while dancing, this conforms to the "double pulse rate" theory. However, there are also gentler disco songs. For example, most of the songs from *Saturday Night Fever* range from 108 to 114 beats per minute. In practice, there seem to be two distinct tempo groupings for disco: a quicker tempo in the 120 to 130 range and a more laid-back tempo in the 108 to 114 range.

---

*By clicking this link, you will be redirected to a third-party site.

Rhythmic Patterns of Disco Songs

What of the rhythmic patterns themselves?

There seem to be two basic elements common to most disco songs. First, all four beats are hit equally; in other words, the typical rock backbeat (emphasis on the 2nd and 4th beats of a quadruple meter) is missing in disco. The quadruple meter is set by the dry thud of a bass drum. Second, there is a subdivision of each beat into four parts (quadruple subdivision, notated as 16th notes), so the basic disco rhythm looks and sounds like the one shown in the figure below.

Disco Rhythm

Click or tap the play button in the Revel course to watch a video exemplifying disco rhythm.

The underlying subdivision of the beat is often played on hi-hat cymbals (with hardwood drumsticks) and reinforced by the rhythm guitar (often using a wah-wah pedal). If this were all there were to it, the disco beat would indeed be as simple and boring as its detractors claim. In fact, there is still room for considerable variance. The basic quadruple subdivision is consistently felt, but actual patterns vary. For example, some songs have a pattern that plays the first, third, and fourth subdivisions (skipping number two—although that missing subdivision too is still *felt*) as shown in the figure below. Click or tap the play button in the Revel course to watch this video.

Disco Rhythm #2

In fact, the missing second subdivision may be present in another part of the texture (e.g., in notes played by the rhythm guitar or in the string or brass lines). Syncopated patterns can be devised that accent larger patterns (over two or four beats) but that are still dependent on the quadruple subdivision. For example, "MacArthur Park" (Donna Summer) includes the patterns as shown in the figure below. Notice that, though the rhythm of no single brass, string, or synthesizer part plays on every one of the quadruple subdivisions (represented visually at the very bottom of the chart), the *composite rhythm* (the vertical combination of all of the various parts) results in at least one of those instrumental parts playing on almost every single one of these 16th-note subdivisions.

Of course, all of these patterns do not occur simultaneously. As each one occurs, it reinforces the basic pattern being provided by percussion, bass, and guitar. The bass, in fact, often plays a *duple* subdivision of the beat, providing a level midway between the basic beat and the quadruple subdivision, as shown in the figure below. Click or tap the play button in the Revel course to watch this video.

Composite Rhythm of the Disco Beat in Donna Summer's "MacArthur Park"

None of these patterns is inherently disco. In fact, the brass pattern (brass III, below) is similar to one used by Blood, Sweat & Tears in "Lucretia MacEvil," which is certainly not a disco tune. Taken all together, though, with the right instrumentation (timbres) and tempo, the aggregate sound is disco.

Disco Rhythm (8th Note Bass)

15.8.2: MacArthur Park

Listen to Donna Summer's single version of "MacArthur Park" (see the Listening Guide below). Try to hear the various rhythmic layers. The bass drum is providing the basic four equal beats (with a very slight backbeat on the snare drum). What is the bass player doing? How about the rhythm guitar? Listen to the string and brass lines: Are they punching up the quadruple subdivision? You may begin to hear more than you thought was there!

With the sounds of disco now firmly planted in your ears, it is time to take your newfound knowledge and turn to your personal library of recordings or your preferred online streaming service to locate other music that shares some of the same stylistic characteristics. In the next section, you will have an opportunity to apply these listening and identification skills directly.

BECOME AN ACTIVE LISTENER: ELEMENTS OF DISCO

Now that you have had a chance to study the evolution of disco presented in this chapter, it is time to return to your own collection of recordings, to your streaming service, or to the Internet to identify, independently, some of the differentiating elements in recordings with which you may be more familiar.

Find examples of these disco elements in the music that you enjoy:
1. A tempo that is equal to our body's "natural rhythm" by conforming to a tempo of about 120 beats per minute
2. An equal emphasis on all four beats in the accompaniment
3. A layered approach to rhythm where syncopations and offbeat patterns are juxtaposed against the regular beat

Listening Guide: "MacArthur Park"[1] (Donna Summer)

0:00–0:03	Introduction (2 measures)	Brief introduction played by strings; the meter here is very tricky: a bar of 3/4 followed by a bar of 3/8.
0:04–0:26	Verse 1 (A)	Voice enters maintaining the ballad-like quality of the introduction; the rhythmic pulse is very subdued.
0:27–1:06	Chorus (B)	Chorus continues the style of the verse with very subdued rhythmic component. Lyrics among the most enigmatic in rock history.
1:07–1:13	Instrumental transition (C)	Disco beat enters, accompanied by Summer's "ah-ha" and the keyboard playing the "brass (II)" pattern[2].
1:14–1:42	Verse 2 (AA)	Second verse consists of two repetitions of the A section but lasts only slightly longer than the first verse due to increased tempo. Note the entrance of the "strings (IV)" pattern at the end of each phrase.
1:43–2:23	Chorus (B)	Lyrics are identical and the melody is very similar to the earlier chorus, but disco accompaniment drastically changes the effect. Note that halfway through the chorus "brass (I)" pattern enters and remains until the final word of the chorus.
2:24–2:45	Instrumental break (C)	Combines all of the various rhythmic patterns described, beginning with the "brass (II)" pattern played four times, modulating to different keys, then leading directly to the synthesizer solo, "synthesizer (V)," as the "brass II" pattern continues as accompaniment.
2:46–3:18	Chorus (B)	Similar to the previous chorus with the disco beat, but Summer takes much more liberty with the melodic line.
3:19–3:33	Extension of chorus	The "brass (I)" pattern provides the foundation for this extension of the chorus, with Summer's high voice soaring above.
3:34–3:47	2nd Instrumental break (C)	Consists of alternation between "brass (II)" pattern and "synthesizer (V)" pattern.
3:48–3:55	Coda	Syncopated "brass (III)" pattern provides a rhythmically intense conclusion.

NOTES:

[1]The timings provided in this Listening Guide are based on the single version of the song rather than the album version.

[2]All rhythmic patterns referenced in this Listening Guide will use the same labels as those used in the Musical Close-Up.

Summary: Dance Music

In this chapter, we explored the world of dance music as it evolved from the mid-1970s into the new millennium. You learned about the newest (at the time) means of promoting new music—MTV—and the manner in which technological developments initiated a variety of changes to the media formats in which recordings were released, including LPs, cassettes, CDs, and digital downloads. We also described how movie soundtracks provided a means of mutually beneficial promotion between the film and music industries. One of the primary musical developments of this period, decried by many at the time, was disco, a style of dance music that became dominant in the late 1970s, especially following the release of the film *Saturday Night Fever*. As a result of this resurgence of dance music, a variety of artists built on the audience's rediscovered desire to "Get On [Their] Feet" (to paraphrase Gloria Estefan) and dance to the music of Michael Jackson, Madonna, Prince, *NSYNC, and the Spice Girls (and other boy bands and girl groups), and other dance music artists. Technological developments provided significantly more capability (and flexibility in the use of those capabilities) for DJs in the context of rave, house, and techno dance music. Finally, the impact of artists from Latin American cultures or influenced by Latin American musical styles was felt clearly in the 1990s, resulting in some of the most enjoyable and commercially successful releases of this period. Dance music had once again become a primary force in the evolution of rock and roll. With that powerful dance beat in mind, we will next turn to subgenres of rock that focus even more fully on the rhythmic component of music: rap and hip-hop.

Take Note: Dance Music

- *How did the rock music industry change during the 1980s and 1990s?*—Several developments transformed the music industry in the 1980s and 1990s. The most important of these was the rise of the music video, thanks to the birth of MTV as an all-music network (initially). Now, the image of the rock star was as important—if not more so—than musical talent. The introduction of the compact disc and digital audio revolutionized the way music was bought by the consumer, replacing the older LP and cassette formats. Portable music players—notably Sony's Walkman and Discman, then the iPod and mobile phones—gave listeners access to music anywhere, anytime.

- *How did dance music make a comeback in the 1970s?*—While most of early rock was intended for dancing, much of the jazz rock, fusion, art rock, and progressive rock of the late 1960s and 1970s was not intended for dancing. During the 1970s, dance music made a comeback with the rise of disco, a new generation of Motown artists, and the group of artists produced by Kenny Gamble and Leon Huff known as the "Philadelphia Sound."

- *What is disco, and who were the leading stars in this musical style?* Disco is a shortened form of the word "discotheque," disco celebrated music for dancing with its heavy, regular beat and lyrics highlighting good times. Donna Summer was a leading disco star; "Love to Love You Baby" became one of the first disco songs to be extended from its original 4-minute length to a nearly 17-minute version designed to keep dancers on the floor. The 1977 film *Saturday Night Fever* helped stoke the disco explosion and also reinvigorated the career of the Bee Gees, who provided many of the film's hits.

- *How was Michael Jackson a major influence on dance music in the 1980s and 1990s?*—Michael Jackson was one of the most successful artists in rock history. His 1979 album, *Off the Wall* (his fifth solo album) included several fast, dance-oriented songs. He followed with *Thriller* (1982), which sold more albums than any other record up to that time. Songs like the title track, "Billie Jean," and "Beat It" featured elaborate videos focusing on Jackson's strong dance skills and innovative choreography. The mini-film for "Thriller," directed by John Landis, established higher expectations for video production standards.

- *What other stars popularized dance music styles during this period?*—Other artists took dance music to the top of the charts during this period, most notably Madonna and Prince. Madonna began her career singing at discos, and many of her early hits were designed for dancing with an updated disco-influenced accompaniment. Through her career, she has been a master at changing her image, but her focus on dance as a part of her highly choreographed stage shows has remained central. Prince's funky beats, catchy melodies, and controversial lyrics have been favorites on the dance floor as well. He achieved his greatest success with the film and soundtrack *Purple Rain* (1984).

- *How has dance music continued to be popular in the 1990s and beyond?*—Pop acts continue to focus on dance music as a means of achieving success on the charts. Boy bands like *NSYNC and girl groups like the Spice Girls and Destiny's Child all incorporated dance moves in their videos and stage shows, while recording a number of upbeat hits designed for the dance floor. Another alternative dance movement arose in the late 1980s and 1990s out of house music and electronica. "Raves" were free-form experiences in which DJs would play records for hours so dancers could move and party to the music.

- *What role did Latin music play on the popular music scene during this period?*—The 1990s brought an explosion of Latin acts to the music scene, many with a heavy dance focus. Gloria Estefan and the Miami Sound Machine established themselves with dance hits like "Conga" and "Get On Your Feet." Estefan, however, was also a master ballad singer and found great success as a solo artist with songs like "Coming Out of the Dark" and "Everlasting Love." Coming out of the Tejano music scene, Selena had a tragically short but successful career primarily catering to a Spanish-speaking audience. Ricky Martin came out of the "boy band" world to achieve success in 1999 with his dance-oriented "Livin' La Vida Loca."

SHARED WRITING

The Rumble Scene: Leonard Bernstein and Michael Jackson

Watch the "Rumble" scene between the Sharks and the Jets in the movie version of *West Side Story*, then view the fight scene in Michael Jackson's "Beat It" video. Compare the choreography of the dancers in these two scenes. In each example, how do the directors, choreographers, and costume designers portray elements of toughness and masculinity? After watching both excerpts, what direct influences do you see from *West Side Story* that appear in Michael Jackson's video? Are there some obvious differences as well? After you have composed your independent response, share it with one or two of your peers as you read their responses.

 A minimum number of characters is required to post and earn points. After posting, your response can be viewed by your class and instructor, and you can participate in the class discussion.

Post

0 characters | 140 minimum

Chapter 16
Rap and Hip-Hop

Learning Objectives

16.1 Explain the influence of technology on music development

16.2 Summarize how rap was introduced

16.3 Describe the evolution of rap

16.4 Identify the factors that contributed to the success of rap artists

16.5 Explain how rap crossed over into the mainstream

16.6 Analyze the vocal delivery of lyrics by various rap artists

We have discussed in this course the significant fragmentation that occurred in rock and roll during the 1970s. One branch of that tree of fragmentation led to a style that, to many, seemed quite foreign. Evolving out of hip-hop culture in the South Bronx, rap emerged from public parks where DJs would spin records and create real-time **mash-ups** using existing recordings. Compared to mainstream rock and the various other subgenres of rock, the focus of rap artists on rhythms and beats—to the exclusion of melody and harmony, some might say—proved perplexing to many listeners at the time. However, over the next two decades, rap conquered mainstream radio and MTV. Technology was a driving force of this evolution, so we shall turn to some of those related developments before diving into the artists and musical styles that defined early rap and its evolution into the new millennium.

16.1: Technology, the Internet, and the Music Industry

OBJECTIVE: Explain the influence of technology on music development

In earlier sections of this course, we have seen how the explosion of electronic technology affected groups such as Emerson, Lake & Palmer; Yes; Passport; Kraftwerk; and Triumvirat. This trend continued unabated through the beginning of the twenty-first century. Not only did synthesizers become capable of performing more and more sophisticated operations, but tools such as samplers, sequencers, drum machines, and guitar and wind MIDI controllers made it possible to create complex, multi-layered compositions electronically, without using any traditional, acoustical instruments. Often, one had to listen with a critical ear to discern acoustic performances from those generated electronically with the use of computer technology.

16.1.1: The MIDI Standard

One of the most significant developments of this era was the creation of the **MIDI** standard in 1983, a language that allowed electronic sound sources (synthesizers, for example) to interact with computers and/or other synthesizers. The MIDI revolution, along with more powerful, smaller, and user-friendly personal computers, had a tremendous impact on all styles of music. The biggest problem created by this trend was that no sooner had one invested time and money in one set of tools when newer models that rendered previous hardware and software outdated, if not obsolete, would hit the market.

In the 1980s, terms such as *technodance* and *technorock* (both subsumed by the more general term **techno**) were applied to groups whose musical style was centered on electronically generated sounds. Representative of the technodance groups was New Order, a group from Manchester, England. If you wondered what happened to disco, listen to a track from *Substance* (1987). The infectious disco beat was back but transformed to the timbres of synthesizers and drum machines. The repetitive accompaniment patterns and monotone vocal delivery may remind us of some new wave bands (like Devo) and some of the minimalists (like Brian Eno). The music may have been a bit monotonous, but that steady repetitiveness made it perfect for dancing.

Less dance-oriented but heavily electronic was The Cure, another British group. Their albums from the early 1980s made little impact in this country; however, they began to enjoy greater acceptance in the late 1980s. Their album *Disintegration* (number 2 in 1987) produced a hit single, "Lovesong" (number 2) that was lighter on electronics than the rest of the album. The Cure delivers rich and colorful walls of synthesized sound, reminiscent of the pioneering group Tangerine Dream, but with a stronger and more defined beat. Still, they rarely go all the way to a neo-disco beat and are, therefore, usually described as technorock rather than technodance.

Depeche Mode's style and popularity curve were similar to The Cure's. Again, techno albums from the early 1980s sold rather poorly in the United States. However, beginning with the single "People Are People," this British band began to receive more recognition. *Music for the Masses* (1987) made the Top 40; *Violator* (1990) reached the Top 10 and produced three Top 30 hits: "Personal Jesus" (number 28), "Enjoy the Silence" (number 8), and "Policy of Truth" (number 15). Like The Cure, Depeche Mode relied heavily on electronically generated sounds over a clearly defined beat that usually stopped short of the typical technodance beat. The result was a type of gentle mainstream rock—heavy on electronics.

16.1.2: Digital Sampling

Another great technological leap forward was provided by digital sampling, a process that involves the conversion of sound energy into a series of numbers representing the sound amplitude at discrete intervals of time; the resulting sound files were called **samples**. Transforming sound energy into a series of numbers in this manner allows the sound to be easily manipulated (e.g., played backward, speeded up, slowed down, combined with special effects, etc.) by using the processing capabilities of a computer.

Prior to the arrival of digital sampling, musicians had attempted to recreate sounds of acoustical instruments by synthesizing the timbre on a variety of electronic keyboard instruments with mixed success (i.e., using additive synthesis, subtractive synthesis, FM synthesis, and other methods). Using sampling, however, the sound of acoustic instruments could simply be recorded digitally, mapped to a key on the synthesizer or controller keyboard, and then played back by pressing the assigned key. Many recordings

of the late 1980s and 1990s incorporated sampling to such an extent that a new song may be entirely based on the musical foundation of previous recordings. For example, M.C. Hammer's hit single "U Can't Touch This" (1990) is based on Rick James's "Super Freak" (1981); his song "Pray" (also 1990) incorporates the rhythm track from Prince's "When Doves Cry" (1984); and "Pumps and Bumps" (1994) uses samples from George Clinton's "Atomic Dog" (1983). Other examples of this sampling technique may be heard in "Ice Ice Baby" by Vanilla Ice (bass line sampled from Queen and David Bowie's "Under Pressure"), "That's the Way Love Goes" by Janet Jackson (samples from James Brown's "Papa Don't Take No Mess"), "Slow Motion" by Color Me Badd (samples from "Spinning Wheel" by Blood, Sweat & Tears), and "Wildside" by Marky Mark and the Funky Bunch (samples from Lou Reed's "Walk on the Wild Side"). Some songs incorporate a multitude of samples from a variety of sources. Use of previously recorded music in this way initiated a serious legal debate concerning copyright infringement that will be addressed shortly.

16.1.3: Auto-Tune

During the first decade of the twenty-first century, another technology became a common element—some would say an overused element—in many recordings. *Auto-tune*, a proprietary manipulation of digital audio created by Antares Audio Technology, allowed a sound engineer to take a melodic line and dramatically alter the intonation and/or timing. The expressive characteristics of the performance could be retained, while "fixing" pitch and rhythmic errors. Early uses of a related technology, the vocoder, can be traced back to the 1970s (e.g., listen to the title track of Herbie Hancock's *Sunlight*, 1977). One of the early uses of auto-tune in rock music was Cher's "Believe" (number 1 in 1999), but many other artists have used the technology to correct errors made in the studio and in live performances. In the mid-2000s, the technology was popularized by T-Pain, a rapper-vocalist from Tallahassee, before the signature auto-tune sound became a near-ubiquitous element of rap and hip-hop recordings. The technology was used to great effect by Auto-Tune the News, a project by a group of musicians known as the Gregory Brothers. Using excerpts of speeches, news reports, and interviews as source material, the group processed this input with auto-tune, resulting in a musical setting for this material with some entertaining, if not particularly earth-shattering, musical results.

16.1.4: New Technologies and the Internet

The final years of the twentieth century witnessed the death of the cassette tape as a viable medium for distributing commercial recordings. Dominance of the compact disc format and the arrival and eventual ubiquitous presence of the CD drive sold with most new computer purchases sealed its fate; these drives not only played CDs but could record data onto them. According to the Recording Industry of America's year-end statistics, between the years 1998 and 1999, sales of cassette versions of commercial recordings dropped from 14.8 percent of the market to 8 percent, and then slid to 4.9 percent the following year, initiating a downward trend that continued until, in 2006, cassette sales accounted for less than 1 percent of the market. LPs have accounted for less than 1 percent of the market since the late 1990s; although during the last half of the first decade of the new millennium, an interesting phenomenon occurred: vinyl LP sales began to rise. Perhaps due to nostalgia, but others might argue that it was a desire for the lost "warmth" of the analog recording medium, some artists (e.g., Radiohead and the Foo Fighters) began to release new recordings on vinyl. Interestingly, more LPs were sold in 2010 than in any year since SoundScan began tracking sales in 1991. (It is worth noting, however, that digital CD sales surpassed LP sales in 1988, several years before SoundScan tracking.) Another set of incompatible media formats, the DVD audio disc (DVD-A) and the Super Audio CD (SACD), provided higher-quality digital audio sound with the capability to reproduce music in surround sound, but neither format succeeded in amassing significant market share. It appeared that the typical consumer preferred portability (see below) over the highest quality sound reproduction.

FILE SHARING The most significant technological innovation impacting the commercial music industry during the 1990s was the arrival of file-sharing capabilities via the Internet. Using this technology, brought into the mainstream by Napster and similar websites, users were able to download digitized music (typically in a compressed format called **MP3**) or share their own files with others around the world. In fact, *Spin* magazine declared that the number 1 album of 2001 was "Your Hard Drive." Many idealistic musicians across the globe saw the Internet as a "great equalizer," giving artists direct access to an audience without the need for an intervening record company. With the dramatic drop in the cost of *digital audio workstations* (DAWs; a personal computer with sequencing, hard disc recording, and audio-editing software), artists could produce near-studio-quality recordings at a fraction of the cost. In reality, however, the continuing need for marketing and distribution to succeed in the music business impeded the rise of all but a few of these hopefuls.

The response of the recording industry, similar to the reaction when the phonograph, radio airplay of music, and the CD recorder were introduced, was initially one of protectionism. The impact of free file sharing on the profit margins of major record companies resulted in a major backlash and eventual legal challenges. After a series of contentious confrontations, the record companies decided

to buy their way out of the difficulty. BMG purchased Napster and Universal acquired MP3.com. For a brief period, this move proved fairly successful at limiting the amount of file sharing involving copyrighted commercial recordings, although other peer-to-peer software packages (e.g., Gnutella, Kazaa, and Morpheus) were still popular.

Some artists effectively used the new technology to introduce themselves to the world and enhance sales of their recordings. For example, prior to signing with a major label, Phish marketed their recordings and hawked band merchandise on the Internet. In association with the software company Sonic Foundry (makers of loop-based music creation software *Acid*), several artists offered their fans a chance to remix tracks from their recordings (http://www.acidplanet.com). Participating artists included Madonna ("Ray of Light," "Music," and "Deeper and Deeper"), Boz Scaggs ("Ms. Riddle"), Static-X ("Black and White"), Garbage ("Androgyny"), Debra Soule ("Amen"), and New Order ("Crystal"). Allowing an audience to have access to the sound files that are used as a foundation for such hit singles is certainly an innovative and enlightened approach. In a sense, the listener is given the opportunity to become a creator, using existing, professionally produced musical materials.

Other artists, including Courtney Love and a coalition organized by Don Henley, began to actively address the inequities inherent in the relationship between recording artists and the corporations that market and distribute their work. According to Don Henley, the goal of his coalition was to use legal action to pressure the major labels to "change the fundamental rules that govern most recording contracts, including copyright ownership, long-term control of intellectual property and unfair accounting practices" (Wild 2002, 17).

ONLINE MUSIC SALES During 2004, the success of online music sales brought change to the industry yet again. Apple's iTunes Store, Real Media's Rhapsody, and even Walmart began offering individual songs in copy-protected digital formats online for between $0.49 and $0.99 each. Entire albums could be purchased, downloaded, and instantly played, most for under $10. This sales model offered the consumer incomparable convenience and immediate gratification since one could purchase, download, and play back the recording in a matter of seconds ... without leaving the house! Around this same time, portable MP3 players (like the iPod) began to overtake a market previously dominated by the Sony Walkman (cassette tapes) and Discman (CDs). As the technology developed and became more affordable, portable units selling for between $150 and $250 could hold a person's entire recording collection (up to 40,000 songs could be stored on a 160-GB model). Later models even allowed the user to access photos and play back video, all capabilities that eventually became common for a typical mobile phone, which ultimately replaced the need for a dedicated iPod or other MP3 playback device.

Because of a significant decline in recording sales, availability of digitized sound files on the Internet (both legal and illegal), and major artists threatening to organize a union and take legal action, the recording industry was in a state of crisis. Following the lead of Apple's iTunes Store and representing the wave of the future, other venders (amazon.com, rhapsody.com, and even Walmart) began to make deals with record companies to allow legal digital downloads of music. While the CD format continued to be the primary means of disseminating full albums, the number of downloaded singles surpassed its nearest competitor (vinyl singles)—by almost 4,000 percent!—immediately upon availability. The sense of immediate gratification and portability had readily trumped higher-fidelity alternatives.

ARTISTS DROPPING RECORDINGS—THE ELEMENT OF SURPRISE   In the new millennium, artists themselves became quite creative about the manner in which recordings were promoted (or not) and released. This partially evolved as a response to recordings that were leaked to the public prior to the intended release date, an unfortunate event that occurred for U2's *How to Dismantle an Atomic Bomb* (2004), Björk's *Vulnicura* (2014), six tracks from Madonna's *Rebel Heart* (2014), and Fall Out Boy's *American Beauty/American Psycho* (2014). Following these events, some artists began to release albums with no advance warning: Drake's *If You're Reading This It's Too Late* (2015). Some artists took an even more drastic approach, simply making the music available online for free, as was the case with Talib Kweli's aptly titled *Fuck the Money* (2015).

In special arrangements with record companies and distributors, "album exclusives" became a popular option during this same period, pitting the numerous music streaming/download sites against one another, since this limited the availability of some recordings to only a single outlet. Examples of such releases, all number 1 albums in 2016, include Beyoncé's *Lemonade*, Drake's *Views*, Frank Ocean's *Blonde*, and Kanye West's *The Life of Pablo*. In exchange for exclusive rights, the distributor (Apple's iTunes Store is a primary participant) funds songs and videos for the artists, showcasing them on TV commercials and online radio stations as a means of promotion. A tipping point arrived in 2016 when Frank Ocean fulfilled the terms of his contract with Def Jam/Universal by delivering *Endless* shortly before he provided *Blonde* (which many considered a superior recording) to Apple as an exclusive. The arrangement regarding exclusive releases troubled some artists. Lady Gaga, for example, informed her label that, if any such exclusive agreement was made on her behalf, she would personally leak her new material.

Going one step further regarding the "surprise" factor, technological advances in the field of holography have provided the means of seeing "performances" by artists who are no longer with us. Among the first to be seen were Tupac (holographic performance at Coachella in 2012), Michael Jackson (at the 2014 Billboard Music Awards), and Ronnie James Dio (at Germany's Wacken festival in 2016). While significant hurdles remain, both technological and legal (performance rights), this development does open the door to some very intriguing possibilities as the rock and roll "live" performance experience continues to evolve.

16.2: Rap's Beginnings

OBJECTIVE: Summarize how rap was introduced

One musical style that continued to flourish despite the overall decline in CD sales was rap. Although many Americans became aware of rap music in the mid-1980s, the style actually dates back to the late 1970s, when it developed in the neighborhoods and boroughs of New York City (especially Harlem, the Bronx, and Brooklyn). A graphic description of a typical "block party" of 1977 is provided by Havelock Nelson and Michael Gonzales in their book *Bring the Noise* (Nelson and Gonzales 1991, xvi):

> A crew of soul brothers (Mod Squad afros, bell bottom jeans) troop down the hill with cartons of records, speakers, two turntables, and a mixer. These are the new gangsters in town, aural outlaws controlling the public airwaves. Slammin' their equipment in front of an old street lamp, their hands move slow, hooking wire and mics and testing a Gil Scott-Heron drumbeat on a Technics turntable. BOOM/BLAST—"Yo, this be DJ Hollywood rockin' da turntables in da hood." Needles bounce, explode with the sound of the new urban blues. BOOM/BLAST—heavy bass riffs lifted from an ancient Stanley Clarke disc.
>
> While Hollywood bellows into the mic', turntable assassin Lovebug Starski plays the role of Doc Magic Hands—spinnin' discs, scratchin' records, borrowing this drumbeat, that keyboard riff. All da ladies in da hood say, "Yeah!" Fem voices roar and the block party erupts.

In the late 1970s, such block parties were part of a collection of urban art forms, labeled **hip-hop**, emerging in the South Bronx. The term, reputedly first coined by Starski himself, was used to describe the lifestyle, fashions, fast-talking comedy, and cultural expressions of this region of New York City (Toop 2007). The "cultural expressions" included **break dancing**, graffiti art, poetry, double-Dutch jump-roping, and music. During the 1980s, as the significance of break dancing and graffiti receded, the term hip-hop became associated primarily with a specific urban musical style. Hip-hop tracks incorporated extant musical sounds, combining these previously recorded segments into new arrangements, if not compositions. It is interesting to note that, at the same time that bands in the punk movement like the Police and the Clash were being influenced by reggae, hip-hop was inspired by Jamaican DJs U-Roy and Lee Perry.

16.2.1: Hip-Hop Emerges from the South Bronx

Setting up their sound systems in parks, school yards, and abandoned buildings, early hip-hop pioneers (known as *"spinners"*) included Kool Herc (often identified as the "founder of hip-hop"), the Fatback Band ("King Tim III [Personality Jock]," 1979), the Sugarhill Gang ("Rapper's Delight," 1980, Kurtis Blow ("The Breaks," 1980), Grandmaster Flash ("The Adventures of Grandmaster Flash on the Wheels of Steel," 1981), and Afrika Bambaataa ("Planet Rock," 1982). Kool Herc began to add masters of ceremony (**MCs**) to speak over the foundation of these rhythmic grooves, sometimes covering up the silence with hand claps or providing improvised prosodic displays as the DJ changed records on one or both of the turntables.

The addition of an MC evolved into the musical form commonly referred to as *rap*. The identity of the MC was an important aspect of the performance, often beginning a rap with a pronouncement (or verbal *"tagging"*): For example, N.W.A.'s "Something Like That" on *Straight Outta Compton* begins with him proclaiming that homeboy Eazy-E was in the house. Spoken rhymes often included references to other rap artists, events, and/or songs, sometimes initiating a back-and-forth, and often confrontational, dialogue from the recordings of one artist to another.

Hip-hop was created primarily by DJs using turntables, rather than by musicians performing on traditional acoustic and/or electronic instruments. A patchwork of musical sounds was woven together to create dance music, often in a manner similar to the technique used by a jazz musician to spontaneously improvise a solo. As in the 1950s, DJs ascended again to a position of prominence in the world of music, this time using a library of pre-existing recordings to create "new" songs to accompany dancing and partying. Some of the favorite musical resources used by early hip-hop DJs, as well as later rappers, included percussion and rhythm tracks from recordings by James Brown, Rufus Thomas, and other soul and funk artists. For example, in 1989, Public Enemy used the rhythmic motif from James Brown's "Funky Drummer" as a basis for "Fight the Power," the theme song for Spike Lee's *Do the Right Thing* (1989). Using two turntables and a mixer, a skilled DJ could create a "seamless blend of beats, riffs and hooks" (Peel 2000, 406) that eventually came to be used as a foundation for early rap music. In addition to excerpts from funk recordings, break sections from 1950s and 1960s rock songs and instrumental compositions were frequently used.

Techniques and Styles of Early Rap Music

The following section will provide an overview of some of the styles and techniques used by early rap artists.

DJs developed techniques for adding their own sounds to the accompaniment. In the late 1970s, hip-hop DJs effectively transformed the turntable, a device used primarily to play back recordings, into a musical instrument. *Scratching*, as the technique came to be known, was accomplished by quickly pushing and pulling records on the turntable, resulting in a variety of effects: loops (short, repeated sections), musical bursts, and backward playback. Some DJs used more than two turntables and developed a technique called *beat mixing*: playing back multiple records simultaneously, while adjusting the speed of each recording to synchronize the resulting complex rhythmic pattern.

There are many examples of dance music recordings that incorporated existing materials into a new context; for exam-

ple, the use of sections from "Good Times" by Chic (1979) for the Sugarhill Gang's "Rappers Delight" (1980), Afrika Bambaataa's use of melodies by Kraftwerk and Ennio Morricone for his own "Planet Rock" (1982) or the use of the Rolling Stones' "The Last Time" (1965) for the Verve's "Bitter Sweet Symphony" (1997).

Soon the personal computer (PC) became the primary workstation for creating the musical accompaniment for rap. The technique of borrowing excerpts from previously recorded material was surrounded by controversy. Many believed that taking brief sections of a composition was well within the poetic license exercised by an artist, while others felt that it was a direct violation of U.S. copyright law. In just one of the many cases that found its way into the legal system, the hip-hop group De La Soul settled out of court for failing to credit the Turtles after sampling a portion of their recording "You Showed Me" (1969). The band had used the excerpt superimposed over a sample from a recording of a French lesson in "Transmitting Live from Mars" from their debut album, *3 Feet High and Rising* (1989).

In its rawest form, rap disposes of melody completely, using instead the rhythmic declamation of a spoken voice (or voices) over a foundation of percussion. Precursors of this declamatory style can be found in the recordings of many soul artists, including Barry White, Isaac Hayes, and Millie Jackson. The lyrical content of rap recordings is often dramatically different from other songs within the rock and roll mainstream. Some subgenres of rap incorporate graphic depictions of violence, objectification of women, and sexually explicit lyrics. Initially, rap audiences consisted primarily of young African American listeners, although during the 1990s, teenagers of all ethnic backgrounds accepted the musical style as their own.

Watch "Rappers Delight" by the Sugarhill Gang

https://www.youtube.com/watch?v=mcCK99wHrk0*

Run D.M.C. in 1986; (L to R) Run, Jam Master Jay, and D.M.C.

SOURCE: Trinity Mirror/Mirrorpix/Alamy Stock Photo

16.2.2: The Commercialization of Rap

One of the first commercially released rap records was "Rapper's Delight" by a Harlem group known as the Sugarhill Gang. Released in 1979, it peaked at number 36 in the early 1980s. By the mid-1980s most people had heard some rap music, but it was still considered a black, underground style, not commercially viable for major recording companies or MTV. Granted, there were a few "cute" raps that did reach the mass audience (e.g., video raps by professional sports teams), but the hardcore style did not gain real national exposure until the mid-1980s. A few rap albums in this period sold sufficiently well to enter the charts: *Run-D.M.C.* (1984) and *King of Rock* (1985) by Run-D.M.C., *Escape* (1984) by Whodini, and *Licensed to Ill* (1986) by the Beastie Boys.

Pioneers of Rap with Commercial Success

The following section will provide highlights from the careers of several of the rap pioneers that emerged during this period: Run-D.M.C., the Beastie Boys, and L.L. Cool J.

Run-D.M.C.—The breakthrough year for rap was 1986. *Raising Hell* by Run-D.M.C. reached the number 3 position and yielded two Top 40 singles: "Walk This Way" (number 4) and "You Be Illin'" (number 29). "Walk This Way" was an update of a 1977 hit by Aerosmith and features the voice and guitar sounds of Aerosmith members Steven Tyler and Joe Perry, respectively (see the Listening Guide below). The rock flavor of Run-D.M.C.'s rap version may account for its national chart success. However, some rap purists resented the intrusion of rock into their style. Because of its commercial success, *Raising Hell* introduced the rap style to a much broader national audience. The Run-D.M.C. trio featured Daryl McDaniels as the MC, Jason Mizell as the DJ (master of turntable manipulations), and Joseph Simmons as second

MC and drummer/keyboardist (also brother of Russell Simmons, cofounder of Def Jam Records). The group took its name from the street names of two of its members: McDaniels was "D.M.C.," Mizell was "Jam Master Jay," and Simmons was "Run." Listen to "You Be Illin'" to get an idea of what DJ Jam Master Jay adds with his turntables; this song also contains a piano bass line and a "live" sax part.

The Beastie Boys—Later in 1986, a white rap trio, the Beastie Boys, broke into the virtually all-black performance style with a number 1 album, *Licensed to Ill*. Adam Yauch ("MCA") and Michael Diamond ("Mike D") began as Young and Useless, a punk-oriented group. After adding Adam Horovitz ("King Ad-Rock") in 1981, they moved to rap and became the Beastie Boys. Their raps cover a range of topics, from sexual promiscuity to drugs and alcohol to political commentary. As with Run-D.M.C., the most commercially successful cut from *Licensed to Ill* was the most rock-oriented single, "(You Gotta) Fight for Your Right (to Party)," which peaked at number 7 in early 1987. In fact, apart from the spoken lyrics, this song is more hard rock than rap. *Licensed to Ill* was the first rap album to hit number 1.

The Beastie Boys' next album, *Paul's Boutique* (1989), was three years in coming as the result of a legal dispute with their record company, Def Jam. The sound of the album was significantly different from their debut, selling far fewer copies and resulting in only one minor hit, "Hey Ladies." Another three years passed before their third album, *Check Your Head* (1992), was released. With the

---

*By clicking this link, you will be redirected to a third-party site.

release of *Ill Communication* (1994) and *Hello Nasty* (1998), the Beasties returned to the top of the album chart where both albums debuted. In 2004, after another long pause, the Beastie Boys released *To the 5 Boroughs*, which, although debuting at number 1 on the album chart, contained no Top 40 singles. Although not prolific in their output, the Beasties continued to release recordings, but the sales figures dropped significantly after the 1990s. In 2011, as if to signal they weren't done yet, the Beastie Boys reached the number 2 spot with *Hot Sauce Committee Part 2*, before losing Adam Yauch to cancer in 2012.

L.L. Cool J—The next rapper to achieve a mass audience was L. L. Cool J. Like Run-D.M.C., James Todd Smith was from Queens. The sales of his first album, *Radio* (1985), were not as impressive as later releases, but *Bigger and Deffer* (1987) rose to number 3 and yielded a hit single, "I Need Love." As with Run-D.M.C.'s "Walk This Way" and the Beasties' "Fight for Your Right," Cool J.'s hit single was not a typical rap song. Instead of being hard-rock oriented, "I Need Love" was a rap ballad, a rap song with a slow tempo, soft beat, gentle accompaniment, and love-oriented lyrics. Although hardcore rappers may have disliked the success of such "impure" rap hits, these songs did bring the general concept of the rap style (rhythmically delivered spoken lyrics) to a wide audience and paved the way to success for more "authentic" rap songs. To gain a sense of the variety of styles by now inherent in rap recordings, listen to "The Do Wop" from *Bigger and Deffer* for an entertaining combination of rap and doo-wop.

Cool J. enjoyed fairly consistent success after 1987, beginning with his album *Walking with a Panther* (1989). By that time, rap had been accepted as a commercially viable style. L. L. Cool J. is cited as an influence by many rappers who came after and was the first rap artist to perform on MTV's *Unplugged* in 1991. His success continued with Top 40 Hits well into the 2000s, as evidenced by his run of releases beginning in the late 1990s: *Phenomenon* (number 7 in 1997), *G.O.A.T. (Greatest of All Time*; identified as "featuring James T. Smith) (number 1 in 2000), *10* (number 2 in 2002), *DEFinition* (number 4 in 2004), *Todd Smith* (number 6 in 2006), and *Exit 13* (number 9 in 2008). One of the most interesting, and perhaps most impactful, recordings with which L.L. Cool J has been involved is a track on Brad Paisley's *Wheelhouse* (2013) entitled "Accidental Racist." Though creating quite a furor on its release, this track appears to be a genuine attempt to address racism, with the lyrics representing a fictional, but highly poignant, conversation between a white southern man and a black man from the northeast, directly communicating their perspectives in a respectful exchange.

Watch "I Need Love" by L.L. Cool J
https://www.youtube.com/ watch?v=NEUX-HYRtUA*

---

*By clicking this link, you will be redirected to a third-party site.

Listening Guide: "Walk This Way" (Run-D.M.C. with Aerosmith)

0:00–0:17	Introduction (8 measures)	Drumbeat and turntable scratching clearly establish the duple meter and duple subdivision and clear hip-hop influence.
0:18–0:26	(4 measures)	Add signature guitar riff to the musical texture.
0:27–0:44	Verse 1 (8 measures)	Rap vocals enter ("now, there's a backseat lover") over an accompanimental guitar riff and solid drumbeat; the rapping technique of alternating between the two MCs is clearly in evidence; notice also the periodic appearance of a third voice: Steven Tyler's recognizable vocal timbre.
0:45–0:54	Interlude (4 measures)	Signature guitar riff returns.
0:55–1:12	Verse 2 (8 measures)	"See-saw swinging"; as before.
1:13–1:30	Chorus (8 measures)	During the chorus, Steven Tyler's shouting vocal dominates, sounding less like a rap single and more like mainstream rock.
1:31–1:39	Guitar solo 1 (4 measures)	Very brief guitar solo over the verse guitar riff.
1:40–1:48	Interlude (4 measures)	Signature guitar riff returns.
1:49–2:06	Verse 3 (8 measures)	"School girl sleazy"; this time the accompanimental guitar riff drops out at the beginning; Tyler is now totally integrated as one of the MCs; listen to the abrupt switching back and forth between rappers.
2:07–2:15	Interlude (4 measures)	Signature guitar riff returns.
2:16–2:33	Verse 4 (8 measures)	Tyler's voice takes the lead role in this verse, **double-tracked** to give it additional prominence.
2:34–2:52	Chorus (8 measures)	As before.
2:53–3:01	Guitar solo 2 (4 measures)	Another very brief guitar solo over a repetitive, monophonic, quadruple subdivision accompaniment. The guitar solo continues from here to the end of the song.
3:02–3:55	(24 measures)	Rhythm guitar accompaniment changes to the signature guitar riff.

3:56–4:13	(8 measures)	Here the second rhythm guitar part continues under the guitar solo, although the signature riff has dropped out temporarily.
4:14–4:36	Interlude (10 measures)	Signature guitar riff returns without guitar solo.
4:37–4:41	Guitar solo returns (2 measures)	Lead guitar solo returns over signature riff.
4:42–4:50	(4 measures)	Returns to second rhythm guitar part without signature riff.
4:51–4:59	(4 measures)	Lead guitar continues without any rhythm guitar accompaniment.
5:00–5:11	Coda (4 measures)	Lead guitar solo ends and drumbeat continues; the song ends as it began, with drums only, creating a kind of musical "arch form."

Watch "Walk This Way by Run D.M.C. with Aerosmith

https://www.youtube.com/watch?v=4B_UYYPb-Gk*

16.2.3: The Rap Explosion

In the transition from the late 1980s to the 1990s, an explosion of rap artists hit the airwaves and the charts, including D. J. Jazzy Jeff and the Fresh Prince (actor Will Smith), the Fat Boys, Public Enemy, Niggaz With Attitude (N.W.A.), M.C. Hammer, Ice Cube, and Vanilla Ice. Although we cannot discuss each of these artists in detail, we will survey some of the changes represented by a few.

New York City may have been the birthplace of rap, but other cities contributed to the growth of the style. D. J. Jazzy Jeff and the Fresh Prince were from Philadelphia; Los Angeles produced Eazy-E, Ice Cube, and N.W.A.; and Eminem emerged from Detroit.

Important Rap Artists Who Appeared During the Transition from the Late 1980s to the 1990s

N.W.A. (Niggaz With Attitude)—N.W.A.'s *Straight Outta Compton* (1989) introduced a large segment of the public to the deepest, most hardcore style of rap, untouched by hard rock, ballads, doo-wop, or any other softening or blending intended to achieve greater commercial success. This album only reached number 37, but it went multi-platinum with over three million copies sold. With *Compton*, many Americans were confronted with a style they had not heard before. One of the original members of N.W.A., Ice Cube, produced an album (*AmeriKKKa's Most Wanted*, 1990) that followed the trend set by N.W.A. (with some interesting samples of pre-existing material). Nelson and Gonzales describe the album as follows (1991, 107):

> From dealers chillin' in front of the projects to rival gangs spraying them with bullets, from the din of children

roaming through the streets of shattered glass to a group of pregnant girlies gulping cheap, sweet wine in front of the local 7-Eleven. With an eye that magnifies brutal characters and violent situations, Ice Cube exposes a world that seems on the brink of exploding in the ear of the listener. This is Black Cali, 1990: Welcome to the nightmare.

N.W.A. and Ice Cube established a sub-style of rap that has become known as **gangsta rap** (discussed later in this chapter).

While some rap groups moved further into the angry, defiant style of gangsta rap (Ice Cube, Snoop Dogg, Ice-T, and Dr. Dre), there were others who played more to the mainstream, two of whom are discussed below. Often defiled by purists (and gangsta rappers) as being fraudulent, they nonetheless achieved great commercial success.

M.C. Hammer—The most successful of the black rappers at the end of the 1980s was M.C. Hammer (Stanley Kirk Burrell), a product of Oakland, California. His first album, *Let's Get It Started,* was reasonably successful, but his second album, *Please Hammer, Don't Hurt 'Em* (1990), was a monster hit, peaking at number 1 and remaining on the Hot 200 for over two years. The antithesis of gangsta rap, Hammer's raps are antidrugs and antiviolence, and speak positively to a young black generation. He even included several rap ballads on *Please Hammer.* Some of the digital samples incorporated into the music were from prior hits by Rick James, Marvin Gaye, the Jackson Five, Prince, and the Chi-Lites. Several singles from the album moved into the Top 20: "U Can't Touch This" (number 8), "Have You Seen Her?" (number 4, a ballad), and "Pray" (number 2). Much of Hammer's popularity certainly stemmed from his dancing, prominently featured in his music videos.

Vanilla Ice—Following close behind Hammer's popularity was a white rapper, Vanilla Ice (Robert Van Winkle). His album *To The Extreme* (1990) sold more than seven million copies. The hit single "Ice Ice Baby" peaked at number 1—the first rap single to do so. As a result of his success, he negotiated endorsement deals with Nike and Coca-Cola, landed a part in *Teenage Ninja Turtles 2: The Secret of the Ooze,* and spent eight months dating Madonna. In an attempt to capitalize on his newfound stardom, Ice starred in the ill-fated *Cool as Ice* (1991), a film that was a spectacular flop. Some black rappers

---

*By clicking this link, you will be redirected to a third-party site.

have accused Vanilla Ice of parodying black music; at the very least, he seems to be a rather pale imitation of "the real thing," and his status as a superstar proved fleeting.

Watch "U Can't Touch This" by MC Hammer

https://www.youtube.com/watch?v=otCpCn0l4Wo*

By the end of the 1980s, rap was firmly entrenched as a new subgenre of rock. Its musical derivation was primarily from James Brown. From earlier in this course, you will recall his steady, unchanging vamps; half-sung, half-spoken "hip" lyrics; and syncopated accompaniments. However, other than the selection of rather clever samples, the musical accompaniment for most rap tends toward simplicity and repetition. In its purest form, there is no melody—only a bass line, a funky beat (often on a drum machine), and rhymes—but the rhymes are the key element. The lyrics of the rhymes range from common love topics to intense social commentary (sometimes positive; sometimes graphically negative).

JOURNAL

Walk This Way – A Comparison

Listen to Aerosmith's original recording of "Walk This Way" (1977), and then listen to Run-D.M.C.'s cover of the song (1986), featuring Aerosmith members Steven Tyler (vocals) and Joe Perry (guitar). Identify at least five differences between the two recordings. What is it that establishes the later recording as rap/hip-hop rather than mainstream rock, which is how most would categorize the original recording? In your opinion, do you identify Run-D.M.C.'s cover version as a rap recording or mainstream rock? Why? Be very specific in your response regarding the musical characteristics that informed your decision.

 The response entered here will appear in the performance dashboard and can be viewed by your instructor.

Submit

16.3: Rap Comes of Age

OBJECTIVE: Describe the evolution of rap

Early in this course, black R&B of the late 1940s and early 1950s was described as the most important musical style leading to the emergence of rock and roll. At that time, it was relatively easy to determine specific musical attributes that distinguished R&B from other contemporaneous musical styles such as Pop or C&W: its typical instrumentation, the hard-driving prominence of its rhythmic component, the simple three-chord harmonies common to the 12-bar blues form, and the shouting vocal style. By the 1990s, such a wide variety of music was being labeled "R&B" that this stylistic descriptor had been rendered practically meaningless. Soulful, but relatively mellow, performers such as Anita Baker, Luther Vandross, D'Angelo, and white vocalist Michael Bolton—followed by Usher and Chris Brown in the following decade—were all identified as R&B artists. At the same time, rappers often lay claim to being R&B artists. Rap music evolved into more than just one of many sub-styles of black music; it became one of the primary directions of popular music for young audiences, regardless of their race.

Rap music also proved to be a potent tool for protest and political activism. Inspired by militant black poets during the late 1960s and early 1970s—for example, the Last Poets in Harlem (New York) and the Watts Prophets (Los Angeles)—musician-poet Gil Scott-Heron released "The Revolution Will Not Be Televised" (1973), popularized by a cover version contained on Labelle's *Pressure Cookin'* released the same year. Early rap recordings initiating this trend include Brother D's "How We Gonna Make the Black Nation Rise?" (1985; featuring Collective Effort) and Grandmaster Flash and the Furious Five's "The Message" (number 4 R&B in 1982), a poignant portrayal of life in the ghetto.

16.3.1: Gangsta Rap

By the mid-1990s, *gangsta rap* became a dominant subgenre of rap. Best-selling rap artists Ice Cube, Snoop Doggy Dogg, Ice-T, Dr. Dre, Cypress Hill, Scarface, and many others incorporated themes of gang-related violence and explicit pornographic depictions into their recordings, often using extramusical sounds such as gunshots and sirens to heighten the effect of the message portrayed in the rhymes. Warner Music Division at Time Warner experienced a tremendous backlash as political and social groups like the National Political Congress of Black Women and various police associations forced them to defend, sometimes at great expense, the distribution of this music, with references to busting off shots and dusting off cops.

Public Enemy

The following section will provide highlights from the career of Public Enemy, a highly influential rap group that was not afraid to make overt socio-political statements through their music.

One of the most influential, politically-oriented hip-hop acts of the time was Public Enemy, boasting a dual MC format, with Chuck D (Carlton Ridenhour) as the authoritative political activist and his sidekick Flavor Flav (William Drayton). The group also included Terminator X and Professor Griff. Public Enemy's backup dancers, known as the Security of the First World (S1W), carried fake Uzis and, in a parody of Motown choreography, performed stiff, martial arts-like movements. In 1987, these self-proclaimed "prophets of rage" released their debut album, *Yo! Bum Rush the Show*, critically acclaimed but not a commercial success.

The band's second album, however, *It Takes a Nation of Millions to Hold Us Back* (1988), sold over a million copies and contained the single "Don't Believe the Hype" (number 18, R&B chart). Chuck D labeled rap music as "CNN for black culture." After recording "Fight the Power" for Spike Lee's film *Do the Right Thing*, Public Enemy released *Fear of a Black Planet* (1990), initiating a series of four consecutive Top 20 albums. This album addressed controversial topics, including white racism ("Burn Hollywood Burn" and "911 is a Joke"), and encouraged African Americans to unite ("Brothers Gonna Work It Out" and "War at 33 1/3").

The powerful messages communicated in many of these songs provided unity and a clear sense of justice as well as inspiration for future artists. Although the lyrics conveyed strong feelings and a passionate belief in correcting the social and economic inequity evident in the treatment of minorities across the United States, the message was not a violent one. Violence, it seems, was left to rappers flooding the airwaves with the new subgenre known as gangsta rap.

Public Enemy's *Muse Sick-N-Hour Mess Age* (number 14 in 1994) criticized this new style of rap, with its extreme portrayal of violence, encouragement of drug use, misogynistic vignettes, and materialism. Although this album entered high on the charts, it quickly faded, suggesting that the young generation may have found a new set of messengers to admire, perhaps precisely those to whom Chuck D was referring pejoratively. In the new millennium, Public Enemy continued to release strong albums, but without the level of commercial success experienced in the early 1990s. Chuck D continued to be politically active, as he delivered impassioned speeches on college campuses and hosted a radio talk show.

Gangsta rap generally had a driving beat, heavy metal guitar style, angry attitude, and violent lyrics. It was viewed by many as a catalyst to the anger of a generation of underprivileged black youth and spawned a fierce debate about the social responsibilities of the recording artists. Rappers who "throw down"—to use their own terminology—such gang-related lyrics often claimed to be merely reporting incidents witnessed in their experience of inner-city, urban life, not giving their stamp of approval to such actions. However, lyrics detailing graphic violence certainly serve to fan the fire of hatred far too common in these troubled urban areas, rather than offering solutions to social and economic problems that certainly exist.

With the rise of successful gangsta rappers on the West Coast (Ice-T, N.W.A., Ice Cube, Dr. Dre, and others), New York's claim to hip-hop preeminence was in question. This rivalry eventually found its way into recordings, with Marian "Suge" Knight (West Coast) and Sean "Puffy" Combs (East Coast) trading threats and insults via their song lyrics. "Dissing" (disrespecting) other competing groups using the imagery of gang warfare was common among gangsta rappers.

Many of the most successful rap artists rose to popularity as part of an ensemble and then departed to pursue solo careers. This *"splinter phenomenon"* has happened frequently throughout the history of rock and roll (e.g., Lionel Richie from the Commodores, Sting from the Police, Peter Gabriel and Phil Collins from Genesis, Bobby Brown and Bel Biv DeVoe from New Edition). Two specific rap groups serve as particularly illustrative examples of this continuing phenomenon.

16.3.2: The Wu-Tang Clan

From housing projects on Staten Island, the Wu-Tang Clan exemplifies a splintered rap group. Two cousins, RZA (Robert Diggs) and GZA (Gary Grice), were the group's founders, enlisting the assistance of Ol' Dirty Bastard (Russell Jones), Inspectah Deck (Jason Hunter), Raekwon (Corey Woods), U-God (Lamont Hawkins), Ghostface Killah (Dennis Coles), Method Man (Clifford Smith), and Masta Killa (Elgin Turner). Their debut album, *Enter the Wu-Tang (36 Chambers)* (1993), infused their ghetto-related lyricism with references to the martial arts. Interestingly, the group's contract with Loud Records allowed each member freedom to negotiate with other labels for the release of solo project work. Method Man was the first to take advantage of this arrangement, releasing *Tical* (number 4 in 1994). Other solo projects from group members included GZA's *Liquid Swords* (number 9 in 1995) and *Beneath the Surface* (number 9 in 1996), RZA's *RZA as Bobby Digital in Stereo* (number 16 in 1998), Raekwon's *Only Built 4 Cuban Linx* (number 4 in 1995), Ol' Dirty Bastard's *Return to the 36 Chambers: The Dirty Version* (number 7 in 1995) and *Nigga Please* (number 10 in 1999), Ghostface Killah's *Ironman* (number 2 in 1996), Inspectah Deck's *Uncontrolled Substance* (number 19 in 1999), and U-God's *Golden Arms Redemption* (number 58 in 1999). Although group members experienced a significant amount of success as solo artists, they continued to record as the Wu-Tang Clan, including *Wu-Tang Forever* (number 1 in 1997), *The W* (number 5 in 2000), *Iron Flag* (number 32 in 2001), and *Disciples of the 36 Chambers* (number 82 in 2004). In November 2004, Ol' Dirty Bastard died after collapsing suddenly in a New York recording studio from a heart attack due to intoxication involving the combined effects of cocaine and Tarmadol. Despite this loss, the group continued to release music, including five Top 50 albums: *8 Diagrams* (number 25 in 2007), *Chamber Music* (number 49 in 2009), *Wu-Massacre* (number 12 in 2010), *Legendary Weapons* (number 41 in 2011), and *A Better Tomorrow* (number 23 in 2014).

16.3.3: N.W.A.

Formed in 1986, N.W.A. (Niggaz With Attitude) experienced great commercial success with *Straight Outta Compton* (number 37 in 1989) and *EFIL4ZAGGIN* (number 1 in 1991; the title is "Niggaz 4 Life" backward). *Straight Outta Compton* resulted in significant controversy due to its inclusion of the track "Fuck the Police," for which distributor Priority Records received a warning letter from the FBI.

Members of the group who went on to highly successful solo careers include Ice Cube (O'Shea Jackson), Eazy-E (Eric Wright), and Dr. Dre (Andre Young). As a solo artist, Ice Cube released *AmeriKKKa's Most Wanted* (number 19 in 1990), *Death Certificate* (number 2 in 1991), *The Predator* (debuting at number 1 in 1992), and *Lethal Injection* (number 5 in 1993). During the 1990s, he also had a very successful acting career, appearing in films such as *Boyz n the Hood* (1991), *The Players Club* (1998; written by, directed by, and starring Ice Cube), and *Three Kings* (1999). Ice Cube's solo efforts continued to sell well into the 2000s. Eazy-E recorded *Eazy-Duz-It* (number 41 in 1988), *It's On (Dr. Dre 187um) Killa* (number 5 in 1993), and *Str8 off tha Streetz of Muthaphukkin Compton* (number 3 in 1996). Eazy-E died in 1995 of complications related to AIDS. Dr. Dre went on to establish Death Row Records with Marian "Suge" Knight. His solo efforts include *The Chronic* (number 3 in 1993) and *2001* (number 2 in 1999). As producer, Dre worked successfully with Snoop Doggy Dogg, Tupac Shakur, and others. Dr. Dre was also responsible for discovering a white rapper from Detroit named Eminem and produced his highly controversial recordings (discussed later in this chapter).

Comedian Chris Rock, addressing N.W.A.'s popularity, pointed out that, for a segment of American society, this rap group was bigger than Nirvana or Madonna. He characterized this era, and N.W.A. specifically, as a "British Invasion for black people" (*Rolling Stone*, December 20, 2013, p. 44).

JOURNAL

Rap Lyrics as Social Commentary

While "Cop Killer" may have stolen the headlines due to its explicit call to arms, a number of tracks on Body Count's self-titled album present social commentary worthy of closer consideration. Listen carefully to the title track of this album, "Body Count," keeping an open mind; I strongly recommend finding a copy of the lyrics online so you can follow along. What do you interpret as the primary message(s) being communicated in this recording? Do you believe that Body Count is successful and effective in accurately delivering this message? Does the music enhance or distract from the message? If you were a famous rap artist who wanted to communicate this message to an audience, what would you have done differently?

▶ The response entered here will appear in the performance dashboard and can be viewed by your instructor.

Submit

16.4: Other Rappers

OBJECTIVE: Identify the factors that contributed to the success of rap artists

Interestingly, while gangsta rap was becoming more extreme in its depiction of violence, milder forms of rap were being accepted into the mainstream of popular music. In the next section, we will review one female rap group that was highly successful during the 1980s and 1990s, and a male rapper who challenged numerous boundaries.

16.4.1: Salt-N-Pepa

One of the first rap groups to cross over successfully to the pop chart, Salt-N-Pepa, consisted of three female rappers: Cheryl "Salt" James, Sandy "Pepa" Denton, and DJ Pamela Greene.

Salt-N-Pepa

SOURCE: Jeffrey Mayer/Pictorial Press Ltd/Alamy Stock Photo

The trio, formed in 1985 (Denton, James, and manager-producer Hurby "Luv Bug" Azor met while working at Sears), released *Hot, Cool, and Vicious* (number 26) the following year. The album resulted in three minor R&B singles: "Show Stoppa," "My Mike Sounds Nice," and "Tramp." Success on the Hot 100 did not come until a San Francisco DJ remixed the B-side of one of these singles, "Push It." The remixed version of the single reached number 19 and was nominated for a Grammy in 1988. That same year, Greene was replaced as DJ for the group by Deidre "Spinderella" Roper. The most successful song from the two following albums, *A Salt with a Deadly Pepa* (number 38 in 1988) and *Blacks' Magic* (number 38 in 1990), was "Let's Talk About Sex" (number 13). The women released *Very Necessary* (number 4 in 1993), attaining their highest chart successes with "Shoop" (also number 4) and "Whatta Man" (number 3), the latter a collaboration with the female vocal group En Vogue. In the mid-1990s, Salt-N-Pepa adopted the image of tough-rapping divas, as exhibited on "Ain't Nuthin but a She Thing" (number 38 in 1995). However, the role of tough females in rap ultimately fell to Queen Latifah and Sister Souljah, who rapped forcefully on the subjects of African nationalism and pro-woman activism. As in the title song from Sistah Souljah's *360 Degrees of Power* (1992), these strident rhymes against racial oppression often contained explicit anti-white sentiments.

16.4.2: Eminem

Rap music originated as an almost exclusively African American art form. As time went by, however, white rappers appeared on the scene. Early examples of nonblack rappers include Vanilla Ice and Marky Mark (Mark Wahlberg, who later earned significant fame as an actor), although neither of these "white boys" could truly hold a candle to the rap style and verbal gymnastics of black MCs. More authentic sounding white rappers followed,

Eminem, 2000.

SOURCE: Pictorial Press Ltd/Alamy Stock Photo

including House of Pain and the Beastie Boys. In the late 1990s, the arrival of Marshall Mathers (a.k.a. Eminem) revealed that rap, gangsta or otherwise, was no longer solely the province of black performers.

The appearance of white rappers provides an interesting parallel to the period when rock music emerged in the 1950s. While nonblack rap artists prior to the appearance of Eminem might be seen as purposefully toning down the angst and subject matter of their African American counterparts to make the style palatable to a wider audience (like Pat Boone covering a tune by Big Joe Turner), Eminem performed rhymes uncensored, emulating the style of his predecessors (like Elvis's comparatively authentic integration of stylistic traits of R&B artists).

Musical Career of Eminem

What of the rhythmic patterns themselves?

Although Mathers's recording debut, *Infinite* (1997), attracted little attention, the follow-up EP won him a recording contract with Interscope and brought him to the attention of one of its influential artists and producers, Dr. Dre. Eminem's second recording was extended into the breakthrough album *The Slim Shady LP* (number 2 in 1999), winning Grammys for Best Rap Album and Best Rap Solo Performance ("My Name Is"). *The Marshall Mathers LP* debuted at number 1 in 2000 and became the fastest-selling rap album of all time, proving that, within the rap genre, Eminem was a force with which to be reckoned. This recording earned him a second consecutive Grammy for Best Rap Album.

His commercial success continued unabated with a series of number 1 albums: *The Eminem Show* (2002), *8 Mile* (2002; he also starred in a movie of the same name and performed on this soundtrack), *Encore* (2004), *Curtain Call: The Hits* (2005), *Relapse* (2009), *Recovery* (2010) and *The Marshall Mathers LP 2* (2013). *Eminem Presents: The ReUp* (number 2 in 2006) is what has become known as a "*crew album*," including appearances by Eminem protégés Obie Trice, D12, Status Quo, Cashis, and Bobby Creekwater. The album peaked at number 2, but critics generally spurned the recording. At the end of 2007, Eminem almost died from an accidental methadone overdose, an event that served as inspiration for *Relapse* and *Recovery*. His influence as an artist and talent scout also proved quite effective with several spinoff projects, including Dirty Dozen (D12) and 50 Cent (pronounced "fitty cen'"). While D12 fell flat, 50 Cent proved to be one of the most successful artists of the first decade of the new millennium. Based on Whitburn's (2010) assessment using an artist's number of charted singles and number of weeks on the chart, 50 Cent was one of the top three artists of the decade, surpassing even Eminem's level of success during that period.

The critical and commercial success of Eminem's recordings was second only to the controversy resulting from concern about his lyrics. Eminem openly ranted about guns, drugs, killing, abuse, homosexuality, misogyny, and many other taboo topics, often seeming to promote and encourage violence. Among the loudest voices in protest against his music were gay rights activists, religious groups, women's groups, and even members of his own family. He was sued by his mother for defamation and by his estranged wife (who he "killed" more than once in his recorded narratives). Like many other rap artists, Mathers wound up on the wrong side of the law, receiving two years of probation for assault and carrying a concealed weapon. The assaulted man allegedly kissed the rapper's wife outside a nightclub.

Why is it that we, as the listening public, give attention to such an individual? Simply put, Eminem was one of the best MCs rapping during the transition to the twenty-first century. His rhyming skills and delivery style rivaled many of the best black performers of the time, winning him the respect not only of the general public, but of many of his peers in the rap community. Second—and this is, admittedly, a slippery slope—the storytelling on Eminem's albums was presented through the eyes of "Slim Shady," a fictional alter ego who was described as "a homicidal comedian through whom Mathers enacted his most outrageous and perverse revenge fantasies" (George-Warren and Romanowski 2001, 304). When Eminem narrates for us a tale of riding in the car with his daughter to a drop-off point, where they will dispose of the lifeless body of the child's mother (along with two other bodies, implied to be the stepfather and a half-brother), as he does in "'97 Bonnie and Clyde," we are to believe that this is simply a storyteller stretching the bounds of poetic license for dramatic effect. There is no doubt that the dramatic impact is great, but once again, one must ask, What of social responsibility?

JOURNAL

Eminem's Rap Lyricism

The track "Rap God" on Eminem's *The Marshall Mathers LP 2* (2013) appears to exist primarily as a showpiece to demonstrate the rapper's lyrical and vocal delivery prowess, though his over-the-top violence and humor are both also on display. Listen to the song a couple of times while following along with the lyrics. Now, do your best to ignore the lyrics (i.e., the semantic meaning of the words) and focus solely on the artistry involved in Eminem's rapping style. Identify two or three sections of the song that you consider the most impressive examples of his rapping ability. What is it specifically about these excerpts that attracted your attention? Do you hear the influence of earlier rappers on Eminem's style? If so, which one(s)?

  The response entered here will appear in the performance dashboard and can be viewed by your instructor.

Submit

16.5: New Jack Swing

OBJECTIVE: Explain how rap crossed over into the mainstream

In spite of the controversy surrounding gangsta rap, developments at the end of the 1980s played a primary role in bringing rap into the mainstream of popular music.

Important People Associated with New Jack Swing

Teddy Riley—Credited largely to the influence of multi-instrumentalist and producer Teddy Riley, a new variety of rap referred to as *new jack swing* (or *neo-soul*) evolved out of New York City, merging a hip-hop beat with light rap and traditional R&B vocals. Guy, Riley's own group,

had an R&B hit with "Groove Me" in 1988 (number 4, R&B chart). Singles by the band were selected for inclusion in the soundtracks of two black urban films, *Do the Right Thing* (1989) and *New Jack City* (1991). Members of Guy went their separate ways after releasing *The Future* (1990), which resulted in three Top 10 singles on the R&B chart: "Let's Chill" (number 3), "Do Me Right" (number 2) and "D-O-G Me Out" (number 8). Following the group's dissolution, Riley assisted Michael Jackson during the recording of *Dangerous* (1991), stamping that release with his trademark production sound. Listen to "Jam," the opening cut on Jackson's recording, to hear Riley's new jack swing influence. The song begins with rhythmically spoken words over a heavy dance beat. Throughout the entire recording, Jackson's vocals seem to take on a more mature, forceful tone. In the middle of the song, following a brief synthesized horn break, there is a straight-ahead rap section performed by Heavy D, giving way once again to Jackson's vocals.

In 1994, Riley formed Blackstreet and experienced continued success with "Before I Let You Go" (number 7 in 1994) and "No Diggity" (number 1 in 1996). A reunion of Guy resulted in *Guy III* (number 13 in 2000) and a hit single, "Dancin'" (number 19).

Babyface—Following Riley's lead, other producers, including Jimmy Jam & Terry Lewis and Babyface, picked up on this eclectic and highly lucrative blend of musical styles. Babyface gained massive critical acclaim for his production talent, working throughout the 1990s with artists such as Paula Abdul, Pebbles, TLC, the Jacksons, Whitney Houston, Boyz II Men, and Bobby Brown. His production work and songwriting skill resulted in an amazing 12 Grammy nominations in 1997, tying the record set by Michael Jackson for *Thriller* in 1982.

Keith Sweat—One of the first artists to popularize the new jack swing sound was Keith Sweat. Working as a commodities broker on Wall Street, Sweat successfully marketed his own demo, succeeded in finding an interested management company, and eventually signed a record contract. His debut single, "I Want Her" (number 5 in 1988), revealed a smooth blend of R&B and hip-hop, becoming the first new jack swing hit to receive national attention and continuing his success through the end of the 1990s.

Other Rap Groups—Some rappers place more importance on the declamatory speaking style and hip-hop rhythms but still incorporate melodic aspects into the song structures. Former band mates of Bobby Brown and Ralph Tresvant in New Edition, Ricky Bell, Michael Bivins, and Ronnie DeVoe, formed Bell Biv DeVoe in 1988. With the encouragement of producers Jimmy Jam and Terry Lewis, the three rappers proved to be a dance music powerhouse for a couple of years. Bell Biv DeVoe's biggest hits ("Poison" and "Do Me!," both number 3) were culled from their debut album *Poison* (1990). All six members of New Edition, including Bobby Brown and his replacement, Johnny Gill, reunited in 1996 to produce *Home Again* (number 1 on both the Pop and R&B charts), including the Top 10 songs "Hit Me Off" and "I'm Still in Love with You." Other examples of this rap-R&B blend can be found in the music of Snap! ("The Power," 1990), Marky Mark and the Funky Bunch ("Good Vibrations," 1991), Color Me Badd ("I Adore Me Amor," 1991), and Arrested Development ("Mr. Wendal," 1993).

Watch "Groove Me" by Guy

https://www.youtube.com/watch?v=PAu2bsV9CiQ*

Watch "No Diggity" by Blackstreet

https://www.youtube.com/watch?v=3KL9mRus19o*

16.5.1: Rap Goes Mainstream

The successful crossing over of rap music into the mainstream of American popular music was completed by the late 1980s. Signs of such a transition had been on the horizon for some time, but with Run-D.M.C. and Aerosmith's version of "Walk This Way" in 1986, the crossover of rap to the mainstream was complete. Further proof of the fact came shortly thereafter with the release of the Beastie Boys' *Licensed to Ill*—the first rap album to reach number 1. Final

confirmation that rap had truly been accepted into the mainstream was provided in the October 11, 2003, issue of *Billboard* magazine. That week, for the first time in rock history, all of the Top 10 singles on the Hot 100 chart were by black recording artists. All but one—the top position—were by rappers:

1. "Baby Boy," Beyoncé (featuring Sean Paul)
2. "Shake Ya Tailfeather," Nelly, P. Diddy, and Murphy Lee
3. "Get Low," Li'l Jon and the East Side Boyz (featuring Ying Yang Twins)
4. "Right Thurr," Chingy
5. "Frontin'," Pharrell (featuring Jay-Z)
6. "Damn!," YoungBloodz (featuring Li'l Jon)
7. "P.I.M.P.," 50 Cent
8. "Into You," Fabolous (featuring Tamia/Ashanti)
9. "Stand Up," Ludacris (featuring Shawnna)
10. "Where Is the Love?," Black Eyed Peas

The evolution of rap produced a wide variety of substyles within this genre of rock. From the raw intensity of gangsta rap to the R&B melodicism of new jack swing to the eclectic sounds of jazz-rap (a rap hybrid initiated by the Jungle Brothers and popularized by US3's "Cantaloop"), the characteristic spoken delivery of lyrics was absorbed into the mainstream of contemporary youth culture. According to Arthur Kempton (2003), as we settled into the new millennium, white customers accounted for 70 percent of hip-hop sales. Rap had entered the mainstream, clearing the way for artists like Jay-Z, Ludacris, T.I., and Kanye West to lead the pack into the new millennium. As further confirmation of "mainstream" status, two events are worthy of notice. First, in November 2009, Jay-Z released his 11th number 1 album, *Blueprint 3*, surpassing Elvis Presley's record for the most number 1 albums by a single artist or group. [Jay-Z's next studio album, *Watch the Throne* (2011), provided his 12th number 1.] Second, according to SoundScan, Eminem sold 32 million albums during the first decade of the twenty-first century; you just can't get more mainstream than that!

JOURNAL

Influence of New Jack Swing

Take some time to listen to a leading rap radio station in your area or select a station via one of the Internet radio streams. Listen until you have identified at least three songs that reveal the influence of new jack swing's combination of rapped lyrics and sung melodies. For each song, record the artist and song title, and then briefly describe how the artist creatively combines these different approaches to musical performance. Of the songs you identified, which is your favorite and why?

 The response entered here will appear in the performance dashboard and can be viewed by your instructor.

Submit

16.6: Musical Close-Up on the Expressive Performance of Rap

OBJECTIVE: Analyze the vocal delivery of lyrics by various rap artists

Music is a highly expressive form of human communication, filled with subtle nuance and meaningful gestures. The same musical phrase performed by two different artists will never be exactly the same. In fact, it is not even possible for the same artist—short of using digital sampling—to perform the same phrase twice in precisely the same way. Subtle changes occur in the **pitch**, **loudness**, **timbre**, and duration of the tones performed. Such changes provide the basis for a human performance. The use of the term *"imperfect"* is sometimes used to describe such alterations, though this would seem to be an inappropriate use of that term. Rather, these subtle changes in basic musical elements add expressive meaning to the musical message. If you want to hear a clear comparison of two performances—one that incorporates **expressive deviations** ("imperfections") and one that does not—simply select any song (e.g., "Yesterday" by Lennon and McCartney). Listen carefully to the original studio recording by the Beatles and notice—beyond the meaning of the lyrics—the mood, style, and emotion that are communicated by the musical performance. Now, use your favorite Internet search engine to locate a MIDI file of this same song. Listen to this "performance" of the song in which all note durations are played mechanically, exactly as they are represented in the musical score and in which there is little, if any, differentiation in loudness from note to note. The very important element missing from this latter music is the expressive performance—the human element that gives music its impressive ability to communicate nonverbally.

Have you ever wondered why there is more than one recording of Beethoven's Fifth Symphony or any other classical masterpiece? It is because the notes on the page provide only a guideline to the performer. Much of the communicative message is added in the performer's interpretive process of changing the notes on the written page into musical sound. Of course, a significant amount of popular music is created and performed without the use of a written score. As revealed by the three *Anthology* volumes released by the Beatles, the creative process often involves multiple attempts to perform a song—in different keys, at different tempos, and with different interpretations. This is an integral part of the creative process. Listening to a number of live recordings of the same song performed by an artist is another way to observe expressive differences. Cover versions of popular songs, as well, often emphasize differences in expressive style to set them apart from the original recording.

When describing a rapper's style of vocal delivery, one can focus on the way the tones are altered in expressive ways. The term *"tone"* might seem out of place in this context because we have maintained that the element of pitch within a melodic framework is typically absent from rap. However, all forms of expressive deviation are available to the rapper—even pitch—through the use of voice inflections. Although many of these artists do not sing, in a traditional sense, there is certainly a pitch contour evident in their spoken delivery—otherwise, the style would become as boring as listening to someone speak in a monotone. Listen carefully to any of the latest rap singles listed on the *Billboard* Hot 100 and see if you can follow the pitch contour of the spoken voice as it moves from low- to high-toned inflection.

In a more general sense, rappers have adopted a variety of styles for rhythmically delivering their rhymes. According to Gioia (2003, 14), the rap artist

> consciously exploits stress-meter's ability to stretch and contract in syllable count. In fact, playing the syllable count against the beat is the basic metrical technique of rap. Like jazz, rap extravagantly syncopates a flexible rhythm against a fixed metrical beat, thereby turning a traditional English folk meter into something distinctively African-American. By hitting the metrical beat strongly, while exploiting other elements of word music, rappers play interesting and elaborate games with the total rhythm of their lines.

16.6.1: Rap Vocal Techniques

In this Musical Close-Up, we will compare the vocal delivery of several of the most highly respected and commercially successful rap artists: Run-D.M.C., Snoop Dogg, Eminem, and OutKast.

Vocal Delivery of Commercially Successful Rap Artists

Passing the Role of MC: Run-D.M.C.—Often, as a means of providing variety, rap groups pass the role of MC between two or more rappers. The pioneering rap group Run-D.M.C. does this, as do N.W.A., Wu-Tang Clan, and the Beastie Boys. One unique characteristic of Run-D.M.C.'s rapping technique is that, rather than the typical form of alternating verses or even lines within a verse, Run and D.M.C. start and finish one another's lines or create a dynamic musical texture by interlocking words and/or phrases. The first few lines of "Peter Piper" (the opening track on *Raising Hell*) show the most dramatic use of this technique.

This kind of alternation is not a new performance technique and, in fact, can be traced back as far as the appearance of **hocket** in the medieval organum (thirteenth century) and the Renaissance motet (fifteenth and sixteenth centuries). In the context of a rap song, however, this technique provides a sense of freshness and innovation. The two lead rappers perform their energetic rap delivery with a high level of rhythmic precision, never straying too far from the beat.

Relaxed Delivery: Snoop Dogg—In contrast, Snoop Dogg's rap delivery is significantly more subdued. In fact, as a quintessential gangsta rapper, the relaxed drawl with which the words of his rhymes are delivered serves to increase the intensity of the meaning of the words. Listen to "Murder Was the Case" (1994), a song from the soundtrack for a documentary film of the same name about Snoop and Dr. Dre. The song was a remix of a track originally released on *Doggystyle* (1993). Note the typically soft, somewhat breathy delivery of the lyrics. He also uses a wide pitch range, as portions of the text are delivered in a near-falsetto voice range. Other significant aspects of Snoop's style are exemplified by his more relaxed rhythmic delivery—lagging behind the beat at some points, while rushing ahead slightly at others—and the lax manner of his rhyming structure. Most of the time, couplet phrases rhyme, but sometimes they do not. To break up the quadruple meter and duple subdivision feel, the rapper periodically inserts triplet rhythms, providing a subtle lilt to the musical delivery.

Intensity of Delivery: Eminem—With Eminem, the intensity of the performance is a direct result of the delivery style. Mathers moves frequently and comfortably between an intense, in-your-face, machine gun-style delivery and taking apparent pleasure in mocking rap music—both his own and that of other artists. As an early example of this artist's rap style, listen to "My Name Is" (on *The Slim Shady LP*). The opening lines, as the title and hook line suggest, tag the recording as being performed by Eminem's alter ego Slim Shady. In particular, notice his use of the high-pitched "chicka-chicka" motive (a recurrent idea appearing on several of his recordings), a vocal attempt to replicate—parody?—a DJ's turntable scratching technique, a prominent element of many rap recordings. Apart from the meaning of the lyrics and the often controversial subject matter, one of the most consistent rhythmic characteristics of this recording is that Eminem's vocal delivery is always ever so slightly behind the beat. Dragging slightly behind the beat proves to be an effective technique to increase the level of tension perceived by the listener and to enhance the sense of urgency perceived while listening to the music, even if these effects remain at a subconscious level.

Melding of Rap with Singing: Outcast—Finally, demonstrating a style with audible ties to new jack swing, OutKast members Dre (a.k.a. Andre 3000) and Big Boi present a musical fabric that alternates between catchy melodic hooks and rap. As a result, OutKast represents a hybrid form of rap that uses the format of two rappers alternating back and forth and, at times, rapping in unison—a style obviously influenced by Run-D.M.C. This rhythmic vocal delivery is contrasted tastefully with melodic hooks. To hear a representative example of this music, listen to "So Fresh and So Clean" (from *Stankonia*). Notice how the syncopated melody of the chorus hook line (i.e., the title of the song) appears periodically between rapped rhymes that constitute the verses. As you listen to the verses, notice how the rhythmic rhyming of both rappers is delivered with a high degree of precision. Even the 16th-note subdivisions are performed nearly flawlessly, laying right in the groove. Also notice in the rapped verses that a line or couplet rhymed by one rapper or the other is often concluded in unison by both rappers. They also incorporate the hocket technique identified in the previous discussion of Run-D.M.C.'s rapping style.

Even without the benefit of beautiful melodies, rap artists have numerous ways in which to embellish an expressive performance: altering the loudness, timbre, duration, and pitch range of the vocal delivery. With the concepts of expressive performance in mind, seek out examples of your own to compare and contrast the approach that various rap artists take to communicate a musical message via the rhythmic enunciation of their rhymes.

BECOME AN ACTIVE LISTENER: RAP VOCAL TECHNIQUES

After studying the evolution of rap and hip-hop presented in this chapter, it is time to return to your own collection of recordings, to your streaming service, or to the Internet to identify, independently, some of the differentiating elements in recordings with which you may be more familiar.

Find examples of these rap vocal techniques in your favorite recordings:
1. Hocketing (alternating voices to complete a single musical phrase)
2. Relaxed "drawl"
3. Intense, in-your-face, machine gun-style delivery
4. Melding of rapped rhymes with singing (new jack swing)

Summary: Rap and Hip-Hop

In this chapter, we explored the exciting developments that led rap and hip-hop into an era of dominance on the rock charts. We reviewed some of the technological developments that contributed to this evolution and mentioned the significance of the Internet, both as a means of listening to music and acquiring digital downloads. Then, the early days of rap were presented, evolving in the South Bronx as part of hip-hop culture. In the mid-1980s, as a result of artists like Run-D.M.C., the Beastie Boys, and L.L. Cool J, rap artists began to experience massive commercial success. That success then spurred a true explosion of rap artists from New York City, Philadelphia, Los Angeles, Detroit, and other cities around the nation, resulting in performance styles that varied widely from gangsta rap to new jack swing. Rap and hip-hop remain a dominant force in the popular music industry.

Take Note: Rap and Hip-Hop

- *How did the Internet and Web technologies influence the development of popular music in the 1990s?*—The explosion of electronic technology had a major impact on popular music. MIDI helped link computers to synthesizers and other musical devices; digital technology provided a streamlined way to manipulate pre-existing recordings. File sharing over the Internet changed how music was experienced by consumers. Portable music players and online music stores replaced compact discs and walk-in music stores as the primary ways music was promoted and distributed.

- *What constituted the beginnings of rap music?*—Rap developed out of hip-hop culture in the South Bronx during the late 1970s. Pioneering DJs set up their equipment in parks and recreation centers, manipulating pairs of turntables to create a rhythmic foundation for an MC's improvised spoken rhymes. Among the first successful rap records was the Sugarhill Gang's "Rapper's Delight," released in 1979; however, the commercial breakthrough that brought rap into the mainstream was Run-D.M.C.'s *Raising Hell* (1986) and the hit single "Walk This Way," featuring two members of Aerosmith.

- *How did rap serve as social protest music?*—While New York was the epicenter of early rap, a related movement grew in Southern California that would spawn a more socio-politically focused style. Public Enemy was a leader in this style of rap (e.g., *Fear of a Black Planet*, 1990).

- *What is gangsta rap, and why was it popular?*—Gangsta rap became popular in the mid-1990s as a reflection of the violence in inner-city communities like Compton in Los Angeles and the South Bronx in New York City. The lyrics were meant to be provocative and shocking; the accompaniments were more aggressive, borrowing from hard-edged rock styles like heavy metal. N.W.A. was one of the most prominent Southern California gangsta rap groups (e.g., *Straight Outta Compton*, 1989).

- *What other rappers achieved major success in the 1990s and early 2000s?*—Many rappers achieved commercial success by creating less confrontational material than the gangsta rappers. Salt-N-Pepa was a highly successful trio of female performers whose songs focused more on issues of relationships and sex. Others, like white rapper Eminem, took the violent imagery of gangsta rap and applied it to more personal issues.

- *What is new jack swing, and how is it related to rap?*—New jack swing developed in the late 1980s and early 1990s as a melding of the contemporaneous R&B vocal style with rap. Producer Terry Riley played a crucial role in popularizing this style, followed by the successful production duo of Jimmy Jam and Terry Lewis.

SHARED WRITING

Addressing Racism Through Music

Listen carefully to country artist Brad Paisley's "Accidental Racist," a song from his album *Wheelhouse*, featuring L.L. Cool J. Locate a copy of the lyrics online and follow along as you listen. The song involves the two artists representing two very different perspectives and entering into a conversation in a sincere attempt—it would appear—to have a meaningful dialogue. Paisley represents a southern white man and Cool J a black man from the North. What do you consider the three most effective aspects of this song in regards to addressing racism directly? Do you feel that the song fulfills the artists' intent? What is your reaction to the song and how does it align with your own perspective regarding race relations? Share your response with two peers as you read their responses. Do you all share the same perspective or are there differences that might lead to additional fruitful conversations as we continue to confront this critically important topic within our society?

 A minimum number of characters is required to post and earn points. After posting, your response can be viewed by your class and instructor, and you can participate in the class discussion.

Post

0 characters | 140 minimum

Chapter 17
Alternative Styles

 ## Learning Objectives

17.1 Analyze the development of alternative rock

17.2 Identify the influences on early alternative rock

17.3 Explain why the punk movement was considered a rebellion against other rock trends

17.4 Relate punk rock to alternative rock styles

17.5 Outline reasons for the popularity of grunge rock

17.6 Differentiate indie rock from other alternative rock styles

17.7 Explain how punk re-emerged as an alternative rock style in the early 2000s

17.8 Describe the emergence of progressive rock

17.9 Evaluate the alternative rock movement

As we near the end of this survey of rock history and the many subgenres it includes, we must acknowledge that rock and roll itself began as an "alternative" to the musical styles of the era in which it emerged (i.e., the mid-1950s). As explained elsewhere in this course, the most popular categories of music at that time included Pop, C&W, and R&B, each with its own clearly defined audience and sales market. Throughout the rock era, numerous "alternatives" appeared. Although that descriptor was not used as a genre category until the 1980s, in this chapter the term is extended retroactively to some developments preceding that decade.

17.1: Boomers and Post-Boomers

OBJECTIVE: Analyze the development of alternative rock

At the end of World War II, the United States experienced a significant increase in the birthrate, continuing into the early 1960s. The resulting bulge in population is often called the "baby boom." Virtually every business in the nation, including the music industry, carefully followed (and attempted to predict) the movement of "the Boomers" as they grew up and became consumers. They are counted not only as numbers, but as dollars. The spending power of the Boomers has continued to be a major market influence on the U.S. economy well into the new millennium.

The Boomers were the first generation that was raised almost entirely on rock music. Although they may have been rebels in the 1960s and 1970s, by the 1980s and 1990s, they began to settle down. By then, they were doctors, lawyers, professors, and successful business executives. They married (usually more than once) and raised families. With the arrival of the twenty-first century, many were beginning to look toward retirement. As is typically the case as individuals age and mature, many also became more conservative. The Boomers continued to be most comfortable with things the way they were and were rather disturbed by the antics of their offspring (sound familiar?). The economic strength of the Boomers continued to be a major influence on the music industry into the new century, as older and more mainstream styles of rock once again became big business.

By the early 1970s, the Boomers had begun having families of their own. As their children moved through their teens, from about the mid-1980s until 2000, they, too, wielded some economic influence. However, if the history of rock music tells us anything, we should expect that the post-Boomers, as was the case with their parents, would be drawn to musical styles that are clearly distinct from their parents' music; in fact, the more distinct—and perhaps even repulsive—to their parents, the better. They sought alternative styles, which leads us to a closer consideration of that adjective: alternative.

17.1.1: Alternative Rock

In the late 1980s and 1990s, certain rock groups and styles were referred to as alternative rock. Considering the entire history of rock music, this term seems redundant. Indeed, most rock music from its very beginning was "alternative" music. The young audiences in 1955 were fascinated by the music of Fats Domino, Chuck Berry, and Bill Haley, precisely because it represented a musical alternative to the Pop styles of Tony Bennett, Nat "King" Cole, and Eddie Fisher. The music of Elvis Presley, Little Richard, and Buddy Holly (and many others) continued this alternative style. When mainstream rock seemed to fade in popularity in the early 1960s, the young audiences again went crazy (literally) over the new sounds of the Beatles and the Rolling Stones. It was an exciting new alternative to the soft rock, Pop, and **rockabilly** that had dominated the charts for several prior years, as presented in another section of this course. One can trace this fascination with the "alternative" throughout rock history. Heavy metal, punk rock, gangsta rap—these and other styles can be seen as reactions against (or alternatives to) styles that enjoyed mainstream popularity. However redundant it may be in the context of rock history, the term *alternative rock* became an accepted descriptor in the 1990s. This chapter will examine more closely the various sub-styles that fall under this category.

Before incorporating the term "alternative" into our discussion, let us consider its implications just a bit further, building upon what has been presented elsewhere in this course. In the early 1960s, we observed a brief period of fragmentation within the music market, but the overwhelming power of the Beatles—at least temporarily—overcame that fragmentation. However, in the 1970s, the fragmentation resumed with a vengeance. "Fragmentation," of course, is simply a word that describes an explosion of alternatives. Generally speaking, we think of alternatives as being good. After all, it is nice to have a wide array of choices. However, is it possible to have too many choices? Can the presence of too many choices virtually paralyze us? Consider coming home from work or school and thinking, "I think I'll listen to some music," but, while perusing the contents of your media player or subscription streaming service, you are stymied. A Beethoven symphony would be nice. Or are you more in the mood for the Rolling Stones? Maybe some light jazz would be pleasant. Do you want to hear Radiohead or Chicago? Frustrated, you say to yourself, "Forget it, I can't decide. Maybe I'll watch some TV instead." Researcher Sheena Iyengar refers to this situation as the "choice overload problem" (Iyengar, 2011).

Perhaps you can imagine similar cases of decisional paralysis—"Oh, forget it!"; for instance, when you are confronted with over 600 television channels, hundreds of kinds of wine, dozens of varieties of mustard, or a dizzying array of magazines. Of course, these decisions (or non-decisions) are not of life-shattering importance. However, what if the multiplicity of choices—alternatives—exists in more important realms, such as values and lifestyles? Easy, you might say. You just figure out what is good (meaning healthy, safe, and wise) and what is bad. Again, what if society has purged those terms and concepts from our vocabulary and thinking? What if things are no longer good or bad, right or wrong, but merely "alternative"? The implication is that all of those choices are equally acceptable.

17.1.2: Anomie

In the late 1960s, the Boomers seriously questioned the values of the "establishment." Among other things, this led to the antihero phenomenon, as represented earlier in this course by the Rolling Stones. In effect, this resulted in a reversal of traditional values to the extent that good became bad and bad became good (this position will be developed further elsewhere in this course). In the intervening decades, there has been an increasing hesitation to render value judgments about what is good or bad, right or wrong, better or worse. This philosophy of egalitarianism—that all things should be equal—was implied in the late 1960s and early 1970s by the phrase "different strokes for different folks." In other words, what is right for one person may not be right for another. There was no firm definition of what was right; it all depended on the person or circumstances. All things were relative, rather than absolute. In the late 1980s and 1990s, some school districts advocated teaching "situational ethics." This philosophy suggested that there is no absolute right or wrong; instead, what was right or wrong varied according to the situation. The desire to avoid stigmatizing some individuals or circumstances led to phrases such as "alternative lifestyles" and "alternatively abled." People spoke of alternative medicine and alternative cuisine. Of course, in addition, we had alternative music. Indeed, the word "alternative" became one of the buzzwords of the 1990s.

Too many choices among equals (or alternatives) can lead to an inability to make any choice at all. The post-Boomers seem to have grown up with little or no guidance regarding values because, after all, if all alternatives are equal, then there is no difference in value (and, hence, no value at all). By extension, there are no standards because all things are simply equal alternatives. There need be no rules because there is no better or worse behavior.

The French have a word that seems to apply in this situation: *anomie*. It refers to a person or society that lacks purpose, identity, or ethical values, thus leading to a feeling of rootlessness. Some writers have referred to the post-Boomers as generations without specific identities, as can be derived from the largely generic labels assigned to these groups: Gen X, Gen Y, Millennials, and Gen Z. Psychiatrists specializing in adolescents tell us that children and teenagers actually need and crave limits, rules, standards, and values, even though they may protest. If this is true, we can understand why those without clearly defined boundaries might feel angry and betrayed. In frustration, they push further and further against what they believe to be society's norms, just to see how far they can go before forcing society to say, "Enough!" The tragedies at Columbine High School on April 20, 1999, and Virginia Polytechnic Institute on April 16, 2007, are just two examples of this attitude taken to its extreme. Keep this in mind as you read about the excesses evident in some styles of rap music, as discussed elsewhere in this course, and the more extreme styles of alternative rock discussed in this chapter. As we consider the music of the post-Boomers, note that oftentimes, the music and lyrics represent anger. Often, the performers appear to be angry, as do their audiences. Whereas young girls used to sob uncontrollably at performances by Frank Sinatra, Elvis Presley, or the Beatles, when listening to some more recent forms of rock, both females and males in the audience often seem to be mad at the world. Could it be that the availability of too many alternatives has led to a generation severely affected with anomie? The baby Boomers protested because they did not like the establishment; their offspring may be protesting because of the lack of an establishment.

17.1.3: The Problem with Definitions

Throughout this course, we have been careful about the use of certain words when they are intended to connote a specific musical style. "Pop," "mainstream," "R&B," and other terms have all maintained an intended distinction based on specific identifiable musical characteristics.

17.1.4: Settling on a Definition of Alternative Rock

As a result of the evolving definitions of these stylistic labels, the distinction between mainstream and alternative artists made in this chapter will be based not on musical

Difficulties in Defining Alternative Rock

The following section will provide an overview of the challenges associated with clearly defining "alternative rock."

Fragmentation of Music—As the twentieth century came to an end, the diversity of musical styles (branches of the rock and roll genealogical tree) became so numerous that it makes the fragmentation during the 1960s and 1970s seem minor by comparison. At the same time, a high level of cross-pollination between styles was occurring, resulting in many new stylistic labels for these various hybrids.

Blurring of Boundaries—Terms that have become familiar from earlier sections of this course have begun to take on different meanings. The term rhythm and blues provides a case in point. This term is no longer used to describe only the branch of the rock music tree that has its roots in the R&B of the 1940s and 1950s, but it is now often used to describe much different music; for example, some subcategories of rap are now considered R&B. Pop, as defined by *Billboard*'s online list of "Top Pop Catalog Albums," includes contemporary artists as diverse as Lady Gaga, Brad Paisley, Adele, The Black Eyed Peas, Eminem, Rascal Flatts, Arcade Fire, Norah Jones, and Taylor Swift. None of these artists would have been a likely candidate for Pop as defined in earlier sections of this course. Further evidence of the blurring of boundaries can be found by listening to the music itself, which represents influences of R&B, dance music, country rock, hip-hop, soul, and some eclectic combinations of these styles.

Use of the term "mainstream," as if discussing a particular musical style, has become particularly problematic. A quick look at albums attaining multi-platinum status—tangible socioeconomic evidence of mainstream appeal—during the first three months of 2011 provides a glimpse of the diversity of taste inherent in the record-buying public at the time (see the table below). At a time when alternative rock (Kings of Leon), rap/hip-hop (Eminem), R&B (Chris Brown), Latin music (Prince Royce), dance pop (Pussycat Dolls), country rock (Taylor Swift and Carrie Underwood), and Pop standards (Michael Bublé) were all listed alongside Elton John, the meaning of *mainstream* had become diluted to the point of being meaningless.

Dilution of the Term "Mainstream"—

A list of multi-platinum albums from early 2011 represents the diversity of styles in the mainstream.

Artist	Category	Album Title	Number of Albums Sold by March 2011 (in millions)
Eminem	rap/hip-hop	*The Eminem Show* (2002)	10
Eminem	rap/hip-hop	*The Marshall Mathers LP* (2000)	10
Elton John	mainstream/ soft rock	*Greatest Hits: 1970–2002* (2002)	5
Taylor Swift	country rock	*Taylor Swift* (2006)	5
Chris Brown	R&B	*Exclusive* (2007)	2
Prince Royce	Latin	*Prince Royce* (2010)	2
Kings of Leon	alternative	*Only By the Night* (2008)	2
Michael Bublé	pop	*Crazy Love* (2009)	2
Pussycat Dolls	dance pop	*PCD* (2005)	2
Carrie Underwood	country rock	*Play On* (2009)	2

style, but on artist intent. We will define *mainstream artists* as those who approached their craft in a manner similar to that of a corporation seeking to turn a profit, using music as a commodity. In contrast, artists in the alternative category, at least in the early years of their professional music careers, actively spurned the trappings of the business side of the industry, seeking rather to express themselves artistically, whether there was money to be made or not. This approach is quite similar to the independent record labels of the 1950s. In fact, many of these artists intentionally chose to associate with an indie, rather than a major label, in an attempt to avoid the corporate money-making machine. Some artists, like Ani DiFranco, even established their own record labels, marketing and distributing their recordings. In this sense, the alternative approach is a state of mind that distinguishes it from the mainstream commercial approach of other artists.

JOURNAL

Finding New Music in an Era of Unprecedented Choice

Open your favorite online music site or a streaming service to which you subscribe. Perform a search for music representing one of your favorite subgenres of rock and roll. How many items were returned in response to your initial search? Continue to narrow down the search, describing in your response the selections you make in the search engine and the results obtained. Keep going until you narrow the search and identify an item that fits that search criteria but that you have never heard before. Listen to that recording. Provide the song title, artist, and describe the sound of the music. Of particular interest, how well does the music found fit into the style of music for which you were searching? Compose a paragraph describing how you typically discover new music in an era when the number of choices available is truly unprecedented.

 The response entered here will appear in the performance dashboard and can be viewed by your instructor.

Submit

17.2: The Beginnings of Alternative Rock in the 1970s

OBJECTIVE: Identify the influences on early alternative rock

Since its earliest days, one of rock music's central themes has been the relationship between the sexes. Whether soft rock and rockabilly artists were singing about love or mainstream artists were implicitly or explicitly singing about sex, the assumption was that both the love and the sex were heterosexual. This is a continuation of the boy-loves-girl traditions (or vice versa) in the roots of early rock and roll. While that type of romantic relationship may have established the foundation for rock, the

level of inclusivity regarding relationships (and openness to alternative lifestyles) was about to increase as we take a close look at some of the alternative rock styles that evolved.

17.2.1: Glitter Rock

In the early 1970s, an offshoot of the British mainstream known as **glitter rock** (or **glam rock**) varied from this norm. Certainly these rockers were presenting an alternative to mainstream music by expressing their own individuality, portraying androgynous stage characters, with little thought for mainstream commercial success.

17.2.2: David Bowie

The unquestioned leader of this early, alternative trend was David Bowie, one of the true enigmas of rock. A musical chameleon, he was able to transform the sound of his music and change his persona radically and seemingly endlessly.

David Bowie on stage as Ziggy Stardust, c. 1972.
SOURCE: Jim forrest/Alamy Stock Photo

When describing Bowie, most writers speak of his theatricality, the role of symbolism in his performances, and his complicated psyche. His music is rarely the central focus.

Musical Career and Style of David Bowie

Indeed, Bowie was not a great musical innovator; he might more accurately be described as an actor who used rock music as his medium of communication.

Bowie (born in south London in 1947) changed his name in 1966 from David Jones to David Bowie to avoid confusion with Davy Jones of the Monkees. As a teenager, he pursued his talent for art by working for a commercial art company and a London advertising agency; his theatrical abilities carried him into a mime company, avant-garde films, and a few commercials. Looking for his own musical style, he tried being a Dylan-like folksinger, an Anthony Newley–type pop singer, and a member of various local rock bands.

After several commercially unsuccessful albums, Bowie produced *The Man Who Sold the World* (1970) containing some rather morose songs about his bizarre upbringing, but it also revealed the potential of an artist in development. The album cover depicted Bowie dressed to resemble either Lauren Bacall (Helander 1982, 49) or a "swishy blunt-cut Beau Brummel" (White 1984, 202). Openly admitting his bisexuality, Bowie soon found his style being referred to as glitter rock or glam rock. He began to project a purposely androgynous image.

He created a character named Ziggy Stardust. His first album as Ziggy, *The Rise and Fall of Ziggy Stardust and the Spiders from Mars* (1972), revealed Bowie's ability to shift his musical gears. The opening moments of "Rock 'n' Roll Suicide" sound like Dylan, "It Ain't Easy" reminds us of R&B, and songs like "Star" and "Suffragette City" are good old mainstream rock and roll. The Ziggy Stardust tour of the United States that same year featured Bowie's peculiar mixture of bizarre makeup and costumes, elaborate lighting and staging, and camp theatricality. Bowie reached a peak of popularity in 1974 with *Diamond Dogs* and a live album, *David Live,* his first Top 10 albums. The Diamond Dogs tour to the United States included a $250,000 set; however, midway through the tour, Bowie scrapped it and changed to a stark, plain style. Gone, too, were the orange hair and the deathly white face. *Young Americans* (number 9 in 1975) contained elements of soul, R&B, and even disco ("Fame," number 1). Promoting that album, Bowie toured in 1976 with a new image: dressed in black, except for a white dress shirt, and blond hair slicked back.

After spending nearly a year in Berlin developing his next dramatic shift, Bowie re-emerged in early 1977 with the first of three albums recorded in collaboration with Brian Eno, a British art rock musician who had once been a member of Roxy Music. These three albums, *Low* (number 11 in 1977), *Heroes* (number 35 in 1977), and *Lodger* (number 20 in 1979), experiment with the heavily electronic minimalist sound of some late 1970s art rock. By 1980, the true actor in Bowie came to the fore. He had appeared in several earlier films (e.g., *The Man Who Fell to Earth*, 1976, and *Just a Gigolo*, 1978), but it was for his starring role in *The Elephant Man* (live on tour and on Broadway) that he achieved significant critical acclaim without standing behind a microphone.

Bowie's success (and his ever-changing image) continued into the new century with CD rereleases of his early recordings, new collaborations (Brian Eno and Trent Reznor), and innovative use of the Internet for marketing his music and new releases. Following a career as a musical chameleon, David Bowie passed away in January 2016, two days after his 69th birthday, the day upon which his last studio album, *Blackstar* (number 1), was released. The single Top 40 hit from this album was "Lazurus," the title song from Bowie's off-Broadway musical production. Bowie was experimenting musically until the very end, as evident from this impressively experimental album, which was recorded with a small combo of New York–based jazz musicians.

In 1976, Bowie had commented, "I consider myself responsible for a whole new school of pretensions" (Miller 1980, 389). Certainly, prior to Bowie, rock had prided itself on its rough-and-ready macho image (even Grace Slick and Janis Joplin belted and shouted lyrics in an aggressive, masculine way) and its unpretentious sincerity, but Bowie's theatrical makeup, orange hair, androgynous image, and fictional stage personae presented a new approach. He was putting on a show; it was not real, it was theater. The effect on other performers (Elton John, Alice Cooper, Kiss, and Boy George) is easily recognized. Although these performers had widely varying musical styles, all devised costumes or makeup and presented their music theatrically.

17.2.3: Boy George

A somewhat similar image to that of David Bowie was projected by Boy George (born George O'Dowd in London in 1961). He combined the androgynous glitter image with a somewhat lighter, soft rock sound. Complete with female makeup, clothing, and hairstyle, Boy George sang in a soft, gentle voice that kept early fans guessing: Was the singer a "he" or a "she"? His group, Culture Club, hit its peak popularity in the early 1980s with a series of Top 10 hits between 1982 and 1984: "Do You Really Want to Hurt Me" (number 2), "Time (Clock of the Heart)" (number 2), "I'll Tumble 4 Ya" (number 9), "Church of the Poisoned Mind" (number 10), and "Karma Chameleon" (number 1). Gradually pulling back from the androgynous look, Boy George's career was derailed by severe drug addiction. Other British acts that aligned with the glitter rock trend included Mark Bolan's T. Rex, Gary Glitter, Mott the Hoople, and Roxy Music.

JOURNAL

Bowie's Influence on the Presentation of Rock

Using YouTube or another of your favorite video archives, locate two or three videos of live performances by David Bowie in the period from 1972 to 1975 (i.e., the Ziggy Stardust, Diamond Dogs, and Young Americans eras). Second, locate a video of a performance of Alice Cooper or Kiss. When you consider the theatrical elements of these performances, what similarities can you identify between Bowie and the other artist(s)? What are some differentiating factors? Identify a more recent artist or group for whom such theatrical presentation constitutes an essential component of their success. In a sentence or two, identify any similarities with and/or differences from Bowie's dramatic performances.

▶ The response entered here will appear in the performance dashboard and can be viewed by your instructor.

Submit

17.3: The Punk Movement Takes Rock Back to the Basics

OBJECTIVE: Explain why the punk movement was considered a rebellion against other rock trends

One of the offshoots of the harder branch of mainstream rock was actually a rebellion against most of the other trends within rock, including soft rock, art rock, jazz fusion, heavy metal, and disco. As was the case with several 1970s rock trends, the focal point of **punk rock** was not musical, but extra-musical. As Keith Richard of the Rolling Stones commented, "I don't think there was anything new musically, or even from the PR point of view, image-wise. There was too much image ... and the music seemed to be the least important thing. It was more important if you puked over somebody" (Shaw 1982, 293).

Punk rock can be considered as (a) the ultimate rebellion against virtually all forms of post-1960s rock and against society in general, (b) the ultimate extension of the harder side of mainstream rock initiated by the Stones and other British blues-based bands, or (c) both of the above. Punk enthusiasts tend to prefer the first explanation because they enjoy the image of being ultimate rebels. Future rock historians may prefer the second explanation because, indeed, most of the elements of punk rock were simply the reduction ad absurdum of hard, mainstream rock. It is also quite possible that the truth is a combination of both explanations.

17.3.1: The British Punks

The harder style of mainstream rock, from the Stones through heavy metal, set itself in opposition to the sophisticated experimentation and artistic ambitions of the post-Beatles, intellectual branch of mainstream rock. Hard rockers stressed simplicity and repetitiveness, they preferred basic rock and roll, and they hoped to shock "straight" society. The punks extended all of these characteristics, playing music that was even simpler, more repetitive, and louder; their lyrics were often patently gross; and their images and antics were far more shocking. While extending these characteristics, they openly rebelled against the long, technically demanding instrumental solos; the serious art rock aspirations; and the wealthy, commercially successful rock star syndrome of many mainstream groups.

THE SEX PISTOLS The first major British punk group was the Sex Pistols, formed in 1975. Basing their act on prior "punk" bands from the United States (the New York Dolls and the Ramones), they played simple, loud rock and roll that reverted to the musical vocabulary of the hardest 1950s style, but typically with considerably less technical skill. Lead singer Johnny Rotten (John Lydon) had never sung before joining the Pistols. But, as Keith Richard said (quoted previously), the music was not really the point. Signed by EMI, the Pistols released a single in 1976, "Anarchy in the UK," that became a minor British hit. In early 1977, the Pistols appeared on London's *Today* television show. When host Bill Grundy asked Rotten to say something outrageous, he responded with several choice profanities. Perhaps as a result of this media exposure, "Anarchy" became an even bigger hit. The Pistols were denounced everywhere, from Parliament to the newspapers, and EMI dropped them like a hot potato. On their 21-date tour, all but three concerts were canceled or stopped in progress.

The Sex Pistols on stage, c. 1977.

SOURCE: Pictorial Press Ltd/Alamy Stock Photo

A&M Records signed the band, now including Sid Vicious (John Ritchie) on bass, and subsequently dropped them—all within one week. Finally, Virgin Records signed them to a new contract and released a sarcastic version of "God Save the Queen," which became a major British hit. Their one and only studio album, *Never Mind the Bullocks, Here's the Sex Pistols*, was released in late 1977. In early 1978, they attempted a U.S. tour, complete with considerable promotional hype. However, the act was a bit too much for American audiences of the time, and the tour was abandoned in San Francisco. Rotten quit (or was fired, depending on which account one believes) and formed a new band, Public Image, Ltd. The Sex Pistols continued as a band through 1978, but, in October, Sid Vicious was charged with the murder of his girlfriend, Nancy Spungen, in Manhattan. He was found dead of an apparent drug overdose in Greenwich Village in early 1979, before he could be tried.

Sex Pistols' performances included vulgar lyrics, shocking onstage antics (sticking large pins in their bodies or slashing themselves with razor blades and broken bottles), and slapping members of the audience. As a social or psychological phenomenon, this type of punk may be deemed significant; as a musical style, it was important only as evidence of just how low rock and roll could go. As Lydon (Rotten) himself said later, "The Sex Pistols were a fiasco. A farce" (Miller 1980, 462).

THE CLASH   Another major British punk band, the Clash, sounded significantly more musical when compared to the Sex Pistols. Slightly less outrageous than the Pistols in terms of lyrics and antics, the Clash nevertheless carried on the musical style of simple, basic, and repetitive harmonies; simple melodies; basic rhythms; and lots of screaming and distortion. The Clash released their first album in 1977. Not unlike the 1960s folkies, the Clash included songs that protested everything: boring jobs, police, America, rock music, violence, and racism. The growing affinity between the punks and reggae music evident during this era was illustrated in "Police and Thieves" and "White Man in Hammersmith Palais." *London Calling* (1979) made the Top 30 in the United States, as did the single "Train in Vain (Stand by Me)." The band actually broke the Top 10 with the album *Combat Rock* (1982) and a single, "Rock the Casbah" (number 8).

Following the lead of the Sex Pistols and the Clash, there were many other punk bands that wielded significant influence over musical developments during the following years, including the Fall and the Mekons.

EMERGENCE OF THE NEW WAVE STYLE   With the negative publicity received in 1978 to 1979 by the Sex Pistols and other punk bands, some artists sought to establish a new name for this music with a less negative connotation. Thus, the term **new wave** was introduced. As Arnold Shaw notes, one can view new wave as an offshoot of punk, somewhat subtler and less prone to the gruesome, the overtly repulsive, and the sadomasochistic; or *new wave* may simply be a term coined to escape the criticism and censure heaped on punk groups (Shaw 1982). As is often the case, the truth is likely to lie in-between. Most bands (and their record companies) can tolerate—and, at times, even encourage—public outrage, unless it becomes so extreme that customers refuse to buy records and concert tickets. Also, it is understandable that impaling oneself with pins and slicing one's chest open with broken glass begins, after a few performances, to lose its appeal, even to the most devoted of performers, if not fans.

The Role of Elvis Costello in New Wave Music

The following section will provide highlights from the career of Elvis Costello, a highly influential, early new wave artist.

Beginning in about 1979, many of the revolutionary punk bands lessened the aggressive sound of their music, making it more palatable and accessible to a wider audience. This explanation could provide a possible basis for the changed sound of the Clash's *Combat Rock*, containing the band's only Top 10 hit, initiating a move toward the new wave style. Elvis Costello (born Declan McManus in 1955) was a leader of this new movement. Whether it was due to his doubly nostalgic pseudonym or the gradual American acceptance of punk rock, Costello's early recordings reached the Top 40: *My Aim Is True* (number 32 in 1977) and *This Year's Model* (number 30 in 1978).

Underneath the punk attitude and the new wave musical veneer, his songwriting for these recordings reveals early signs of a skilled craftsman at work. In 1979, he launched his third major album, *Armed Forces*, with an American tour. The album rose to number 10, but, in the midst of the tour, an incident occurred that had a transforming effect on Costello. He had been capitalizing on the mean, angry punk image quite successfully, but one night, in a Columbus, Ohio, bar, Costello publicly referred to Ray Charles as a "blind, ignorant nigger" and then went on to make similar comments about James Brown. Chastened severely in the press, Costello was embarrassed by the incident and subsequently apologized. According to Ken Tucker, Costello would "tone down his aggressive demeanor for the rest of the tour, and, indeed, for the next few years" (Ward, Stokes, and Tucker 1986, 569). In some ways, that incident may have been a significant line of demarcation between punk and new wave.

Costello's songwriting talents began to be appreciated once the prohibitive shield of punkdom was penetrated. In fact, several of his songs have been covered by such singers as Linda Ronstadt and George Jones. Costello seemed to mellow somewhat, often recording oldies (*Taking Liberties*, number 28 in 1980) and country-flavored material (*Almost Blue*, number 50 in 1981). In the mid- to late 1990s, he teamed with pop songwriter Burt Bacharach for several successful albums, one of which (*Painted from Memory*, number 78 in 1998) resulted in a Grammy Award. Costello's output was prolific from his initial album through the late 1990s, and he continued to record in a wide range of musical styles: a collection of piano ballads that he composed, orchestrated, and conducted (*North*, number 57 in 2003) and an orchestral composition (*Il Sogno*, 2004). He then returned to his rock roots and his longtime band, the Imposters, for six more albums between 2004 and 2010, several of which reached the Top 40: *Delivery Man* (number 40 in 2004); *My Flame Burns Blue*; *River in Reverse*; *Momofuku*; *Secret, Profane and Sugarcane* (number 13 in 2009); and *National Ransom* (number 39 in 2010).

While new wave provided a much different sound when compared to the raw energy and distortion inherent in the punk style that preceded it, the style incorporated a similar musical simplicity and directness. We will now turn to punk-related developments in the United States.

17.3.2: America's Punk Mini-movement

Although the punk movement made its greatest immediate impact in England, its roots lie in a handful of early to mid-1960s American bands. Two prototypes for American punk were the Motor City Five (MC5) and the Velvet Underground. Formed in a suburb of Detroit in 1965, the MC5 released a series of influential recordings, including *Kick Out the Jams, Back in the USA*, and *High Time*, from 1969 to 1971. The MC5 were a critically important group in initiating the violently antiestablishment ideology upon which punk rock was founded. From 1967 to 1968, the group became known as the "house band" for John Sinclair's radical White Panther Party, releasing their debut album, recorded live, *Kick Out the Jams* (number 30 in 1969). When Sinclair was locked up on marijuana charges and they were dumped by Elecktra (at least partially due to the prominence of the word "motherfucker" in the anathematic title song's hook), the band was left without a manager or a record label. Atlantic took the opportunity to sign the band, releasing *Back in the USA*, a critically acclaimed album that fell short on commercial success, reaching only number 137 on the Hot 200. After being dropped by Atlantic, the band moved to England but dissolved soon thereafter.

VELVET UNDERGROUND Also coming together in 1965, the Velvet Underground was an eccentric band from New York City. Organized by classically trained pianist Lou Reed, the Underground defies categorization: Not only were they not in the mainstream, it would be difficult to assign them to any "stream" but their own. Joining with John Cale, a classically trained violist and pianist from South Wales, guitarist Sterling Morrison, female drummer Maureen Tucker, and German-born female singer Nico, Reed christened the new group the Velvet Underground (after the name of a paperback book that was a survey of sadomasochism). The band became a part of Andy Warhol's traveling "happenings," called the Exploding Plastic Inevitable.

Signed by MGM Records, the band released *The Velvet Underground and Nico* in 1967. Containing several explicit songs about drugs ("Heroin"), drug dealers ("I'm Waiting for the Man"), and sadomasochism ("Venus in Furs"), the album received very little radio play and died after reaching the number 171 position. Nico left the group, but the others released a highly experimental second album called *White Light/White Heat* in 1968. The title track was another drug-related song; "The Gift" consisted of a surrealistic, sex-oriented spoken lyric over a noisy, repetitive accompaniment. "I Heard Her Call My Name" was an early experiment in distortion and feedback; the 17-minute "Sister Ray" contained half-sung, half-spoken sexually explicit lyrics over a heavily distorted, repetitive accompaniment. This avant-garde album peaked at number 199. The Underground staggered along for several years before finally disbanding in 1972. Only a single Velvet Underground album cracked the Top 100: *VU* (number 85 in 1985). As an anticommercial, antiestablishment, avant-garde band, complete with a focus on drugs and sex, the Velvet Underground was an early forerunner of the punk movement.

IGGY POP Not far behind the Underground was Iggy Pop and the Stooges. James Osterberg (Iggy Pop) was from Ann Arbor, Michigan. In 1967, he formed a quartet that specialized in loud, simple, and repetitive music that served as a background for Osterberg's outrageous antics. According to Brock Helander (1982, 577), "Over the years, his notoriety grew with deeds such as threatening and vilifying audiences, cutting himself with broken bottles, pouring hot wax over his body, intentionally smashing his teeth, and throwing up, even urinating on audiences and allowing ardent fans to perform fellatio on him."

Iggy and the Stooges' 1969 debut album was produced by the Velvet Underground's John Cale. After this and the follow-up album fared poorly, the band went to England to work with David Bowie. Bowie produced their third album, *Raw Power*, which is often cited as an

Iggy Pop, 1992.

SOURCE: Pictorial Press Ltd/Alamy Stock Photo

archetype, not only for the punk trend, but also for heavy metal. By 1974, the band had disintegrated. Several years later, Iggy teamed up with David Bowie again and released several more albums. In the early 1980s, he made another tour, complete with more outrageous antics. Iggy Pop, even more so than the Velvet Underground, became the prototype of the punk style of the late 1970s.

OTHER AMERICAN PUNK PERFORMERS If the punk style flourished anywhere in the United States, it was in New York City. Following in the footsteps of the Velvet Underground came Patti Smith, who recited her poetry over the sounds of a drummerless duo or trio of instrumentalists. The Patti Smith Group released four albums during the 1970s, two of which, *Easter* (1978) and *Wave*

(1979), made the Top 20. Smith dropped out of the music scene in the early 1980s, when she moved to Detroit and married MC5 guitarist Fred "Sonic" Smith. In the late 1980s, she returned to the recording studio and released a series of albums, including the politically scathing election-year release of *Trampin'* (2004).

From Queens came the Ramones, a quartet that established an early punk image with their torn T-shirts and black leather jackets. The relatively small punk movement in the United States stayed loyal to the Ramones, allowing two of their albums to crack the Top 50 (*Rocket to Russia*, 1977; *End of the Century*, 1980). They specialized in very brief songs with simple lyrics that were performed at breakneck speed.

Crossing between the punk movement and the glitter rock trend were the New York Dolls. Adopting eccentric costumes and androgynous makeup, the Dolls combined an amateurish primitivism with raw violence. Their brief appearance on the scene yielded two albums, released in 1973 and 1974: *New York Dolls* and *In Too Much Too Soon*, respectively. After two albums, the band was dropped by Mercury Records due to disappointing sales. By 1975, Johnny Thunders (guitar) and Jerry Nolan (drums) left the Dolls. Shortly thereafter, David Johansen initiated a solo career, evolving into Buster Poindexter, a lounge-singing alter ego. At the request of Morrissey (former vocalist for the Smiths and a one-time president of a New York Dolls fan club in England), remaining band members reunited to perform at a music festival in 2004. In 2006, the group released *One Day It Will Please Us to Remember Even This*, a new studio album. In 2011, the two surviving, founding members of the Dolls (singer David Johansen and guitarist Sylvain Sylvain) released *Dancing Backwards in High Heels*. Despite being highly influential on the evolution of punk and glitter rock, no Dolls album cracked the Top 100.

NEW WAVE EMERGES OUT OF AMERICAN PUNK The two 1970s new wave bands that have secured a significant place in rock history are the Talking Heads (led by David Byrne) and the Police (led by vocalist-bassist Sting).

Punk and New Wave Bands in America

Though they began with relatively simple musical styles, each evolved in a unique way. Details about the Talking Heads and The Police be provided in the following section.

Talking Heads—Emerging from the New York punk scene in 1977, the Talking Heads led the way from punk to new wave. They generally avoided eccentric costumes and onstage antics and drew on contemporary classical trends to create a more

sophisticated style. Their early lyrics often emphasized the struggle between the individual and society.

The Heads' first four albums were produced by Brian Eno at about the same time he was collaborating with David Bowie. Eno experimented with the latest in electronic technology: synthesizers, tape manipulation, and computerized keyboards. By the beginning of the 1980s, Eno was forming a bridge to a subcategory of contemporary classical music often called **minimalism** (sometimes referred to as *pattern music* or *process music*). The minimalists created their music by designing a limited number of tonal sequences or patterns of unequal length; then, as these patterns repeated over and over, they created a constantly shifting overall sound—a kind of sonic metamorphosis. The basic concept of the minimalists' simple, repetitive patterns was naturally appealing to rock musicians (and vice versa). In late 1970s New York City, rock musicians such as Eno, Robert Fripp (also formerly of Roxy Music), and Fred Frith were drawn to the music of minimalist composers like Philip Glass (*Koyaanisqatsi*, 1983, and *Einstein on the Beach*, 2005) and Steve Reich (*Piano Phase*, 1967, and *Three Tales*, 2002).

Talking Heads' albums like *Remain in Light* (number 19 in 1980) illustrate a rock-style adaptation of minimalist principles. When transferred to rock, the patterns were modified to conform to a regular, quadruple meter, but one can hear the reliance on steady, unchanging patterns layered throughout the instrumental accompaniment. The result is an elaborate drone effect: It sounds rather robot-like and emotionless, as if some great machine were grinding out the music. For example, in "The Overload," a steady drone persists throughout, the drum pattern is unchanging, the vocal line is sung as if it were a somber chant, and only various electronic sounds color the otherwise unchanging sonic environment. In songs like "Once in a Lifetime" and "Houses in Motion," with their reliance on spoken lyrics over a constantly repetitive accompaniment, one can hear the influence of Velvet Underground's music of the late 1960s. Influences of reggae and other black styles are also readily apparent in the music of the Talking Heads; "Houses in Motion" is a good example. In 1983, the band had a Top 10 hit with "Burning Down the House." The Heads continued to evolve through the mid-1980s, and lead singer David Byrne continued an impressively prolific solo career into the twenty-first century.

The Police—Also derivative of the punk movement (with associated reggae elements) and influenced by the new wave trend were the Police, a British trio headed by lead singer Sting (born Gordon Sumner in 1951). Originally formed in 1977, it was not until 1980 that major success came with their third album, *Zenyatta Mondatta*. The Police's peak came in 1983 with *Synchronicity*, their only number 1 studio recording. The album included mainstream rock in the form of the title song (parts 1 and 2), reggae references ("Walking in Your Footsteps"), punk influence ("Mother"), soft rock (the number 1 song "Every Breath You Take"), and even a touch of jazz influence ("Tea in the Sahara"). As was often the case with the Police, the lyrics were quite introspective and intellectually oriented, with hints of new age philosophy. After the band broke up, Sting's musical career as a solo artist proved quite impressive, including ten Top 10 albums between 1985 and

2010 and over a dozen Top 40 singles. Confirming the magnitude of his star power, Sting placed his performance of a collection of music by John Dowland, an influential English composer and lutenist of the late sixteenth and early seventeenth centuries (*Songs from the Labyrinth*, 2006), at number 25 on the *Billboard Hot 200*.

In 2007, all three original members of the Police came together for a long-anticipated but short-lived reunion tour. Then, following in the style of *Songs from the Labyrinth*, Sting released an album of Christmas carols, *If On a Winter's Night* (2009); rather than the familiar songs heard commonly during the holiday season, however, these were fourteenth-century carols, along with other songs created by adding lyrics to the music of Bach and Schubert. It is a testament to Sting's star power that even this album reached number 6. His next album, *Symphonicities* (also number 6 in 2010) consisted of covers of classic Police and solo tracks, reimagined with orchestral accompaniment; some of these versions vary greatly from the sound and style of the original recordings. Sting toured briefly with Peter Gabriel in 2014, and then, in collaboration with author-lyricist Brian Yorkey, he created "The Last Ship," a musical loosely based on his childhood in post-war England. The play opened on Broadway in October of that year, but, unfortunately, closed after only three months. He continues to release new music well into the new millennium, including *57th & 9th* (number 9 in 2016), an album named after an intersection he crossed daily to get to the recording studio. The style of this album is much closer to the sound of his early solo albums than to the lute-tinged, medieval influence of most of his recordings since 2007. Few artists boast as eclectic a catalog of releases as Sting. In his own words, "I really do what the fuck I want" (*Rolling Stone*, Aug. 11, 2016, 14).

Other New Wave Groups—Growing out of the new wave movement were other groups, including Devo, Blondie, and Pere Ubu. Devo (from Akron, Ohio) took the idea of machine-like, repetitive patterns and created a robot-like sound using short, clipped vocals and instrumental lines. The result was an antiseptic rock sound, seemingly devoid of emotion—almost as far from soul music as one could get. Pere Ubu (from Cleveland) was similar in some ways, but the vocals of David Thomas varied from blunt, choppy declarative phrases and repeated words to sudden bursts of emotive squawks and shouts. Generally (with the exception of the Talking Heads and the Police), new wave seems to have been a brief fad during the transition to the 1980s, although both Devo (*Something for Everybody*; number 30 in 2010) and the Cars (*Move Like This*; number 7 in 2011) reunited to release new studio albums and tour well into the new millennium.

17.4: Alternative Styles Evolve

OBJECTIVE: Relate punk rock to alternative rock styles

The roots of alternative music can be found in the return to the basics of rock considered essential by the punk movement: Keep the music simple, limit the number and length of instrumental solos, and play "with an attitude." Harbingers

of these dissenters from the mainstream of rock began to appear in the 1960s; for example, as described elsewhere in this chapter, the Velvet Underground (laying a foundation for the punk movement) and Captain Beefheart (eclectic pioneer of art rock). A similar reversion to musical simplicity and overt antisocial behavior were the distinctive characteristics in the split between the fans of the Beatles and the Rolling Stones during the 1960s, discussed in other sections of this course. Although one of the difficulties inherent in any discussion of alternative music is the wide range of styles subsumed under this heading, it is possible to identify three main trends: post-punk hardcore music, thrash metal, and grunge. Having discussed **thrash metal** elsewhere in this course, we will now take a close look at hardcore and grunge, along with their derivatives, all of which are commonly referred to as part of "alternative rock."

17.4.1: Post-punk Hardcore

A number of bands, both in America and England, refused to follow the new wave directions, developing instead into the hardcore movement of the early 1980s. These hardcore bands form a direct link between the punk rock of the late 1970s and the emergent forms of alternative music in the 1980s and 1990s. Formation of the SST record label in Southern California provided a means for bands like Black Flag (whose guitarist Greg Ginn had founded the label) and the Minutemen to record and distribute their music without the support of a major record company. Following in the footsteps of their punk rock progenitors, the hardcore bands took loudness, intensity, tempo, and nihilism to new extremes.

Two premier hardcore bands of the early 1980s, X and Black Flag, served as prototypes for hard-rock bands of the post-punk era. Combining the hyperactive guitar banging and pulsating drum rhythms of punk rock with lyrics expressing dark disillusionment and distrust, John Doe (John Nommensen, bass and vocals), Exene Cervenka (Christine Cervenka, vocals), Billy Zoom (Tyson Kindale, guitar), and Don J. Bonebrake formed X in 1977, evolving out of the Los Angeles punk scene. "Nausea," "Sex and Dying in High Society," and "We're Desperate," provide examples of the band's sound and message. In addition to founding SST Records, Greg Ginn (guitar) and Charles Dukowski (bass) added a "party animal" aesthetic to the nihilistic angst of the hardcore movement, establishing Black Flag. Exuding a feeling of disillusionment, Henry Rollins (Black Flag's vocalist since 1981) professed to be the typical product of a dysfunctional family. In discussing his feelings about life, he said, "I don't know jack shit about love, or about feeling a relationship with a blood relative. That shit means nothing to me" (Szatmary 2007, 296). Such sentiments were expressed musically in Black Flag songs like "Depression," "Dead Inside," and "Life of Pain" to the accompaniment of loud, distorted guitars and driving rhythms.

A large number of other bands could be included in the hardcore rock category, some of the most prominent of which were the Germs, Hüsker Dü, the Replacements, Dead Kennedys, the Circle Jerks (formed by founding Black Flag vocalist Keith Morris), and Suicidal Tendencies. However, because the hardcore movement served as a bridge between the punk music of the 1970s and the alternative movement of the late 1980s, we will turn now to developments relevant to these later musical styles.

17.5: Grunge

OBJECTIVE: Outline reasons for the popularity of grunge rock

During the late 1980s, a rock revolution emerged in the Pacific Northwest. Influenced by hardcore punk and heavy metal, Seattle became a musical hub for this movement, combining distorted guitars and angst-ridden lyrics. What began as a regional phenomenon expanded quickly to a national level driven by the most commercially successful groups (Nirvana, Soundgarden, and Pearl Jam), and then gradually extended to an international audience.

17.5.1: The Pixies

One of the most influential bands of the late 1980s, the Pixies laid the musical foundation upon which **grunge** and much of the alternative music that followed is based. Cited as a primary musical influence by Nirvana's Kurt Cobain, within a three-year period, the Pixies placed three albums in the Top 100: *Doolittle* (number 90 in 1989), *Bossanova* (number 70 in 1990), and *Trompe Le Monde* (number 92 in 1991). Formed in Boston in 1986, Black Francis (born Charles Michael Kitteridge Thompson IV, [guitar and vocals]), Joey Santiago (guitar), Kim Deal (bass), and David Lovering (drums) began as Pixies in Panoply, releasing an EP in 1987, followed the next year by their first full-length recording, *Surfer Rosa*. A staple of the Pixies' musical style was the use of a soft verse alternating with a hard-rocking chorus, a style frequently adopted later in the music of Nirvana. Although the Pixies recordings continued to be released in the early 1990s, the high level of tension between band members resulted in a series of solo projects and the eventual breakup of the group. Solo projects by Black Francis and those by Kim Deal (both the Breeders and the Amps) exerted a significant impact on the burgeoning alternative music scene. In a surprise chain of events, the Pixies reunited for a world tour in 2004, performing a series of sold-out tour dates, and toured again in 2009 to celebrate the twentieth anniversary of the release of *Doolittle*, and continued to tour well into the second decade of the new millennium.

17.5.2: Nirvana

Although Sub Pop's first real success story came with two EPs by Soundgarden, *Screaming Life* (1987) and *Fopp* (1988), credit for placing the sound of Seattle grunge into the mainstream of rock and roll goes to Nirvana.

Foundation of Grunge

The following section will provide an overview of the emergence of grunge in the Pacific Northwest and the rock styles that proved heavily influential on these musicians.

Emerging from the Seattle area at the end of the 1980s, grunge proved to be the most commercially successful subgenre of the alternative music scene. Driven by the belief that the basis of artistic freedom was to provide an outlet so musicians could maintain artistic control over their material instead of turning this responsibility over to a major record company, Bruce Pavitt turned an unsuccessful record store venture into a highly successful regional label: Sub Pop Records.

Of course, it is likely that many of the bands that found their way to Sub Pop could not have attracted the attention of any major label due to their raw musical style and the state of the music industry at the time. As a result, Pavitt began his career in the recording business by releasing a compilation of music written and performed by regional bands from the Pacific Northwest entitled *Sub Pop 100*. The label's next release was an EP by Green River, a local band with a sound that would soon become associated

with the Pacific Northwest. Two members of Green River left to form Mudhoney in 1988, one of the earliest grunge bands and Sub Pop's biggest-selling group during these early years. The other two members of Green River formed Mother Love Bone (one of the first Seattle bands to sign with a major label) and later achieved superstardom as members of Pearl Jam.

Musical characteristics of this early form of grunge were closely related to the hardcore sound and, therefore, to punk rock of the 1970s. The apparent purpose behind grunge and, for that matter, hardcore or thrash metal is not aesthetic beauty of the sort revered by mainstream pop culture. Rather, these alternative artists reveled in dissonance, the sound that purposely pervades their music at almost every turn, as if challenging the listener to move away from the comfortable place of the familiar, the tried, and the true.

Although the musical characteristics of grunge were often intentionally uncomfortable to listen to, there was an element of tolerance in the lyrics. Songwriters like Kurt Cobain of Nirvana were openly pro-gay and pro-woman. Whereas the lyrics of punk rock commonly spewed messages of hate at the establishment and the world in general, grunge artists tended more toward self-reflection, taking that same intense hatred and turning it inward, often in a form of self-loathing.

Musical Journey of Nirvana

The following section will provide highlights from the brief career of Nirvana, a highly influential band that was one of the primary groups responsible for bringing grunge to a national (and international) audience.

Early Career

Nirvana; (L to R) Dave Grohl, Kurt Cobain, and Krist Novoselic.
SOURCE: Roy Tee/S.I.N./Alamy Stock Photo

Influenced musically by local punk band the Melvins, Black Flag, San Francisco's Flipper, Black Sabbath, and the Pixies, Kurt Cobain and childhood friend Krist Novoselic formed Nirvana in 1987. The group signed with Sub Pop Records the following year. Typical of the production that went into recordings made by most of their grunge contemporaries, Nirvana's debut album (*Bleach*, 1989) was recorded for a total cost of $606.17 (Romanowski and George-Warren 1995). "School," "Blew," and their cover of Shocking Blue's "Love Buzz" exemplify the fast-paced early style of the band. It is the melodicism of the ballad "About a Girl," however, that revealed the underlying talent and songwriting craftsmanship that was to carry Nirvana to a level of success far beyond that attained by most other Seattle bands. Receiving critical acclaim for this album, the band signed a recording contract with David Geffen's DGC label, hoping to deliver the musical style of the Pacific Northwest to a national audience. In 1990, they added drummer Dave Grohl.

Commercial Success —Nirvana attained impressive commercial success with the release of *Nevermind* (number 1 in 1991), eventually selling over 10 million copies. In addition to successful album sales, two songs from the album were Top 40 hits: "Smells Like Teen Spirit" (number 6) and "Come As You Are" (number 32). "Smells Like Teen Spirit" (see the Listening Guide at the end of Section 17.5.2.) was a breakthrough not only for Nirvana but for the entire alternative music scene. With its release, alternative music was accepted by many white, middle-class post-Boomers as the music of their generation. African American youth had accepted rap/hip-hop as their own, and now a second segment of the American youth population had a musical style from which teenage anthems began to emerge. "Smells Like Teen Spirit" is the first such song to evolve from the alternative tradition and to make a mark in the mainstream arena of rock and roll, stating explicitly what some perceived as the expectations of the post-boomer generation: that they were here, and needed to be entertained. After releasing a collection of early singles and outtakes in 1992 (*Incesticide,* number 39), the band issued *In Utero* (1993), which debuted at number 1. Although this recording resulted in no Top 40 hits, both "All Apologies" and "Heart-Shaped Box" became favorites on *AOR* (album-oriented rock) radio stations. Cobain had wanted to name the album *I Hate Life and Want to Die*—an uncanny, if tragic, harbinger of events to come—but the record company eventually convinced him otherwise.

Effects of Success—Success at the level experienced by Nirvana affects artists in different ways. There are those, such as the Beatles, the Rolling Stones, and Van Halen, who seem to thrive on attention and economic success as a confirmation of their ability. Others respond differently. Kurt Cobain's level of personal happiness and satisfaction seems to have been inversely related to the level of Nirvana's success. The greater the heights to which their popularity rose, the more Cobain felt his audience was blind to the antiestablishment message of their music. In response to those who accused him of selling out to the influences of a major label, Cobain provided a terse reply in the liner notes for *Incesticide* (1992). He offered a "big fuck you" to anyone who considered him so naïve that he would allow himself to be controlled by the industry. He goes on to communicate his complete lack of guilt for the commercial exploitation of what he considered to be a totally depleted youth culture, claiming that, in his eyes, punk rock was largely dead.

The need to justify commercial success seems to be a common trait among alternative bands and artists. Emerging as strong adherents of the artistic freedom associated with independent record labels, many alternative bands found themselves a few short years later signed with major labels and selling records at a rate comparable to—sometimes even surpassing—their mainstream rock counterparts.

Tragic End—During a period of time that, by all normal accounts, should have been extremely uplifting for him—unprecedented popularity for the band, his marriage to Courtney Love (vocalist for Hole), and the birth of their healthy baby—Cobain began to show signs of extreme discontent. Beginning in the spring of 1993, his unhappiness was manifested through a series of drug overdoses

and a domestic assault incident. Revolver in hand, Cobain threatened to commit suicide in his own home on March 18, 1994. Following this event, he checked into a recovery center at the end of March but sneaked away after only two days. One week later, on April 8th, he shot himself in the head with a 20-gauge shotgun.

The news of Cobain's death was as devastating to the post-Boomers as the earlier deaths of Jimi Hendrix, Janis Joplin, and Jim Morrison had been to the baby boom generation. Nirvana's fans, along with hosts of radio stations and MTV, mourned their loss for weeks. Later that year, *Unplugged in New York* (an album of Nirvana's live appearances on MTV the previous year) debuted at number 1. During the period following Cobain's death, Novoselic and Grohl assisted to compile a collection of live recordings, *From the Muddy Banks of the Wishkah* (1996), which also reached the top of the chart, appropriately capping the career of one of the most significant rock groups of the early 1990s. A documentary entitled *Kurt Cobain: Montage of Heck* (2015) provides a candid glimpse into the life of this tortured artist, responsible for producing some of the most recognizable music of the 1990s.

Life of Members in the Post-Nirvana Era—The member of the trio who has continued most effectively in the post-Nirvana era is, without a doubt, Dave Grohl. Moving from behind the drums to lead vocal and guitar, Grohl established the Foo Fighters in 1995 and released nine Top 25 albums and several Top 40 hits over the next 15 years. In 2011, *Wasting Light* debuted at number 1. Grohl returned to drums temporarily in 2009 to form Them Crooked Vultures with Josh Homme on vocals (Queens of the Stone Age) and John Paul Jones on bass (Led Zeppelin). Their eponymous debut album reached number 12 that same year. Grohl then took an interesting detour into filmmaking, producing two compelling documentaries: *Sound City* (2013) and *Foo Fighters: Sonic Highways* (2014). The first was an homage to the studio where *Nevermind* and many other classic albums were recorded, while the latter presents a virtual tour of seminal recording studios in various cities across the nation, each of eight episodes focusing on an identified "music capital" (including Chicago, Nashville, Seattle, Washington D.C., Austin) and the important role of the chosen studio in creating the music scene for that region. The soundtrack album for this series peaked at number 2. While working on the soundtrack for *Sound City*, Grohl had the opportunity to work with many leading artists, the most famous of whom was, undoubtedly, Paul McCartney. In collaboration with Grohl and Novoselik, Sir Paul penned a heavy rocker entitled "Cut Me Some Slack," which won the Grammy for Best Rock Song in 2013. After releasing *St. Cecilia*, an EP that didn't quite make it into the Top 100, Foo Fighters released *Concrete and Gold* (2017), which debuted at the top of the chart.

Click or tap the video title to listen to "Smells Like Teen Spirit" by Nirvana.
https://www.youtube.com/watch?v=hTWKbfoikeg*

Click or tap the video title to listen to "All Apologies" by Nirvana
https://www.youtube.com/watch?v=m0drC8qVMRk*

*By clicking this link, you will be redirected to a third-party site.

Listening Guide: "Smells Like Teen Spirit" (Nirvana)

0:00–0:24	Introduction (12 measures)	Begins with rhythm guitar on the chord progression that serves as the foundation for each chorus section (C). In the fourth bar, a drum fill leads to the entry of the full ensemble.
0:25–0:33	Verse 1 (20 measures total) (A = 12 measures)	The verse consists of two basic musical ideas. The A section of the verse begins with a 4-bar instrumental prelude.
0:34–0:49		Continuing the A musical idea, the vocal enters in the fifth measure.
0:50–1:05	(B = 8 measures)	With a change of the accompanimental chord progression and the entry of the lyric "hello … low?" this B section of the verse provides a transition to the chorus.
1:06–1:30	Chorus (16 measures total) (C = 12 measures)	The chorus also consists of two sections. The C musical idea from the introduction initiates the chorus.
1:31–1:38	Instrumental break (D = 4 measures)	Continuing the chorus with a progression containing a surprising chromatic chord at the end of the first and third measures, this D section is answered at the end of each phrase.
1:39–2:03	Verse 2 (20 measures total) (A = 12 measures)	As before, begins with the 4-bar instrumental prelude; the vocal enters in the fifth measure.
2:04–2:19	(B = 8 measures)	The B section returns.
2:20–2:44	Chorus (16 measures total) (C = 12 measures)	As before: the C musical idea …
2:45–2:52	Instrumental break (D = 4 measures)	… followed by D.
2:53–3:24	Guitar solo (A, B, & C = 16 measures)	The guitar solo—actually just an instrumental performance of the vocal melody for A, then B over the heavy instrumental accompaniment to the chorus C section. It is in this instrumental section that three of the four musical ideas (A, B, and C) included in this song are all performed.
3:25–3:49	Verse 3 (20 measures total) (A = 12 measures)	As before, begins with the 4-bar instrumental prelude (this time with a sustained lead guitar chord over this opening subsection); the vocal enters again in the fifth measure.
3:50–4:05	(B = 8 measures)	The B section returns.
4:06–4:29	Chorus (21 measures total) (C = 12 measures)	As before, the C musical idea …
4:30–5:01	Coda (C = 9 measures)	This ending musical phrase uses the same instrumental accompaniment as the C section of the chorus, but the vocalist simply repeats a single phrase nine times, until the final sustained chord.

NOTE: In the Listening Guide above, it is worth noting that the sections labeled "A," "B," and "C" are all based on the same chord progression but are distinguished within the musical form due to the dramatic differences in texture and timbral content.

"Smells Like Teen Spirit" was Nirvana's highest-charting single, reaching number 6; in fact, it is the band's only Top 10 hit. Though the sound of the group varied from soft ballads to highly charged punk, this song provides a prime example of the musicians at their anathematic best, merging elements of punk, heavy metal, and mainstream rock. Also clearly evident is Kurt Cobain's lyrical creativity.

17.5.3: Pearl Jam

Another group that is widely credited with bringing the Seattle sound to national attention is Pearl Jam. As mentioned previously, bassist Jeff Ament and guitarist Stone Gossard had been members of Green River, one of the earliest grunge bands. Following the breakup of that band, the two musicians joined vocalist Andrew Wood to form Mother Love Bone. Wood died of a heroin overdose shortly after the band completed its first album. Adding Mike McCready (guitar), Eddie Vedder (vocalist from San Diego), and Dave Krusen (drums), the band began performing under the name Mookie Blaylock in honor of the New Jersey Nets basketball star. Shortly thereafter, they changed their name to Pearl Jam, a reference to a "psychedelic confection" made by Vedder's half-Native American great grandmother (George-Warren and Romanowski 2001).

Musical Career of Pearl Jam

The following section will provide highlights from the career of Pearl Jam, another band responsible for bringing grunge into the mainstream of rock.

Ten—Apparently not exhibiting the aversion to major labels shared by some Seattle groups, Pearl Jam signed initially with Epic Records and released their debut album (*Ten,* number 2 in 1992); the name of the album was the number on Mookie Blaylock's jersey. Particularly noteworthy examples of Pearl Jam's early musical style are "Even Flow," "Alive," and "Jeremy." In 1992, shortly after Nirvana brought alternative music to mainstream rock radio, Pearl Jam surpassed Nirvana in record sales, combining the riff-heavy guitar sound of 1970s rock with the angst of 1980s post-punk. All the while, however, they continued to provide their listeners with catchy guitar riffs, hook lines, and memorable choruses. Shortly after the release of their debut album, drummer Kusen left the band, to be replaced by Dave Abbruzzese.

Vs.—In contrast to the relatively consistent hard-rock style of *Ten,* Pearl Jam's second album, *Vs.* (debuting at number 1 in 1993), revealed an impressive variety of musical styles. Contrast, for example, the hard-rock sound of "Go" or "Leash" with the folk influence apparent in both "Elderly Woman Behind the Counter in a Small Town" and "Indifference."

During this early period of their career, the band made some risky business decisions. Although their rise to popularity was greatly enhanced by MTV hits and their appearance on the second Lollapalooza tour, spurning the accepted conventions of the recording industry, the band refused to release videos to promote *Vs.* In addition, during the promotional tour for the album, Pearl Jam chose to perform in smaller auditoriums and on college campuses, rather than in the stadium settings that had become commonplace for "arena rock" concerts. In an incredibly gutsy move, the band canceled the summer portion of their tour because Ticketmaster was pressuring the promoters to charge more than $20 for concert tickets. Pearl Jam took legal action against Ticketmaster for unfair business practices, though the Justice Department eventually ruled in favor of the ticket agency.

Vitalogy—The band's third album, *Vitalogy* (number 1 in 1994), is shrouded in lyrical messages of death and despair; it provides a soundtrack for the 1990s through the eyes of several post-Boomers. Like *Vs.*, this album consists of both heavy rock songs ("Spin the Black Circle" and "Last Exit") and ballads ("Nothingman"

and "Better Man"). In addition, the band includes some of their most eclectic tunes yet: the funk rhythms and trance-inducing repetitions of "Aye Davanita," the odd two-chord accordion vamp underneath "Bugs," and the art rock–influenced sound collage, "Stupid Mop."

No Code—With the release of *No Code* (1996), Pearl Jam challenged their association with the grunge movement to an even greater degree. Along with the typical hard rock and punk influences clearly evident in "Hail, Hail" and "Habit," this album reveals a level of musical experimentation beyond that normally associated with alternative—and, specifically, grunge—bands. From the opening measures of "Sometime," with its soft guitar tone, fretless bass, and the sound of rolling thunder, the music promises to be different. "Red Mosquito," providing a waltz-like feel with its triple subdivision of the beat, alternates dramatically between instrumental sections reminiscent of San Francisco acid rock and verses that take on an almost folk rock or country character. Undoubtedly influenced by Vedder's collaboration with Pakistani vocalist Nusrat Fateh on the soundtrack to the motion picture *Dead Man Walking* (1995), "Who You Are" incorporates droning guitar parts, tribal-sounding drums, and a Buddhist lyric.

Yield—Also in 1995, the band collaborated with Neil Young on his album *Mirror Ball*. Returning to their hard-rock roots, Pearl Jam released *Yield* (number 2 in 1998), accompanied by the release of their first video since 1991.

Continued Success—In the fall of 2000, Pearl Jam made recording history. In one week, they simultaneously released 25 live double albums. Five of these entered the *Billboard* Hot 200 simultaneously. The band continued releasing live recordings from its 2000 tour, reaching a total of 72 releases by mid-2001. The concert from Seattle, Washington, on November 11, 2000, a three-CD set, proved the most popular. Although hailing from the grunge capital of the world, Pearl Jam moved beyond the boundaries of alternative music, revealing the influence of eclectic, Zeppelin-style 1970s rock and even some Beatlesque experimentation. Confirming these ties with earlier rock and roll, Vedder was the vocalist asked to take the place of Jim Morrison when the remaining members of the Doors reunited for their induction into the Rock and Roll Hall of Fame in 1993. The continuing success of *Riot Act* (2002), *Lost Dogs* (2003), *Pearl Jam* (2006), and *Backspacer* (2009)—three of which were Top 5 albums—suggests that Pearl Jam remained an important and influential rock band of the 2000s.

Click or tap the video title to see "Jeremy" by Pearl Jam.

https://www.youtube.com/watch?v=MS91knuzoOA*

17.5.4: Riot Grrrl

As part of the "Women in Rock" thrust that gathered steam during the late 1980s and came to undeniable fruition by the mid-1990s, female performers also found their way into alternative and other punk-influenced musical styles.

The Riot Grrrl Phenomenon

The following section will provide highlights of the Riot Grrrl movement, identifying some of the primary artists involved.

Unlike many of rock's other stylistic developments, the official establishment of the **Riot Grrrl** phenomenon can be traced to a specific date: August 20, 1991. On that day, indie music fans from the Pacific Northwest swarmed to Olympia, Washington, for the International Pop Underground Convention: "Love Rock Girl Style Now," which featured a number of all-female groups. The event launched the *Riot Grrrl movement*, which highlighted all-female alternative music but also included activists and writers as well, coming together periodically to perform music and address relevant social issues. Early meetings consisted of discussions about music and specific bands, but also more serious issues confronting females, including violence against women and domestic abuse. As a result, "Riot Grrrl meetings were similar to the consciousness-raising sessions held by 70s-era feminists—with the added desire to create music" (Experience Music Project 2002, para. 2).

There were certainly pioneers from previous decades whose efforts effectively opened the door for this fresh wave of artists. Suzi Quatro and Joan Jett (and her early all-female band, the Runaways) are two examples of female performers of the 1970s and 1980s who performed hard-rock music, receiving a significant degree of both critical and commercial success. The Riot Grrrl sound took on a more aggressive feminist tone than the music of these hard-rock performers, however. Finding solid roots in the female punk bands of the late 1970s (e.g., the Slits and the Raincoats), Riot Grrrl bands typically adopted a *DIY (do-it-yourself)* aesthetic that required no prior musical training. Much like the early punk rock bands, Riot Grrrl spurred female artists to break out of the stereotypical crooning ballad mode, encouraging women to let go of their inhibitions and open themselves to multiple modes of self-expression and creativity.

By the summer of 1992, Riot Grrrl was being touted as the "next big thing" to come from the Pacific Northwest, considered by many at the time to be the hotbed of innovative, energetic musical activity. The success of Nirvana's *Nevermind* (as discussed previously) focused attention on the Seattle area and assisted in bringing national attention to some of the more successful and deserving Riot Grrrl bands; Bikini Kill and Calamity Jane, for example, both opened shows for Nirvana. By the mid-1990s, however, many of the original Riot Grrrl groups had disbanded. Nonetheless, the movement promoted and inspired a wave of female singer-songwriters during the late 1990s, including Ani DiFranco, Jewel, Alanis Morissette, PJ Harvey, Sheryl Crow, Norah Jones, and Sarah McLachlan—music sung by women, for women, primarily about issues important to women. The torch of feminist empowerment was passed from Riot Grrrl to Lilith Fair, McLachlan's touring women's music festival.

17.5.5: Pop Punk

As alternative music continued to work its way into the mainstream in the early 1990s, an interesting subgenre emerged from within the punk scene. Maintaining the high energy, punk attitude and dissonant, distorted guitar sounds of its progenitor, some artists began to incorporate melodic hook lines and tuneful choruses, resulting in **pop punk**. This odd mix of seemingly contradictory musical styles is best exemplified by the tremendous success of Green Day. Childhood friends in Berkeley, California, Billie Joe Armstrong (guitar and vocals) and Mike Dirnt (bass) formed the band in 1989, naming it after a frequent activity of the self-described "potheads." After adding John Kiffmeyer on drums, the trio released a series of EPs and one full-length album before Kiffmeyer was replaced on drums by Tre Cool (born Frank Edwin Wright III). The band built a solid following in the Berkeley hardcore music scene, before signing with Reprise Records to release its first major label album, *Dookie* (number 4 in 1994). The album won a Grammy for Best Alternative Music Performance and earned Green Day plenty of MTV time as well as spots on the Lollapalooza tour and at Woodstock 1994. The band's early style, consisting of easily accessible, three-minute song forms with memorable hook melodies, helped them sell over 10 million copies of this album.

Green Day's Billie Joe Armstrong on stage in 2009.
SOURCE: London Entertainment/Alamy Stock Photo

Click or tap the video title to see "American Idiot" by Green Day.

https://www.youtube.com/watch?v=Ee_uujKuJMI*

associated with the Seattle grunge scene and **nü metal** (discussed in another section of this course)—it was accepted, warts and all, into the mainstream of 1990s youth culture, leading into the twenty-first century.

Green Day and the Punk Attitude

On September 21, 2012, Green Day was the penultimate group performing at the iHeartRadio Music Festival in Las Vegas. They were to play a 45-minute set, but, because some earlier bands ran over their allotted time, were told to cut it down to 30 minutes. For each festival performer, the time remaining for their set was prominently displayed on a large video screen. As the time remaining for Green Day dropped to 1 minute, just as they were about to launch into some of their recent material for which they should have had another 15 minutes, Billy Joe Armstrong took the opportunity to express clearly his thoughts on the matter. Watch the video of this two-minute tirade on YouTube. What do you derive about Armstrong's "punk attitude" from his statement. Do you agree with his perspective? Why or why not?

▶ The response entered here will appear in the performance dashboard and can be viewed by your instructor.

Submit

With *American Idiot* (number 1 in 2004), Green Day proved they had matured significantly as musicians, releasing a concept album that might even be considered a rock opera. Two of the tracks ("Jesus of Suburbia" and "Homecoming") constitute what are essentially multi-movement suites, each over nine minutes in length and incorporating an impressive range of musical styles. The title track, overtly political in its message, presents the band's reaction to the confusing and warped environment that constituted post-September 11 American pop culture. In 2009, in collaboration with Armstrong, the album was transformed into a musical that opened in Berkeley and then moved to Broadway, where the lead singer charismatically performed the role of St. Jimmy for dozens of performances before the show closed in 2011. Equally ambitious and perhaps even more comprehensive as a story-telling narrative, *21st Century Breakdown* (number 1 in 2009) focuses biting criticism on what Green Day views as America's fear culture ("American Eulogy"), government-supported war ("21 Guns"), and Christian hypocrisy ("East Jesus Nowhere").

The maturity evident in Green Day's transition from three-minute song forms to these two fully developed concept albums represents one of the most impressive musical evolutions within the punk movement. The band released a trio of albums within a two-month period in 2012: *Uno!* (number 2), *Dos!* (number 9), and *Tre!* (number 13). In 2013, Bill Joe collaborated with Norah Jones on *Foreverly* (number 19), a complete cover of *Songs Our Daddy Taught Us*, an album released by the Everly Brothers in 1958. Armstrong then composed music for *These Paper Bullets!*, an off-Broadway update of Shakespeare's *Much Ado About Nothing* in which a "fab four from Liverpool" try to find true love in London as they attempt to record an album in seven days. Green Day roared back to the top of the chart in 2016 with *Revolution Radio*.

Despite pop punk's success, punk always remained on the periphery, never attaining widespread appeal relative to that of mainstream rock. In this respect, alternative music has far surpassed the punk movement in terms of commercial success and national attention. Rather than being glossed over and repackaged as a more palatable musical style, the way punk elements evolved into the emergence of new wave, alternative music—primarily that

17.6: Indie Rock

OBJECTIVE: Differentiate indie rock from other alternative rock styles

In earlier sections of this course, we have used the term "indie" in reference to the independent record companies operating during the mid-1950s. In an effort to succeed in a time when the popular music industry was dominated by the major labels (not much has changed, has it?), independent record labels initially attempted to compete by connecting with a smaller audience to whom they could deliver their product cheaply and efficiently. By the 1990s, **indie** referred to music that, in some manner, placed itself in opposition to the mainstream in musical sound, fashion, and/or image. An "indie kid" would typically don clothing that gave a "thrift shop" appearance, Buddy Holly-style dark (sun)glasses, and Converse tennis shoes—all readily available at any Urban Outfitters retail store. By adopting this look, indie kids attempted to convince their peers that appearance was not important. Of course, this specific dress *was* important and played a central role in the social structure of the new indie culture. "The OC" on Fox network was one example of a show that provided entertainment for the indie culture, a set of characters with whom they could closely identify. It also provided a soundtrack for a generation, with selections available for purchase on a series of CD releases. Groups that fit into the indie

---

*By clicking this link, you will be redirected to a third-party site.

category of rock include Weezer and Beck, revealing strong musical influence exerted by Sonic Youth and the Pixies. Dashboard Confessional, Coldplay, Modest Mouse, Jimmy Eat World, and Starsailor are sometimes included in the indie subcategory of **emo** (emotionally oriented rock).

17.6.1: Beck

Influenced during his teens by the music of Sonic Youth and Pussy Galore and his upbringing in the bohemian environs of a street-musician father and an artist-musician mother, Beck Hansen proved to be the ultimate indie kid. Eventually, as is often the case with creative musicians saddled with such a stylistic label, he began stretching the boundaries this moniker imposed. After a brief stint in New York City in the late 1980s, Beck returned to his Southern California birthplace and began performing in a number of artsy coffee shops. Encouraged by Tom Rothrock, owner of Bongload Records, Beck recorded and released "Loser," an interesting combination of folk music and rap. The single became a huge regional hit on Los Angeles's alternative radio station and initiated a major label bidding war. After signing an agreement with DGC that allowed him to continue recording concurrently for small indie labels, Beck released *Mellow Gold* (1994), including "Loser" (number 10), his only Top 40 hit.

After two independent releases in 1994, Beck returned to the spotlight with *Odelay* (1996). With this album, he won Grammys for Best Alternative Music Performance and Best Rock Male Vocal Performance ("Where It's At"), while receiving Album of the Year recognition from major publications, including *Rolling Stone, Spin,* and the *Village Voice.* Through the 1990s, Beck continued to build his songwriting skills and versatility as a musician. *Midnite Vulture* (1999) is a particularly significant departure from the sounds of his previous albums. On this recording, Beck sometimes sounded like a Prince clone; the influence of neo-soul and R&B are evident throughout this self-produced recording. Consider, for example, the use of falsetto on the tune "Debra" or the Stax-Volt horn section on "Sexx Laws"; both represent a dramatic change from the sound of his earlier material. However, with *Sea Change* (2002), Beck returned to a quieter and more introspective musical style, promoted before its release with a brief acoustic tour. Along with *Sea Change*, the release of *Guero* (2005; a return to the sound of *Odelay*), *The Information* (2006; a hip-hop-influenced recording), and *Modern Guilt* (2008; an eclectic mix of tracks produced by Danger Mouse) resulted in a series of four Top 10 albums for this innovative artist. In 2005, while shooting the video for "E-Pro," the opening track on *Guero*, Beck suffered a debilitating spinal injury. Three years later, his range of motion remained limited during his tour for *Modern Guilt*, and he was unable to play his guitar or sing in the same way he had prior to the accident. He was concerned that his career might be over.

As he recovered post-*Modern Guilt*, Beck took on a broad range of projects, including one-off collaborations with Jack White, Dwight Yoakam, and others; motion picture scores (*Twilight: Eclipse*, 2010, and *Scott Pilgrim vs. the World*, 2010); and songs composed for television shows (*True Blood*). In 2009, Beck announced his intention to create a "Record Club," selecting a classic album to reinterpret and providing an opportunity for various musicians to record an album in a day (search for "Beck Record Club" on Vimeo or YouTube). The albums in the series included *Velvet Underground & Nico, Songs of Leonard Cohen, Oar* by Skip Spence, *Kick* by INXS, and *Yanni Live at the Acropolis*. The artist then released *Beck Hanson's Song Reader* (2012), a hardcover book containing 20 new songs in sheet music form, none of which had been recorded; that is quite a unique way to release one's compositions to the world, as if saying, "Here, see what *you* can do with this!" Several artists took the challenge and, in 2014, Jack White, Norah Jones, and other artists released *Warby Parker Presents Song Reader: 20 Songs by Beck*. The artist came roaring back with *Morning Phase* (2014), which won a Grammy for Album of the Year, and *Colors* (2017).

17.6.2: Other Early Alternative Rock Artists

Although Seattle was the epicenter of the grunge movement, the national prominence attained by that style of alternative music resulted in a proliferation of alternative bands from all over the United States: Smashing Pumpkins (Chicago), Sonic Youth (New York), Dinosaur Jr. (Amherst, Massachusetts), Soul Asylum (Minneapolis), Pavement (Stockton, California), Stone Temple Pilots (San Diego), Hole with Courtney Love (Los Angeles), and No Doubt with Gwen Stefani (Orange County, California). Showcasing some of the top alternative bands, the annual Lollapalooza concert tour, begun by Jane's Addiction vocalist Perry Farrell, combined the talents of some of alternative music's headliners with up-and-coming artists, allowing fans an opportunity to see their favorites and to be introduced at the same time to the next generation of likely stars. A significant number of alternative bands performed at Woodstock 1994 and Woodstock 1999, the 25th and 30th anniversaries of the 1969 rock festival. Following the crowd violence and bad press associated with these two festivals, and the challenging economic climate of the period, a planned 40th anniversary event did not come to fruition.

The Musical Versatility of Beck

As described above, Beck, like David Bowie and Elvis Costello, was a musical chameleon. Listen to "Where It's At," "Debra," and "Sea Change." In what rock subgenre (or combination of subgenres) would you categorize each of these recordings? Which of these songs do you like best? Comparing the sound of your chosen recording to the other two, compose a paragraph explaining the reasons for your choice, using your musical vocabulary to clearly identify the musical elements that influenced your decision-making. Identify one of your favorite artists whose music also includes a broad range of styles, and enumerate three or four songs from her/his catalog that represent widely varying musical styles.

▶ The response entered here will appear in the performance dashboard and can be viewed by your instructor.

Submit

17.7: Neo-Punk Propels Rock into the New Millennium

OBJECTIVE: Explain how punk re-emerged as an alternative rock style in the early 2000s

During the late 1990s and early 2000s, a renewed interest in authentic punk rock emerged (i.e., returning to the roots of the movement that initiated grunge), including its early reggae influence. The raw aesthetic of the White Stripes' early recordings and the slicker, modestly pop-infused sound the Strokes provide two examples of this approach.

17.7.1: The White Stripes

Formed in 1997 in Detroit, the White Stripes were an enigmatic, bass-free duo consisting of Jack White (born John Anthony Gillis) and Meg White (born Megan Martha White). Jack and Meg were elusive regarding the true nature of their relationship. Assumed at various times to be brother and sister or husband and wife, the two musicians contributed significantly to the neo-punk genre in the transition to the new millennium. The duo was interestingly reminiscent—visually, if not musically—of the Carpenters, in which Karen played drums and Richard played keyboards. Typically dressed in red and white outfits, the White Stripes exuded a striking stage presence, while their unique sound—Jack on guitar and vocals, Meg on drums, and no bass—provides an interesting contrast to the typical punk rock instrumentation. In 1997, the Stripes debuted with two singles: "Let's Shake Hands" and "Lafayette Blues." Released in 1999, their eponymous full-length debut

provided a mix of interesting covers (Dylan's "One More Cup of Coffee" and Robert Johnson's "Stop Breaking Down Blues") with the band's own blend of original music. Their second album, *De Stijl* (2000), was named after the Dutch minimalist art movement, cited as a source of inspiration for their own stripped-down band sound. With *White Blood Cells* (2002), the duo extended their audience and received attention for a single from this album entitled "Fell in Love With a Girl." *Elephant* (number 6 in 2003) was recorded using only analog equipment and an eight-track recording system, rather than a typical state-of-the-art digital recording facility; it won a Grammy for Best Alternative Album, and one of its tracks, "Seven Nation Army," won the Grammy for Best Rock Song, though not making the Top 40. *Elephant, Get Behind Me Satan* (number 3 in 2005) and *Icky Thump* (number 2 in 2007) each reached the Top 10. Jack White became involved in numerous side projects, including the Raconteurs and the Dead Weather (with Alison Mosshart of the Kills) and made a DVD with guitar greats Jimmy Page and the Edge (*It Might Get Loud*, 2008). In 2011, via a posting on Jack White's Third Man Records website, the White Stripes announced they had broken up. Shortly after this dissolution, Jack White released a series of solo recordings, beginning with *Blunderbuss* (2012) and *Lazaretto* (2016), both reaching the top of the album chart. Following his initial solo tour to promote the former album, White's Third Man Records reissued a series of recordings by depression-era blues icons, including Charley Patton, Blind Willie McTell, and Mississippi Sheiks.

17.7.2: The Strokes

Forming in 1999, the Strokes were relative latecomers to the revival of the punk aesthetic, although the neo-punk of the 1990s was slick and clean in comparison to its 1970s precursor. Image, even if an illusion, was a high priority. These bands were willing to spend loads of time and money, if necessary, to ensure that their clothing was "vintage" and their hair was mussed just right, resulting in the "authentic" look of a punk rock band. In 2003, during the transition to the twenty-first century, around the same time that the Strokes emerged, a whole group of bands sharing a similar punk aesthetic appeared: the Hives, the Vines, the White Stripes, and the Yeah, Yeah, Yeahs.

By the time of the release of their full-length debut album (*Is This It?, 2001*), the Strokes were already one of the most popular club bands in New York City, a position that was fueled by their initial EP, *The Modern Age* (2001). Pairing the energy and DIY aesthetic of punk with catchy hook lines, *Is This It?* reached the Top 40. Two contrasting examples of the band's early style are provided by the title track and "Last Night." While the former starts with random tape noises followed by a drum machine-like beat pattern to introduce the verse that pairs a droning guitar riff and a relaxed vocal by Julian Casablancas, the latter reveals an up-tempo alternative sound with moderate reggae influence (notice the accent on the upbeat in the rhythm guitar part), but with a more aggressive lead vocal. The success of their debut album prepared the way for two number 4 albums: *Room on Fire* (2003) and *First Impressions of Earth* (2006). While *Room* essentially provided a polished version of their earlier work, *Impressions* revealed the band stretching out in a number of musical directions. It was five years before their fourth studio album was released; returning to the garage band sound of their initial two albums, *Angles* (2011) also reached number 4 on the album chart.

It is too early to tell how far-reaching will be the effect of bands representing this recent incarnation of punk-influenced music. Their popularity and the sheer number of groups sharing similar musical influences leave little doubt, however, that the infusion of punk elements into the rock mainstream will continue to be an important influence for the foreseeable future.

17.8: Prog Rock

OBJECTIVE: Describe the emergence of progressive rock

Amid all the noise and hubbub of the most basic alternative subgenres, there were some bands that began with the alternative mind-set and then evolved gradually into music that can rightly be referred to as high art. Not unlike the music created by art rock performers of the late 1960s and 1970s, these artists once again set about pushing beyond the common boundaries of rock music. Two of the most important of these, Radiohead

and Björk, will be discussed at length; other bands that deserve mention in the **progressive rock** category include Tool, Nine Inch Nails, Sigur Ros, and God Speed You Black Emperor!

17.8.1: Radiohead

Thom Yorke (vocals and guitar) and Colin Greenwood (bass) were former schoolmates who formed Radiohead in 1991, changing the band's name from On a Friday at the request of EMI, dangling a six-album deal. Adding Ed O'Brien (guitar), Phil Selway (drums), and the bassist's younger brother Jonny (guitar and keyboards), the band quickly built a local following in Abingdon in the Oxfordshire region of the UK.

Radiohead in 1992.
SOURCE: Johnny Greig/Alamy Stock Photo

Musical Career of Radiohead

The following section will provide highlights from the career of Radiohead, a group that continues to expand the boundaries of rock and roll.

Their debut album, *Pablo Honey*, was a hit in both England and the United States (where it was number 32 in 1993). Undoubtedly influenced by the Seattle grunge movement, the lyrics evidence a similar self-loathing (e.g., "Creep," number 34). The band's musical maturation was clearly evident on *The Bends* (1995). Like Nirvana before them, the heavy rock sound was balanced, at times, by interesting musical experimentation and, at others, by a surprising Beatlesque melodicism ("High and Dry").

OK Computer (number 21 in 1997) proved to be the breakthrough album for Radiohead, winning a Grammy for Best Alternative Music recording. Although not intended as a concept album, several songs ("Karma Police" and "Paranoid Android") communicate a concern with the ubiquitous presence of technology in our lives and the implied fear of losing control. "Paranoid Android" provides an excellent example of the band's tight formal structures with adventurous musical elements. Sections of the piece utilize septuple meter (seven beats per measure), changing tempo, polyphonic vocal textures, and the use of changing loudness levels for dramatic effect (e.g., a dramatic crescendo that increases from the relatively soft acoustic guitar sounds heard at the beginning to distorted electric guitars and shouting vocals). There were no Top

40 singles from the album and, reminiscent of the folk rock trend of the late 1950s and early 1960s, Radiohead's commercial success derived primarily from album sales.

In the late 1990s, a number of guitar-centric British bands emerged that were obviously influenced by Radiohead's sound (e.g., Travis and Coldplay).

Radiohead returned in 2000 with their anxiously awaited *Kid A*. The album was originally scheduled for a simultaneous premiere via MTV2 and the BBC, but three weeks prior to the scheduled release date, bootleg copies began to appear on the Internet. Despite this fact, however, and what appeared to be an intentional anti-marketing campaign (e.g., no videos for MTV rotation and no singles released), the album shot to number 1. The signature sound of Greenwood's guitar, so prominent on previous recordings, no longer provided the primary foundation for the accompanimental tracks. Instead, synthesizers and other electronic sounds dominated the musical texture.

The album opens with the sound of an electric piano and heavily processed vocal fragments, while the lyrics—once Yorke's vocals enter in earnest—assure us that "everything [is] in its right place," an interesting commentary on the radical change in the band's sound. Electric guitar sounds are completely absent until the third track, "The National Anthem," when the electric bass guitar provides a driving rock beat. When the electric guitar does appear, it is just as likely to be in the form of feedback, providing another layer to be mixed into the complex musical fabric, rather than the riffs that have made the guitar a central part of a rock ensemble since the time of Chuck Berry's early recordings. In addition, many tracks on *Kid A* contain significantly longer instrumental sections, often providing ambient contrast to the vocals, instead of inserting a predictable guitar solo into the musical form. "Treefingers," a song completely without vocals, is an interesting example of an almost four-minute composition that verges on ambient music, suggesting influence of the work of Brian Eno. None of the songs from this album were released as singles, and the album was not supported, as was typically the case for rock albums, by extensive promotional touring.

Amnesiac (2001), containing some tracks recorded during the same sessions as *Kid A*, debuted at number 2 and left no doubt about the band's penchant for musical experimentation. In 2003, the band released yet another critically acclaimed recording, *Hail to the Thief* (number 3).

Following a bit of a lull in recorded output from the band, Thom Yorke released a solo album, *The Eraser* (2006), which reached number 2 on the album chart. With bassist Flea from Red Hot Chili Peppers, Yorke formed a side project named Atoms for Peace, releasing *Amok* (number 2 in 2013). In late 2014, he released *Tomorrow's Modern Boxes* over BitTorrent with no advance warning. Other members of the band also took on outside creative projects. Guitarist Jonny Greenwood pursued a career composing orchestral music, including film scores (*Bodysong*, 2004; *There Will Be Blood*, 2008; *Norwegian Wood*, 2011; *The Master*, 2012; and *Inherent Vice*, 2014) and art music for live orchestral performance, influenced significantly by the work of Polish composer Krzysztof Penderecki. An album released in 2012 contains two compositions by Penderecki ("Threnody for the Victims of Hiroshima" and "Polymorphia") and two by Greenwood ("Popcorn Superhet Receiver" and "48 Responses to Polymorphia"). Drummer Phillip Selway also initiated a solo career in 2011 with *Familial*.

Click or tap the video title to see Radiohead's "Paranoid Android."

https://www.youtube.com/watch?v=fHiGbolFFGw*

UNIQUE STRATEGIES FOR PROMOTING COMMERCIAL RELEASES In addition to their creative musical output, Radiohead provided a model for how the Internet, and even Napster, could be used effectively to market and promote commercial releases. About six months before the release of *Kid A*, for example, the band created 15-second video animations (what they called "blips") that they made available to fans via the Internet. Fans were encouraged to trade the clips like "electronic postcards" (Knopper 2001, 69). Given the album's success on its release, making these materials available—including MP3 files of some of the tracks—seems to have whetted the appetite of the record-buying public, who were ready and willing to purchase the recording, once it was available. Presenting a further challenge to a recording industry already reeling from a drop in music sales and the industry's apparent inability to adapt quickly enough to the changing landscape of legal music downloads, Radiohead released *In Rainbows* (2007) for download from their website. Having fulfilled their six-album contractual agreement with EMI, the band chose to release this album using Internet-only distribution, and rather than assigning a set price, they allowed fans to determine the amount they were willing to pay … many choosing to download the tracks for free. Even after the online release, when CD copies were made available in stores, the album still topped the *album chart*! For *King of Limbs* (number 3 in 2011), subscribers to Radiohead's website were notified about the album's availability with an invitation to pre-order the recording. Unlike iTunes and some other online music distributors, Radiohead offered the album both in compressed format (MP3 at 320 kbps) and CD-quality sound files (WAV), the latter at a slightly higher price. The long-term impact of these unorthodox distribution methods is not yet known but provides yet another sign that Radiohead is challenging tradition both in their approach to the music creation process and in the business model used to disseminate their recordings. Five years later, Radiohead released *A Moon Shaped Pool* (number 3 in 2016).

---

*By clicking this link, you will be redirected to a third-party site.

17.8.2: Björk

The music of Icelandic singer Björk Gudmundsdóttir reveals a very different but equally adventurous approach to the creative process.

Björk, 2006.

SOURCE: Thorvaldur Kristmundsson/Icelandic photo agency/Alamy Stock Photo

Click or tap the video title to watch "It's Oh So Quiet" by Bjork

https://www.youtube.com/watch?v=htobTBlCvUU*

Another shift occurred within the realm of rock music during the 1990s. Alternative music infiltrated, and then dominated, the mainstream of popular culture. During the same period, however, many artists continued to stretch the boundaries of rock and roll. It was an exciting decade, the influence of which continues to carry into the present.

_____

*By clicking this link, you will be redirected to a third-party site.

Musical Style and Career of Björk

The following section will provide highlights from the career of Björk, another artist who refuses to be limited by the boundaries of mainstream rock.

A performer from an early age, Björk completed her first album when she was 11 years old. The singer experienced significant success in Iceland performing in a hard-rock band that eventually took the name the Sugarcubes before recording *Life's Too Good* (number 54 in 1988). This album was well-received critically in the United States and the United Kingdom; a video for the song "Birthday" was placed into rotation on MTV.

After recording several less-successful albums with the band, Björk left to pursue a solo career. Her first release as a solo artist, aptly titled *Debut* (1993), contained a single entitled "Human Behavior," which rose to number 2 on the Modern Rock chart, though not cracking the Hot 100. In 1995, Björk released *Post* (number 32), a widely varied collection of songs, revealing the influence of electronica ("Army of Me"), ambient music ("Hyperballad"), and even big band jazz ("It's Oh So Quiet"). The singer's unique vocal quality makes her easily identifiable, and her stream-of-consciousness lyrics manage to draw the listener into her (rather strange) world.

Although the earlier albums provided a strong sense of Björk's creative potential, musicality, and arranging skill, *Vespertine* (2002) left little doubt that she was a force with which to be reckoned. Consisting largely of what can most accurately be described as sonic montages, the singer performs her flowing vocal melodies over a primarily electronic foundation, so it is not surprising that this album did not enter the *Billboard* 200. Some

selections ("Cocoon," "It's Not Up to You," and "Heirloom") are highly rhythmic, integrating many interesting sampled source materials into the mix (e.g., electronic pops and clicks, phonograph needle noise, and escaping steam). Add to this unique and highly creative mix the singer's inimitable vocal style and the result is highly interesting and quite distinctive.

Björk composed the soundtrack and starred in *Dancer in the Dark* (2000), a critically acclaimed motion picture alternating between a dark reality and the lead character's imaginative fantasy world. In a career marked by innovative musical experimentation, Björk's most stunning departure from popular song form came with the release of *Medúlla* (2004). Built almost completely of vocal sounds (sometimes heavily processed), the resulting sonic montage, which also includes synthesizer textures, is truly an artistic masterpiece, although the recording presents an undeniable challenge to the listener who yearns to hear a hit single.

Pushing the boundaries not only for the sound of popular music but also the manner in which it is distributed, Björk released *Biophilia* (number 27 in 2011). The album was concurrently released as a suite of 10 interactive iPad apps, one for each song with animations that provide a visualization of the music (or a complete musical score) and the lyrics as the song plays, a truly innovative means of presenting a rock album. Navigating this interactive release is an experience, and I hope that you will be motivated to seek it out so that you can have that experience yourself. Björk's prolific and innovative musical releases continued with *Vulnicura* (number 20 in 2015), addressing the grief associated with lost love accompanied by lush orchestral sounds, and *Utopia* (number 75 in 2017), on which the strings are replaced by interesting combinations of synths; birdsong; harp; lutes; choir; and, as typical, heavy amounts of sonic manipulation.

Björk and Musical Adventurism

Play "The Pleasure is All Mine," the opening track on Björk's *Medúlla*. Listen carefully for the duration of the recording. When it ends, write two to three sentences describing your reaction to the sounds you heard. Now, listen to the entire track a second time. After completion, copy-and-paste the sentences you previously wrote into a new paragraph, editing the content based on your perception of the second pass. Then, listen to the track a third time. After listening the third time, follow the same copy-and-paste procedure, editing your comments for the second listening based on this third hearing. Repeated listening is a critically important skill, essential to an informed listener. As you become a more experienced listener, you will notice that, especially with more complex music, you hear more details with each pass. In a final paragraph, respond to the following questions: Do you think this track fits appropriately into the category of rock music? Why or why not?

▶ The response entered here will appear in the performance dashboard and can be viewed by your instructor.

Submit

17.9: Musical Close-Up on Alternative Views of Alternative Rock

OBJECTIVE: Evaluate the alternative rock movement

Have you ever thought to yourself (or perhaps even said), "Life is just too darned complicated!"? Indeed, if one steps back far enough to consider the entirety of human evolution, it does seem that there has been a consistent tendency for us to move from the simple to the complex. When the complexities of life begin to overwhelm us, we often yearn for a simpler existence—and so it is with music. Remember the 12-bar blues form we discussed in another section of this course? It was a very simple idea and, in its most basic form, worked well for thousands of songs; but, inevitably, the human tendency to tinker with things had its effect. Over the years, chords were substituted, meters were changed, the AAB lyric structure and melodic scheme were modified, and there were even measures added or deleted.

Rock and roll began as a rather simple style of music, but, as we have seen with the Beatles, Brian Wilson, Radiohead, and others, there were ever more creative manipulations to almost every one of its musical elements: harmony and tonality, rhythm and meter, timbre, and form. This all-pervasive evolution from simplicity to complexity was not an absolutely straight line. At frequent points along the way (whether one is considering blues, jazz, rock, or any other aspect of the human experience), there are those who yearn for a return to simplicity. Their rebellion often takes the form of a "return to basics" or "roots" movement. And so it was with the punk rockers and those who followed in their footsteps. How are we to evaluate, musically, these alternative styles? Does the product of this rebellion have true musical value, or is it simply the noisy ranting of charlatans? Let us consider several alternative—pun intended—answers to these questions.

17.9.1: Alternative Rock as a Valid Musical Component of Rock History

The emergence of the mainstream rock sound of Little Richard, Jerry Lee Lewis, Elvis Presley, and other artists in the mid-1950s offered an alternative to the sound of Pop artists of the era.

Cyclic Pattern of Complexity and Simplicity

This section presents a brief explanation of a common pattern in the evolution of musical styles, moving from simplicity to complexity that is then followed by a return to simplicity, beginning the cycle anew.

One of the primary musical distinctions between Pop music and early rock was the raw energy of the rock recordings. In contrast to the carefully arranged instrumental parts and highly trained vocal stylings of the crooners, the R&B-influenced rockers presented a musical style that was—if imperfect in its performance— full of youthful energy and vigor. A similar contrast can be made during the late 1960s, if one compares the music of the Beatles and Rolling Stones. The musical style of the Beatles continued to evolve dramatically, resulting in recordings that some (not the present author) might consider pretentious, while the Stones, after an initial foray into such experimentation, returned to their mainstream rock roots. Considering the evolution of rock music over the past several decades, one can identify specific musical trends that represented a return to a more basic style.

Of course, rock is not the only musical genre to have experienced such a cyclical pattern of complexity and simplicity. In its long history, Western art music has experienced many similar cycles. To focus on only one example, consider the remarkable change from the late Baroque style to the early Classical style. By the end of the Baroque period, complex polyphonic textures were the norm, perhaps best exemplified by the fugal compositions of J. S. Bach. The Classicism of Haydn and Mozart was, among other things, a move away from the intricate polyphony of Bach toward simpler textures, singable melodies, and more easily perceived, symmetrical musical forms. By the end of the Classical period, however, extreme complexity was again dominant in works such as Beethoven's Ninth Symphony and *Grosse Fuge.* Similar alternation between simplicity and complexity in art music composition can be traced right up through the twentieth century and into the new millennium.

This same cycle of action and reaction has occurred numerous times in the context of rock music. Generally, the punk movement resulted in a return to a rawer, harder-edged sound. This reflexive return to a simpler style can be viewed as a valid reaction to (against?) two existing trends: a move toward musical complexity and increased reliance on technology. Recall that the transition to the 1960s represented an initial fragmentation of the rock market. The resulting branches of the rock and roll genealogical tree included a variety of musical styles. As the decade proceeded, new styles emerged that were dramatically more complex than those that had come before. Two examples are jazz rock and art rock (both discussed in earlier sections of this course). In comparison to most other subgenres of rock, the music of Blood, Sweat & Tears; Chicago; Yes; and Emerson, Lake & Palmer during the late 1960s and early 1970s represented a significant increase in musical complexity.

During this same period and the years that immediately followed, the music of Queen, Steely Dan, Pink Floyd, Styx, and others represented a vigorous pursuit of perfectionism in studio recording technique. As a result, some of the highest quality and most innovative recording productions in the history of rock were released during this time. Although many previous artists (Buddy Holly and Brian Wilson, for example) had used the studio as a musical instrument, the level of attention given to every detail of the recording process during the mid-1970s represented a new level of sophistication. One need only listen to the "operatic" section in Queen's "Bohemian Rhapsody" from *A Night at the Opera* (1975) or "Deacon Blues" from Steely Dan's *Aja* (1977) to hear the incredibly high production quality evident in these recordings, incorporating numerous overdubs and retakes. However, other listeners felt that rock music had begun to lose its connection to the energy inherent in the immediacy of a live performance. In fact, such listeners might argue, many early R&B recordings were made by simply hanging a single microphone and capturing a live performance, imperfections and all.

The initiation of the punk movement was at least partially intended to deflate the balloon of the contrasting perfectionist trend, suggesting instead that a DIY aesthetic was more appropriate to rock and roll. Why should the creation and performance of music be reserved for a few highly trained musicians and recording engineers? Punk rockers joyfully celebrated the imperfections of live musical performance and were more than willing to trade the studio perfection of art rock bands—a sound they believed to rep-

resent a sanitized and pretentious version of rock—for the energy and immediacy of their own radical musical style. Perhaps it is no coincidence that the Sex Pistols were formed in the same year as the release of Queen's *A Night at the Opera,* and that their most important recording (*Never Mind the Bollocks, Here's the Sex Pistols*) was released the same year as Steely Dan's *Aja.*

During the 1980s, technology was used to an ever greater extent as a performance tool in popular music. Dance music frequently replaced a live drummer with rhythms "performed" by a drum machine, and many of the bass lines and keyboard parts were created using computer sequencers, not performed by live musicians. Even the parts that were performed by human hands were typically *quantized*—adjusted temporally for rhythmic accuracy—to make the performance more perfect than humanly possible. Listen carefully to Michael Jackson's "Speed Demon" from *Bad* (1987). Following the vocal phrase "speed demon" in the chorus, notice the mechanically perfect performance of the 32nd note runs of the bass synthesizer. Although highly trained musicians possess superb technical skills, the accuracy with which this musical line is performed (and repeated numerous times without deviation) is simply beyond human capability. Music by many artists during the mid- to late 1980s (e.g., Madonna, Prince, George Michael, Stacy Q, and Nu Shooz) incorporated these same technologies. Live performance of certain parts (e.g., electric guitar, saxophone, and vocals) was often incorporated to balance the lack of expressivity in the technically perfect performances of these instrumental parts. Prince, for example, typically used a live drummer *and* a drum machine as a means of getting the best of both worlds: a high degree of rhythmic and metrical accuracy, without giving up completely the expressivity of human performance.

By the mid-1980s, another punk-influenced musical revolution was initiated to counter this move toward computer-based musical performance: grunge rock, emerging from the Pacific Northwest. Grunge bands were influenced musically by heavy metal and mainstream bands (Led Zeppelin, Black Sabbath, AC/DC, and Aerosmith) but were also heavily derivative of hardcore punk groups like Black Flag, the Melvins, Butthole Surfers, and Circle Jerks. Much of the music produced by Sub Pop Records during the 1980s was raw and intentionally simplistic. Volume and energy were the prime elements; listen, for example to Mudhoney's "The Rose," Green River's "Hangin' Tree," or Nirvana's "Spank Thru." However, with Nirvana's *Nevermind* (1991), the punk aesthetic found a mainstream audience. Other bands, including Soundgarden, Pearl Jam, and Alice in Chains, emerged from the Seattle area to become some of the most popular groups of the 1990s.

Thus, the punk rockers and their progeny can be seen in the larger context of action–reaction. As has been the case throughout music history (and human history, in general), these rebellions against complexity and technological perfection sought a return to simpler, more human values. Taken in this light, they take their legitimate place beside countless others who have tried to balance the scales against the seemingly unstoppable human propensity for increasing complexity and sophistication.

17.9.2: Alternative Rock as a Form of Musical Charlatanry

In the preceding section, alternative rock was viewed as a legitimate reaction to more complex styles of rock music. However, it is also possible to consider this apparent rebellion against complexity in a far different light.

Circumstances That Can Lead to Rebellion Against Complexity

After all, there are two very different circumstances that can lead to such a rebellion. First, one may understand and appreciate complexity but consciously opt for a simpler style, or one may simply be incapable of dealing with the complexity (for one reason or another) and, therefore, have no choice but to pursue simplicity.

Consciously Opting for a Simpler Style—As an example of the former, consider the analogy cited above in Classical music. It is true that Haydn and Mozart rebelled against the complex polyphony of Bach and other late Baroque composers. However, both Haydn and Mozart were thoroughly schooled in the intricacies of the polyphonic styles that preceded them. They *chose* to develop a very different style. To find a more appropriate parallel to the punk rockers, we would need to identify some composers contemporaneous with Mozart who had no formal musical training and wrote music that was significantly simpler, and potentially bombastic, as a means of artistic expression. No one could legitimately suggest that Haydn and Mozart wrote in their style because they were incapable of writing complex polyphonic music (in fact, they did so at times). Although they adopted a somewhat simpler texture, their music was extremely sophisticated in other ways.

Incapability of Dealing with the Complexity—Far different is the person who adopts a simpler style, because, lacking the informed understanding of the styles of preceding musical eras and the developed compositional technique needed to work in a more complex style, there is simply no other choice. In the case of some of the punk bands (not all, of course), as one representative style of alternative rock, their so-called rebellion against complexity and perfectionism could be nothing more than a convenient rationalization that masks an inability to sing, play an instrument, or work creatively with the musical elements at a more sophisticated level. Their product sells to consumers who, like themselves, may be less capable of appreciating anything other than the most basic musical styles. At times, the rock press legitimizes these bands and their simplistic product because to do otherwise would force a value judgment—and remember from the beginning of this chapter that, in today's egalitarian culture, there is no "better" or "worse," no "good" and "bad"; all things have equal value and are simply "alternatives."

Let us return to a question that was posed in articulating part of the alternative rock philosophy: "Why should the creation and performance of music be reserved for a few highly trained musicians and recording engineers?" One potential answer might be, "Because they know what they are doing!" Let us consider an analogy. Suppose we restated our question as follows: "Why should the practice of medicine be reserved for a few highly trained doctors?" Medicine has become incredibly complex and technologically sophisticated. We now have laser surgery and the ability to perform intricate operations that actually replace human hearts, hips, and knees—all monitored closely by elaborate computer hardware and software. What if you or someone you care about were faced with a life-threatening medical emergency? How would you feel if your doctor announced a strong belief in a "back to the basics" philosophy and, as a result, recommended bloodletting, a few well-chosen leeches, and an old fifteenth-century incantation? That is a type of alternative medicine you would probably do well to avoid!

So, is alternative rock a valid musical response to the excessive musical and technological complexity of more advanced styles of rock, or is it just a smokescreen for the musical "wanna-be" (and an audience that is less capable of appreciating more challenging styles)? The answer will probably come with time. Because of the natural tendency of the human race to move from simplicity to complexity, it seems likely that some punk-influenced groups will gradually inch toward greater sophistication, if they are capable of doing so; in this chapter, Green Day was provided as one such example. Others will stagnate and disappear rather quickly into anonymity.

17.9.3: A Final Note About Complexity and Simplicity

Before leaving this discussion of complexity and simplicity, we need to be certain that we have not led the reader to believe that complexity is inherently superior to simplicity. When we use the terms *complex* and *simple,* we mean to describe, as objectively as possible, the level of creativity demonstrated in the manipulation of the musical elements (as defined in other sections of this course). The music of the Beatles is more musically complex than that of the Rolling Stones. That is simply a fact based on an objective, analytical study of the music. However, this observation does not imply any kind of value judgment (that the Beatles' music is "better" than that of the Rolling Stones). In fact, there is no inherent connection between complexity/ simplicity and good/bad. "Good" and "bad" are value judgments based on a matrix of personal tastes, backgrounds, educations, and experiences.

Too often, we meet people who have limited capability to appreciate the complex or the simple. They thrive on one and denigrate the other. Such people are living only half a life, musically speaking. The truth is that both simple and complex music can have a rewarding function in our lives. There are times when we desire and appreciate the challenges afforded by the sophisticated music of the Beatles; Blood, Sweat & Tears; Emerson, Lake & Palmer; Radiohead; or Björk. However, there are other times when we crave the simpler, more visceral appeal of Little Richard, the Rolling Stones, James Brown, the Velvet Underground, Willie Nelson, or Britney Spears. This is no different than selecting a television show to watch. There are times when you might be ready for a show like *Law and Order: Special Victims Unit*, one that will cause you to think about complicated ethical or legal dilemmas. There are other times when you just need to "veg out," watching a rather mindless sitcom. Both have a function in our lives.

In previous sections of this course addressing the British Invasion and jazz rock, we encountered a song entitled "Sympathy for the Devil." The original song (by Jagger and Richard) was simple and repetitive. The arrangement by Blood, Sweat & Tears, however, was remarkably complex. A non-musical analogy can be made using two technological developments: a supercomputer and a mobile-phone calculator. One is very complex; the other is relatively simple. However, both have practical functions for which the other is ill-suited. Thus, you would not want

America's next space shuttle to be designed and controlled by the hand-held calculator, nor do you need to drag a supercomputer along with you to the market to determine which brand of toothpaste is cheaper per ounce. Such is the case with the two versions of "Sympathy for the Devil." One is more complex; the other is simpler. The truly fortunate person is the one who can enjoy each for what it is. If you honestly prefer one and find little to like about the other, that is a matter of personal preference and is absolutely your prerogative. What is truly unfortunate is if you cannot tell the difference!

BECOME AN ACTIVE LISTENER: ELEMENTS OF ALTERNATIVE ROCK

After studying the evolution of alternative rock presented in this chapter, it is time to return to your own collection of recordings, to your streaming service, or to the Internet to identify independently some of the differentiating elements in recordings with which you may be more familiar.

Find examples of these alternative elements in the music that you enjoy

1. An emphasis on musical simplicity over virtuosity
2. An acceptance of, or even emphasis on, imperfections in the musical production
3. Use of "real" musical instruments versus electronically altered sounds

Summary: Alternative Styles

In its (r)evolutionary path, rock music has been influenced by a wide array of musical styles, some closely related to mainstream rock, others vastly different. The punk aesthetic has proven to be no different. In fact, the initial punk movement of the 1970s—not a dramatic commercial success on its own—realized its most lasting influence as its musical elements were subsumed in new wave, a subgenre that did experience a degree of commercial success. In the 1980s, punk influenced the grunge phenomenon that truly brought alternative music into the rock mainstream. By the time of the neo-punk movement of the 1990s, some of the most commercially successful recordings were by artists identified as belonging to one of any number of punk-influenced musical categories, many of whom have been discussed in this chapter. While the long-term impact of and resulting musical development following the neo-punk movement of the late 1990s and early twenty-first century is yet to be fully determined, one thing is not debatable: The cyclical infusion of punk elements into the rock and roll mainstream continues to serve as a periodic reminder that rock music, at times, may take itself a little too seriously and move beyond the realm of accessibility and

mainstream popular appeal. The punk message is reflected by a return to the basics from which rock emerged. Much as an emergency room physician uses electricity to return animation to a human heart that has stopped beating, the punk aesthetic provides a sense of renewed vigor, frenetic energy, and immediacy to rock music at times when the music appears to be in need of such an infusion.

Take Note: Alternative Styles

How did the Boomer and post-Boomer generations influence the development of rock music?—The Boomers were the first generation raised almost entirely on rock music. Their children, the post-Boomers, naturally sought their own alternative musical styles to enjoy. Faced with so many options, many of the post-Boomer generations were loathe to make any choices or value judgments at all.

Why is alternative rock so hard to define?—Alternative rock is difficult to define because mainstream rock itself has become so diverse. Within this chapter, the term "alternative" is used to describe those artists who—at least in the beginning of their careers—shunned mainstream success and focused on expressing themselves through their music, spurning (supposedly) commercial success for artistic authenticity.

What were alternative rock's beginnings?—Rock and roll began as an alternative to Pop music of the 1950s and has continued to evolve numerous "alternatives" as it has developed. Using the term as defined in this chapter, David Bowie can be considered among the early alternative artists whose music and stage presence added a highly theatrical component to what had become the norm for mainstream rock. In the 1970s, his glam-rock style challenged contemporary notions of sexuality, while assuming a variety of personas—most notably Ziggy Stardust—that underscored the distance between performer and audience.

How was punk rock a rebellion against other trends in rock?—The punk rock movement began as a reaction against the increasing commercialization of mainstream rock. British groups like the Sex Pistols celebrated their lack of musical abilities, while their lyrics disputed mainstream social values. Punk dress, body piercing, and hair styles all were intended to shock mainstream society. Some punk bands, like the Clash, were more musically and politically sophisticated, leading to the development of new wave artists like Elvis Costello. American punk groups included Iggy and the Stooges and Black Flag. On the new wave end of the spectrum in the United States were groups like the Talking Heads and the Police.

How did grunge rock become one of the most successful styles of alternative rock during the late 1980s and early 1990s?—Grunge rock developed out of the Seattle alternative music scene in the late 1980s, led by groups like the Pixies. These groups combined a hardcore punk style with more progressive lyrics, often focusing on meaningful social issues (e.g., women's rights). Among the most successful grunge groups were Nirvana and Pearl Jam. The Riot Grrrl phenomenon grew out of grunge as women formed bands specifically to address female issues and provide an alternative

to the traditionally male-dominated rock scene. Pop punk groups like Green Day brought a modified version of punk into the mainstream, adding catchy melodies and hooks to the punk aesthetic.

What was indie rock, and how did it differ from other alternative styles?—In the early 1990s, indie rock took up the mantle of opposing the mainstream. However, unlike the earlier punks who were openly hostile toward rock, the indie movement was more bohemian in nature, a kind of return to the earlier hippie days of the late 1960s. Beck was a prolific and versatile exemplar of the indie movement.

How did punk re-emerge as an alternative style at the beginning of the twenty-first century?—Authentic hardcore punk returned in the early twenty-first century with bands like the Strokes and the White Stripes. However, unlike earlier punks who celebrated their back-to-the-basics approach, these bands featured musicians (Jack White of the White Stripes and Julian Casablancas of the Strokes) with significantly higher levels of musicianship, as is evident from their recordings, despite the DIY approach to production.

How did prog rock return as an alternative style?—Several groups have returned to an interest in creating an intentionally "artistic" music in the manner of the original prog rockers of the late 1960s through the mid-1970s. Radiohead's *OK Computer* (1997) was a breakthrough album for the band, featuring sophisticated song forms, unusual rhythms, changing tempos, and frequently changing musical textures. The group also pioneered a new way of marketing itself with the Internet release of their album *In Rainbows* (2007), inviting fans to pay whatever they felt the album was worth to access the downloadable sound files. Björk takes a different approach to her uniquely innovative music, combining her unusual vocal style with electronic sources and samples of real-world sounds to create widely varying and extremely interesting compositions, some of which pose a significant challenge to listeners adapted to the Top 40 hit single format.

SHARED WRITING

The Influence of Simplicity and Complexity on Your Favorite Music

Throughout this course, you have been introduced to subgenres of rock that represent a wide spectrum of styles from the very basic to the highly complex, let's apply that understanding to the music you prefer. Select one of your favorite artists and reflect on a recent release; please choose an album rather than a single. Write a paragraph of three to five sentences communicating the extent to which you hear influences of simple rock styles (basic mainstream rock, punk, etc.) and more complex styles (art rock, jazz rock, prog rock, etc.)? Be as specific as you can. Show your response to two or three other students, providing a link to at least one track recorded by this artist that you think best exemplifies the artist's style. Read the responses of these students and provide feedback regarding their evaluation and identifying additional influences as you are able.

▶ A minimum number of characters is required to post and earn points. After posting, your response can be viewed by your class and instructor, and you can participate in the class discussion.

Post | 0 characters | 140 minimum

Chapter 18
An Overview and an Editorial

 ## Learning Objectives

18.1 Summarize the eight basic statements of rock and roll

18.2 Outline the concerns with the continued evolution of rock and roll

Other sections in this course have provided detailed information about the evolution of rock and roll from its emergence in the mid-1950s up to (almost) the present day. Along the way, you have been introduced to an amazingly diverse set of rock subgenres, selected artists representing each, and some of the social and political movements with which they were associated. You also learned a musical vocabulary and concepts that will enable you to communicate effectively about music of any kind, including rock, jazz, classical, and world musics. Hopefully, this will provide you the tools you need to better understand and to talk with friends about your favorite music and about your own musical preferences. The purpose of this chapter is quite different, as explained below.

18.1: Eight Basic Statements

OBJECTIVE: Summarize the eight basic statements of rock and roll

At the beginning of this course, it was made clear that the intention of this history of rock and roll is to maintain as objective a perspective as possible, stating the facts and allowing the readers to draw their own conclusions. Any evaluative statements made regarding musical content have, it is hoped, been based on valid musical analysis and estimates of the relative importance that various performers have achieved, since that tends to be a central task of any historian.

This chapter, however, is different … an overview that contains a number of subjective evaluations, and the subsequent editorial is highly personalized. It is hoped that the perspective will prove provocative or instructive; if not, perhaps the reader will at least find them interesting or entertaining.

Beginning with a mixture of R&B, C&W, and Pop music, early rock and roll settled into three basic styles: mainstream rock, rockabilly, and soft rock. In the 1960s, other influences were added (e.g., folk, jazz, gospel, and classical music), resulting in several new subgenres. In the 1970s, rock fragmented into a bewildering array of individualized subgenres, most of which continued unabated through the 1980s and 1990s and on into the new century. Given the path we have followed, is it possible to step back and attempt to draw a series of conclusions that might apply to all of the history of rock? That is the purpose of this chapter. The eight basic statements that follow seem to apply across the entirety of rock. They are stated in no particular order, except that the most important point will be saved for last.

18.1.1: Basic Statement 1

Rock and roll may be here to stay, but individual artists and styles are not. In other words, although rock as an inclusive, overarching musical category may be permanent, its component parts are extremely transitory. Rock and roll is much like the weather: If you do not like it now, wait a while. For every Chicago or Rolling Stones, there are hundreds of performers who are here today and gone tomorrow.

For many years, the author conducted a survey on the first day of his university rock history classes. One item on the survey asked students to provide a list of their five favorite current groups or artists. Another item asked students to identify the three groups or artists who they consider the most influential in the history of rock. The results of those surveys make an important point: Over time the current performers listed vary significantly, while the artists considered most influential remain relatively consistent.

There is one other observation that relates to basic statement number 1: Nothing is as "out" as that which is most recently out. Very often, there is a cycle: popularity to derision to nostalgia. In a 1984 survey, Michael Jackson was the biggest vote-getter; when his name was mentioned in class in 1986, the responses varied from snickers to outright guffaws. As time passed, the Jackson stigma passed, and Michael became a nostalgia item from the "good old days" of the 1980s. This phenomenon is particularly noticeable with the harder rock styles, especially with heavy metal. The principle in operation here seems to be that the more the appeal of a group is based on rebellion and shock, the more likely it is to pass from "super in" to "super out." After all, what is outrageously shocking today will be "old news" in two years—which brings us to the next observation.

18.1.2: Basic Statement 2

What were once vices are now habits. The principle of one-upmanship is quite powerful within the rock industry. The title of the Doobie Brothers album (quoted as basic statement number 2) makes a profound statement related to rock history. Again, this principle applies with increasing strength in the harder styles, especially where rebellion and shock are major factors. Competition within the rock industry is tremendous. Countless new bands form each year in the United States, England, and around the globe. All hope to "make it"—to see their albums rise to the Top 10 and to play sold-out stadiums.

Unfortunately (or fortunately?), 99 percent will never come close to their dreams. Somehow, out of all those thousands of bands, only a decimal of one percent actually attain significant success. Thus, publicity becomes crucial—good or bad matters little (there is an old show biz proverb that "all publicity is good publicity"). To grab the spotlight from the current stars, a new band must attract attention to themselves, playing louder, having more elaborate props, dressing more outrageously, wearing more spikes and chains, shouting more obscenities, or biting the heads off more bats. If not, they run the risk of being submerged in obscurity forever.

Thus, one-upmanship is a fact of life for many aspiring bands. The only problem is that one-upmanship is a game that no one wins for long. The rules of the game mean another group will soon come along with more powerful amps, even more elaborate props, more revealing costumes, and even more explicit songs—and they will bite the heads off of more bats … and a baby rabbit.

The troublesome result of the one-upmanship game is that it implies a staggering future. If the game continues as it has for the last 50 years, where will rock and roll be two decades from now? Just how loud can it get? How sexually explicit? How outrageous? It is certainly a cause for concern.

18.1.3: Basic Statement 3

Good is bad, and bad is good. The one-upmanship game would not be a concern if each group were merely trying to play better music, make ever more uplifting statements, and set increasingly better lifestyle examples. This is, in fact, close to the nature of the game in the early and mid-1960s, when love, peace, and racial tolerance were themes. With the division of the mainstream in the mid-1960s into Beatles and Stones, though, an interesting change occurred. The Stones represented the antihero concept. Part of their popularity resulted from "being bad." They acted badly, they sang badly (compared to the Beatles, at least)—they *were* bad … and bad was good. In fact, the word "bad," said with the right inflection, means "good."

This inversion of traditional evaluative criteria developed through the 1970s, and the message seemed to be that the worse you were, the better you were (and vice versa). Distortion was deliberately added to the music. Thus, rock consumers bought more and more sophisticated stereo systems—presumably as free from any distortion as possible—so they could hear the distortion better. Singers who screamed and shouted out of tune were praised, whereas singers who sang in tune were sometimes derided. The "best" or "real" rock groups were those who played with the least sophistication; any attempt to sophisticate the music was condemned as a sellout to commercialism or as a disreputable attempt at musical snobbery.

After all, the more sophisticated and complex the music, the more that is required of both the performers and listeners. Some effort must be put forth to perform or listen intelligently to the more sophisticated compositions within any style of music—but it is an effort worth making. There must be something inherent in the finest music that allows it to last for hundreds of years, whereas less thoughtful work often totally disappears within a matter of weeks.

Some rock writers say, though, that "real" rock (meaning simple, three-chord, 4/4 rock) is for the "real" people (the average middle and lower income working classes). This is surely the most offensively prejudicial position one can take. It implies that only the privileged socioeconomic classes have the intelligence, inner drive, and discipline to learn to play or to listen to more sophisticated styles of music and that a "regular person" cannot possibly appreciate more than three chords or four beats. Such a position is not only grossly offensive, it is also dead wrong. Anyone can learn to listen more actively and intelligently to music. One need not know every chord, every metrical pattern, or every musical form to respond to better music (in whatever style). As with anything else (football, baseball, politics, etc.), the more one knows, the more one enjoys.

By the way, the foregoing discussion should not be interpreted to mean that one ought to prefer more sophisticated music and shun simpler music. Musical preference is a complicated issue with which profound minds have been grappling for a long time. There is absolutely nothing wrong with liking simpler styles of music. What is wrong is to disdain more complex styles just because they are more complex. That would be just as bad as disdaining simpler styles just because they are simple. The ideal goal would be to develop a broader taste that can accept and enjoy both simple music and complex music (and everything in-between), while recognizing each for what it is. Fortunate is the listener who can enjoy Emerson, Lake & Palmer or Blood, Sweat & Tears, appreciating their musical complexities, and then fully enjoy Little Richard or the Rolling Stones, while recognizing their music as being pure and simple fun. In other words, one need not validate one's own musical preference by disparaging other styles.

18.1.4: Basic Statement 4

"My album may be number 1, but I'm not commercial!" One of the basic ironies in the rock industry is that virtually everyone is striving for commercial success, while loudly proclaiming just the opposite. As was mentioned earlier, in our discussion of indie rock, for example, one of the most damning charges one can make is that a performer has "gone commercial," but rock music is not only a musical phenomenon, it is a commercial enterprise. There need not be a stigma attached to the word "commercial." The crux of the issue may be whether or not (and to what extent) a group alters its style simply to achieve commercial success. Thus, if a group maintains its style and gradually becomes popular enough to enjoy a wide appeal, they have simply carried their style to a wider audience. That should be a compliment to the musicians and to their early fans, validating their musical preference.

More problematic is the case of a band that consciously alters its musical principles solely to achieve commercial success. This rings of hypocrisy and raises embarrassing questions about musical authenticity. Sometimes it is difficult to know whether such a change is genuine or simply done to make a buck.

As we have seen, the word "commercial" is often slapped onto performers whose talents are versatile enough to enable them to perform in a variety of styles. If a musician has the musical talent to perform convincingly in a variety of styles, he or she should be respected, not condemned. Such condemnation often reflects the narrow-mindedness of the critic more than the lack of integrity of the performer.

In any event, the word "commercial" ought not to be used as a pejorative term. It means nothing musically; it tells nothing about the harmonies, melodies, forms, and so on. It is an economic term. So beware the next time you hear someone disparage a performer for being commercial. Try to think (and listen) more deeply than that.

18.1.5: Basic Statement 5

Not all music is art; most of it is simply product. Have you ever stood in stunned appreciation while some musical whiz sat at a piano and improvised almost any tune you could name, or have you been amazed at the seemingly mysterious ability of some guitarist to invent tunes and chords at a moment's notice? It is a vestige of nineteenth-century romanticism that we tend to view musical talent with awe and to invest it with an aura of mysticism. In earlier centuries, musicians were often viewed merely as skilled technicians, not much different from our modern-day auto mechanics, electricians, or plumbers.

The fact is that only a small percentage of musical talent is mysterious. A much larger percentage is simply the result of plain old hard work. There is a standing joke about composition: that it is 10 percent inspiration and 90 percent perspiration. That is about right. In his superb book, *Outliers: The Story of Success*, Malcolm Gladwell determines that, to become an expert in some area (including music, sports, and technology development), an individual must invest about 10,000 hours of time, focused on that activity (Gladwell, 2008). A musician (or athlete or computer developer) gets a musical idea in the same way one gets ideas about other things—"from somewhere." Then come the pure hard work, discipline, and practice to turn that idea into a full-blown reality.

A true work of art seems to appeal not only to a large number of people, but to generations of people across many centuries; it is as though the art object transcends time. A product, however, is a more mundane thing. Usually, a product begins with someone assessing what will sell, figuring out the technology required to produce it, and then going to work manufacturing it, promoting it, and selling it. Usually, such a product serves an immediate function and (as we all know too well) soon wears out or becomes obsolete and is discarded. This process applies to products as varied as automobiles, computers, and electric toothbrushes.

In every century and in every musical style, there have been very few true artists and a large number of musical manufacturers. The former create art; the latter make products. In Mozart's time, there were many composers who understood the musical language of the time and then went about producing music that utilized that language. They knew the skill of creating tunes, chords, and forms that were currently in style. Only a handful of composers of that time had that "something extra" that made their music rise above the level of product to the status of art. Several centuries later, we have forgotten many others, but we still remember Mozart.

Things are not much different now. Especially in a heavily commercialized industry like rock music, one can be sure that works of art will be few and far between, whereas 95 percent (likely, significantly more) of what we hear is mere product. Many composers, performers, and engineers have learned the technical skills necessary to manufacture a marketable musical product; hence, they go about their business, grinding out those products day after day. Fifty years from now (much less 200), almost all will be forgotten; only a trace will remain.

So beware when rock musicians attempt to hide behind so-called "artistic freedom." In most cases, they are merely successful manufacturers of a product. As such, they have the same responsibilities to society as manufacturers of automobiles, cigarettes, and lawn mowers.

You might ask, "Is artistic freedom not necessary for the creation of true art?" Well, Bach worked from Sunday to Sunday for the church; he wrote many musical masterpieces within the strict confines of what was acceptable to his employer. Yet he still managed to create musical works that live several centuries later. Was he free as an artist? Absolutely not. How far do you think he would have gotten if he had popped a few satanic messages or sexually explicit songs into the Sunday morning church service? Or consider Haydn, who worked for years for an Austrian prince. Each week, he had to create chamber music, solo literature, or orchestral music for the court. In addition, he composed many pieces for the baryton, a bass string instrument, because Prince Nicholas Esterházy (his patron) played the instrument. Because Haydn was a true artist, he created masterpieces within the boundaries imposed upon him. Whether such limitations are set by the church, the state, the employer, a patron, or society as a whole, art can and has flourished within these limitations. Composer Igor Stravinsky famously stated, "The more constraints one imposes, the more one frees one's self of the chains that shackle the spirit."

18.1.6: Basic Statement 6

The audience for rock is getting both older and younger. In its beginnings, rock and roll was the music of teens and very young adults (generally seventh grade through college years), but, as we entered the 1970s, an inevitable fact became obvious: those 1950s teenagers were entering middle age, and they still liked rock. A baby born in 1940 was 15 years old when "Rock Around the Clock" hit number 1. In 1970, that same person turned 30 but very likely still liked Elvis, the Beach Boys, Dylan, and the Beatles, and, in 2000, that baby was 60 years old and, in all probability, still

liked those artists as well as a few more recent ones. Notice the number of "classic rock" and "adult rock" radio stations on your FM dial? Those are aimed at a relatively affluent segment of the population that is roughly 50 to 75 years old. While these people are past their peak earning years, many continue to have expendable income (a fact of considerable interest to radio advertisers), and they want to hear their favorite artists from the 1950s and 1960s as well as a few of the more conservative acts of the 1970s through 1990s … and, depending on their interests, perhaps a few even more recent. Indeed, the rock market now extends to 80-year-olds, with many of the long-term rock performers in their 70s.

The other end of this demographic expansion is with preteens. The lowering of the age of rock consumerism accelerated with the arrival of MTV and other televised rock video formats. It should come as no surprise to anyone that children—little children—like television, and many can get around the Internet much more proficiently than their parents or grandparents. Now the 7-, 9-, and 11-year-old has immediate (and free) access to the most up-to-date rock videos. While parents and older siblings are at work, school, or elsewhere, the latchkey preteen is left to the electronic babysitter—television or a computer with Internet access. The child has a choice of cartoons, reruns, game shows, or rap videos. Rock videos have brought an increasingly younger population into the world of rock and roll.

This lowering of the age of pop music awareness is reflected at rock concerts, where the average age is steadily lowering. Whereas it was not so long ago that the rock concert was the province of those 16 to 24 years of age, it is gradually becoming evident that the majority of concertgoers are 12 to 19, with a heavy sprinkling of preteens at most concerts. Whereas in 1957, the typical 12-year-old would only stare in astonishment at older brother's new pink and black outfit and greasy ducktail, today's 12-year-old might be a carbon copy of Katy Perry or Nicki Minaj. Today, it is not uncommon to attend a concert by one of the remaining "classic rock" stars (the most recent I attended was Paul McCartney) and see an audience ranging in age from preteens to those well into their 80s, all rocking, smiling, and singing along.

Thus, the rock market of the early 2000s extends from the early elementary school students to 80-year-olds. True, the teenager is still the center of the market, but to call rock and roll "teen music" is simply no longer accurate.

18.1.7: Basic Statement 7

*Rock is no longer the counterculture—it **is** the culture.* This statement naturally follows the previous statement. Rock and roll no longer stands as a teen-oriented, countercultural phenomenon. It now pervades our entire culture and has had significant impact on a global scale. It cuts across all economic groups, social levels, and ethnic groups. The rock style permeates movie soundtracks, music for television, jazz, athletic events, church, and just about any event. Granted, within rock, there are countercultural trends, but as a generic entity, rock so permeates our entire culture that all other styles of music (jazz, classical, pure C&W, etc.) are considered on the fringe, admired by small subcultural groups.

18.1.8: Basic Statement 8

Music, including rock and roll, affects behavior. Perhaps the most oft-quoted statement in this regard was made by Andrew Fletcher in 1703: "Give me the making of the songs of a nation and I care not who makes the laws." In other words, music may be even more influential in shaping the attitudes and behaviors of a nation than its constitution, legal system, and government. Fletcher was hardly the first to recognize that fact. Socrates's and Plato's mentor, Damon, said that music, "being chaste, has the power of disposing our minds to virtue and, being the contrary, to vice." Centuries later, Martin Luther would say, "Music is one of the greatest gifts that God has given us; it is divine and therefore Satan is its enemy. For with its aid, many dire temptations are overcome; the devil does not stay where music is."

In our own century, anthropologist Alan P. Merriam wrote, "The importance of music, as judged by the sheer ubiquity of its presence, is enormous …. There is probably no other human, cultural activity that is so all-pervasive and that reaches into, shapes, and often controls so much of human behavior" (Merriam, 1964, 218). We have known intuitively for centuries that music can make us feel relaxed, scared, patriotic, ambitious, mad, sad, happy, romantic, and reverent. The ability of music to affect human behavior is the basis of the entire field of music therapy and innovative research in the field of music perception and cognition.

THE SCIENTIFIC STUDY OF MUSIC   In the past few decades, scientists have learned more and more about the ways in which we are affected by music. We know for certain that music affects us both physiologically and psychologically. Various musical stimuli can affect our heartbeat, respiratory rate, glandular secretions, and the production of electricity through the skin, but, with all we have learned about the intimate relationship between music and people, there is even more that we do not know. Music psychology—closely related to music therapy—is an exciting field of research. In future decades, we are sure to learn much more about how and why we react the way we do to music.

The fact that music is such a powerful tool in manipulating human behavior has been reflected in our society for years. Drums and bugles accompanied armies into battle,

partly to spur feelings of patriotism and courage. Film and television producers spend much time, energy, and money ensuring that just the right music accompanies each love scene, horror scene, or chase scene. As Arnold Perris points out, music "reaches the emotions easily, often [always?] ahead of intellectual awareness" (Perris, 1985, 6). Perris uses the example of the movie *Jaws,* in which "a melodic motive in the bass arouses our fear of the shark each time we hear it, whether or not the terrifying creature appears before our eyes" (1985, 6).

Businesses have picked up on this impact, carefully selecting music that is appropriate for their intended audience. Recorded music, whether piped in from a paid source (e.g., Muzak) or streamed from the Internet using an app like Pandora or iHeartRadio, is carefully programmed throughout the day to calm, stimulate, or otherwise affect the behavior of office workers. Doctors and dentists use music in their waiting rooms to help calm their anxious patients. The ability of music to make repetitive physical tasks easier or even fun has given rise to jazzercise and spin classes, in which people congregate to do coordinated calisthenics or ride stationary bikes to the accompaniment of pop and rock music. They do 100 jumping jacks and think they are having fun (and pay for the privilege). Doing it without the music would be work.

MUSIC AND MEMORY   In a Musical Close-Up earlier in this course, we noted the intimate relationship between lyrics and music. Music's ability to help us remember verbal messages has been demonstrated repeatedly by commercial jingles. When an advertiser wants to be sure that a product name, a sales slogan, or even a telephone number becomes lodged in the consumer's mind, he or she turns to music as an aid. Decades later, most people who watched television in the 1950s can still recall the product name from an old jingle, "See the U.S.A. in your ———."[1] They are likely to be able to sing the tune quite accurately. Do such jingles actually affect consumer behavior? Advertisers invest millions each year in the belief that they do, and research has confirmed its efficacy.

Sesame Street has used this principle for years. Noting that children could reproduce commercial jingles they heard on television, the *Sesame Street* creative team decided to run "commercials" for the letter "j," the number 9, and so on. Thousands of youngsters learned the "advertised" letters and numbers through these repetitive "commercials." Psychologists believe the association of verbal messages with simple and catchy musical phrases helps embed those messages in our minds, ready for instant recall years later.

THE IMPACT OF MUSIC ON HUMAN BEHAVIOR   Certainly, rock musicians have understood the power of music

---

[1]Chevrolet.

to affect human behavior. After all, they see the principle in action as they face thousands of screaming fans in arenas and stadiums night after night. They can play the crowd with uncanny insight. Certain songs tend to settle a crowd down, while others can bring the concert to a fever pitch. If they are not careful, artists can create a situation beyond even their own control, as the crowd's animation becomes potentially violent, sometimes even threatening the safety of the onstage performers themselves. Recall the Stones' reaction to the tragic developments at Altamont, turning intuitively from the frenetic pace of "Sympathy for the Devil" to some blues to calm the audience.

The folkies and folk rockers of the 1960s relied heavily on music's ability to affect behavior. Their "message songs" were intended to reinforce and even change people's attitudes toward violence, war, and racial prejudice. David Crosby once remarked, "I figure that the only thing to do was to steal the kids. I still think it's the only thing to do. By saying that, I'm not talking about kidnapping. I'm just talking about changing young people's value systems, which removes them from their parents' world very effectively" (*Rolling Stone Interviews* 1971, 410). The acid rockers also knew of music's power. Jimi Hendrix is reported to have said that "you can hypnotize people with music, and when you get people at their weakest point, you can preach to them into their subconscious what we want to say" (Peters and Peters 1984, 76).

On several occasions we have noted that music has the capacity to both reflect society and change it. As composer Roger Sessions noted, "Bach and Mozart and Beethoven did not reflect Germany, they helped to create it" (Augros & Stanciu 1984, 139). In his excellent study of the use of music as a force for change, Arnold Perris attempts "to demonstrate that composers in many times and places have consciously used their craft to change the world outside their studio" (Perris, 1985, 222). Perris discusses various examples of the use of music in totalitarian societies as an important agent of controlling thought and behavior. Regarding Hitler, he quotes Hellmut Lehmann-Haupt, who said that the dictator "does not think of art as a luxury or a pastime, a pleasant embellishment of life .... He has a very healthy respect for it. He knows that there is hardly a better way of getting hold of a person ... his inner life, the subconscious, hidden personality—than through art" (1985, 209). Perris shows how leaders from Saint Augustine to Mao have all understood music's ability to affect human behavior.

If music possesses such power, there is both good and bad news. The good news is that music can be used to uplift us, to help us learn, and to make us more tolerant. The bad news is that music can also encourage drug abuse, increase violence and rebellion, reinforce suicidal tendencies, and influence our purchasing decisions. Far too many writers of rock music get themselves into an embarrassing and untenable position. Their enthusiasm leads them to point with pride to the undeniable affects music has had on clothing, hairstyles, and lifestyles; they praise music for its pivotal role in the civil rights and antiwar movements. Harry Belafonte, a motivating force behind "We Are the World," remarked that "the power of artists is unlimited .... There are no boundaries on art; its universal power is absolutely unlimited" (Bronson 1988, 605). However, many of the same commentators pull a quick about-face when confronted with potentially negative examples. What about drugs, suicide, violence, and misogyny? Suddenly, the party line changes. Music inexplicably becomes impotent; some claim that it is not an influence where these negative behaviors are concerned. Music, such writers would say, is just harmless, good-time entertainment, utterly devoid of any affective power.

The problem is that one cannot have it both ways. If we acknowledge that rock music has had positive effects (and it has), we must also be willing to admit that it has had negative effects (as it also has). The person who proudly proclaims, "Oh, I listen to the music, but it doesn't affect me" is either hopelessly naive or grossly ill-informed.

As people have known for centuries (from Damon to Hendrix), and as scientists have begun to document, music is one of the most powerful tools known to humankind. In Perris's words "Music is doing something to everyone who hears it all the time" (Perris, 1985, 6).

JOURNAL

Challenge the Eight

The eight basic statements above are intended to communicate a perspective regarding rock music, but it may not be your own perspective. It would be surprising for anyone to read through such a subjective set of items and agree completely with each and every one. Select one of the eight statements with which you disagree most vehemently. State your counter perspective and compose a paragraph providing a clear rationale for your position.

 The response entered here will appear in the performance dashboard and can be viewed by your instructor.

Submit

18.2: Editorial

OBJECTIVE: Outline the concerns with the continued evolution of rock and roll

Let us review the eight basic statements from the preceding overview:

1. Rock and roll may be here to stay, but individual artists and styles are not.
2. What were once vices are now habits.
3. Good is bad, and bad is good.

4. "My album may be number 1, but I'm not commercial!"
5. Not all music is art; most of it is simply product.
6. The audience for rock is getting both older and younger.
7. Rock is no longer the counterculture—it *is* the culture.
8. Music, including rock and roll, affects behavior.

The editorial comments that follow draw in varying degrees on these eight basic statements.

18.2.1: Pushing Limits

Since its birth in the mid-1950s, rock and roll has changed dramatically. Elvis Presley sang about hound dogs and pleaded with his lover not to be cruel. Chuck Berry sang of school days and teenage would-be rock and rollers ("Johnny B. Goode"). Elvis bumped his hips; Chuck Berry duck-walked across the stage; Little Richard and Jerry Lee Lewis played the piano every way imaginable.

More recently, Prince told us that incest is not so bad and rapper Ice-T yearns to "dust" (kill) a cop. In concert, W.A.S.P. lead singer Blackie Lawless simulated intercourse using a buzz saw, Slayer simulated the cannibalization of women, Alice Cooper symbolically abused a baby doll, and satanic symbols adorn numerous stage settings. Album covers show meat hooks pressed into nude breasts, chewed-up body parts beneath the blood-drenched mouth of a rock star, and fantastic scenes representing hell. Videos revel in sado-masochism, misogyny, and violence. To paraphrase a popular commercial slogan, "We've come a long way, baby!"

All a matter of degree, you may say. Little by little, inch by inch, year by year, we have "progressed" from Elvis swiveling his hips through Hendrix humping his guitar and Morrison exposing himself to W.A.S.P. simulating intercourse with a saw blade. Yes, it is just a matter of degree—but when does a difference in degree become a difference in kind? After all, 110 degrees Fahrenheit is simply a difference in degree from 15 degrees, but the former most of us think of as hot and the latter we call cold—opposites, in fact. At what point does temperature become "hot"—at 83? At 92? At 100? We are not certain; each of us has a different tolerance for heat, but we would probably all agree that when the thermometer rises above 100 degrees, we are hot. Somewhere, at different temperatures along the way, we became hot—we crossed a line. Has rock and roll, while "progressing" by degrees, crossed a line? Recall five of our basic statements:

1. the one-upmanship principle
2. the inverted-values principle
3. the younger rock audience
4. the rock-is-the-culture principle
5. the music-affects-behavior principle

If these principles continue to operate for the next 10 years, as they have for the last several decades, what will rock and roll be like 10 years from now? What will today's 18-year-old face in the attempt to raise a child in the rock culture in a decade or so?

Increasingly, thoughtful observers have begun to wonder just how much is too much. Has the one-upmanship game gone too far? Even though not all agree as to when and where the line was crossed, many reasonable people agree that things have gotten a bit out of hand. Rock and roll has gradually become something different in kind, not simply different in degree. Former Doobie Brothers member Michael McDonald has commented on the apparent dichotomy between the energy created by earlier rock groups as contrasted with more recent groups. According to McDonald, earlier groups exuded energy to make their audiences feel better, whereas many more recent groups use their energy to intimidate (Woodward 1985, 82). Certainly, there is an element of hatred and violence in much of today's rock that simply has not been present in any style of music previously. Something is different.

CRITICS OF ROCK MUSIC Whereas rock's critics have traditionally been fundamentalist religious groups, another segment of the population has joined the fray. In June 1984, the National PTA, representing 5.6 million members, adopted a resolution calling on record companies to advise consumers when their products contained material with explicit language or sexual references and inferences not commonly recommended for all age groups. At the instigation of the Parents' Music Resource Center (PMRC), a hearing was held before the U.S. Senate Committee on Commerce, Science, and Transportation on September 19, 1985. Among those testifying were representatives of the PTA, the PMRC, the recording industry, the radio industry, a psychiatrist, a music educator, and performers John Denver, Frank Zappa, and Dee Snider (lead singer of Twisted Sister). The purpose of the hearing was not to foster legislation to control rock music, nor was it antirock, as some writers have erroneously reported (e.g., "Even as the PMRC was mounting its antirock campaign ..."; Ward, Stokes, and Tucker 1986, 620). The hearing did attempt to focus attention on a certain segment of the music industry that may have "crossed the line." It called on the music industry to clean up its own act and practice social responsibility. The hearing further encouraged companies to label potentially offensive albums for the purpose of informing the consumer (a standard practice in other segments of the marketplace, from movies to cigarettes to children's toys). Commenting on this topic in a 1985 interview, Neil Young correctly described rock albums as products (like packaged food for the mind instead of the body). He, therefore, suggested that labeling according to content would be entirely appropriate. (Note that Young's opinion reflects our basic statement 5.) Frank Zappa further suggested that lyrics be printed on the outside of albums, a suggestion that met with near-unanimous approval. Although some called this "censorship," that was a false issue. Neither the labeling of the product nor the printing of lyrics qualifies as censorship; in fact, such procedures represent the increased dissemination of information, not the suppression of information—in other words, exactly the opposite of censorship.

According to basic statement 8, music—including rock and roll—affects behavior. Will our culture be affected more by Bruce Springsteen, Michael Jackson, Huey Lewis, and Lionel Richie, or by Snoop Dogg, Eminem, and Venom? The answer rests in the delicate interplay between the consumer and the industry. If consumers buy more of one and less of the other, the industry will be quick to react. After all, they are merely manufacturing a product to sell. To a large extent, though, the industry can determine what consumers think they want to buy. For example, referring to the selling of Sha-Na-Na, a 1950s-style rock revival group of the 1970s, Neil Bogart of Casablanca Records said,

> To build this group, we created a music industry trend. We called it rock 'n' roll revival. With slogans, stickers, buttons, and industry and consumer contests, and even black leather jackets for our promotion staff, we brought back the fifties.

Bogart concluded that "talent may be compared to commercial products—the cigarettes you smoke, the TV set you watch, or the car you drive. You select that brand of product that you have been convinced is the one you should buy" (Szatmary 1991, 223–224).

David Szatmary points out the importance of the rock critic in creating the consumer's "free will." He quotes columnist and author Richard Goldstein, who maintained "illusions about the value-free purity of rock until the day in 1969 when my agent informed me that a large music publisher would pay me $25,000 for three presentations on the state of popular music. It was understood that I would favor this company's artists in my reviews" (Szatmary, 1987, 171). Some companies provide up to six copies of each new release, worth up to $10,000 per year, to major, well-placed rock journalists (Szatmary 1987). It is simply naive to believe that the rock industry functions with a free-willed consumer purchasing the artistic expressions of an idealistic group of musical creators.

The Issue of Censorship Concerning Rock Recordings

You have undoubtedly seen album covers containing the word "Explicit" or have seen that word in parentheses at the end of a song title for a digital download. After reading the section above, do you consider this requirement to be a form of censorship? Compose a paragraph supporting your response.

 The response entered here will appear in the performance dashboard and can be viewed by your instructor.

Submit

18.2.2: Toward Improvement

Can the situation improve? Yes. A remarkably valid solution was suggested by none other than Frank Zappa at the Senate hearings in 1985:

> Children in the "vulnerable" age bracket have a natural love for music. If, as a parent, you believe they should be exposed to something more uplifting than "Sugar Walls," support Music Appreciation programs in schools. Music Appreciation costs very little compared to sports expenditures. Your children have a right to know that something besides pop music exists. (U.S. Congress, 1985)

A respected author on the topic of American culture (and especially on the media and our educational system) was the late Neil Postman, former professor of communication arts and sciences at New York University. In *Teaching As a Subversive Activity*, Postman (1979) suggests that an educational system should serve as a counterbalance to the existing cultural environment. In other words, education should provide what the culture does not. He bravely suggests a curriculum that provides substantive education in areas absolutely essential to the development of human culture, but unlike so many "back to basics" prescriptions, Postman wisely includes music and the arts among the essentials.

In considering music a cultural essential, Postman is on absolutely solid anthropological ground. Music has been one of the few consistent characteristics of every society since the beginning of recorded history. No matter how basic; no matter what continent; and no matter what the ethnic, economic, or social profile, every society has had music. Anthropologists have concluded, therefore, that all societies have felt the need for some type of musical expression. It is, apparently, a necessity of human existence. This anthropological evidence runs exactly counter to the oft-held position that music is a luxury, a nonessential that may be jettisoned from the educational curriculum at the first provocation. How often have you heard some educational reformer angrily demanding that the educational fluff be cut out of the curriculum? In most cases, music is cited as one example of fluff. One can hardly imagine a more historically ill-informed position.

What kind of music should we teach? Again, Neil Postman has a valid suggestion. Consistent with his philosophy that education should provide a counterbalance to the cultural environment, Postman recommends that schools should stay as far away as possible from contemporary works, especially avoiding products of the popular culture. That idea sounds so reactionary that it is downright revolutionary, but Postman's idea makes good sense. After all, teaching rock and roll to high school students is like teaching a fish to swim. Postman argues that the so-called First Curriculum (by which he means television and other electronic media) supplies a glut of information about contemporary popular culture; hence the Second Curriculum (the school curriculum) should provide a counterbalance—that is, it should inform students about alternative artistic products from other (including past) cultures. Thus, he is saying almost exactly what Frank Zappa said about the advisability of exposing youth to other styles of music beyond "pop music."

FINDING A SOLUTION We are in the age of relevance—knowledge for knowledge's sake is an unappreciated concept—but relevant to what? Today, most students might reply, "Relevant to making money!" If it applies to operating a computer, running a business, or setting up a wireless network, it is relevant (the "STEM"-obsessed society in which we find ourselves); if it deals with the philosophy of religion, the history of government, or the music of Schubert, it is irrelevant. Worse, it is boring! Thus, we have the materialistic-world Madonna referred to in her song "Material Girl."

Even though we may agree with Postman's idealistic suggestions, we must also face reality. Perhaps the solution lies somewhere in-between. For example, perhaps we should study rock and roll but, in doing so, perhaps we should try to distinguish between art and product. What is it about the music of the Beatles that continues to enliven the interest of both the average listener and the musically educated? Why do popular music scholars find works by Blood, Sweat & Tears and Emerson, Lake & Palmer so fascinating? What was it that these groups (and others) did that seems to set them apart from the others? Maybe the answer has to do with genuine musical creativity—the talent some musicians have, to take whatever musical language they prefer (classical, jazz,

rock, etc.) and manipulate it (via melody, harmony, form, timbre, rhythm, etc.) in new and imaginative ways. If students can begin to appreciate true musical creativity in rock (and also to recognize the more pervasive musical mundanities), it often follows that they crave further musical stimulation, seeking it out (and finding it) in other styles, such as jazz or classical music. This may not happen in every case, but it happens more often than one might expect.

Rock and roll, just like almost anything else you can name, is neither all good nor all bad. Someone who criticizes a certain aspect of rock should not be labeled automatically as "antirock." In fact, just the opposite may be true; the criticism may stem from an abiding love of rock music and a belief in its validity as a form of musical expression. Such critics want rock to be the best it can be … a creative musical style that enhances our society, rather than one that debases it.

JOURNAL

Music (Not) in Schools

In recent years, we have seen a significant drop in the number of opportunities for students to study the arts, specifically music, in K–12 schools in America. Many of you reading this text were likely impacted by this decision. After reading the section above and reflecting on the recommendation made by Frank Zappa's during the 1985 Senate hearing, what is your position regarding the role of studying music as a part of one's formative education?

  The response entered here will appear in the performance dashboard and can be viewed by your instructor.

Submit

Summary: An Overview and an Editorial

Trying to forecast trends in the unpredictable music industry is risky business. During the 2000s, rock and roll turned 50 years of age. Jazz was about that age when it experienced its popular decline, and it was not long after that the new kid on the block—rock and roll—took over. Many wondered whether a similar fate awaited rock and roll. Would the early decades of the new millennium witness the death of rock?

It has not yet happened. One of the points made earlier in this chapter was that rock has become totally integrated into our culture. By now, there is such a multitude of rock styles—each with its own audience, from preteens to folks in their 70s or 80s—that it seems highly unlikely that rock will die anytime soon. (For that matter, jazz did not die, it just receded from its position of prominence to a less prominent place in the world's musical fabric.)

Like jazz, rock is unlikely to die suddenly in the early decades of the new millennium, but there is historical precedent for the emergence of a new style that could cause the harder rock styles to decline in their commercial impact.

As we have mentioned, harder rock styles are based to a large degree on the one-upmanship principle. Many heavy metal bands and rap artists have raced, pell-mell, down a very steep path of explicit sex, graphic violence, anger, and defiance. Coupled with numbing similarity and often dubious musical value, this appears to be a path that may well face an eventual dead end. Although there may always be an audience for such music, the early decades of the twenty-first century may find a larger number of listeners who have tired of rock degradation and negativism.

The probability is that the children of the Millennials will be listening to a musical style that we cannot yet imagine. Suppose you had told people in 1946 that in 10 years, most of the music they were listening to would be obsolete, replaced by a raucous new style called "rock and roll." They would have laughed at you and had no concept of what such music would be like. Just as was true then, the seeds of the next new style are probably around us now, but we are not able to recognize them.

In spite of our inability to predict the future, we can hazard a few guesses about the music of the coming decades. Certainly, there is no reason to think that the technological trend will slow down; thus, it is likely that digital sampling, computer workstations, software synthesizers, and other manifestations of music technology will continue to be important elements of whatever popular styles emerge.

Also, the softer styles of rock seem to have had a consistent appeal throughout the rock era, and there is no reason to expect anything to change in that regard.

Finally, people like to dance. Whether it was swing, the twist, disco, or technodance, dance music seems to have a consistent appeal in every era. In fact, since music is most often an important element of social events, it serves to bring people together. The need to come together with friends and family is one aspect of culture that is unlikely ever to change. Therefore, we can be confident in the prediction that some form of dance-oriented music will continue to be successful well into the future.

Rock has a wonderful, colorful, and exciting history. From Bill Haley and the Comets through Presley, Dylan, the Beatles, the Stones, Motown, Chicago, ELP, Jackson, Springsteen, Garth Brooks and Jay-Z—it is a fascinating story and one that shows no signs of ending—or even slowing down—any time soon. The author hopes that this and the preceding sections of this course have helped you develop a meaningful perspective related to the history of rock. Perhaps the next time you hear of an exciting new group or new style, you will have a better idea of how it fits into a larger picture and from whence it came.

SHARED WRITING

Your Prediction for the Future of Rock and Roll

For the final written assignment for this course, take time to reflect on the many musical styles you have listened to and studied during the past weeks. (It might be helpful to review the table of contents to remind yourself of the many topics covered.) Though no one is expected to be a fully accurate prognosticator, do your best to think forward two decades and envision what you believe the rock music scene will sound—and look—like at that time. What specific current musical trends do you believe will continue to evolve into that future period, and how do you predict they might change? What trends do you believe will disappear? Share your answer with two other students as you read their responses. Do you find yourselves largely in agreement or with widely varying perspectives? (You might want to save this response to share with your children or grandchildren, who will be fully immersed in the music of their time.)

A minimum number of characters is required to post and earn points. After posting, your response can be viewed by your class and instructor, and you can participate in the class discussion.

Post

0 characters | 140 minimum

Discography

A Basic Recorded Library of Rock and Roll

Spending a lot of money on recordings is no problem; anyone can do it. However, the Discography that follows is an attempt to reduce the seemingly endless possibilities to a manageable collection. Despite this strategic effort, there are still approximately 300 entries, equaling an estimated expenditure of between $3,000 and $4,500 to acquire these recordings in a media format (e.g., CD or vinyl) or via digital download. Of course, the arrival of music subscription services (e.g., Spotify, Rhapsody, and Apple Music) allows you direct access to many of these recordings.

This Discography is intended to provide a representative sampling of styles since rock's emergence in the mid-1950s. Needless to say, it was difficult to make the decision regarding what to include and what to leave out. Of course, no two rock discographers would ever come up with the same list. In this case, it is also necessary that artists and songs explicitly discussed in the text are appropriately represented in the Discography.

In trying to keep the list as short (and inexpensive) as possible, some inevitable trade-offs were accepted. First, in a number of cases, greatest hits compilations were listed. While such compilations are a cost-effective way to acquire the "biggies" by a given artist, it is important to be cognizant that some of the given artist's most creative work may not be among the most popular Top 40 hits but found in the other tracks of various albums. The compilations remaining were determined judiciously, opting for specific albums in cases where the artist's best work might be lost on a greatest hits album.

A second trade-off involves anthologies or compilations (listed separately). Here again, one gains in cost-effectiveness (e.g., why buy an entire album of the Kingsmen when all one wants is "Louie, Louie"). However, most anthologies contain a certain percentage of significant material, plus a balance of filler. Also, there is inevitably some duplication among similar anthologies. Again, there are many anthologies available; those listed were thoughtfully selected for breadth and coordination with the text.

One final note: If your funds are limited, please note the asterisks in the Discography. The selections marked with an asterisk constitute a very basic library of just over 100 items (approximate cost: $1,250) that would seem to be the minimum required to establish a basic sampling of rock's recorded history. In the cases in which multiple recordings are listed for a group or artist, you will find an asterisk preceding the specific album(s) that warrant, in the opinion of the author, this "most significant recording" status. Another option that has recently become available is purchasing individual songs for around $1 each from a music download service, using a computer-based media player. Two of the most popular options at the time of publication are Apple's iTunes (http://apple.com/itunes/) and Spotify (http://spotify.com). Although this may be seen as an economic option, it should be considered a distant second in terms of purchasing music to build a library. After all, purchasing an entire album, containing both hit singles and album cuts, provides a much broader perspective on the output of any given artist or group. You can find two Spotify playlists of recordings to go with this text: a "required" list and a supplementary "recommended" list. When you open Spotify, simply type "Lipscomb Rock and Roll" into the search box (or select Edit > Search; shortcut = Command/Control + L).

Selected Discography

AC/DC, *Back in Black*, Epic 80207

Aerosmith, *Greatest Hits (1972–79)*, Columbia 57367; *Big Ones*, Geffen 24716

Air Supply, *The Definitive Collection*, Arista 14611

Alan Parsons Project, *The Turn of a Friendly Card*, Arista ArCD-8226

Alice Cooper, *Greatest Hits*, Warner 78129

Allman Brothers Band, *Best of Allman Brothers Band*, Polydor 823-708

America, *Premium Gold Collection*, EMI 837638

Animals, *Best of the Animals*, ABKCO 4324

Baez, Joan, *Diamonds and Rust*, Mobile Fidelity 646; *Hits/Greatest and Others*, Vanguard 79332

Beach Boys, *Pet Sounds*, DCC 1035; *The Greatest Hits Vol. 1: 20 Good Vibrations*, EMI 21860; *The Greatest Hits Vol. 2: 20 More Good Vibrations*, EMI 20238

Beastie Boys, *Licensed to Ill*, Def Jam 4464

Beatles, *Abbey Road*, Capitol 46446; *The Beatles* (White Album), Capitol 46443; *Sgt. Pepper's Lonely Hearts Club Band*, Capitol 46442; *Please Please Me*, Capitol 46435; *Revolver*, Capitol 46441; *Rubber Soul*, Capitol 46440

Beck, *Odelay*, Geffen 24823

Beck, Jeff, *Blow by Blow*, Epic 85440

Belafonte, Harry, *Calypso*, RCA 53801

Berry, Chuck, *The Anthology*, Chess 112304

Björk, *Post*, Elektra 61740; *Vespertine*, Elektra 62653

Black, Clint, *Greatest Hits*, RCA 66671

Black Sabbath (see also *Osbourne, Ozzy*), *Paranoid*, Victor 61711

Blondie, *Parallel Lines*, Chrysalis 21192

Blood, Sweat & Tears, *Blood, Sweat & Tears*, Legacy 63986; *Blood, Sweat & Tears 3*, Mobile Fidelity 2013; *Blood, Sweat & Tears 4*, Columbia 66422

Bon Jovi, *Slippery When Wet*, Mercury 538089

Boone, Pat, *Pat Boone's Greatest Hits*, MCA 10885

Bowie, David, *Ziggy Stardust*, Virgin 21900

Boy George (see *Culture Club*)

Boyz II Men, *Cooleyhighharmony*, Motown 6320

Brooks, Garth, *No Fences*, Capitol 93866

Brown, James, *20 All Time Greatest Hits*, Polydor 511326

Buffalo Springfield, *Box Set*, Rhino 74324

Byrds, *The Notorious Byrd Brothers*, Legacy 65151; *Greatest Hits*, Sony 9516

Campbell, Glen, *The Very Best of Glen Campbell*, Capitol 46483

Carey, Mariah, *#1s*, Columbia CK 69670

Carpenter, Mary Chapin, *Come On Come On*, Sony 48881

Carpenters, *Yesterday Once More*, A&M 75021-6601

Charles, Ray, *Ultimate Hits Collection*, Rhino 75644

Chase, *Chase*, Endorphin 001

Checker, Chubby, *Greatest Hits*, Prime Cuts 1334

Chic, *C'est Chic*, Atlantic 81552

Chicago, *Chicago Transit Authority*, Rhino 76171; *Chicago VII*, Chicago Records 3007

Clapton, Eric, *461 Ocean Blvd.*, Universal International 9158; *Cream of Clapton*, Polydor/Chronicles 31452 7116; *Unplugged*, Reprise 45024

Clash, *The Clash*, Sony Japan 520; *London Calling*, Epic 63885

Coasters, *The Very Best of the Coasters*, Rhino 71597

Cooke, Sam (see also *Soul Stirrers*), *Greatest Hits*, RCA 67605

Costello, Elvis, *The Very Best of Elvis Costello*, Rhino 76652

Cream, *The Very Best of Cream*, Polydor/Chronicles 523752

Creedence Clearwater Revival, *Chronicle: The 20 Greatest Hits*, Fantasy 2

Croce, Jim, *Photographs & Memories*, Atlantic 92570

Crosby, Stills, Nash, and Young, *Déjà Vu*, Atlantic 82649

Culture Club, *Colour by Numbers*, Virgin 86180

Daniels, Charlie, *Million Mile Reflections*, Columbia 35751

Dave Matthews Band, *Before These Crowded Streets*, RCA 67660; *Crash*, RCA 66904

Davis, Miles, *Bitches Brew*, Columbia 65774

Deep Purple, *Gemini Suite*, Cleopatra 234; *Deepest Purple/The Very Best of Deep Purple*, Warner Brothers 2-3486

Denver, John, *The Very Best of John Denver*, BMG 67442

Depeche Mode, *Violator*, Sire 9260812

Derek and the Dominoes, *Layla*, Polydor 9167

Devo, *Freedom of Choice*, Warner 3435

Diamond, Neil, *12 Greatest Hits, Vol. II*, Columbia 38068

Dixie Chicks, *Wide Open Spaces*, Sony 68195

DJ Shadow, *Endtroducing*, Mo Wax 124123

Domino, Fats, *My Blue Heaven*, Astan 20082 (LP)

Donovan, *Greatest Hits and More*, EMI 1333

Doobie Brothers, *Best of the Doobies*, Warner 78096

Doors, *Best of the Doors*, Elektra 5035 (LP)

Dr. Dre, *The Chronic*, Death Row 6300

Dylan, Bob, *The Essential Bob Dylan*, Columbia 85168; *The Freewheelin' Bob Dylan*, Columbia ck-8786; *The Times They Are a-Changin'*, Columbia 8905; *Highway 61 Revisited*, Sony 90324; *Blood on the Tracks*, Sony 377

Eagles, *Their Greatest Hits*, DCC 2051; *Hell Freezes Over*, Digital Sound 1006

Electric Light Orchestra, *Greatest Hits*, Jet 4775002

Emerson, Keith (and the Nice), *Here Come the Nice: Immediate Anthology*, CASTL CMETD055

Emerson, Lake & Palmer, *Brain Salad Surgery*, Atlantic 19124; *Emerson, Lake & Palmer*, Rhino 72223; *Tarkus*, Castle 434; *Pictures at an Exhibition*, Rhino 72225; *Trilogy*, Rhino 72226

Eminem, *The Eminem Show*, Interscope 493290; *The Slim Shady LP*, Interscope 90287; *The Marshall Mathers LP*, Interscope 490629

Estefan, Gloria, *Greatest Hits*, Sony 86729

Everly Brothers, *All Time Original Hits*, Rhino 75996

Flack, Roberta, *Softly with These Songs: The Best of Roberta Flack*, Atlantic 82498

Fleetwood Mac, *Greatest Hits*, Reprise 25801

Focus, *Focus III*, Red Bullet 66189

Four Seasons, *Anthology*, Rhino 71490

Frampton, Peter, *Frampton Comes Alive!*, Mobile Fidelity 678

Franklin, Aretha, *Amazing Grace*, Atlantic SD2-906; *Soul '69*, Rhino 71523

Gaye, Marvin, *What's Going On?*, Motown 530883

Genesis, *The Lamb Lies Down on Broadway*, Virgin 1

Grateful Dead, *Live/Dead*, Warner 1830; *Workingman's Dead*, Warner 1869

Green Day, *American Idiot*, Reprise 48777; *Dookie*, Reprise 45529

Guns N' Roses, *G N' R Lies*, Geffen 24198; *Appetite for Destruction*, Mobile Fidelity 699

Haley, Bill (and the Comets), *Universal Masters Collection*, Polygram 112174200088

Hancock, Herbie, *Thrust*, Sony 86568

Harrison, George, *All Things Must Pass* [boxed edition], Capitol 46688

Harvey, PJ, *Dry*, Island 555001

Hendrix, Jimi, *Electric Ladyland*, MCA 11600; *Are You Experienced?*, MCA 11602

Holly, Buddy (and the Crickets), *The Buddy Holly Collection*, MCA 10883

Houston, Whitney, *Whitney: The Greatest Hits*, Arista 14626

Iron Butterfly, *In-A-Gadda-Da-Vida*, Atco 33250

Iron Maiden, *Number of the Beast*, Sony 86210

Jackson, Janet, *Rhythm Nation 1814*, A&M 75021-3920

Jackson, Michael, *HIStory: Past, Present and Future, Book 1*, Epic 59000; *Thriller*, Sony International 504422

Jackson Five, *The Ultimate Collection*, Motown 530558

Jay-Z, *Vol. 2: Hard Knock Life*, Roc-a-Fella 558902

Jefferson Airplane, *Surrealistic Pillow*, Cloud 9 84791

Jethro Tull, *The Very Best of Jethro Tull*, Emi 532614

Jett, Joan, *Fit to Be Tied: Greatest Hits by Joan Jett*, Blackheart 31

Joel, Billy, *Greatest Hits Vols. 1 and 2*, Columbia 40121

John, Elton, *Greatest Hits*, DCC 2013; *Goodbye Yellow Brick Road*, Universal International 9107

Joplin, Janis, *Cheap Thrills/I Got Dem Ol' Kosmic Blues Again Mama!/Pearl* [boxed set], Sony 64804

Journey, *Escape/Frontiers/Infinity* [boxed set], Columbia 61387

Judas Priest, *British Steel*, Columbia ck-36443

Kansas, *Leftoverture*, Columbia 34224

King, Carole, *Tapestry*, Song International 4931805

King Crimson, *In the Court of the Crimson King*, Discipline Gm 501; *Larks' Tongues in Aspic*, Virgin 849935

Kingston Trio, *Story*, EMI 576219

Kiss, *Lick It Up*, Polygram International 120499

Lauper, Cyndi, *She's So Unusual*, Song 38930

Led Zeppelin, *Led Zeppelin II*, Atlantic 7567-8268-2/4; *Led Zeppelin IV*, Atlantic 11614

Lennon, John, *Lennon Legend*, Capitol 21954B

Lewis, Huey, *Sports*, Mobile Fidelity 509.

Lewis, Jerry Lee, *25 All-Time Greatest Sun Recordings*, Varese 066129

Lewis, Ramsey, *Sun Goddess*, Columbia 33194

Linkin Park, *Hybrid Theory*, Warner Bros. 47755

Little Richard, *Good Golly! Ten Greatest Original Hits*, RSP 53314

L.L. Cool J, *Bigger and Deffer*, Def Jam 527353

Lynyrd Skynyrd, *Best of the Rest*, MCA 31006

Madonna, *The Immaculate Collection*, WEA International 10843

Mahavishnu Orchestra, *Birds of Fire*, Legacy 66081

Malmsteen, Yngwie, *Eclipse*, Polydor 843361

Mamas and the Papas, *Greatest Hits*, MCA 11740

Mangione, Chuck, *Greatest Hits*, A&M 540514

Manilow, Barry, *Platinum Collection*, Arista 17545

Mannheim Steamroller, *Fresh Aire 4*, American Gramaphone 5004

Weezer, *Weezer* [Blue Album], DGC 24629

White Stripes, *Elephant*, V2 27148

Who, The *Tommy*, Polygram International 9196;
Quadrophenia, Polygram International 9200; *Who's Next*,
Mobile Fidelity 754; *My Generation: The Very Best of The
Who*, MCA 11462

Williams, Hank, *40 Greatest Hits*, Mercury 821233

Wings (see *McCartney, Paul*)

Wonder, Stevie, *At the Close of a Century*, Motown 153 992

Wu-Tang Clan, *Enter the Wu-Tang (36 Chambers)*, BMG 2120367

Yardbirds, *Ultimate*, Recall 184

Yes, *Close to the Edge*, WEA International 6292; *Fragile*,
Atlantic 82524; *The Yes Album*, Atlantic 7567826652

Zappa, Frank, *Freak Out!*, Video Arts 1203; *Uncle Meat*,
Video Arts 1208

Anthologies

American Graffiti (MCA 8001): includes Bill Haley, Del
Shannon, Frankie Lymon, Buddy Holly, Diamonds,
Beach Boys, Chuck Berry, Platters, Joey Dee, Fats
Domino, Flamingos, Silhouettes, Five Satins, Buddy
Knox, DelVikings, Big Bopper, Skyliners, Mark Dinning,
Spaniels, Booker T. & the M.G.s, and others.

Atlantic Blues (Rhino 82309): four-CD box includes Jimmy
Yancey, Professor Longhair, Joe Turner, Meade Lux
Lewis, Ray Charles, Dr. John, Stick McGhee, Guitar Slim,
Stevie Ray Vaughan, Ike and Tina Turner, B.B. King,
LaVern Baker, Wynonie Harris, Esther Philips, Rufus
Thomas, Bobby Bland, Aretha Franklin, Howlin' Wolf,
Muddy Waters, Freddie King, and others.

Atlantic Rhythm and Blues: 1947–1974 (Atlantic 82305):
seven-CD box includes Stick McGhee, Ray Charles, Joe
Turner, LaVern Baker, Clyde McPhatter, Chuck Willis,
Coasters, Drifters, Ben E. King, Carla Thomas, Solomon
Burke, Booker T. and the M.G.s, Otis Redding, Sam and
Dave, Percy Sledge, Wilson Pickett, Rufus Thomas,
Esther Philips, Don Covay, Joe Tex, Brook Benton, King
Curtis, Aretha Franklin, Roberta Flack, Donny Hathaway,
Les McCann and Eddie Harris, The Spinners, and others.

Dick Clark's #1's: 50's to 70's (Rhino 74350): six-CD box with
an eclectic selection of major artists and hits.

Hair (RCA 1150): the original Broadway cast recording.

History of British Rock (Sire 1CD65471/2): includes Fleetwood
Mac, Donovan, Beatles, Chad and Jeremy, Animals,
Derek and the Dominoes, Troggs, Dusty Springfield,
Billy J. Kramer, Gerry and the Pacemakers, Cilia Black,
Searchers, Manfred Mann, Freddie and the Dreamers,
Cream, Bee Gees, Peter and Gordon, Kinks, and others.

Hitsville USA: The Motown Singles Collection 1959–1971
(Motown 636 312): four-CD box featuring virtually every
Motown artist and/or group during these years.

*Hitsville USA Volume II: The Motown Singles Collection
1972–1992* (Motown 159 027): four-CD box representing
later Motown hits.

Jesus Christ Superstar (Decca 11542): the original London
studio recording, featuring Ian Gillan (vocalist for Deep
Purple) performing the role of Jesus.

O Brother, Where Art Thou? (Mercury 170069): the original
motion picture soundtrack album.

Outlaws, The (SPA 55407): includes Willie Nelson, Waylon
Jennings, Tompall Glaser, and Jessi Colter.

Saturday Night Fever (Mobile Fidelity 716): includes Bee
Gees, MFSB, Tavares, K.C. and the Sunshine Band,
Kool and the Gang, Walter Murphy, Yvonne Elliman,
and others.

Sub Pop 200 (Sub Pop Records 25): includes Nirvana,
Soundgarden, Green River, Mudhoney, Screaming Trees,
and others.

Woodstock (Atlantic 500): includes Joan Baez; The Who;
Jefferson Airplane; Crosby, Stills, Nash & Young;
Country Joe and the Fish; Sly and the Family Stone;
Santana; Butterfield Blues Band; Jimi Hendrix; Arlo
Guthrie; and others.

Music DVDs and Rockumentaries

The Beatles Anthology (5-DVD set; Apple C9 7243) is an
exhaustive collection of recordings, interviews, and
performances by the Beatles.

The Complete Monterey Pop Festival (3-DVD set; Criterion 167)
was recorded during the summer of 1967 and includes
defining performances by Jefferson Airplane, Janis
Joplin, The Who, Jimi Hendrix, Simon and Garfunkel,
Ravi Shankar, Otis Redding, the Mamas and the Papas,
Canned Heat, the Animals, and others.

Don't Look Back (Docurama NVG-9447) is a documentary
about Bob Dylan by D. A. Pen nebaker filmed during a
three-week concert tour of England during the spring
of 1965.

Elvis: The Great Performances (3-DVD set; Rhino R2 976096)
captures many defining performances throughout the
various periods of Elvis Presley's career.

Foo Fighters: Sonic Highways (RCA Records, 2014) is an
eight-episode HBO series by Dave Grohl (Nirvana &
Foo Fighters) in which each episode focuses on a
specific studio and its influence on the local music
scene.

Gimme Shelter (Criterion 99) is a documentary film based on
the Rolling Stones' tour leading up to and including
Altamont.

History of Rock 'n' Roll (5-DVD set; Warner 34991) is an
exhaustive overview of five decades of rock music,
including performances by too many artists to mention
and commentary by famous rock musicians who were
influenced by the performers you see.

The Last Waltz (Special Edition; MGM 1003426) is a
documentary film directed by Martin Scorsese that
captures the final concert by The Band; it includes guest
appearances by Bob Dylan, Eric Clapton, Neil Young,
Joni Mitchell, Van Morrison, Muddy Waters, Ringo Starr,
Paul Butterfield, and others.

Muscle Shoals (Dogwoof, 2016) is a documentary about the
famous Muscle Shoals studio in Alabama where many of
the most important music of the area was recorded,
including songs by Wilson Pickett, Aretha Franklin,
Percy Sledge, and the Rolling Stones.

Woodstock: 3 Days of Peace & Music (Director's Cut, 2-sided
DVD; Warner 13549) is a beautiful documentary
including performances by Joan Baez; The Who;
Jefferson Airplane; Crosby, Stills, Nash, and Young;
Country Joe and the Fish; Sly and the Family Stone;
Santana; Butterfield Blues Band; Jimi Hendrix; Arlo
Guthrie; and others.

Bibliography

Belz, Carl. *The Story of Rock*. 2nd ed. New York: Harper Colophon Books, 1972.

Bronson, Fred. *The Billboard Book of Number One Hits*. Rev. ed. New York: Billboard Publications, 1988.

Classic Albums: Anthem to Beauty (1997, DVD). Isis Productions.

Coleman, Ray. *Lennon*. New York: McGraw-Hill, 1984.

DeCurtis, Anthony, and James Henke. *The Rolling Stone Illustrated History of Rock and Roll: The Definitive History of the Most Important Artists and Their Music*. New York: Random House, 1992.

Dickerson, James. *Women on Top*. New York: Billboard Books, 1998.

Dictionary.com. "iconoclastic." Dictionary.com Unabridged. Random House, Inc. http://www.dictionary.com/browse/iconoclastic (accessed March 6, 2018).

Dylan, Bob. *Writings and Drawings*. New York: Alfred A. Knopf, 1973.

Experience Music Project. "Riot Grrrl Retrospective: Evolution of Grrrl Style." http://www.empsfm.org/exhibitions/index.asp?articleID=668 (accessed August 29, 2007), 2002.

Fulford-Jones, Will. "House." In *The New Grove Dictionary of Music and Musicians,* 2nd ed., edited by S. Sadie, p. 758. London: Macmillan, 2000.

George-Warren, Holly, and Patricia Romanowski. *The Rolling Stone Encyclopedia of Rock & Roll*. 3rd ed. New York: Fireside, 2001.

Gillett, Charlie. *The Sound of the City: The Rise of Rock and Roll*. Rev. and exp. ed. New York: Random House/Pantheon Books, 1983.

Gioia, D. "Disappearing Ink: Poetry at the End of Print Culture." *The Hudson Review*, Spring, 2003.

Gladwell, Malcolm. *Outliers: The Story of Success*. New York, NY: Little, Brown and Co. 2008.

Goodman, Fred. "Music Business Sings the Blues: Declining Sales Spark New Layoffs." *Rolling Stone*, February 14, 2002.

Gorbman, Claudia. *Unheard Melodies: Narrative Film Music*. Bloomington: Indiana University Press, 1987.

Haislop, Neil, Ted Lathrop, and Harry Sumrall. *Giants of Country Music: Classic Sounds and Stars, from the Heart of Nashville to the Top of the Charts*. New York: Watson-Guptill, 1995.

Helander, Brock. *The Rock Who's Who*. New York: Schirmer Books, 1982.

Hirshey, Gerri. *Nowhere to Run: The Story of Soul Music*. New York: New York Times Books, 1984.

Hopkins, Jerry. *Elvis: A Biography*. New York: Simon and Schuster, 1971.

Iyengar, Sheena. "How to make choosing easier." TEDTalk at TEDSalon. New York, NY; November, 2011.

Jackson, Blair. *Grateful Dead: The Music Never Stopped*. New York: Delilah, 1983.

Kempton, A. *Boogaloo: The Quintessence of American Popular Music*. New York: Pantheon Books, 2003.

Knopper, Steve. "Radiohead: Band of the Year." *Spin*, January 2001.

Leaf, David. *The Beach Boys*. Philadelphia: Courage Books, 1985.

Lewis, Myra (with Murray Silver). *Great Balls of Fire*. New York: William Morrow, 1982.

McDonough, Jack. *San Francisco Rock*. San Francisco: Chronicle Books, 1985.

Merriam, A. P. *The Anthropology of Music*. Chicago: Northwestern University Press, 1964.

Miller, Jim E., ed. *The Rolling Stone Illustrated History of Rock and Roll*. Rev. and updated ed. New York: Rolling Stone Press, 1980.

Naisbitt, John. *Megatrends: Ten New Directions Transforming Our Lives*. New York: Warner Books, 1982.

NBC. 1968. "Comeback Special. " Released in DVD format by Sony Legacy, 2006.

Nelson, Havelock, and Michael A. Gonzales. *Bring the Noise: A Guide to Rap Music and Hip-Hop Culture*. New York: Harmony Books, 1991.

Nettl, Bruno, et al. "Improvisation." In Grove Music Online. Oxford Music Online, http://www.oxfordmusiconline.com.floyd.lib.umn.edu/subscriber/article/grove/music/13738 (accessed April 14, 2011).

nielsen.com [Nielsen]. "2016 U.S. Music Year-End Report." http://www.nielsen.com/us/en/insights/reports/2017/2016-music-us-year-end-report.html (accessed December 28, 2017).

Norman, Philip. *Symphony for the Devil: The Rolling Stones Story*. New York: Linden Press/Simon and Schuster, 1984.

Otto, Shawn. *The War on Science: Who's Waging it, Why it Matters, What We Can Do About It*. Minneapolis, MN: Milkweed Editions, 2016.

Peel, Ian. "DJ(ii)." In *The New Grove Dictionary of Music and Musicians*, 2nd ed., edited by S. Sadie, pp. 406–7. London: Macmillan, 2000.

Perris, Arnold. *Music as Propaganda: Art to Persuade, Art to Control*. Westport, CN: Greenwood Press, 1985.

Peters, Dan, and Steve Peters. *Why Knock Rock?* Minneapolis, MN: Bethany House, 1984.

Postman, Neil. *Teaching As a Conserving Activity*. New York: Delacorte Press, 1979.

Reynolds, Simon. "Laptop Punk and Powerbook Pop." *Spin*, August 2001.

RIAA. "Recording Industry Releases Yearend 2001 Latin Music Statistics." http://www.riaa.com/print.php?id=3C1F4FCC-B2E6-B822-0C57-696C892EEF9A (accessed August 29, 2007).

Rolling Stone. "Women Rule the Charts in 2010," March 4, 2010.

Rolling Stone. "Paul McCartney Looks Back: The Rolling Stone Interview." April 9, 2014, p. 39.

Rolling Stone. "The Ballad of Mike Love." February 25, 2016, pp. 42–47.

Rolling Stone Interviews. Vol. 1. New York: Warner Paperback, 1971.

Romanowski, Patricia, and Holly George-Warren, eds. *The New Rolling Stone Encyclopedia of Rock and Roll*. Rev. ed. New York: Fireside, 1995.

Rosen, Craig. *The Billboard Book of Number One Albums: The Inside Story Behind Pop Music's Blockbuster Records*. New York: Watson-Guptill, 1996.

Schaffner, Nicholas. *The Beatles Forever*. Harrisburg, PA: Stackpole Books (Cameron House), 1977.

Selvin, Joel. *Altamont: The Rolling Stones, the Hells Angels, and the Inside Story of Rock's Darkest Day*. New York, NY: HarperCollins Publishers Inc. 2016.

Shaw, Arnold. *Dictionary of American Pop/Rock*. New York: Schirmer Books, 1982.

Sherman, B. L., and J. R. Dominick. "Violence and Sex in Music Videos: TV and Rock and Roll." *Journal of Communication* 36 (1986), pp. 79–93.

Sisario, Ben, Alexandra Alter, and Sewell Chan. "Bob Dylan wins the Nobel Prize, redefining boundaries of literature." *New York Times*, October 13, 2016. https://www.nytimes.com/2016/10/14/arts/music/bob-dylan-nobel-prize-literature.html (accessed September 4, 2017).

Szatmary, David P. *Rockin' in Time: A Social History of Rock and Roll*. Englewood Cliffs, NJ: Prentice Hall, 1987.

Szatmary, David P. *Rockin' in Time: A Social History of Rock and Roll*. 2nd ed. Englewood Cliffs, NJ: Prentice Hall, 1991.

Szatmary, David P. *Rockin' in Time: A Social History of Rock and Roll*. 6th ed. Upper Saddle River, NJ: Pearson Prentice Hall, 2007.

Toop, David. "Hip hop." Grove Music Online. http://www.grovemusic.com (accessed August 29, 2007).

U.S. Congress. Senate. Committee on Commerce, Science, and Transportation. "Hearing Before the Committee on Commerce, Science, and Transportation: Contents of Music and the Lyrics of Records." 99th Cong., 1st sess., September 19, 1985.

Walley, David. *No Commercial Potential: The Saga of Frank Zappa and the Mothers of Invention*. New York: E. P. Dutton, 1972.

Walser, R. "Heavy metal and the highbrow/lowbrow divide." In *The Rock History Reader*, edited by T. Cateforis. New York: Routledge, 2007.

Ward, Ed, Geoffrey Stokes, and Ken Tucker. *Rock of Ages: The Rolling Stone History of Rock and Roll*. New York: Rolling Stone Press, 1986.

Whitburn, Joel. "*Billboard*'s Top 3000 Plus, 1955–1990." Menomonee Falls, WI: Record Research, 1990.

Whitburn, Joel. *The Billboard Book of Top 40 Hits*, 6th ed. New York: Billboard Books, 1996.

Whitburn, Joel. *The Billboard Book of Top 40 Hits*. 9th, rev. and exp. ed. New York, NY: Billboard Books, 2010.

White, Timothy. *Rock Stars*. New York: Stewart, Tabori, and Chang, 1984.

Wild, David. "Musicians Unite Against Record Labels." *Rolling Stone*, January 31, 2002.

Wilson, Brian (with Ben Greenman). *I am Brian Wilson: A Memoir*. Philadelphia, PA: Da Capo Bress, 2016.

Wise, Herbert, ed. *Blood, Sweat, and Tears*. New York: Amsco Music, 1971.

Woodward, Josef. "The Darker Side of Michael McDonald." *Musician* 86 (1985): 76–83, 106.

Glossary

8-bar blues. A musical form related to the 12-bar blues; although there are frequent variations to the basic pattern, the 8-bar pattern often has the following chord progression (one chord per bar): I-I-IV-IV-I-V-I-V.

12-bar blues. A musical form that is extremely common in R&B, rock, and jazz (also found in country music); consists of three 4-bar phrases; the basic chord progression (one chord per measure) is shown in the following:

first phrase:	I	I (or IV)	I	I
second phrase:	IV	IV	I	I
third phrase:	V	V (or IV)	I	I

In the most traditional blues form, the lyrics (and often the melody) follow an AAB pattern.

12-tone composition. An approach to composition in which the 12 tones of the chromatic scale are arranged in a specific order determined by the composer and guides the compositional process. The primary rule is that no note of the chromatic scale can be repeated until all other notes have been used, minimizing the potential for perceiving the hierarchical relationship of tones within a key that had been common since the establishment of functional harmony in the late 16th and early 17th centuries. This technique is sometimes known by the name "dodecaphonicism" (a synonym or "atonality") or "serialism," the latter of which can refer to not only the application of this technique to pitch order but to other musical elements including note duration, loudness, and timbre. See *atonality*.

a cappella. Without accompaniment.

A-side. A term developed in the 1950s in reference to the 7-inch vinyl record ("single"); the A-side is the featured song—the one the record company expects to be the hit. (See *B-side*.)

accent. An emphasized note or sound that causes it to stand out in comparison to surrounding musical events. The most common form of accent is to play the accented note louder, but increased duration and other modifications can also result in increased salience.

acid rock. A style of rock developed in the late 1960s that was associated (sometimes correctly, sometimes incorrectly) with LSD; frequently characterized by high-volume levels, long improvised solos, and drug-related lyrics; loosely interchangeable with *psychedelic rock*.

album-oriented rock (AOR). An FM radio format that concentrates on longer album tracks, album sides, and even entire albums (as opposed to Top 40 singles); developed in the 1960s.

alternative rock. Emerging in the 1980s as a category of rock and roll, though its roots can be traced back to punk rock of the 1970s, a style of music by performers who typically record for independent record companies and subvert, at least to some extent, the musical conventions of mainstream rock.

anomie. A French word for a person or society that lacks purpose, identity, or ethical values, thus leading to a feeling of rootlessness; without these qualities, the individual (or society) may be less capable of making decisions, viewing all alternatives as equivalent.

arch form. A musical form in which a series of sections is performed and then repeated in reverse order, ultimately creating a mirror symmetry; in its simplest form, ABA would represent an arch form, while ABCBA would be a slightly more complex example.

arpeggio. Playing the notes of a chord consecutively, in quick succession, rather than simultaneously; a technique that is often used in keyboard and guitar performances.

atonality. Music that does not imply a key (tonal center) or utilize the hierarchical relationship between pitches within the key that provides a sense of arrival or completion when landing on a tonic chord; a very different sound compared to functional harmony, which is evident in most music composed from the seventeenth through nineteenth centuries and almost all popular music. See *12-tone composition*. (For related terms, see *key center* and *tonic chord*.)

augmentation. Lengthening the note values of a previously stated melody (e.g., doubling the length of each note in a given theme or tune).

auto-tune. A proprietary manipulation of digital audio that allows a sound engineer to take a melodic line and dramatically alter the intonation or timing while retaining the general expressive performance aspects of the digital recording (created by Antares Audio Technology).

B-side. A term developed in the 1950s in reference to the 7-inch vinyl record ("single"); the B-side (sometimes called "flip-side") is a song that is not expected to be a hit. On some singles recorded by very popular artists, both sides of the record become hits. (See *A side*.)

backbeat. Extra emphasis on the second and fourth beats in quadruple meter; a basic characteristic of rock and roll (and some of its predecessors and later offshoots).

backmasking. A technique in which a musical and/or lyric passage is mixed into a recording, backward.

bar. A notational device that allows for the grouping of beats (delineated by a vertical line at the beginning and end of each group); used interchangeably with *measure*.

barbershop quartet. An ensemble of four voices (traditionally male) that sings pop songs a cappella in four-part consonant chordal homophony. See *homophony*.

barre chord. A common guitar chord used in rock and roll, for which the instrumentalist places the index finger of the hand flat over the fretboard, such that it presses all of the strings to the neck of the guitar. The other fingers of that hand are then placed appropriately to create the other notes of the desired chord. This term is sometimes misspelled as "bar chord."

beat mixing. In the performance of hip-hop and rap, playing back multiple records simultaneously, while adjusting the speed of each recording to synchronize the resulting complex rhythmic pattern.

Beatlemania. A term that was coined to describe the extreme frenzy of popularity related to the Beatles; Beatlemania (both the phenomenon and the term) began in England in 1963 and hit the United States in 1964.

beats. Metrical pulses found in most music; usually grouped into recurring patterns. (See *meter*.)

block chords. A series of chords in which the notes of each chord all move simultaneously to the notes of the next chord; thus, all voices are dependent on each other (no independent movement).

blue note(s). One of a set of tones (usually the lowered 3rd, 5th, or 7th of the diatonic major scale) used by blues, gospel, rock, and jazz performers to add emotional expression (a "bluesy feel") to a performance, which results from the dissonance these tones create within a major key context.

boogie (boogie-woogie). A piano style popularized in the 1930s; usually based on the 12-bar blues and characterized by a rhythmically active and repetitive bass pattern (left hand) accompanying elaborate improvisations (right hand).

break dancing. A style of dancing that developed in the 1970s relating to the hip-hop culture; practiced by individuals (not couples), the style is characterized by high-energy, improvisational, gymnastic elements.

bridge. A section of a song that provides a musical contrast, which can differ from the preceding section(s) melodically, harmonically, or both.

cadence. A brief harmonic progression that closes a phrase or section of a song.

cadenza. Virtuoso solo (often improvised) inserted into a movement of a classical concerto or other work.

call-and-response. A musical performance in which one singer or instrumentalist performs a melody or rhythm and another person or group echoes that musical idea, alternating back and forth; sometimes called *statement-and-answer*.

calypso. A popular style of music developed in the Caribbean, especially Trinidad and Jamaica; originated in the very early twentieth century; since the 1940s, associated with the timbre of steel drums.

changing meters. A musical excerpt in which the number of beats in a measure is not consistent from measure to measure. While the meter rarely changes in every measure, the resulting change in rhythmic patterns give the music a high level of complexity. In the discussion of jazz rock, the section on Chicago provides a number of examples of changing meter.

chitlin' circuit. A series of venues in the eastern and southern United States that catered to African-American performers and audiences; such night clubs and theaters thrived in the 1940s to 1970s (although there are venues that were successful before and after those decades).

chord. Three or more pitches sounded simultaneously.

chromatic (chromaticism). The melodic and/or harmonic use of pitches not contained in the diatonic scale of a given key. See *diatonic*.

close harmony. A type of harmonization in which at least the three upper voices are within the range of an octave; typically, the top voice takes the melody note, and the second and third voices take the nearest adjacent chord tones.

coda. The closing section of a musical form.

codetta. The closing section of an internal part of a larger musical form.

complex or asymmetrical meters. Meters in which the grouping of subdivisions is irregular (asymmetrical) instead of regular (symmetrical); for example, in quadruple meter, the eight subdivisions might be grouped as 3 + 2 + 3 instead of the normal 2 + 2 + 2 + 2.

composite rhythm. The rhythm resulting from a combination of the individual sound events across all instruments (and voices) performing within a musical texture across time; an amalgamation resulting in a kind of overall rhythm.

compound meter. A meter that has three subdivisions per beat.

concept album. An album in which all (or most) of the songs are related to a single idea or story; very different from the more traditional practice that simply gathers a series of unrelated songs onto an album.

conjunct. A melodic style characterized by primarily stepwise motion (i.e., each note moves up or down to the nearest note in the key); creates a very smooth melodic contour. See also *disjunct*.

contour (pitch contour). The overall linear shape of a melody as the pitches rise and fall.

countermelody. A secondary melody; it coexists with the primary melody and adds interest to the overall musical texture, resulting in *polyphony*.

cover versions (covers). Subsequent versions of an original song almost always recorded by another artist or group.

crooner. A singer in the Pop style, characterized by a rich, resonant voice, wide melodic range, and carefully trained enunciation and intonation; the term has traditionally been applied to male ballad singers; opposite of *shouter*.

crossovers. Songs that originate in one segment of the music market but achieve success in one or more other segments.

death metal. A style of rock that combines the loudness and distortion of heavy metal with the tempo and driving rhythm of speed metal, with lyrical references to graphic images of death and destruction.

deejay (DJ). A label assigned to those radio personalities in the early 1950s and throughout much of the history of rock who selected, introduced, and played hit records, primarily in the Top 40 radio format. Many DJs rose to significant prominence as a result of this role, moving beyond the radio station into concert promotion and other areas of the music industry. With the rise of hip-hop and rap, the label "DJ" was also used to describe the person spinning records, while the label "emcee" (MC) was assigned to the rapper. See also *veejay*.

diatonic. The melodic and/or harmonic use of the pitches of a given key's scale.

diegetic music. A type of film music that is assumed to be audible to all characters in the on-screen narrative. See *nondiegetic music*.

digital audio workstations (DAWs). A personal computer with sequencing, hard disc recording, and audio-editing software on which artists could produce near-studio-quality recordings at a fraction of the cost.

dirty saxophone. A style of playing the saxophone characterized by a "growl" (produced by humming a different note than the one being played); especially popular in R&B and 1950s rock bands.

disco. A popular dance music of the mid- to late 1970s (a shortened form of "discotheque").

disjunct. A melodic style characterized by leaps (i.e., notes moving to nonadjacent notes); creates a more angular melodic contour. See also *conjunct*.

dissonant (chord). Chords that contain one or more dissonant intervals; increased dissonance adds more tension (or "bite") to a given harmony; psychologically, we are conditioned to perceive increased dissonance as "uglier" and increased consonance as "sweeter."

dissonant (interval). Intervals other than those contained in the major or minor triad, thus seconds, sevenths, and tritones; psychologically, we have been conditioned to expect these intervals to resolve to more stable intervals (e.g., thirds, fourths, fifths, sixths, octaves, unisons).

DIY (do-it-yourself). A musical development evident in both the punk and alternative music scenes that actively challenged the separation of contemporary society into listeners and trained music specialists; bands such as the Sex Pistols and White Stripes exemplify this approach (even though some of the participating musicians may attain relatively high levels of musical ability); sometimes referred to as a "garage band ethic."

doo-wop. A style of R&B and soft rock characterized by the use of nonsense syllables; in its most basic form, it features a small vocal group (e.g., trio or quartet) singing *a cappella* (without accompanying instruments); the addition of vocal rhythmic patterns (the use of nonsense syllables) takes the place of the missing instrumental accompaniment and provides a stronger rhythmic element.

double entendre. Double meaning (often used when one meaning has a risqué connotation).

double-tracking. An audio recording technique that involves singing or performing an instrumental part, recording the same part on a different track, and then mixing them together to create a richer, thicker sound; the fact that the same part is played distinguishes this technique from *over-dubbing*, in which different parts are recorded one after another.

dub. Developed primarily by producer Lee "Scratch" Perry, this music consists of a remix of existing reggae recordings that provides a foundation for improvised vocal solos; the addition of reverberation, echo, and sound effects by the DJ are common.

duck walk. A stage movement made famous by Chuck Berry; consists of a series of forward jumps on one leg, while moving the other leg back and forth; sometimes, Berry would add a bobbing head motion to heighten the effect.

dynamics. Refers to the varying degrees of loudness in music and indicated using a variety of musical notations; e.g., piano (*p*) for soft, forte (*f*) for loud, etc.

echo effects. An audio effect that records a signal and then plays it back after the desired delay (ranging from several milliseconds to several seconds); originally achieved using tape loops; now accomplished digitally.

electronica. Heavily influenced by Chicago house and Detroit techno, a musical style that consists of danceable grooves, loose song forms, and a primary focus on finding a new sound; most early electronica was danceable, but some later styles were intended for listening; eventually fragmented into numerous subgenres and fusions, including ambient house, experimental techno, electrotechno, and many others.

emo. "Emotionally oriented rock"; a subgenre of *indie rock*, characterized by lyrics that are deeply personal and often include intimate confessions uncharacteristic of many of the harder styles of rock.

EP (extended play). A record format that became popular in the 1950s (although it existed both before and after); typically, an EP contained four songs (two per side) on a 45-rpm, 7-inch disc; more recent EPs are released on CD or via digital download, so they are distinguished solely by the smaller number of tracks rather than the size of the media.

expressive deviations. Intentional, often subtle, alterations in basic musical elements (pitch, loudness, timbre, and duration) by a performer that communicate nonverbal emotional cues to the listener.

falsetto. The male voice singing in a female range (usually alto).

feedback. The result of a sound loop between an audio input and output (e.g., a signal received by a microphone is amplified and broadcast through a loudspeaker; the speaker output, in turn, is received again by the microphone and is further amplified and sent, again, to the loudspeaker, thus creating the loop); in most settings, feedback is unintentional and undesirable; however, many rock bands have intentionally created and manipulated feedback for musical purposes.

folk ballad. A song (traditionally from unknown origins) that narrates a simple incident, story, or plot; typically in strophic form, the folk ballad uses acoustic guitar or guitar-like instruments to accompany one or more singers.

folk music. Music (song) of unknown origin that has been conveyed by the aural tradition from generation to generation (often with changes to melody and lyrics); some of the songs of the folk revival were true folk songs; others (most) were newly composed in the style of traditional folk music.

folk rock. A style developed in the mid-1960s by artists such as the Byrds and Bob Dylan; combines some folk elements (e.g., strophic forms, serious lyrics) with rock elements (e.g., electric instruments, drum sets, backbeat, rock bass lines).

folknik. A fan of folk music (usually applied to the folk subculture that thrived in the late 1950s and early 1960s); also referred to as "folkies."

form. The organizational structure of a piece of music; overall form is determined by the sequence of sections in a given composition and how each section relates to earlier sections (e.g., repeated content, contrasting content, or restating repeated content incorporating variation).

formatting. Programming certain styles of music for a specific audience, members of which typically purchased a predictable set of advertised products.

free jazz. A style of jazz developed in the 1950s and 1960s as a reaction to conventional jazz styles; characterized by improvisation that may have little or no discernable relationship to a pre-existing tune, chord progression, meter, or tempo.

fugue. A classical style of composition in which a relatively brief theme (subject) is stated in one voice and then imitated successively by the other voices; when not playing (or singing) the subject, voices may state a countersubject (a secondary theme) and/or develop motives contained within the subject or countersubject.

funk. A term applied to both jazz and rock styles to denote a combination of earthiness, emotionalism, and spirituality associated with the African-American culture; often used interchangeably with *soul*, funky styles blend elements of R&B and gospel; characterized by repetitive riffs, a strong quadruple beat, and prominent bass lines.

fuzz tone. A distorted tone that results when an electric guitar signal is processed through a fuzz box (a commercially available electronic device that adds distortion to the incoming signal).

gangsta rap. A subgenre of rap with lyrics that emphasizes the violence of street life, including gang warfare, misogynistic vignettes, encouragement of drug use, and materialism.

genre. A category or style, usually within one of the arts (e.g., music, art, literature, dance, architecture).

glissandi. A continuous sliding movement through a series of musical pitches (e.g., by sliding the fingers up and down the piano keyboard or sliding over a series of adjacent pitches on string instruments, trombone, or clarinet).

glitter rock. A style developed in the early 1970s that often involved sexual ambiguity (androgyny) and extreme costumes and makeup; more popular in England than the United States, glitter rock was less of a musical style than a theatrical style; also known as "glam rock."

glottal stop. The momentary closing of the glottis (the opening between the vocal cords in the larynx); to feel the glottal stop, say the word "uh-oh"; used in rock vocals to subdivide syllables (such as Buddy Holly's "Peggy Sue-ooh-ooh").

grunge. A subgenre of alternative rock that emerged in the late 1980s from the Pacific Northwest, combining heavy metal and post-punk elements; primarily responsible for bringing alternative rock into the mainstream.

half cadence. A *cadence* is a two-chord progression, occurring at the end of a musical phrase, that provides a sense of closure; the half cadence is a special case of this type of progression that provides a much less musically satisfying conclusion, since it ends on the dominant chord (V) rather than the tonic (I).

hardcore. A subgenre of punk rock that originated in the United States in the late 1970s and early 1980s, serving as a transition between punk and the more intense form of heavy metal known as thrash metal; songs by hardcore bands were often short, loud, and distorted, providing passionate expositions on topics ranging from politics and anarchy to the hardcore culture itself.

harmonic rhythm. The temporal rate at which the chords change within a given musical composition; for example, a song in which the chords typically change at the beginning of every measure has a faster harmonic rhythm than a song in which the chords change every other measure.

harmony. A sequence of *chords*, often creating a sense of expectation for what sounds are likely to come next.

heavy metal. Emerging in the late 1960s and early 1970s, this style of rock music had clear roots in blues-based rock and psychedelic rock; heavily guitar-centric and incorporating lightning-fast guitar solos and a relentlessly pounding drumbeat, heavy metal was louder, simpler, more distorted, and more rebellious than preceding forms of rock. (Sometimes called simply *metal*.)

hip-hop. A collection of urban art forms emerging in the South Bronx during the late 1970s, including lifestyle, fashions, fast-talking comedy, break dancing, graffiti art, poetry, double-Dutch jump-roping, and music; as an urban musical style, hip-hop tracks incorporated extant musical sounds, combining these previously recorded segments into a new composition performed on dual turntables by a DJ.

hocket. A technique in which a melody is passed back and forth between two or more vocal or instrumental parts, smoothly alternating such that when one part stops, the other part picks up where the other left off, providing the illusion of a continuous melodic line; occurring in polyphonic textures, it was used in both art music and popular music of the thirteenth and fourteenth centuries; a similar style of back-and-forth delivery is evident in some rap music, especially that of Run-D.M.C.

homophony. A type of musical texture in which there is one predominant melody to which other parts are secondary; examples include melody and accompaniment homophony (typical of most popular styles, including rock) and chordal homophony (in which all parts move in the same or similar rhythm, as determined by the primary melody).

hook. Usually a specific line of lyrics and its associated melody in a song that is intended to be particularly appealing and memorable; the hook line is usually repeated often throughout the song; sometimes a hook can be instrumental (e.g., the riff in "Satisfaction" or the unusual cadence in George Harrison's "Something").

horizontal organization. An approach to musical composition (including improvisation) that is oriented more to melodic considerations than harmonic (vertical) considerations; with horizontal improvisation, the player is more concerned with the ongoing musical line and working with scales and motives than with conforming to underlying chord progressions. See *vertical organization*.

house. A style of dance music that emerged from Chicago's Warehouse Club during the early 1980s, obviously influenced by disco of the preceding decade; characteristics include a repetitive quadruple meter maintained by a drum machine, with bass drum pounding on every beat and hi-hat on offbeats, simplistic synth bass lines, and heavily synthesized string orchestrations reminiscent of the disco era.

improvisation. The performance of a newly created melody, spontaneously, as it is being performed, which can range from a modest elaboration of an existing melody (a form of variation) to a brand-new sequence of notes and rhythms that the performer has never before played; sometimes the word *extemporization* is used as a synonym for improvisation.

indie (music). Refers to artists who intentionally placed themselves in opposition to the mainstream in musical sound, fashion, and/or image.

indies (record companies). An informal term for an independent record company; small, individually owned companies that are distinct from the larger major record labels.

instrumentals. Songs without vocals, performed purely on musical instruments.

jam. A performance style that is typically less formal than a mainstream rock performance and in which each performer is granted a high degree of freedom and spontaneity.

jam bands. Groups with a highly eclectic sound, integrating country, folk, bluegrass, rock, jazz, and even punk influences into highly energized musical performances in which improvisation plays a significant role; for jam bands, studio recordings often took a backseat to their live performances.

jam-grass. An outgrowth of the jam band style with its emphasis on improvisation; strongly influenced by mountain music and bluegrass.

key. A combination of pitch relationships that establishes one of the pitches as the tonal center; used interchangeably with *tonality*; for example, a "family" of pitches (F-G-A-Bb-C-D-E-F) creates the key (or tonality) of F major.

key center (tonic). The pitch that begins and ends the scale of a given key (or tonality) and gives the key its name (e.g., the key of E major); the tonal center of the key.

key signature. An arrangement of the sharps (or flats) needed to create the scale of a given key; a notational device that appears at the beginning of the musical staff.

lead singer. The primary vocalist in a band or vocal group.

licks. Short, recognizable melodic motives or phrases (e.g., "blues licks"); blues and jazz musicians build up a library of such musical ideas that can be recalled at any time and in any key during improvisation.

loop-based composition. A method of music creation in which preexisting musical ideas (called "loops") are arranged into a complete composition. These musical components can either be digital recordings of acoustic or electronic instruments or MIDI files. Two of the most popular software packages that allow this type of composition were *GarageBand* (for Apple computers) and *Acid* (for Windows-based computers).

loudness. A word used to describe sound (including music) in terms of its intensity, whether loud or soft; the more technical term is amplitude, which refers to the amount of displacement of a vibrating body or air molecule; the greater the displacement, the higher the loudness level (sometimes referred to as "volume," though, to be precise, this latter phenomenon includes several acoustical parameters, of which amplitude is but one).

LP. A recording format introduced in 1948 that became the standard album format, until replaced by CDs in the 1980s; originally a 10-inch vinyl disc, a larger 12-inch disc became the standard; LPs turn at 33 1/3 RPMs and usually contain about 50 minutes of music (about 25 minutes per side); "LP" stands for "long playing" record.

LSD. The chemical compound *lysergic acid diethylamide*, a mind-altering drug espoused by the hippie counterculture of the 1960s; originally created in 1938, its recreational use began in the 1950s among a few health professionals and socially/politically elite individuals; such usage expanded dramatically in the 1960s; banned in the United States in 1971.

macroform. The larger aspects of musical form (e.g., the sequence of movements, the overall form of individual movements). See *microform*.

major triad. A specific type of three-note chord in which the middle note is four half-steps above the lowest pitch and the top note is seven half-steps above the lowest pitch; often perceived as brighter and happier sounding than the minor triad. See *minor triad*.

majors. A small group of record companies—beginning with RCA Victor, Columbia, Capitol, Mercury, and Decca in the 1950s—that dominated the music industry with a large number of artists under contract; the majors developed and maintained sophisticated and effective promotion and distribution systems and frequently involved ties to radio and television networks or subsidiary sheet music publishing operations.

mash-up. The process of combining two or more existing pieces of music in a manner that creates a new song; in some cases, an instrumental track from one recording might be combined with a vocal track from another.

MC (master of ceremony). In the context of rap, refers to the individual who speaks rhythmically, often with improvised lyrics, over the musical foundation laid down by a DJ.

measure. See *bar*.

melisma. Extending one syllable of text over many notes; although used in many styles, it is a central characteristic of soul music.

Mellotron. An electronic keyboard instrument developed in the early 1960s; based on a series of audiotapes, each of which carries about 8 seconds of a prerecorded tone played by an acoustic instrument (or group of instruments) or voices; playback heads beneath each key activate the tape assigned to that key.

melody. A series of pitches and note durations (i.e., notes) typically perceived by the listener as an organized musical unit; in traditional music (including all popular music styles), the series creates a recognizable and memorable tune.

Memphis Mafia. The informal name for a collection of friends, employees, and associates of Elvis Presley; some performed specific duties while others were present primarily for companionship.

Mersey sound. Refers to the rather vague blend of rock and roll, doo-wop, R&B, and skiffle produced in the early 1960s by Liverpool groups (e.g., the Beatles, the Searchers, Gerry and the Pacemakers); used interchangeably with "Liverpool sound," the name derives from the Mersey River that runs through Liverpool.

metal. See *heavy metal*.

meter. The organizational grouping of beats; various meters are identified according to the number of beats that are grouped together; thus, duple meter organizes the beats into groups of two, triple meter organizes beats into groups of three, and so on. The vast majority of rock music is in quadruple meter (beats occur in groups or cycles of four); within each of these (and other) meters, there is a differentiation of stronger and weaker beats.

metronome. A mechanical or electronic device that provides a consistent tempo based on the number of beats per second (bps), sometimes referred as a metronomic marking (mm). More recent electronic versions (e.g., those available for download as mobile apps) can provide very complex mappings of multiple beat patterns concurrently.

microform. The smaller, more detailed aspects of musical form (e.g., the relationship of phrases, the number of measures per phrase, the form of internal sections of a piece of music). See *macroform*.

minimalism. A compositional style characterized by persistent repetition (sometimes with gradual variation) of short phrases or motives, a steady pulse, and relatively consonant harmonies; developed in the 1960s as a reaction to the complexities and dissonant atonality of serial music, minimalism became a predominant style of "serious" composition in the last decades of the twentieth century. (Sometimes referred to as *"pattern music"* or *"process music"*).

minor triad. A specific type of three-note chord in which the middle note is three half steps above the lowest pitch and the top note is seven half steps above the lowest pitch; the middle tone is one half step lower than in a major triad; often perceived as darker or sadder sounding than the major triad. See *major triad*.

modes. Collections of pitches, including scales, spanning an octave (i.e., from one pitch to its next recurrence); each mode (or scale) can differ from others both by the number of pitches and by the pattern of intervals between adjacent pitches; in modern usage, *mode* usually refers to one of the seven modes derived (generally) from the old Greek modes and church modes (Ionian, Dorian, Phrygian, Lydian, Mixolydian, Aeolian, and Locrian); in informal usage, *scale* usually refers to either the major or minor scale, although in a broader sense, the word can refer to any octave-spanning collection of pitches, including modes (e.g., pentatonic scale, whole-tone scale, chromatic scale).

monophony. A type of musical texture in which there is only one line or melody, with no accompanying parts.

motive. A short, rhythmic and/or melodic idea; to be recognized as such, a motive should be distinctive enough to establish its identity and retain that identity through subsequent usage in a given piece of music.

Motortown Reviews. Traveling live package shows sponsored by Motown Records to highlight new artists and new releases by more established artists.

Motown. The record company established by Berry Gordy, Jr., in Detroit; thrived throughout the 1960s and into the 1970s with African American artists whose backgrounds were in gospel, R&B, and doo-wop styles; by combining elements of these styles with Pop styles, Motown and its various subsidiary labels appealed to a wide audience of both blacks and whites.

MP3 (MPEG Audio Layer 3). A popular and highly compatible compression format for digital audio files that is commonly used in portable media players; the use of psychoacoustic models in determining how to alter the full-quality sound file allows the process to eliminate auditory components that are less audible to the listener, retaining a high-quality sound but a significantly reduced file size.

music piracy. The act of stealing music by illegally duplicating a commercial recording in lieu of purchasing a copy; with the rising popularity of computer-based music, portable media players, and the Internet beginning during the 1990s and 2000s, piracy presented a significant challenge to the music industry.

Musical Instrument Digital Interface (MIDI). A technology that enables real-time communication between electronic musical instruments and computers; this industry-standard protocol, developed in the early 1980s, allows for successful interface among a wide range of digital technologies.

musical theater. The presentation of a story or play, most often using sets and costumes, in which a performer or the entire ensemble breaks into song periodically; sometimes referred to as simply a "musical." The art form began in the 19th and early 20th century known as "light opera" or "musical comedy." The most successful musicals are found on Broadway in New York City. (See *opera*.)

new jack swing (neo-soul). A hybrid form of rap, merging a hip-hop beat with light rap and traditional R&B vocals, initiated by New York-based artist and producer Teddy Riley.

new wave. A sanitized descendent of punk rock, incorporating the musical simplicity and repetitiveness of punk packaged into a more palatable product for mass consumption.

nondiegetic music. A type of film music intended to set the mood by highlighting (or contradicting) the action of the narrative; this music is assumed not to be heard by on-screen characters and often remains at a subconscious level for audience members. See *diegetic music*.

novelty song. Usually a humorous or whimsical song that is counter to the prevailing popular style; using a catchy hook, novelty songs may gain unexpected popularity; some novelties take the form of parody (e.g., songs by Stan Freberg); others use a variety of gimmicks (e.g., the Chipmunks).

nü metal. A subgenre of rap, combining the musical elements of heavy metal with the spoken vocal delivery style of rap.

octave. The distance from a given pitch to its next occurrence in the musical alphabet (e.g., from the note G to the next higher or lower G: G-A-B-C-D-E-F#-G); the frequency (number of vibrations per second) of the higher pitch is twice that of the lower pitch.

opera. In classical music, an opera is a dramatic story that is set to music and staged with sets and costumes, typically accompanied by orchestral instruments; strictly speaking, an opera is distinct from musical theater, since the former is set to music from beginning to end, whereas the latter includes spoken dialogue to advance the narrative. (See *musical theater* and *rock opera*.)

ostinato. A short musical pattern that is repeated persistently throughout a section of a song (or, more rarely, the entire song); representative examples in popular music include the bass pattern in boogie-woogies and the bass riffs of many rock songs.

overdubbing. A recording technique in which one or more tracks are added to previously recorded tracks. See *double-tracking*.

package show. An entertainment format in which a roster of performers goes on tour as a collection of artists (i.e., "package"); typically, lesser-known acts begin the show, and the hottest act closes the show.

payola. An illegal practice in which payments or other inducements are offered by record companies to broadcasters to play specific recordings.

pedal point. A note that is sustained or persistently repeated (traditionally in the bass), while harmonies in the upper voices change; over the centuries, the concept has broadened to include "pedal points" in upper voices (with harmonies changing below); this is sometimes referred to as an inverted pedal point.

phasing. An audio effect in which the original signal is passed through one or more filters that have nonlinear phase responses and then is applied back to the original signal; the result is a unique change in the timbre of the original signal. Flanging is a specific type of phasing that adds the original signal to a uniform time-delayed copy of itself; phasing and flanging sound rather similar (sometimes described as a "hollow" sound or as "the wind blowing through the music"); also referred to as "phase-shifting" or "flanging."

phrase. A short section of a musical composition. Similar to the linguistic meaning from which it derives, a phrase makes up a portion of a melody or theme in the same way that a linguistic phrase represents a smaller section of a sentence or paragraph.

pitch. A sound created by a vibrating body in a repetitive pattern; the greater the frequency of vibration, the higher the resulting pitch is perceived to be; sometimes used interchangeably with *note* or *tone*.

pointillistic. A term borrowed from the world of painting and applied to a style of musical composition in which pitches are presented in widely varied ranges and often in varying timbres; in painting, small distinct points of color are used to create an overall impression; the analogy in music resides in the use of small distinct points of pitch and timbre to create an overall effect.

polyphony. A type of musical texture in which there are two or more simultaneous, independent, and equally important melodic lines.

pop. Short form of *popular music*; in the broadest sense, refers to widely disseminated music aimed at the general audience and includes various styles of rock, jazz, country, soul, folk, etc. In this textbook, *Pop* (with a capital "P") refers more specifically to the style of music that was by and for the general (white) population of the United States in the first half of the twentieth century; based largely on the Tin Pan Alley tradition, the music was frequently associated with Broadway musicals and the Hollywood movie industry.

pop punk. A subgenre of punk that maintains the high energy; punk attitude; and dissonant, distorted guitar sound of its progenitor but incorporates melodic hook lines and tuneful choruses; emerged in the early 1990s.

progressive rock. A term that replaced *art rock*; refers to the 1970s extension of the late 1960s art rock trend; sometimes shortened to "prog rock."

psychedelic. Related to hallucinogenic drugs or altered states of awareness.

psychedelic soul. A descriptive term applied to music that combines elements of psychedelic rock with elements of soul music; popular in the late 1960s and early 1970s; associated primarily with Sly and the Family Stone.

punk rock. An excessively rebellious musical form that branched from the harder rock mainstream during the mid-1970s in Britain; representing an initial foray into the *DIY* ("do it yourself") aesthetic, the music was played loudly and aggressively by working-class performers; compared to the mainstream rock styles, punk rock was simpler, more repetitive, and louder.

quantize. In the digital realm of music making, a temporal manipulation of the notes played such that the rhythmic accuracy is made perfect, rather than containing the slight imperfections that result from human performance; it is worth noting, however, that it is these slight imperfections (playing a note slightly before or after the temporally accurate time) that result in the perceived expressive or emotional qualities of music. In the conversion from an analog signal to a digital signal, quantization also refers to the constraints of a system (8-bit, 16-bit, 32-bit, or more) from the continuous (analog) signal to an assignment of the value measured at a consistent time interval (sample rate) to the closest of a discrete set of numerical values (usually integers).

quartal. Based on the musical interval of a fourth; may be applied to harmonies (chords built on the interval of a fourth) and melodies (tunes that rely heavily on the interval of a fourth); distinct from the more traditional tertian harmonies and melodies (based on the interval of a third).

range. The distance between the highest and lowest pitches in a musical excerpt; thus, the range of a melody might be quite narrow or very wide; this term can also be used to refer to the range of a singer's voice.

rave-ups. Improvisational jam sessions featuring extended instrumental solos; developed in the mid- to late 1960s by certain British bands (e.g., the Yardbirds).

rhythm and blues (R&B). A style of popular music primarily associated with the African American market, especially from the 1940s to the 1960s; characterized by prominent rhythms, strong melodic bass lines, shouting vocals, and a reliance on the 12-bar blues form; typical instrumentation includes piano, electric guitar, bass, drums, saxophone, and vocals; R&B was the strongest and most direct progenitor of rock and roll during the late 1940s and early 1950s.

rhythm.   The interrelationship between music and time, created through a sequence of notes with varying temporal durations.

rhythm section.   The accompanying (or rhythm) instruments in a jazz or rock group, typically including the keyboard, rhythm guitar, bass, and drums.

riffs.   Short, repetitive instrumental passages that are pre-planned, not improvised; may be repeated identically or varied slightly to fit an underlying harmonic pattern.

Riot Grrrl.   An all-female subgenre of alternative music that emerged from the Pacific Northwest, coalescing in 1991; heavily influenced musically by its punk roots and a *DIY* aesthetic, the message of the music took on a clearly aggressive feminist tone; not limited to female musicians, it included male activists and writers.

ritard.   Short form of *ritardando*; a gradual slowing of the tempo.

rock opera.   A genre within art rock (and, later, progressive rock) that utilizes the musical style of rock in an operatic context; thus, it is a larger form that includes a series of songs, developing various characters within a narrative plot. Some rock operas were never actually staged; those that were emulated opera by including sets and costumes. Strictly speaking, rock opera (e.g., *Tommy, Jesus Christ Superstar*) are distinct from rock musicals (e.g., *Hair, Godspell, Grease, The Wiz, Evita*), since the latter include spoken dialogue, whereas a true rock opera is set completely to music throughout.

rockabilly.   One of the early trends in rock and roll, influenced most heavily by country music; with roots in both R&B and C&W, rockabilly eventually developed into the various styles of country rock.

rondo.   A musical form that consists of a series of sections, the first of which (often called the "refrain") recurs a number of times, normally in the *tonic* key, between other sections (often called "episodes") that contain contrasting musical material before returning to the refrain to conclude the composition.

root.   The fundamental (or generating) pitch of a chord; thus, in the C major triad, the root is C.

salsa.   A style of Latin rhythm characteristic of the music of Cuba, Puerto Rico, and the Spanish Caribbean that began to be incorporated into jazz, pop, and R&B during the 1960s and re-emerged during the late 1980s and 1990s; an important component of this rhythmic style is a syncopated rhythm performed on the claves, a pair of cylindrical hardwood sticks; characterized by heavy reliance on a variety of percussion instruments and brass.

samples.   (1) in rap, the use of previously existing music as the basis for a new composition; an early example of this technique is the Sugarhill Gang's "Rapper's Delight"; (2) electronically, the conversion of sound energy into a series of numbers representing the sound amplitude at discrete intervals of time; once transformed, the music can be easily manipulated (e.g., played backward, sped up, slowed down, combined with special effects, etc.) using the processing capabilities of a computer.

San Francisco sound.   The style associated with the San Francisco bay area countercultural bands of the late 1960s and early 1970s; characterized by lengthy instrumental improvisations, very loud volumes, and lyrics that were either drug oriented or poetic (often focused on peace, love, brotherhood, harmony with nature, spiritual self-realization).

scale degree.   The numbered position of a pitch within a scale; may be indicated by number (e.g., first, second, third, fourth, fifth, sixth, or seventh degree) or name (tonic, supertonic, mediant, subdominant, dominant, submediant, leading tone, respectively).

scratching.   A technique used to transform a turntable into a musical instrument, quickly pushing and pulling records on the turntable, resulting in a variety of effects: loops (short repeated sections), musical bursts, and backward playback.

sequencer (step).   Developed in the 1970s, the step sequencer was an electronic instrument that, when programmed, triggered a sequence of pitches, rhythms, timbres, and loudness levels on the synthesizer; once programmed, the sequencer cycled the programmed pattern repetitively; in recent decades, the term *sequencer* has been broadened to include any device (including computer software) that allows the user to record, play back, and edit musical patterns.

sheet music.   Printed musical notation in the form of symbols (e.g., quarter notes, time signatures, etc.) that provide a guide to musicians who can read music, allowing them to easily play (i.e., decode) the music represented, whether rock, jazz, or classical. This is in contrast to the process of "playing by ear," in which a musician listens to a performance and plays it back without the aid of such notational symbols.

shouter.   Vocalists who, at times, purposely add a harsh, raspy sound to their voices by oversinging; often encountered in R&B styles, the shout carried over into rock and roll (e.g., Little Richard); opposite of *crooner*.

shuffle beat.   A rhythm derived from the shuffle dance step, a dance of indefinite southern African-American origin, characterized by a subdivision of the beat into uneven triplets and usually played at a relaxed tempo; the word *shuffle* is onomatopoeic, representing the rhythm's alternation of long and short syllables (SHUF-fle, SHUF-fle, etc.).

singer-songwriters.   Performers who write the lyrics, compose the music, and sing their own songs; in many cases, they provide their own instrumental accompaniment; an extension of the folk music tradition; thrived especially in the 1970s.

sitar.   A long-necked lute instrument common to the classical music of north and central India; a typical instrument consists of five main strings, two drone strings, and a dozen sympathetic strings, the latter of which vibrate in response to pitches plucked using a plectrum on the other strings.

situational ethics.   A philosophy that suggests there is no absolute right or wrong; instead, what was right or wrong varies according to the situation.

skiffle.   Folk-like British popular music in which homemade instruments (e.g., washboard, cigar-box fiddle, kazoo, musical saw, comb, and paper) provided the accompaniment for simple songs; although developed in the first half of the twentieth century in the United States, skiffle enjoyed a revival in England in the 1950s; several British rock bands (most notably the Beatles) began as skiffle bands.

song cycle.   A group of songs that creates a larger musical unit; typically, the songs share a relationship to a common general theme or narrative.

speed metal.   A sub-style of heavy metal that exudes the high level of intensity inherent in thrash metal but incorporates even faster tempos and a persistent, driving quadruple subdivision of the beat.

strophic form.   A form in which each stanza of lyrics is set to the same music; especially common in folk music and hymns (also in many classical songs).

subdivision.   A secondary pulse within a beat of music; the most common subdivisions are duple, triple, and quadruple, consisting of two, three, and four equal subdivisions of the beat, respectively.

suite.   A series of shorter musical pieces conceived of and performed as a larger single work; in classical music, suites are instrumental; in rock, some suites include vocal sections (e.g., *Gemini Suite* by Deep Purple).

symmetrical form.   Characterized by uniform, regular, and balanced lengths; for example, many 32-bar popular song forms can be subdivided into two 16-bar sections, four 8-bar sections, or eight 4-bar sections; contrast such symmetry with some Beatles tunes that have irregular lengths (e.g., "Hello Goodbye" with a 15-and-a-half-bar section that subdivides into phrase lengths of 4, 4-and-a-half, 4, and 3 bars each).

synthesizer.   An electronic device that allows the user to generate and manipulate electronic signals to create music; although music synthesis can be traced back to the late nineteenth century, the practical use of synthesizers began in the late 1960s and was made accessible to most musicians in 1970 by the introduction of the Minimoog, a prepatched, portable synthesizer developed by Robert Moog.

talking blues.   A song style associated with folk music and country music in which the "singer" speaks a narrative over an instrumental accompaniment (usually acoustic guitar); developed by "Leadbelly" (Huddie Ledbetter), the style was popularized by folk singer Woody Guthrie, who, in turn, influenced Bob Dylan; talking blues may be autobiographical or provide social or political commentary.

techno.   A dance music style emerging directly from the disco era that blended an incessant disco beat with the high energy and attitude of punk; typically incorporates segments of previously recorded music, drumbeats, television chatter, and other "found sounds" into a style that is intentionally repetitive and noisy to provide a background for dancing and all-night partying.

teddy boy.   A youth culture that developed in England in the 1950s; associated with American rock and roll; teddy boys ("teds") dressed in long drape jackets (often with velvet trimmed collars and pocket flaps) and "drainpipe" pants; hair was greased into a pompadour and a ducktail; some teddy boys created gangs that could be violent. (p. 86)

Tejano music.   A general term for Mexican-influenced popular music that emerged from southern Texas; related to norteño and conjunto styles, but with more American influences; sometimes performed by larger ensembles, including primarily acoustic instruments, horns, and accordion.

tempo.   The relative speed of the musical beat; may be described subjectively (e.g., fast, slow, moderate) or objectively (e.g., 120 beats per minute).

ternary.   A three-part musical form, most often symbolized as ABA. In this brief musical form is encapsulated the fundamental principles of repetition (A) and thematic contrast (B).

texture.   A term that describes the number of musical lines and the way those lines relate to each other; thus, the musical texture may be thick (many musical lines or events occurring simultaneously) or thin (only one or a few musical lines or events); also, the relationship among the various musical lines (*monophonic*, *homophonic*, or *polyphonic*).

theremin.   An electronic instrument invented around 1920 by Leon Theremin; utilizes two oscillators and two antennas to generate a single tone; the player controls the pitch and volume by moving hands in varying proximity to the antennas; the result is an eerie or alien sound; the most familiar usage is in "Good Vibrations" by the Beach Boys.

thrash metal.   A blend of late 1970s heavy metal with the speed and intensity of post-punk hardcore rock.

through-composed form.   A musical form in which each successive section is new; earlier material does not return; in songs, new music is composed for each new verse; an example of this infrequently used form is *Karn Evil 9*, "Second Impression," by Emerson, Lake & Palmer.

timbre.   Tone color; refers to the tone quality of various instruments or voices.

Tin Pan Alley.   The nickname for a small section of Manhattan that housed the music publishers that dominated popular music in the United States in the late nineteenth century and the first half of the twentieth century; also used in a broader sense to refer to the Pop style that was the predominant product of these publishers.

tonality.   See *key*.

tone.   See *pitch*.

tonic chord.   A chord, the *root* of which is the tonic note (or key center); usually refers to a triad; thus, the tonic chord in G major is the G-B-D triad.

tonic note.   See *key center*.

trade-offs.   An improvisational technique in which players alternate the lead for a given number of measures; thus, players may "trade (or swap) fours," meaning they will alternate 4-bar improvisations; related to the call-and-response practice found in African music and religious ceremonies.

trance.   A subgenre of house dance music of the late 1980s and 1990s, emerging from the rave scene; characterized by fast tempos, soft electronic percussion, and repetitive chordal homophonic synthesizer parts.

tremolo bar.   A lever attached to the bridge or tailpiece of an electric guitar that allows the player to vary the tension (and sometimes the length) of the strings; the result can include effects such as vibrato, pitch-bending, and portamento (a slide from one pitch to another).

triad. A chord consisting of three different pitches.

trip hop. A style of club dance music that emerged in the mid-1990s; closely related to hip-hop, though the tempos are slower quadruple meters with sparse instrumentation (typically including keyboards and percussion, but rarely an MC, guitars, or synthesized string parts); arrangements emphasize the bass line (often synthesized), repetitive riff-based musical ideas, and minor keys.

tritone. Two notes that are three whole-steps apart (example: the tritone from F to B includes whole-steps from F to G, G to A, and A to B); it has several unusual characteristics that have led to special usage in music history (e.g., it divides the octave exactly in half; also, unlike any other interval, the inversion produces the same two-note tritone).

tune. A more informal equivalent of *melody*. See *melody*.

upbeat. (1) An informal term used to describe faster tempos. (2) The beat that precedes the downbeat (first beat) of the next measure of music; thus, in quadruple meter, the upbeat is the fourth beat of the measure.

vamp. A repeated accompanimental chord progression performed by the rhythm section (and horn section, if present), as they await the entrance of a vocal or instrumental soloist; the precise time frame for this accompaniment is often unknown and repeats until that entrance actually occurs.

veejay (VJ). A video jockey; one who introduces videos on a broadcast channel or in a streaming format that features music videos; similar to a deejay (disc jockey) in a music-based format. See also *deejay*.

verse-and-chorus form. A form in which verses alternate with choruses; each verse has new lyrics but the same music; each chorus repeats the same lyrics and music.

vertical organization. An approach to musical composition (including improvisation) that is oriented more to harmonic considerations than melodic (horizontal) considerations; with vertical improvisation, the player adjusts melodic lines to fit the underlying chord progressions. See *horizontal organization*.

vibrato. A slight fluctuation in pitch to enrich or intensify the sound; the listener perceives a fast wobble in the pitch; some popular music singers begin a given pitch with a straight tone (no vibrato) and then initiate vibrato.

vocal interpolation. The insertion or interjection of sounds, often highly emotive, into a vocal melody; common in many types of rock music but perhaps most prominent in gospel, R&B, and soul, in which phrases like "hey," wo-wo," etc. can often be heard.

voice box. An effect pedal, used most often on the guitar, that allows the sound of an instrument to be shaped by the performer's mouth and vocal cavity, resulting in what sounds like a talking instrument; Peter Frampton popularized the voice box in his live recording of "Do You Feel Like I Do?" in 1976.

volume. See *loudness*.

worksong. As its name suggests, the primary purpose of this type of music is to facilitate and/or make more tolerable the completion of repetitive tasks; during the late nineteenth and early twentieth centuries, freely extemporized songs were used for this function by field laborers, railroad workers, and prison chain gangs; the call-and-response nature of many of these songs passed directly into the musical style of the blues, R&B, and many early rock songs.

yodel. A vocal technique characterized by rapid shifts from the normal voice to falsetto (for female voices, from full or chest voice to head voice); with each shift, there is a new syllable and a new pitch; developed in the Swiss and Austrian Alps but adopted by country music singers.

Text Credits

Chapter 4

Page 60: David Leaf, *The Beach Boys*, New York: Courage Books, 1985, 90.

Chapter 5

Page 66: Anonymous - Negro tribal song.; p. 72: "Norman, Philip. Shout! The Beatles in Their Generation. New York: Warner Books, 1982." p. 74.; Maureen Cleave, Interview, Evening Standard (4 March 1966); p. 87: Beatles, "I Saw Her Standing There," *Please Please Me*, 1963, Sony ATV.

Chapter 7

Page 110: Shawn Otto (2016). *The War on Science: Who's Waging It, Why It Matters, What We Can Do about It*. Minneapolis, MN: Milkweed Editions.; Page 115: Copyright © 1964, 1965 by Warner Bros. Inc.; renewed 1992, 1993 by Special Rider Music. All rights reserved. International copyright secured. Reprinted by permission.

Chapter 8

Page 127: Gerri Hirshey, *Nowhere to Run: The Story of Soul Music*, Times Books, 1984. Copyright (c) 1984 by Gerri Hershey, published by Da Capo Press. Reprinted with permission of the Carol Mann Agency.; pp. 129, 132, 134: Joseph Scriven and Charles Crozat Converse, "What a friend we have in Jesus."; p. 130: Extract by Gerri Hirshey 1984, 283; "Mister James Brown: The Godfather of Soul Is Back" Rolling Stone, LLC.

Chapter 9

Page 142: J. McDonough, *San Francisco Rock*, Chronicle Books (1985), vii.; p. 145: Jefferson Airplane, "White Rabbit" 1967 RCA Victor.; p. 146: *Classic Albums: Anthem to Beauty* (1997, DVD). Isis Productions.; p. 148: *Blair Jackson, Grateful Dead: The Music Never Stopped*, Plexus, 1983, 77.

Chapter 11

Page 180: David Walley, *No Commercial Potential: The Saga of Frank Zappa and the Mothers of Invention*, Penguin, 1972, 64, 80.; pp. 180–181: Ed Ward, Geoffrey Stokes, and Ken Tucker, *Rock of Ages: The Rolling Stone History of Rock and Roll*, Simon & Schuster, 1986. 619.; p. 181: "Help, I'm a Rock" by Frank Zappa, 1966.

Chapter 14

Page 239: Twisted Sister, Stay Hungry, 1984.; p. 242: Ed Ward, Geoffrey Stokes, and Kevin Tucker, *Rock of Ages: The Rolling Stone History of Rock & Roll*, Rolling Stone Magazine, 1986.; p. 243: Brock Helander, *The Rock Who's Who*, Cengage, 1996.; p. 250: "Tool", Lateralus, Schism lyrics © BMG Gold Songs 2001.

Chapter 16

Page 278: Nelson Havelock and Michael A Gonzales, *Bring the Noise: A Guide to Rap Music and Hip-Hop Culture*, Random House, 1991.; p. 281: Run-D.M.C., "Walk This Way," 1986.; p. 282: Nelson Havelock and Michael A Gonzales, *Bring the Noise: A Guide to Rap Music and Hip-Hop Culture*, Random House, 1991.; p. 289: Dana Gioia, *Disappearing Ink: Poetry at the End of Print Culture*, Graywolf Press, 2013.

Chapter 17

Page 312: "Radiohead, Everything in Its Right Place," *Kid A*, 2000.

Chapter 18

Page 323: A. Perris, *Music as Propaganda: Art to Persuade, Art to Control*, Greenwood Press, 1985.; p. 324: David Crosby in *Rolling Stone Interviews*, New York: Warner Books, 1971.; p. 326: David Szatmary, *Rockin' in Time: A Social History of Rock and Roll*, 6th ed., Upper Saddle River, NJ: Pearson Education, 2006, pp. 223–224, 171.; p. 326: Frank Zappa – Statement To Congress, September 19, 1985.

Index